PEDOLOGY

BY

JACOB S. JOFFE

Professor of Pedology, Rutgers University, College of Agriculture
and
*Research Specialist in Soils, New Jersey Agricultural Experiment
Station, Rutgers University*

With an introduction by the late

CURTIS F. MARBUT

*Principal Soil Scientist, Division of Soil Survey, Bureau of
Chemistry and Soils,
United States Department of Agriculture*

Second Edition

Pedology Publications

New Brunswick, New Jersey

1949

FIRST EDITION, 1936

SECOND EDITION, REVISED AND ENLARGED

PRINTED BY THE SOMERSET PRESS, INC., SOMERVILLE, N. J.

To the memory of my father, Israel, the lover and student of nature, with whom the author, as a child and youth, roamed the woods, tramped the fields, and enjoyed the lake and rivers of the little town of Kupishok, formerly Russia, now Lithuania; to my scholarly brother, Raymond; and to my beloved mother, Tona, now living in Lithuania,—this book is affectionately dedicated.

(From first edition)

PREFACE TO THE SECOND EDITION

When the first edition of this volume appeared, the subject of *pedology* had just begun to make inroads into the Western world among scientific agriculturists in general and soils men in particular. They have discovered at long last a base on which to build a system of soil management that stems from the fundamental properties and characteristics of the soil as such. To this end, this volume has contributed in a measure that is not for the author, but for the future historian of pedology, to judge.

For the record, it may be told that the first edition of this volume was practically sold out within the first 3 years after its publication. World War II had put a stop to the distribution of the remaining less than a hundred copies. By the end of the war, the volume was out of print. A revision was to have been undertaken in 1940, but it was not until 3 years ago. However, the material for revision has been assembled ever since the publication of the first edition.

Almost every page of the text was rewritten, subject matter brought up-to-date, and topics revamped and reorganized. The latest advances, developments, and ideas in the realm of pedology that have appeared within the last 10 years were incorporated in the text. These items have also been used in clarifying, interpreting, and systematizing the original text. A chapter has been added on *Soil Organic Matter,* and the one on *The Soils of the United States* was omitted. Some pertinent points of the latter chapter have been blended in with the respective topics throughout the volume.

The 12 years since the publication of this volume have witnessed an expansion of pedologic investigations. Contributions have appeared at an accelerated tempo (the war years, of course, have markedly reduced the pedologic investigations) not only from Russia, but also from all corners of the world. Because of this, the choice of reference material to illustrate the topics discussed, a task that had burdened the author while preparing the first edition, became more difficult. An effort was made to screen out the poor papers that have come out during the last 10 years, and to avoid clogging the text with reference numbers. A critical review of the papers was the aim, or at least a bibliographic note. However, the folly of reference-mentioning has not been fully avoided. Neither has the virtue of critical analysis received its full share of recognition. To accomplish the two aims, one negative and one positive, would have meant to expand this volume into a pedologic encyclopedia. This would have defeated the purpose of this volume to serve as a balanced text in pedology.

In preparing the revised edition, the author has tried to cover fully

v

the Russian contributions. First of all, the Russian pedologists are still the masters in the field. Secondly, few pedologists of the Western world have access to the Russian literature because of language difficulties. On the other hand, the accessibility to the English, French, German, and Spanish contributions made it less imperative to scrutinize the published material.

In preparing the new edition, the author has utilized his experience in a first hand study of the different soil types (in pedologic sense) while traveling through most of Europe, North Africa, the Near East, through 40 states in the United States, the provinces of Canada, and some sections of Central America. These experiences have served admirably well in developing a more critical analysis and in crystallizing, in some measure, a viewpoint in interpreting the prevailing theories and pressing problems of pedology.

JACOB S. JOFFE.

New Brunswick, N. J.
   July 1, 1948.

PREFACE TO THE FIRST EDITION

Pedology is a branch of soil science or of the science of soils. Its scope is the study of phenomena presented to us by the soil body in its natural position. *Pedology is thus that realm of natural science which has as its objective the elucidation of the natural laws governing the origin, formation, and distribution of soils.* Pedology should not be confused with soil science, which is a broader subject, embracing pedology and the applied phases, such as soil fertility, soil technology, soil reclamation, soil physics, soil chemistry, and soil biology or rather the physics, chemistry, and biology of soils. Pedology is not a fundamental science as is physics, chemistry, or mathematics; it is, however, an independent science dealing with the soil as a natural body, just as botany is an independent science dealing with the plant as a natural body, or zoology dealing with the animal as a natural body.

This book is primarily, as stated by Marbut in the introduction, "a treatise on soils and their development. It is not a discussion of soil productivity." It seems to the author, that a pedological perspective is imperative for the rational approach to problems of soil productivity. Soil genesis, as expounded by pedology, is the cornerstone on which the applied sciences in agriculture are to be built. The agronomist, the horticulturist, the forester, the practical dairyman, the irrigation engineer, the many other representatives of applied agriculture, and the intelligent tiller of the soil will find in the presentation of the characteristics and properties of the zonal and intrazonal soil types valuable information applicable to their respective fields of study and their problems.

The newer knowledge of pedology eliminates the contingent and empirical method in soil fertility studies. It recognizes that the physical and chemical variations in the profile of the respective soil zones dictate a definite method of fertilization, type of fertilizer, and tillage practice. To be concrete: the pedologist would not subscribe unconditionally to deep plowing of podzols in the spring which would bring into circulation the immobilized R_2O_3 constituents from the B horizon. Under certain conditions subsoiling the A_2 horizon of podzols has been found to be very practical and valuable. On the other hand, deep plowing of chernozem may be of tremendous value in conserving moisture and releasing plant food constituents, under conditions of irrigation. Normally these soils need not be plowed deep. It is futile to irrigate a hidden solonchak, unless we are certain that we can establish contact with the ground waters. It is dangerous to use sodium nitrate on a sodium solonetz, but it would be perfectly harmless to use it on solonetz largely saturated with Ca or Mg. These are just examples of the many implications pedology offers to the student of fertility. To elaborate on these would mean to digress into the realm of agropedology, a subject still awaiting the master-craftsman. In this treatise, we are concerned with pedology, the fundamental prerequisite to agropedology.

A clear understanding of the intricate makeup of the soil zones will give us a better chance to realize successfully our altruistic motives in the study of soils—to increase soil productivity and to conserve fertility resources.

In writing this book, the author made use of the wealth of material scattered in the contributions of the Russian pedologists. The texts of Zakharov and of the late Glinka were consulted for both arrangement and subject matter, and the author's tribute to them is hereby expressed.

In selecting material for the book from the thousands of contributions, the guiding principle was reliability and pertinence to the subject. In bringing together the voluminous data, the author was frequently in a dilemma as to the choice and the proper balancing of the various subjects under discussion. In many instances it was a problem not of finding material but of eliminating the less valuable. Wherever possible, examples were drawn from contributions of our American research institutions. An attempt was made to interpret the data in the light of our modern concepts of physical chemistry and wherever possible to incorporate the latest ideas and data available. Undoubtedly omissions will be noted, and the author will be grateful for having his attention called to these and for frank criticism.

The author wishes to express his indebtedness to his inspiring teacher, Dr. J. G. Lipman, Director of the New Jersey Agricultural Experiment Station, for his sympathetic attitude and encouragement during the preparation of the manuscript; to Dr. C. F. Marbut, Chief of the Division of Soil Survey, Bureau of Chemistry and Soils, U. S. Department of Agriculture, for his interest in the author's effort to write the book, his many helpful suggestions, his reading of the manuscript, and finally his writing of the introduction; to the many friends, colleagues in the same field, in the United States and in foreign lands who have shown an interest in the writer's book; and to the graduate and special students who had the patience to listen to the author's lectures in pedology, all of whom have stimulated the author to undertake the writing of this book.

New Brunswick, N. J.
May, 1935.

JACOB S. JOFFE.

INTRODUCTION

Every American pedologist should familiarize himself with at least the broad lines of the history of the development of pedological science in Russia. Russian work brought the study of soils out of the chaos and confusion of the geologic, agronomic, chemical (Liebig) points of view and established it firmly as an independent science with criteria, point of view, method of approach, processes of development applicable to the soil alone and inapplicable to any other series of natural bodies. That work determined a definite relationship between the soil and the environment in which the soil is found, thus showing the soil to be related, on the plane of development, to biological bodies and not wholly physical.

At the time when western Europe was still engaged in the futile assertion that the soil as soil is dominated in its general features by the materials out of which it has been built, the Russian workers had already shown that the soil is the product of process rather than of material and is, therefore, a developing body rather than a static body. They allied the soil to life rather than to death.

Fortunate in the mid-continental location of the country in which they worked, equally fortunate in its broad geographic extent, the relatively slight extent to which man had interfered with the normal course of Nature's processes and the clearness with which the results of her processes in soil development are expressed, the Russian workers were able to see, with remarkable clearness, relationships that in western Europe are either obscurely expressed or not expressed at all.

In the clearness and simplicity with which the great soil features, as well as their relation to environment, are expressed, Russia occupies a place in the development of pedology comparable to that of the western United States in the development of the science of land form development. Whether our Russian colleagues are to be praised or merely congratulated may be a debatable question, but that the fundamental principles of the science of the soil were first laid down by them on the basis of conditions and facts in their own tremendously varied country is not debatable. Dokuchaev and his co-workers occupy the same position in pedology as do Sir Charles Lyell and his co-workers in geology, and Linnaeus in botany.

The Eurasian and North American continents include the two great continental areas of the world lying within the temperate zone. The other continents have their greatest exposé in the tropics and taper to narrow widths in the south temperate zone. While these considerations show us that the science of pedology in its particularities and as it now stands is applicable to the temperate zones, at the same time other considerations make it evident that the basic principles of the science, geographically limited though they are as yet, must be applicable to the world as a whole.

Since pedology is a science concerned with bodies so peculiarly a part of their environment, it is evident that only in identical environments will soils be identical. Absolute identity of environments in different continents does not seem to exist, hence the necessity of the exercise of great caution in the direct application of results obtained in one continent to another, even where environments are much alike.

Notwithstanding these considerations, the shifting of attention from materials to processes and the demonstration that soils as bodies are both products and factors of the geographic environments in which they lie were fundamental contributions of eternal value and significance and constitute principles applicable to all parts of the world. For these fundamental principles the world is indebted to Russian scientists.

These principles fundamentally consist of or concern soil relationship to the climatic environment with less clear and less decisive emphasis on the biological factors of the environment. It is possibly more correct to say that the recognition of the biological factor of the environment was clear but that emphasis was laid more strongly on the significance of the climatic factor than would be the case at present. This arose certainly from the fact that the relationship of climate to organic life in the Russian environment was everywhere the same, and this experience led to the assumption that the invariable association of a humid climate with forest vegetation and of a dry climate with grass is the same throughout the world. As long as this relationship was accepted as universally applicable, emphasis on the climatic factor of the environment was entirely justifiable, the inference being clear that the vegetation is itself merely an expression of the climate and deserves no independent recognition.

The assumption that this relationship exists and is universal and a vital one throughout the world was unnecessary and, in the light of subsequent observation, unjustified. It was unnecessary because it was not needed as a supporting factor for the fundamental principles formulated; they were in their essential nature true regardless of this. But it carried with it unfortunate consequences to the extent that it tended to cause acquiescence in the assumption that the biological factors had no independent action of their own and that an attempt to differentiate between the action of the one and the other factor was unnecessary.

Professor Joffe, like a great many Russians and other Europeans, assumes that a soil not now fitting into a climatic environment must have fitted the environment that existed in the locality at the time when it was developed and that its existing characteristics have been inherited from some former climatic condition different from those now existing. He concedes that in the special case concerned the special characteristics may possibly have developed under the influence of local conditions which have since disappeared.

The facts are interpreted by American pedologists as expressions of normal soil development in a case where biological factors (plants) have been given an opportunity to operate in a direction directly opposite to that toward which climate tends. As explained above, climate-plant relations are in Eurasia everywhere alike so that a given association of climate-plant produces the same result at all places where it occurs and each kind of climate-plant relationship is constant all over the continental area. A given climatic condition is everywhere associated with, in general, the same kind of plant life. Because of this, it has been impossible to determine by geographic correlation the character of work done in soil development by each of the two factors.

In the United States this is not true. A given climatic condition is not always associated with the same biological conditions. In Eurasia a humid climate is invariably associated with forest, and a dry climate with grass. If this association be not everywhere of this character it is so dominant that any other association is neglected and regarded as an accident with no significance.

In the prairies or humid grasslands of the United States, the climatic conditions are those which constitute the climatic part of the "Podzolic Type of Soil Formation" in Russia and elsewhere in Eurasia. In the United States the soils associated with this climate are in the surface horizon to a depth of 2 feet identical with those in a "Chernozem Type of Soil Formation" in Eurasia. Doctor Joffe, like most Europeans who have always given the climate the dominant role in soil making, cannot harmonize this relationship except on the assumption that the existing relationship has existed a short time only and that the soils are the product of development under a pre-existing relationship identical with that in Eurasia. The American pedologists interpret the existing climate-plant relationship as a permanent one, permanence being defined in terms of the time required to produce existing soil conditions. Their interpretation is based on three lines of evidence:

1. If the soil be the product of Eurasian conditions existing at some former time, existing relationship of environment to soil is an environment of degradation. The prairie soils are not degraded.

2. If the soil be the product of Eurasian conditions existing at some former time evidence of a change of conditions should be found. Recently discovered facts indicate that if any climatic change has taken place recently, it has taken place in a direction opposite to that assumed by the Eurasian pedologists.

3. The existing soils of the prairies are the normal product of the dominant factor in the soil developing environment, the biological factor of the American prairies being the first large area of the world in which the relationship of climate to plant is such that the specific quality and effectiveness of the plant in soil development can be measured for the first time. It is shown that it is by far the dominant factor.

Doctor Joffe's explanation of the development of the prairie soils cannot be accepted by the writer of this introduction. It seems to be a reflection of pedological habit rather than of critical analysis. This constitutes, however, a very minor factor in Doctor Joffe's book and one that may be considered theoretical and more or less academic.

Russian pioneer work on soils has not been confined to morphology, genesis, and environment relationships. In the development of a science concerned with a body of unindividualized material or bodies, facts of observation must be accumulated and their characteristics must be determined by observation or by the combined senses with the aid of simple experiments. On the basis of these characteristics tentative units or individual bodies must be created by definition or by the isolation into one unit body of all natural units wherever found having identical characteristics. These two stages of observation or accumulation of facts and definition of units are inevitable in the development of a science concerned with a series of natural bodies whether consciously or unconsciously performed, and the further work of development stands on the basis of the units thus defined.

A third inevitable step is that of organizing these units into groups of different degrees of comprehensiveness, which can be done only by establishing relationships of similarities and differences.

Up to this point the work is concerned exclusively with the material and the bodies defined on the basis of its features with no consideration whatever of their relationship to other bodies or with the establishment of relationship to forces not residing in the bodies themselves.

In this and all the preceding stages of the work the student is concerned almost exclusively, if not entirely, with field methods—with the accumulation of facts and their comparison, one with another, and with those of other bodies. It is primarily a work in morphology and classification up to where relationships with foreign bodies and forces are being established.

The establishment of a relationship to forces is the work of the geneticist who, by establishing an invariable and exclusive relationship of a given force or process to a given group of characteristics, already used as a basis for creating individual bodies, determines thereby a probable if not actual genetic relationship. Up to this point, however, the geneticist has not concerned himself with that phase of observation and comparison carried out under control and designated as experimentation.

Experimentations in soil morphology and genesis, however, have not yet been developed as a well-established means of attack on the problems involved.

The matter has been attacked, however, by the determination of characteristics and relationships to a much more refined degree than can be performed by observation, through an attack by chemical methods. This, however, is not a method of actual experimental attack on the problem of genesis. It is merely a means of obtaining facts that cannot possibly be obtained by the method of simple observation.

The utilization of these facts in the solution of problems of genesis is effected entirely and in the same way as are the simpler or at least more obvious facts determined by direct observation—in other words, by the indirect method of interpreting.

This refined method of attack cannot be utilized until the problem or problems have been presented. This presentation is wholly and exclusively the function of the field observer, or of the morphologist, the taxonomist, and the geneticist.

Up to about three decades ago the Russian work proceeded primarily along the last three lines. By it the genetic problems were presented. By it and by it alone, the work of the chemist was defined. His opportunity was presented by the problems encountered in the earlier work.

Nothing inherently residing in the fundamental nature of this chemical work made it necessary that it should be initiated in Russia and by Russians. The fact that the problems were necessarily encountered first in Russia gave the opportunity first to chemists of that country. That opportunity was seized, and, in the pioneer chemical work of Gedroiz on the colloid materials of soils, not only was real soil chemistry presented with a previously unknown method, but it is practically true that real soil chemistry, rather than that involved merely in the chemistry of the soil material, was created. For the first time in the history of science, soil chemistry attacked the problem of soil genesis—the problem of the very existence of the soil as a distinct natural body. By Russian work in soil morphology and genesis, soil chemistry was given the opportunity to exist. The pioneer work in developing that phase of the science of the soil was performed also by Russians.

In western Europe and the United States, soil chemistry did not exist until well after the close of the World War. A chemistry of the soil material has existed since the time of Liebig but it has had and, in so far as it continues to exist, still has no significance as a method of accumulating data that by interpretation may lead to the solution of the problems of soil genesis.

It could not do so, because the soil as a body had no existence in the minds of chemists and most others concerned with American agriculture until after the World War. Problems of soil genesis, therefore, could have no existence. Until the soil as a distinct individuality among natural objects had begun to exist through a determination of its unique characteristics, there could be no questions in the minds of men regarding its genesis. As long as it was merely rock material from which something had been removed, it could have had no genesis, since that word has no meaning except as a designation of a constructive process. It cannot be applied as a designation for lingering but uninterrupted approach toward death. The development of the soil, expressing itself in its morphology, is a constructive process, and until its morphology has begun to exist for man through having been determined by conscious observation of its characteristics, it can have had no genesis in the strict sense of the term and, therefore, no genetic problems.

While knowledge of the unique existence of the soil had penetrated somewhat into western Europe and the United States before the war, chemists had not yet attempted to attack its genetic problems. Since these problems had been created by the Russian work they were attacked by Russian chemists. The opportunity to do so, however, was not exclusively Russian.

Existing books on soils by American authors consist practically exclusively of textbooks. Handbooks on the subject have not been prepared by American authors. Soils are almost universally looked upon in the United States as producers of crops. In no institution of learning is the subject of pedology ever thought of as a so-called "culture subject."

In American textbooks on soils, soils as bodies are treated in an incidental way as though that phase of the subject were a curiosity with no close relationship to the subjects treated in the body of the texts. Such consideration as is given to soils as bodies is relegated to the end as a sort of appendix and is treated as foreign matter. These books discuss soil texture, soil moisture, the content of the elements generally regarded as food for plants, and the processes of rock and plant material decomposition. Until very recently, such chemical treatment as the subject has received consisted of the mere consideration of percentages of the various substances present, mainly the percentages of nitrogen, phosphorus, potassium, and calcium present in so-called "available forms."

No discussion of the processes of soil development worthy of the name is attempted in American books on soils. A good deal of attention is usually given to the description of rocks and minerals and still more to the processes of rock decomposition. These are destructive processes and are limited entirely to the processes of soil material accumulation, but the constructive processes of soil development receive practically no consideration. This arises because of the continued inability of the average textbook writer to think of the soil as a body and as the product of constructive processes.

Since practically the only attention given to soils in the United States is given in the agricultural colleges, the agronomic relationship of soils is necessarily given a great deal of attention in textbooks. The treatment of soils as such is not considered "practical," and the subject must be made practical at all hazards. To be practical the two features of soil texture and the contents of the plant food elements must be given a great deal of attention. The whole field of the significance of the soil as a body in plant production remains wholly uncultivated because of the dominance, even in the third decade of the 20th Century, of the ideas of Justus Liebig.

Professor Joffe's book is a treatise on soils and their development. It is not a discussion of soil productivity. It concerns the development under the influence of environmental conditions of the outer layer of the earth's crust. It concerns that part of the earth's crust which is itself both the product and the indispensable support of organic life on the earth. The soil lies on the twilight of life, a connecting link between the living and the non-living, between material animated by vital forces and material subjected to physical forces. No American pedologist nor any one interested in the manifold branches of soil science can fail to find it valuable.

CURTIS F. MARBUT, *Principal Soil Scientist;*
Chief, Division Soil Survey, Bureau of Chemistry
and Soils, U. S. Department of Agriculture.
[Written in November, 1934.]

TABLE OF CONTENTS

Part I: Soil Genesis

CHAPTER   PAGE

Part II: Soil Systematics, Climatogenic Soil Types

Part III: Soil Systematics, Climatogenically Subdued Soil Types

LIST OF ILLUSTRATIONS

Part I
Soil Genesis

CHAPTER I

PEDOLOGY AS A SCIENTIFIC DISCIPLINE

Introduction

In introducing the subject of pedology, the distinctive contribution of the Russian school to soil science, it seems worth while to review the approaches made to the study of soils. Historical perspective helps to fix in our minds the intricate phases of the subject.

As an independent science, pedology originated in Russia with the classical researches of Dokuchaev and of his pupils. Because of language barriers—the Russian language was not much studied outside of Russia—and the isolation of Russia until World War I and the subsequent revolution, this accumulated store of knowledge remained a terra incognita to western Europe and the New World. Though some ideas of the Russian school had penetrated western Europe during the first decade of the century, a pronounced change has come about only since then.

In the United States, we owe much to the late Doctor Marbut, of the erstwhile Bureau of Soils, United States Department of Agriculture, for the present interest in the modern scientific viewpoint on soils. Marbut was the first in the United States to appreciate fully the far reaching possibilities in the study of soils as presented by the Russians, after he became acquainted (through a German translation) with the views of the late Doctor Glinka, probably the most prominent pupil of Dokuchaev.

The Russian school made it clear that the principles applied in elucidation of the natural sciences, such as zoology and botany, are applicable also to soil science. The soil is looked upon as a distinct organism, with definite morphologic and constitutional (physiological) features, with specific physical properties, chemical composition, and biological makeup in its various parts. The pedologic method in the study of the soil is analogous to that used in the fundamental sciences: chemistry, physics, and biology.

Crystallization of Soil Studies

Mankind gradually acquired knowledge as a result of a struggle for existence. Medicine was, in consequence, one of the early scientific disciplines. Botany also belongs to one of the oldest scientific disciplines because of the keen interest in plants as ingredients for compounding medicines, and hence as vehicles of medicinal virtue. The mysteries of the skies—changes from day to night, the recurrent appearance of the sun, and other incomprehensible phenomena—undoubtedly engendered a curiosity which stimulated the early advent of astronomy. Other scientific disciplines found their way into the sanctuaries of human intelligence as need required, but those needs which were not of immediate concern had to await a diversification of mankind's pressing interests. The soil lay at man's feet but he looked to the inaccessible heavens for help and salvation.

From the time man emerged from the nomadic state and took to settled agriculture he has been confronted with soil problems. As his needs increased, or as the land became exhausted and refused to yield sufficiently to meet requirements, man commenced to seek new lands. From the fabulously rich lands of the valleys of the Euphrates and Tigris, early man wandered from fertile to less fertile soils. A single exception may be found in the history of the United States where colonization took place first on the relatively less fertile soils of the Coastal Plain along the Atlantic seaboard, then on the more fertile soils of the Piedmont Plateau, and finally on the still more fertile soils of the Mississippi Valley and the Great Plains.

As long as there was enough good land, there was no pressing need for soil studies. With the increase in population, the demand for living space was met in many ways. One of these was the building of colonial Empires, with the disastrous results of neglecting the soils of the mother country. The fall of the Roman Empire has been in a large measure attributed to the decay of its home agriculture. This relation of human activity to soils retarded the development of soil science. As time went on, the land hunger could not be satisfied adequately by territorial conquests. The land on hand had to be managed to produce more, and scientific investigations of soils came in to meet the problem.

Some fruitful ideas about soils, primarily with reference to productivity, have developed all through recorded history. Systems of soil management, such as fallowing the land, use of legumes, and converting cultivated land into pasture, meadow, or some form of sod, have been employed from time immemorial. The Bible prescribes resting the land once in seven years. Burning the steppe country in late summer to improve the pasturage, a practice still in use, originated in the nomadic period of human history. These ancient practices, which forshadowed modern studies in soil fertility, were known to the Hebrews, Egyptians, Chinese, Greeks, and Romans.

The history of the various scientific disciplines in relation to soil studies tells us that every science had a claim on soils as being an adjunct of its domain. The soil as a distinct body in nature was not recognized until pedology had formulated its principles.

Physical Sciences

The rapid and fruitful advances made by chemistry in the early part of the nineteenth century overshadowed for a while the development of all other scientific disciplines. It appeared as if chemistry would solve most problems of animate and inanimate nature, including, of course, the soil productivity problem. The remarkably clear and scholarly contributions of Boussingault in France on agricultural chemistry and the more sensational researches of Liebig in Germany mark an important milestone in the development of soil science. Liebig's bold assumptions and his postulation of the mineral theory nurtured the subject of soil fertility. The chemist, with his analytical trend of mind and activity, overlooked the soil as a natural body and sought a solution in analyses of soil material. The imposing position gained by chemistry hindered the independent development of the study of the soil as a distinct scientific discipline. Soil studies became a subordinate branch of chemistry. This does not, of course, minimize the tremendous service of chemistry in promoting the science of soils. The methods worked out by the soil chemist and the application (even though in a limited way) of the fundamental laws of gases, solutions, and solids in the study of soils as media for crop production could be fully utilized by the pedologist in studying the soil body. The voluminous data on soil acidity, liming, soil solution, and soil colloids represent a wealth of knowledge which has been utilized in elucidating the pedogenetic characteristics of soils.

Physics also laid claim on elucidating the complex nature of the soil. But the soil physicist, like the soil chemist, devoted his attention to the soil material rather than to the soil body. Notable contributions on the specific gravity, volume weight, capillary pore space, moisture regime, texture and structure of soils, and mechanical analysis have been made. These contributions may easily be applied in studies which scientifically interpret soils as an independent natural body.

An analysis of the evolution of the science of soil as a distinct scientific discipline would be incomplete without mention of geology. Indeed, geology with its allied branches, petrography and mineralogy, makes a strong appeal to the student of soils. Soils form the uppermost layer of the earth's mantle, and, very frequently, are formed in situ, retaining some of the rock fragments and minerals of the underlying geologic formations. But, while looking for the fragments of native rock, the geologist failed to scrutinize the soil in its natural habitat. Had he done so, he would have noted that the characteristics of soils in Georgia derived from granite are entirely different from those of soils in California derived from similar granites. He would have realized that the soil is in itself a unit object in nature. Although geology served as a great aid in the recognition and evaluation of certain soil properties, it was inadequate to explain the complex processes of soil formation. It remained for pedology to solve the difficulty. By recognizing the soil as an independent natural body in relation to the processes responsible for its formation, pedology had justified its claim to an independent status of a scientific discipline.

Microbiology and Soils

As elemental constituent of the soil is its organic matter, the product of biological agencies in the process of soil formation. Decomposition and synthesis reactions brought about by microbes in the soil are important in elucidating some fundamental properties of the soil.

Ever since the days of Pasteur, microbiologists have dwelt upon the riddles of the soil flora. Fundamental contributions have been made on the processes of organic matter transformation in the soil, ammonification, nitrification, and nitrogen fixation. Notables among the pathfinders in these fundamental investigations are: Schloesing, Warrington, Hellriegel and Wilfarth, Winogradsky, Beijerinck, Omelyansky, Marchal, Löhnis, and J. G. Lipman.

Microbiologists have not investigated the relation of microbial activities to the processes of soil formation. Their investigations dealt primarily with the soil mass as a medium for microbes and the effect of their activities on crop production. In this respect, soil microbiology has been leaning rather towards agronomy and plant physiology than to the science of the soil in general and still less to pedology.

In recent years, soil microbiology has turned to studies on the relation of microbiological reactions to the processes of soil formation and the evolution of the soil as a body in nature.

Agronomy and Soils

The agronomic point of view stresses the fertility of the soil expressed in yields per acre. Tillage and other soil management practices, compensation for crops taken off, and systems of cropping are the criteria which guide the agronomist in his pursuits. For him, the soil is the abode of plants. His chief concern, therefore, is the cultivated soil, even though he realizes the potentialities of the virgin soil. The agronomist, unlike the pedologist, does not look upon virgin soil as a stable condition, but as a temporary state which, after several years of cropping, runs down and requires the attention of the artisan.

Agronomists have concentrated on empirical soil studies, limiting their attention to the surface soil and occasionally the subsoil and interpreting yield data in terms of the physical, chemical, and biological properties of soils. The title and, in a large degree, the content of Sir John Russell's *Soil Conditions and Plant Growth* illustrate the agronomic viewpoint.

The rich store of facts accumulated by the agronomists helped to advance a more rational system of crop adaptation to soils, furthered better methods of tillage and land utilization, and clarified the problems attendant on the agricultural value of sundry soils. The agronomist, however, failed to perceive the soil as a unit in the scheme of natural sciences. He did recognize the difference between a virgin and cultivated soil, but failed to appreciate the value of studying soils in their virgin state. Not until pedology had emerged as an independent science devoted to a study of the soil as a natural body did the virgin soil receive its due share of attention. Hilgard (Ch. 2,30) is an outstanding exception to this general disregard of virgin soils. In speaking of the failures of soil studies in the past, he remarked: "Foremost among these is the fact that until within recent times, soil studies have been concerned almost entirely with lands long cultivated and in most cases fertilized: thus changing them from their natural condition to a more or less artificial one, which obscures the natural relations of each soil to vegetation."

Pedology and the Pure and Applied Sciences

Scrutnizing the achievements of the chemists, geologists, and agronomists in the study of soils, one cannot but recognize that our knowledge has now advanced in proportion to the efforts made. Each one of the approaches contributed a great deal to our understanding of many properties of the soil material; but the facts were recognized only in conjunction with the advancement of the particular science with which the soil investigator was more familiar. An interesting illustration in this connection is the impetus which the introduction of the pH concept has given to soil investigations. It gave a new fillip to some phases of soil studies that were stagnant at the time. Another illustration is the stampede to studies on ion adsorption and exchange in soils.

The contributions of the older schools of soil science dealt with soil material in relation to crop production. In developing this phase of soil studies, the help of the fundamental sciences has been invoked. In this manner, the science of soils became subordinate to the pure and applied sciences.

Pedology presents the soil as a unit in nature; it deals with its origin, formation, and distribution through a study of its constitution and its life

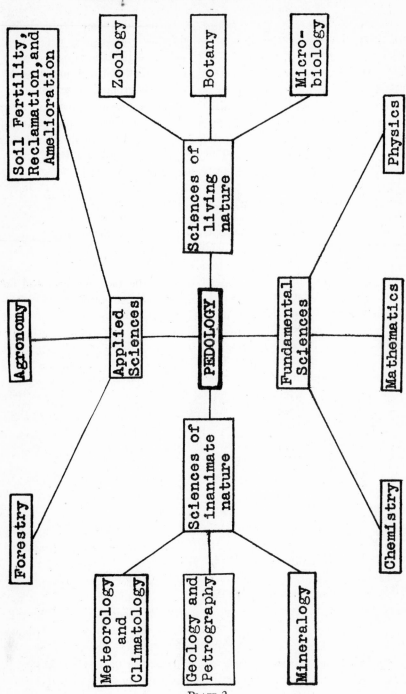

PLATE 2
Relation of pedology to other scientific disciplines
(After Zakharov)

and dynamics. The soil body as found in nature, its anatomy and physiology, its behavior, and its responses to the forces responsible for its creation are the concern of pedology. It occupies an intermediate position between the sciences of animate and inanimate nature. It mobilizes the findings of the natural sciences and applies them in elucidating the concept of the soil in relation to the biosphere, hydrosphere, atmosphere, and lithosphere. In working out the laws governing the factors of soil formation, pedology has emerged as an independent scientific discipline. Its relation to the pure and applied sciences is graphically presented by Zakharov (Ch. 2, 91), reproduced with slight modifications in plate 2.

The Soil Profile

Historically, the modern concepts of pedology stem from the classical researches of Dokuchaev on the genesis of Russian chernozem. It was not a laboratory study of soil samples, but a comprehensive field and laboratory investigation of virgin and cultivated soils of the chernozem belt which extends through European Russia into Siberia and which can be traced throughout the world.

Following the methods of the natural sciences, Dokuchaev started out with the descriptive phase. The soil body was dissected, cut open vertically, and the exposed anatomy noted and described. In a mature state, the soil body revealed a definite constitution, consisting of distinct layers, known as horizons which have similar broad morphologic features, irrespective of the geographic position of the soil and of the underlying geologic formation, provided it is located in identical climatic belts. Not only were the morphologic characters of the soil found to be similar, but also its internal properties—physical, chemical, and biological—and even its agronomic behavior. *The genetically related exposed horizons of a vertical cut in the soil body, taken as a unit, comprise what is known as the soil profile.*

The alpha and omega of soil studies, from the pedologic point of view, is the profile of the soil body with "no reference to other considerations," as expressed by Marbut.

The pedologist is to present as many facts as possible on the physical, chemical, and mineralogical properties of the soil profile. Therein lie the secrets of soil productivity, the ultimate aim of the science of soils.

Soil Zonal Types

The laws governing the distribution of soils in nature were brought to light by the discoveries of Dokuchaev and his pupils who showed that a systematic regularity and orderliness exist in the geographic location of soils. Each type of soil formation, with its inherent characteristics and properties, could be identified within a definite climatic zone, moulded by a series of homologous and, at the same time, specific soil-forming processes. For example, the zone of the podzol soils is typical of the temperate humid regions; the chernozem is found in the semiarid-subhumid regions; the lateritic soils and laterites are typical of the subtropics and tropics. Specific types of soil formation are noted in the arid and semidesert and desert regions. The geographic distribution of soils thus follows the climatic zones or belts, giving rise to zonal soil types.

One of the fundamental laws of pedology, in the words of Glinka (Ch. 2, 27), is "the law of the adaptability of soil types of the globe to definite natural (primarily climatic) conditions." This law was formulated by Dokuchaev and Sibirtzev, and the latter based thereon his theory of the zonal distribution of soils. This law opened a new viewpoint in the study of soils: it showed that the soil may and should be studied not simply as soil material but as a geophysical formation. The properties of the material comprising the soil body should be studied, not in relation to the soil in general, but in relation to each zonal type in particular.

Considering the climate as the primary factor in delineating the zonal soil groups, one should not lose sight of the geomorphological features of the earth that modify the atmospheric elements. The Sierras and the Cascade mountain chains on the Pacific coast serve as barriers for the air masses moving from the Pacific Ocean. They can not climb across the hump and therefore, before getting to the Divide, condense the moisture they carry. The result is forested western slopes, with an abundance of rainfall; and bare rugged arid eastern slopes approaching conditions of semidesert, with a paucity of precipitation. In the back of the Scandinavian mountain chain lies the dry region of Central Norway. Behind the Scotland Plateau is the dry eastern coast. In the Harz mountain zone of Central Europe and in the Alps, we find steppe conditions in the valleys, and conifer forests on the moisture laden mountain slopes. On the Iberian peninsula, the western parts of the Cantabrian mountain and Sierra Estrella (in Portugal) get an abundance of precipitation; the rest of Spain and Portugal have a continental dry climate. Similar phenomena obtain in Italy and the Balkans.

In discussing the displacement of climatic elements, one naturally must point out the Gulf Stream and related movement of ocean currents and their effects on climate. These climatic displacements also affect the distribution of the zonal soils.

CHAPTER II

SOIL AS A NATURAL BODY

Vernadskii (83) defines a natural body as "any object in nature which attains the status of individuality, endowed with an independent existence, capable of being distinguished and isolated from its environment, with an internal constitution, and controlled by specific laws in nature."

When the physical sciences began to unravel the secrets of nature, it became clear that nature itself is a composite number which can be factored and subdivided into unit objects or bodies. For a thorough understanding of nature and for the purpose of harnessing it into the service of man, it became necessary to study the objects as such. It was realized that by this method it would be easier to handle the objects for the purposes wanted. In the case of the soil, we find that the representatives of the various scientific disciplines looked upon the soil in the light of their respective sciences, usually from the utilitarian point of view.

Berzelius (5), the pioneer Swedish chemist, called the soil "the chemical laboratory of nature in whose bosom various chemical decomposition and synthesis reactions take place in a hidden manner." This purely chemical view was shared also by Liebig (44), whose theories in soil fertility and chemistry for a time overshadowed all other currents in the study of soils. To Liebig, the soil was the test tube into which one might introduce plant nutrients. The chemical composition of the plant was the criterion by which he judged soils. In his sensational letters on agriculture (44, p. 122), Liebig accepted without reservations the definition of soils advanced by Gustav Walz, Director of the Agricultural Academy at Hohenheim, Stuttgart: "The soil consists of disintegrated rocks, and either rests upon these same rocks or on others elsewhere; the transported soil may, nevertheless, have remained the same and corresponds at least to the rocks from which it has its origin." Liebig, the exponent of the classical "mineral theory," considered soils as the storehouse of the chemical compounds supplied by minerals.

Thaer (76) was one of the first to present a scheme of appraising soils on the basis of definite physical and even chemical properties. Thaer's theoretical considerations were embryonic in nature, but we must remember that they were presented in the first decade of the nineteenth century, when the natural sciences had just begun to muster their forces for their subsequent rapid development. He stated (p. 60) :

The surface of our planet consists of a crumbly loose material called soil. It is an accumulation and mixture of various substances. To the layman, earth and soil are synonymous, but natural science does not include in the group of earths some substances found in the soil. The chief components of the soil are: silica, alumina, lime, and at times also magnesium. To these components of the soil some iron and other substances, in small amounts, are attached. Besides these simple bodies, any fertile soil —one which is capable of producing useful plants—contains a complex substance which is known as plant-decay material, vegetable mold, or plant-animal earth. This substance is so different from earth that it should not be identified as such and it should be designated by the Latin name *humus,* a term accepted by many. The difference between the two is that this decay-material is decomposable, while earths are not.

Thaer appreciated certain natural properties of the soil body, even though to him the soil was merely loose surface material. He classified soils on the basis of the relative proportion of the various mechanical fractions: loam soil, clay soil, loamy sand, sandy loam, etc. This classification system had a pronounced influence on his followers. Schmalz (65) borrowed as an epigraph for his book a citation from Thaer. To Schmalz, the tax appraisal value of soils was the first consideration in classifying them. A similar view was presented by Kortes (36). Even Schübler (66), the prominent soil physicist of his day, made no attempt to broaden the view of Thaer, and his grouping of soils is very similar to that of Thaer. His definition of soils was utilitarian-agronomic: "The soil is the upper layer of the earth which serves as a support and as a source of nutrition for plants, and is composed of remnants of rock material formed in the process of weathering" (66, pt. II, p. 2).

The work of Davy (9) in England on the importance of the physical properties of soils marks the beginning of soil physics, later developed by Schübler. He may be classed also with the proponents of the chemical viewpoint. To him "the soil is the laboratory in which the food is prepared." In his lectures on soils, Davy discussed the constituents of soils, their analysis, "the rocks and strata found beneath the soil." He stated (p. 174) : "It is evident from what has been said concerning the productivity of soils developed from rocks, that there must be at least as many varieties of soils as there are species of rocks exposed at the surface of the earth." Such utterances are typical of the geologic viewpoint.

Hausman (28) considered soils in relation to the native rock. He classified soils on the basis of the rocks from which they originated. In the first class he placed those which formed from quartzite, siliceous shales, and porphyry; in the second class—from limestone rock; in the third class —from basalt and trap rock, etc. It is a petrographic point of view, and the primary purpose of such subdivision was the economics of soils. It is of interest to note that Hausman published his treatise in Latin.

Hundeshagen (32) did not advance the subject any further than did Hausman, even though one could, by a stretch of the imagination, attribute to him an appreciation of the climatic factor. In the first chapter of his work on "soil, climate and their mutual effect on plant growth," Hundeshagen mentions that the climatic forces—water, heat, light, and oxygen—must react in unison in order to form a productive soil.

Krause (42) analyzed the soil-forming processes in relation to soil productivity, correlating the latter with the climatic factors. He recognized that plants, as weathering agents, penetrate into the crevices of the rocks, split them, decompose them, and utilize some of the constituents. His view might be considered economic-geologic.

The work of Sprengel (72) marks an important milestone in the development of the idea that the soil is an independent natural body. He formulated a theory on the origin of soils, basing it primarily on the humus complexes. By raising the question of the age of the soil, he focused attention on the soil as a definite object in nature, but he did not go far enough to recognize it as an independent natural body. To him, the soil was a mass of material derived from minerals containing the decomposition products of plants and animals.

Sprengel introduced the purely natural historical outlook in the study of soils. To him "the forces which decompose native rocks and convert them into soil were: water, oxygen, carbon dioxide of the air, heat and cold, vegetation, and electricity." On the face of it, Sprengel appreciated the climatic factors and biological agencies of weathering which go to make up the soil body. But a more critical examination of his work shows that he failed to recognize the harmony of these factors and agencies in building up a new natural body, the soil. He associated each one of them primarily in relation to organic matter decay and accumulation. Sprengel correlated the climate with soil productivity and with the perplexing problem of organic matter in the soil. On pages 145-146 he stated: "The value of the soil depends not only on its physical and chemical properties, but also on its position in relation to the climate. One and the same soil may be very fertile in one climate and not in another." On pages 274-276 he stated: "Where the climate is cold, less ammonia and nitrates are formed in the process of organic matter decay, and since it is known that these substances are of important significance to plants, it is concluded that, in this respect, the warm climate should be preferred to the cold. All organic bodies decompose and decay more slowly in cold climates than in warm climates. Manure therefore persists much longer in the soils of the cold climate and more of it has to be added. Though the soils in the cold climates contain more organic matter, the yields are relatively smaller. In warm climate, the soil gives two crops, and where the winter is short, agricultural operations continue throughout the year." The soil, as such, with its distinctive constitution, characteristic makeup, habitus, and genetic relationships of horizons, was unknown to Sprengel; it remained for his followers to develop the idea.

Credit is due Fallou (20-22) for the attempt to treat soil science as an independent science and soil as a separate formation. Yarilov (90), the prominent historian of pedology, considers Fallou as the father of pedology. In his first important contribution on the soils of Saxony (20), Fallou stated: "Geologically, and in a general scientific sense the soil is looked upon as the product of weathering with the aid of which 'father time' is unceasingly gnawing the hard mantle rock of our planet and gradually decomposing the compact soil mass." In the same publication, the following passage on the origin of soils is significant: "The general idea about soils in the natural-historical sense is that they may be subdivided into two categories: weathered soils and washed-in (alluvial) soils. Such an understanding deals not with origin of the soil, but with its make-up and deposition. No soil could form by a washing-in process even though water takes part in weathering and deposition. It is nothing more than that an already existing soil is being transported by the streams." The last sentence makes it clear that soil material and a true soil were interchangeable in Fallou's nomenclature. And yet, Fallou considered the soil a distinct formation, as exemplified by the following quotation: "Soil is decomposed, more or less disintegrated native rock, distinct and separate from the compact, undisturbed native rock, with an admixture of organic materials; the rock has changed and metamorphosed in its form and infrequently also in its makeup. Soil as such does not therefore belong any more to the rock formation, but is a formation by itself."

According to Fallou, the utility standpoint prevented the crystallization of a scientific appreciation of the nature of soils. He criticised severely the chemical theory of soils: "Recently, the millenium for agriculture was looked for from the chemist; it was thought that a chemical analysis of the soil would give a complete idea about the soil. . . . Soil science was recognized not as a science by itself, but as a branch of agricultural chemistry. . . . Soil science is an empirical science. Nature itself is its source. Observations on soils in their geognostic relations, or in their relation to the strata formation and to the underlying rock are of special importance."

The views of Fallou appear modern, and are in line with the scientific appreciation of the soil as a natural body, even though the geologic point of view is apparent. A closer analysis of his work, however, shows that he failed to grasp the significance of the soil forming processes, and his ideas on soil as a natural body are, for this reason, not clear. A citation from his latest work (published in 1875) will illustrate the aforesaid: "This (organic) portion of the soil may naturally originate not before the soil has formed, since plants and animals require food and they can obtain this only from the soil and not from the air."

Fallou attributed variations in soils primarily to the petrographic nature of the soil-forming rocks. He examined vertical soil cuts but failed to detect the profile constitution of the soil, which is the characteristic feature of the soil body. For this reason, his attempts to separate the soil as a distinct body, of which he had a notion, were fruitless and found no support in later years. Fallou's embryonic ideas on soils were correct, and their significance as something new was recognized by his contemporaries. Jul. Kühn (43) wrote with great enthusiasm about the work of Fallou. He said: "The real untangling of agrology became possible only after it gained a pedologic foundation through the work of Fallou on soils in situ and that of Bennigsen on water transported soils."

An extensive study of soils, made contemporaneously with Fallou, was presented by Cotta (7, 8). It was primarily an investigation dealing with the fertility of the soil in relation to the specific geological formations. To the appreciation of the soil as such, Cotta, in the words of Glinka (25), contributed nothing. The following quotation from Cotta, taken from Glinka's paper, illustrates this point: "The weathered mantle rock on any bed rock belongs to the latest and, in most cases, most recent historical formations, and this is what the farmer calls soils. It originated from the weathered mantle rock by the admixture of a certain amount of organic matter (humus). The soil did not originate in situ from the weathered native rock; quite frequently the soil was brought in by the action of water." The voluminous work of Cotta contains information for the geologist, the geobotanist, the geographer, and the tiller of the soil, but not for the pedologist.

Girard (23), another contemporary of Fallou, devoted most of his book to the minerals and rocks which are supposed to be the foundation of the soil cover. Very little can be found in his writings on the processes of weathering and soil formation. His views about the role of organic matter agree closely with those of Fallou, as the following quotation illustrates: "The component organic portions of the soil do not determine the existence of the soil as such, for apparently, the soil existed before the appearance of organic life."

Senft (67) considered soils as the product of the rocks, and rocks as ancient compressed soils. Braungart (6) looked upon soil science as a part of petrography and stratigraphy.

Werner (86), the founder of modern geology, did not even attempt to separate soil science from geology. To him soil was the "thin black layer which covers the dry solid mass, consisting of easily crumbled small particles of rock material and earth and of dead remains of vegetation and animals. The soil is a medium in which plants thrive well, root themselves, grow, and bear fruit."

The true geologic point of view on the process of weathering and soil formation was presented by Berendt (3). To him pedology is "a neglected but inseparable part of geognosy and only within its boundaries it may attain its proper development . . . Pedology is not at all the study of the soft, loose, or earthy rock materials, distinct from the solid materials, as contended by many. Both formations are embraced by geognosy, the study of the present earth's crust." Mentioning the differences between the loose formations and the solid rock, Berendt pointed out that "neither time, place, nor mode of formation, nor their composition can divide these into separate scientific disciplines . . . Every soil with which the farmer or forester deals is nothing more than the belt of weathering of a geognostic layer. One might thus conclude that soil science represents the study of the origin, general composition, and transformation of the belt of weathering which appears at the earth's surface . . . Petrography, pedography—the study of native rocks—and pedology are branches of the same science—geognosy." He distinguished between "Boden" and "Grund." The latter is "the native rock which appears to us in undisturbed solid form." The former is "the surface native rock which is mellowed mechanically in contact with the air, which changes it chemically."

Berendt even attempted to attach agronomy to geognosy. Geologic maps were considered by him as an important adjunct to the study of soils, inasmuch as they gave an idea of the parent materials underlying the soils. A specific trait in Berendt's views was the distinction between the loose surface sedimentary materials and soils. This was a decided step forward from the ideas of Fallou, his contemporaries, and his immediate followers. In this respect, his ideas represent a third period in the development of pedology: from Thaer to Fallou, representing the first period, and from Fallou to Berendt, the second.

Ramann (60) shared the views of Berendt and for a long time—until he became acquainted with the ideas of Dokuchaev—he was one of the ardent exponents of the geologic—chemical viewpoint on soils. In his book, "Bodenkunde," Ramann points out that "the relation between precipitation and evaporation, temperature and vegetation will remain the cardinal basis for soil distribution. The chemical and physical properties of the soil, as well as its geology, will remain as subordinate conditions." And yet, the true relation between the building of the soil body and the climate, the regularity of the distribution of climatogenic soils, was not appreciated by Ramann. He did not differentiate between the process of weathering and the process of soil formation. As shown elsewhere in this work, the specificity of the process of soil formation was not recognized until the genetic school of pedology brought out the facts and factors of soil formation. Ramann, even as late as 1917, in his work on "The Evolution and Classification of Soils," (Ch. 3, 53) still clung to the pure geologic point of view in eludicating the processes of soil formation.

Hilgard (30), in his extensive studies of the soils in the United States, could not help but notice the regularity of the distribution of soils under the various physico-geographical conditions of the land. He had the genetic approach, noting the relations of the various soils with the different natural conditions and factors of soil formation. In discussing the relation of soils to climate, Hilgard (29) said: "Since soils are the residual products of the action of meteorological agencies upon rocks, it is obvious that there must exist a more or less intimate relation between the soils of a region and the climatic conditions that prevail or have prevailed therein." He (30, p. 49) also pointed out that "climatic differences may materially influence the character of the soils formed from one and the same kind of rock." He failed, however, to see soils in their morphologic constitution as a result of the soil-forming processes. Fundamentally, the parent rock was the starting point of Hilgard's elucidation of soil characteristics and features, and in this respect he may be considered as an adherent of the geologic school of soil science.

Orth (52) was among the first investigators to appreciate the soil in its constitutional makeup. He pointed out differences in the layers, but failed to correlate them and to recognize the sum total of the layers as a distinct natural unit, the soil body.

The geologic point of view dominated the work of the other early American students of soils. Thus, to Shaler (68), soil was "a mixture of decayed rock and organic matter." Johnson (33) simply stated that "soils are broken and decomposed rock." King (35), one of the keenest of American soil students, and Hopkins (31), another illustrious American student of soils, also held the geologic point of view. Hopkins considered soils more from the standpoint of agronomy. His field was primarily soil fertility. Similarly, the workers in the Bureau of Soils, especially Whitney (87) and Whitney and Cameron (88), disregarded the soil as an object for study. Its manifestations in terms of fertility were of primary consideration. The views of the last three—Hopkins, Whitney, and Cameron—were also, in a way, a chemical approach to the study of soils.

Richthofen (61, 62) was a follower of Fallou, but his wide experiences as a geologist and geographer gave him the geographic concept of the distribution of soils. His great service consisted in his early recognition of the correlation of the environment, especially climate, with the processes of the decomposition of rocks and their formation anew. The soil as a separate and distinct natural body was, however, unknown to Richthofen. To him, geologic formations in their historical perspective were the alpha and omega of the physio-geographic distribution of soils. "The entire earthy cover, as well as the native rocks, are objects of geologic investigation . . . Soil is a loose surface formation, a kind of pathologic condition of the native rock." Richthofen was too intensely preoccupied in his geographic-geologic investigations to note soil formations distinct from geologic formations. His classical researches on loess in general and of China in particular are a source of invaluable information on the relation of parent material to soil formation.

Walther (85), a follower of Richthofen, considered the distribution of soils not from the standpoint of their origin and formation, but from their position with reference to the geologic materials upon which the soils rested.

Dokuchaev, as a trained geologist, started out with the geologic point of view on soils, current in those days. As he came in contact with the vast stretches of Russian chernozem, his keen eye noted the specific characteristics and features (morphology) of the soils in a definite geographic region. In 1879 (12) he stated:

Whether we admit that the southwestern portion of Russia was submerged under the sea in the beginning of the post-tertiary period, as some geologists think, or it was covered by glaciers, as other geologists think, or it was dry land, as still another group of geologists think, matters little. For us it is important, that after this or the other of the given phenomena the upper layers of the soils were apparently subject to various processes due to weathering and to processes due to vegetation; both of these were instrumental in changing the upper horizon of the parent material to a greater or lesser depth. The parent materials which have undergone changes by the mutual activities of air, water, and plants, I call soil. Soils are the surface mineral and organic formations, always more or less colored by the humus, which constantly manifest themselves as a result of the combined activity of the following agencies; living and dead organisms (plants and animals), parent material, climate, and relief.

Dokuchaev appreciated the complex of natural agencies responsible for the processes of soil formation and differentiated, also, the conditions which go to make up the chernozem or any other soil-forming process. In this manner, he laid down the principle of the geographicity of soil formation. The soil as a formation differs from geologic formations inasmuch as its distribution is governed by natural laws in the same manner as are living organisms. Each climatic belt is endowed with a definite flora, fauna, and soil type. The geologic rock formations are distributed with no relation to the climatic conditions of the region. From this point of view, Doku-chaev formulated the fundamental thesis, called by Zakharov (91, p. 7) *the first soil axiom,* that soil is a distinct and independent, natural-historical body. The factors of soil formation, in any climatic zone over a geographic region, determine the type of soil in its genetic constitution as manifested in the profile. "If we know the factors of soil formation, we can predict what the soil would be like." This was one of the theses in the summary of Dokuchaev's doctoral dissertation. The corollary of that is self-evident: "if we know the soil, we can tell the factors (climatic and biotic) prevailing in the region where the soil is located."

In Dokuchaev's interpretation, the soil as a natural formation must be linked with our contemporary climate, and Glinka (27), in discussing Richthofen's work, justly states: "When one speaks of geographical posi-tion, he understands the existence of a natural relation between the present distribution of climatic elements and the present geography of the soil cover. The regionality, as described by Richthofen, has at times no con-nection with the present climatic conditions. Thus, the region of glacial denudation, the accumulation, the river denudation, the abrasion, and the material of volcanic transport exist on the surface of the earth entirely independently of the present climatic condition."

Dokuchaev considered all the factors of soil formation as a complex. Sibirtzev (69), Dokuchaev's collaborator and disciple, integrated them and established their differential role in soil formation. He advanced the idea of the zonal distribution of soils following the climatic zonality. He also developed the idea of intrazonal soils, which explains the occurrence of soils of a particular climatic zone within another zone where its presence cannot be anticipated. In recent years, Afanasiev (1, 2) furthered the idea of the zonality of soils.

Sibirtzev considered moisture as the primary climatic factor in soil formation. In this respect his views coincide with those independently developed later by Hilgard (29) who divided the soils, on the basis of moisture relationships, into arid and humid. To quote Sibirtzev: "More important than the temperature is the humidity of the climate. Elsewhere enough was said about the primary and manifold influence of moisture on mechanical and chemical weathering. It is quite clear that in any isothermic belt the weathering of rocks varies (qualitatively and quan-titatively) with the moisture condition." In speaking of the climatic condi-tions in North America, Sibirtzev stated: "The humidity conditions of the American climate change in an entirely different direction from those of

European Russia: the loss in moisture does not follow the northwest-southeast direction, as in the southern half of European Russia, but the east and west direction. The eastern states are humid; the precipitation is twice as high as in our southern provinces. The western states, on the other hand, are very dry and are known among the Americans by the very inappropriate name 'arid region.' Correspondingly goes the distribution of soils." The views of Sibirtzev (70), why the new concept of soils did not develop in the west are of interest:

> The causes which impeded the independent scientific study of soils in the west, and prevented the establishment of a genuine genetic classification of natural soils, were local, more or less accidental, due to external conditions, and were by no means of an essential nature. Western-European scientists had to deal either with feebly developed soils, mixed with geologic deposits of varying thickness, or with eroded soils; and besides, the soils have changed appreciably through cultivation.
>
> The methods of intensive and deep cultivation of the soils in the west, leaving out of consideration the introduction of various fertilizers, make them an artificially loosened mixture of natural soil material and of the underlying parent rock. The characteristic morphological horizons of the natural soils are hardly distinguishable. The color and structure of the soils are altered, and its composition tends to approach the parent material. Hence, the wide popularity of the geologic-petrographic and physico-chemical ideas on soil classification among the European scientists.

Sibirtzev was the first to expound clearly Dokuchaev's ideas of the soil as a "natural-historical body." His book "Pochvovedenie" marks the introduction of a course in pedology (71).

Dokuchaev's discovery marks the end of an age long period of groping in the dark over the position of the soil in the scheme of natural phenomena. The soil was finally placed as one of the harmoniously organized bodies in nature that can be easily recognized and comprehended. One only wonders how this discovery had not been made earlier. As with many new discoveries, the simplicity becomes apparent only after the light of genius has illumed it. To be sure, there is a measure of scholasticism in some of Dokuchaev's theories. Fundamentally, however, the postulates advanced by him on the position of the soil as an independent body in nature stand the test of scientific analysis and inquiry.

Dokuchaev's discovery ushered in a new glorious epoch in the study of soils. As yet, the modern teachings of pedology have not been fully appreciated. Pedology is becoming the cornerstone upon which all phases of soil studies are being built. Great strides have been made by the pupils and followers of Dokuchaev in elucidating some of the unknown facts, in augmenting the available data, and in expanding and broadening his fundamental ideas. More and more we become cognizant of pedology as a force in advancing our knowledge on soils as such and as medium for crop production.

Glinka's volume (27) on the geographic distribution of soils, after its translation into German and English, had a profound influence on the penetration of Dokuchaev's views into Germany and the United States. Glinka tested the new science, developed it, and compiled the accumulated knowledge in his comprehensive volume "Pochvovedenie" (27). A unique contribution of Glinka, sometimes overlooked, is his researches on buried soils, which offer a great array of facts not only to the pedologist but also to the geologist and climatologist. This work has been furthered by his close friend and associate, Polynov, (55, 56), who has contributed invaluable investigations on the relation of pedology to geology and many other problems on the genesis of the soils.

Nabokikh (48, 49) subjected the new ideas of Dokuchaev to a critical analysis and questioned the validity of some of them. His arguments evoked a heated discussion, with Glinka (26) championing the cause of Dokuchaev. Ototzkii (54), under whose learned leadership the famous Russian soil science journal "Pochvovedenie" (Pedology) was edited for 17 years (1899-1916), made important contributions on the hydrological conditions of various soil zones. Similar investigations were conducted by Vysotskii (84), who is to be remembered in connection with his researches on the moisture régime in the chernozem soils. He also contributed a great deal to the problem of forest soils, the development of the glei horizon, the movement of soluble salts in the soil profile, and many other problems.

Prasolov (57-59) carried on a series of soil surveys. There is practically no corner in the vast stretches of the colossal empire of the U.S.S.R. that Prasolov and his students have not investigated from the standpoint of soil genetics. After the death of Glinka, Prasolov, as the head of the Dokuchaev Soil Institute at the Russian Academy of Science, undertook extensive investigations on the morphological, physical, and chemical properties of soils. The realm of soil cartography may be in a large measure credited to Prasolov. He edited and published Glinka's posthumous contribution: "A Soil Map of the World" (59) and was responsible for the new soil map of the world.

Similar work was carried on by Zakharov (91), another disciple of Dokuchaev. He furthered the principle of vertical zonality of soils developed by Dokuchaev and Sibirtzev. His work on the mountain soils is a distinct contribution. A summary of the Russian school of pedology, as well as his own contributions in pedology, was made available by Zakharov in his textbook "Kurs Pochvovedeniya," A Course in Pedology.

With Prasolov and Zakharov we may link the soil geographer Afanasiev (1), whose contributions on the zonality and classification of soils are unique. He advances many new ideas and presents new facts which corroborate fully the fundamental principles of Dokuchaev and Sibirtzev. Neustruev (50), another illustrious pupil of Dokuchaev, was the pioneer exponent of his teacher's principles by the method of geographic correlation. He was the founder of the school of pedologist-geographers, and his long years of research on the soils of Turkestan, Siberia, and other regions in Russia were summarized in his book "Elements of Soil Geography."

The contributions of Tumin (82) have stimulated greatly the study of the morphological characteristics of the profiles in the various soil zones. He clarified several perplexing problems in the genesis of the different soil types, especially the podzols.

A critical and scholarly analysis of the Dokuchaev School of Pedology has been made by Kossovich (89, 90). He applied the methods of chemistry and physics in interpreting the genesis of soils and in characterizing the morphological features of the various soil types.

Mention should be made also of the notable contributions of Kostychev (41) on the origin and formation of chernozem; of the early investigations (the later contributions made in the United States are discussed presently) of Nikiforov(ff) (51) on the chernozem soil complex and the profile features of the soil in it; of Tanfiliev (74, 75) and of Berg (4) on the same soils and on the problem of loess formation, origin of steppe, and extension of forest region in the northern and southern latitudes; of Korzhinskii (37, 38) and of Kassatkin and Krasyuk (34) on the extension of chernozem into other zones and on the field methods in the study of the soil profile; of Dimo (10, 11), of Dranitsyn (17), and of Sukachev (73) on the profile characteristics of the desert, semidesert, and tundra soils; and of the many other pupils and followers of Dokuchaev, whose investigations are summed up by Glinka (26) in his report to the First International Congress of Soil Science.

Besides their pedologic investigations, many of the workers mentioned have contributed to researches in hydrology, mineralogy, soil solution, and chemistry, physics, and biology of soils. All of these investigations radiate from one central idea and revolve in an orbit around the fundamental principles laid down by Dokuchaev.

Outside of Russia, researches on soil genesis in the pedologic sense have been practically unknown until the first decade of the 20th century. Ramann (60) contributed to our knowledge of soils from a viewpoint closely related to pedology. His system of soil classification is based on climatic elements. He lacked, however, an appreciation of the soil as a natural body. Murgoci (46, 47) from Rumania and Treitz (78-81) from Hungary were among the early disciples of pedologic principles. Treitz and Timko studied under Glinka at the Novo-Alexandria Station in Russia, and Timko published a series of papers on the pedologic aspects of the soils of Hungary.

Outside of Russia, Marbut was the most prominent worker in the field of pedology to appreciate and apply fully the ideas of pedology. Today, his views on the genesis of soils as expounded in his studies on the soils of the United States, South America, and Africa, are undoubtedly as far reaching as those of the most outstanding pedologists in Russia. His contribution *The Soils of the United States* may compare favorably with the best of the prominent Russian pedologists. It is well to remember that in preparing this monumental work Marbut had no pedologic data to speak of, except his personal observations.

With chemical and mechanical data on soils, sampled in most cases with no reference to the constitution of the soil profile and designed for a utilitarian purpose, Marbut had to build single handed a genetic system of soil distribution in the United States. Marbut had no access to the wealth of pedologic material of the Russian masters and had to depend on his own keen observations and logical thinking in developing pedologic principles.

A memorial volume *Life and Work of C. F. Marbut* was published by the Soil Science Society of America. Of the many contributions in this volume,* those that lean on the remarks and sparkling thoughts of Marbut are the most interesting and instructive. They give an insight into the manners of his methods of work that might be worth while to follow. In this respect, the highest honors go to Louise Marbut Moomaw, Marbut's daughter, who has enriched the pedologic literature with the biography of her great father. More than many of Marbut's associates has she caught the spirit of the pedologic principles that have kindled the fires of Marbut's genius. Her brilliant appreciation of her father's work is a fitting tribute from a daughter to a great father. Louise Marbut Moomaw shows a profound knowledge of pedology, and it is regrettable that she has not followed up her calling.

American soil workers, with very few exceptions, have not appreciated what Marbut has done for them and for soil science in the United States. Instead of taking hold and advancing his ideas and extending his methods, his successors have drifted into the business of dramatizing the story of the soils as an object of would be national preservation or suicide, or once more a return to the old utilitarian motive. However, the edifice built by Dr. Marbut, his monograph on "The Soils of the United States,"

---

*It is not the author's intention to give a critical review of this volume. Readers of this book are urged to consult the memorial volume. In this connection, the author wishes to point out that the compilers of this volume have not, for one reason or another, found it necessary to include in the Marbut bibliography his *Introduction* to this book. This contribution of Marbut was probably one of the last major papers he had written.

contains the riches of knowledge which is of permanent value. The great heritage associated with the international master, the great American pedologist, Curtis F. Marbut, is still to be evaluated. The memorial volume is to be looked upon as an introduction to a much more comprehensive analysis of the work of Marbut. It is a task awaiting the new generation of pedologists.

Short Biographical Notes

PLATE 3

FR. ALB. FALLOU

(1794-1877)

Fallou, Fr. Alb., was born in 1794 in Saxony. He studied jurisprudence at the University of Leipzig. Mineralogy became a hobby with him, and his love of nature turned his attention to soils. He was poetically inclined and wrote verse. The last 25 years of his life he lived the life of a dervish, close to nature, away from the hustle and bustle of the city. He never married and died at the age of 83 in 1877. (Quoted from Yarilov.)

PLATE 4

VASILII VASIELEVICH DOKUCHAEV

(1846-1903)

Dokuchaev, Vasilii Vasielevich, was born February 17, 1846, in the village of Milukovo, Smolensk. His father was a priest and he wished his son to be one. The young Dokuchaev, therefore, attended the Theological Seminary. Upon graduation, he was awarded a fellowship at the Theological Academy in St. Petersburg. After the first year he turned to the natural science. An episode of Dokuchaev's student days, related by Ototzkii [The Life of Dokuchaev. Pochvovedenie (1903) 5: 319-342], characterizes some of the erratic tendencies which apparently burdened him all his life and cut it short. When Dokuchaev had to choose a subject for his graduation thesis, he approached Professor Puzyrevskii, in charge of the courses in mineralogy. The following conversation took place between the ambitious young student and the elderly learned professor, a man of experience, full of wisdom and with a highly developed sense of humor. Said Puzyrevskii: "Tell me, young man, what are you occupied with primarily?" The answer was frank, direct, and brief: "Playing cards and drinking." To this the professor remarked: "Great! Continue and do not spoil life with dry science."

Dokuchaev specialized in mineralogy and geology, became curator of the geological laboratory at the St. Petersburg University in 1872. His geological studies brought him in contact with soils, a study of which remained his life work. He was connected with the university as a lecturer in mineralogy, led extensive expeditions studying soils, and was in contact with the most important investigations of the soils of Russia. His publications, which began to appear in 1877, were immediately recognized as a harbinger to pedology. His famous book "Russian Chernozem" appeared in 1883. He died October 26, 1903, after a prolonged illness, from a complication of diseases.

PLATE 5

NIKOLAI MIKHAILOVICH SIBIRTZEV

(1860-1899)

Sibirtzev, Nikolai Mikhailovich, was born in Archangelsk in 1860, and studied in the Theological Seminary and in the St. Petersburg University, where he took up the natural sciences. Upon his graduation from the university in 1882, he was invited by Dokuchaev to serve as a professor at the university in connection with the soil researches of the Nizhnenovogorod government. In 1894 he was called to the newly established chair of pedology at the Novo-Alexandria Agricultural Institute, with which he was connected to the end of his short life. He died in 1899 from tuberculosis. In the short span of his life he succeeded in bringing out a series of important contributions in which he developed the new ideas of Dokuchaev. Among his most outstanding works are his book *Pochvovedenie,* the first of its kind on the new Russian school of soil science, and soil maps of Russia and of the world. (After Barakov and Glinka in *Pochvovedenie* (1900), V. 2, No. 4).

PLATE 6

KONSTANTIN DIMITRIEVICH GLINKA

(1867-1927)

Glinka, Konstantin Dimitrievich, was born in Smolensk in 1867, and was graduated from the St. Petersburg University in 1889, where he studied mineralogy under Dokuchaev. He was retained by the latter as an assistant. When Dokuchaev took up the reorganization work at the Novo-Alexandria Agricultural Institute, Glinka was invited to occupy the chair in mineralogy and geology. Upon Sibirtzev's death, in 1899, Glinka succeeded as professor of pedology. He conducted many soil research expeditions throughout Russia and western Europe, and the culmination of all these were his books "Pochvovedenie" and "The Great Soil Groups of the World and Their Development." The latter was first translated into German about 1914 by Stremme and later, in 1928, into English by Marbut. Since then the Dokuchaev school has been penetrating western Europe and America. Glinka, more than any other of the pupils of Dokuchaev, became known to the western world and was recognized as the leader of the new school of pedology.

The personal contact of the author with the late Doctor Glinka during his stay in the United States in 1927 in connection with the First International Congress of Soil Science served as a great stimulus to a more profound study of the Dokuchaev school of pedology. It was the imposing personality of Glinka, the encouragement given in conversations from day to day during this brief but close contact, that prompted the author to undertake a series of lectures at the New Jersey College of Agriculture on the Dokuchaev School of Pedology. At this Congress Glinka was elected president of the International Society of Soil Science, but he did not live long enough to inaugurate the plans he had for the Second International Congress of Soil Science. Soon after his return from the United States, Glinka became seriously ill. His malady was diagnosed as cancer of the stomach, and on November 2, 1927, he died, surrounded by his many pupils and mourned by pedologists the world over.

PLATE 7
EUGENE WOLDEMAR HILGARD
(1833-1916)

Hilgard, Eugene Woldemar,* was born January 5, 1833, at Zweibrücken, in Rheinish Bavaria. His father was a lawyer, holding the position of chief justice of the court of appeals of the province. Judge Hilgard, having been born and educated in the shadow of the French Revolution and being of pronounced liberal views, stoutly opposed the supersedence of the Code Napoleon by the liberal laws of the old régime. In 1836 he emigrated to the United States with his family and settled on a farm at Belleville, Illinois. The son Eugene was sent to the University of Heidelberg in 1849 and graduated with honors and a doctorate in 1853. He also studied at Zürich and at Freiberg in Saxony. Returning to America he began geological exploration work in Mississippi in 1855 and was appointed state mineralogist in 1858. In 1860 he visited Spain for the second time, married, and upon his return to the United States, resumed his work. During the intervention of the Civil War he pursued the chemical work required by the Southern Confederacy. In 1866 he was chosen professor of chemistry in the University of Mississippi, then professor of geology, zoology, and botany. In 1872 he left Mississippi to take a position on the faculty of the University of Michigan, and in 1874 he was called to California where he remained until he died, January 8, 1916.

While developing agricultural instruction in the University of California, he proceeded with research work and published his first results in 1877. His work in the investigation of soils in connection with their native vegetation, of the influence of climate on the formation of soils, and especially of the so-called "alkali soils" achieved for him a reputation as wide as the world of science.

Hilgard's pedological investigations began with his work as a geologist. In 1860 he published an extensive "Report on the Geology and Agriculture of the State of Mississippi." In the 400 pages of this report the ground work of Hilgard's long years of research was laid. His book *Soils* published in 1906 is still, for the serious student in soils, a source of knowledge and inspiration. He was not only a pedologist

---

*The biographical sketch is from a reprint of a paper "In Memoriam Eugene Woldemar Hilgard." Univ. of California Chronicle, V. 18, No. 2 (1916).

but also an agronomist, botanist, and, of course, geologist. Among the Russian pedologists Hilgard is considered as one of the few great scholars, and his works are
well known. Tulaikov, a prominent Russian pedologist-agronomist, upon his visit to
California, wrote a paper on Hilgard and his work; the last paragraph is characteristic of the esteem which Hilgard commanded: "We pedologists owe to Hilgard more
than any of the agronomists. It might appear to us, pedologists of the Russian school,
that we look upon the soil from a broader point of view than Hilgard, but I would
not undertake to answer the following question: Is not the view on soils of the old
pedologist-agronomist Hilgard more vital and fruitful than the view of the 'pure'
pedologist in our own fatherland?" (From N. M. Tulaikov's paper in Pochvovedenie
(1910) 12: 217-226).

PLATE 8

EMIL RAMANN

(1851-1926)

Ramann, Emil, was born April 30, 1851, in Dorotheenthal, near Erfurt. He received his early training from his father, who was interested in the natural sciences. After his father's death, young Ramann prepared for publication his father's unfinished work on "Butterflies." Originally Ramann took up pharmacy and later studied chemistry at the University of Berlin. In 1880 he received his first appointment as assistant at the Eberwalde School of Forestry, and in 1886, he became director of the Department of Forestry at the Prussian Forestry Experiment Station. In the year 1900 he was appointed to the chair of soil science and agricultural chemistry at the University of Munich as the successor of Ebermayer and remained there until 1925. At the same time he was director of the Soil Science Institute of the Bavarian Forest Experiment Station.

His most important experimental work was done on forest soils. His researches, observations, and investigations during his many journeys cover many phases of soil formation from geological, geobotanical, and chemical viewpoints. In all these fields he was the master-mind. His book *Bodenkunde,* the first edition of which appeared in 1893 under the title of "Forstliche Bodenkunde und Standortslehre," is a classic in the field of pedology and soil science in general. In a later book (published in 1918) *Bodenbildung und Bodeneinteilung* (this was translated into English by Whittles in

1928 under the title *The Evolution and Classification of Soils*), Ramann summarized his life-long experience and investigations on soils. He came very close to the genetic point of view, apparently under the influence of the Russian pedologists whose views at that time began to penetrate into western Europe. We read in the introduction to his book: "We shall arrive at a clearer understanding of the processes of soil formation if we take climate as our starting point." He constructed a climatogenic system of soil classification even though he failed to appreciate the views of the genetic school of pedology, the so-called Dokuchaev school.

The teachings of Ramann embody the best that could be found in the pseudo-pedological researches (in reality these were the applied phases of pedology collectively known as "soil science") of Germany and western Europe with a definite pedologic slant. In this respect, Ramann may be compared with the savant of American pedology, Hilgard. His name will remain among the chosen few great pedologists of the generation that has just passed into history.

PLATE 9

CURTIS F. MARBUT

(1863-1935)

Marbut, Curtis Fletcher, was born July 19, 1863, in Spring River Valley, Missouri, on his grandfather's homestead where his mother stayed while her husband served in The Union Home Guard during the Civil War. His father was a farmer in Barry County along Little Flat Creek. From the biographical sketch written by Marbut's daughter, published in *The Life and Work of C. F. Marbut*, it is clear that it was Marbut's mother who encouraged his love for learning. His school attendance began in a one room hewn-log schoolhouse with no windows. The school terms were of only 4 months duration, beginning in July. At the age of 17, we find young Marbut teaching school, and with the earnings of 4 months ($20.00 per month) he managed to attend the county school where he learned Latin and a little Greek. In 1885 he entered the University of Missouri and graduated in 1889. In 1893 he enrolled as a graduate student at Harvard and received the Master of Arts degree and completed his residence requirement for Doctor of Philosophy in 1895. His thesis on *The Physical Features of Missouri* was published in 1896. He left the University in 1895 without taking the oral examinations for his degree and started his career as a geologist with the Missouri Geological Survey where he stayed until 1910. The last 5 years of this period he had directed the Soil Survey of the State. Upon the invitation of Dr. Whitney, Marbut joined the Bureau of Soils, United States Department of Agriculture, as the head of the Division of Soil Survey. He entered the field of soil studies with the broad outlook of a scientific geographer having travelled extensively in Europe, South America, and Africa and valuable perspective as a geologist in charge of the geologic survey of Missouri. He was influenced by the teachings of Shaler, the author of the classical monograph *Origin and Nature of Soils,* and also by the work of Hilgard.

In the formative period of the U. S. Soil Survey, the fieldmen hopelessly strove to classify something with which they were in intimate contact, but the fundamental features of which they did not recognize. The Soil Survey was inaugurated to develop a system of classifying soils for land utilization. The survey, therefore, followed these lines in describing soils: 1, geologic origin; 2, texture; and 3, agriculture. Gradually, the survey broadened its system of characterizing soils and developed the concept of *soil type* as the fundamental unit of classification. This system embraced the textural characteristics of the soil under the name of *soil class* (loam, sandy loam, etc.); and group characteristics, such as color of surface soil and subsoil, relief, drainage, and geologic origin of material, under the name of *soil series* (Sassafras, Marshall, Barnes, etc.), using a geographic term which usually refers to a locality.

When Dr. Marbut became acquainted, in 1915-1916, with the Russian genetic school of Soil Science, better known as the Dokuchaev school, he seized the opportunity of rebuilding the classification system, fitting in the series into the natural soil zones in their geographic distribution. Marbut was not satisfied with the then existing classication and had expressed his concern over the prolific naming of soil series.

From the genetic point of view, the series name is of minor importance, the descriptive material adding little to the pedogenic characteristics of the soil groups. The information made available is of a local nature, designed primarily for utilitarian purposes. However, some of the facts on the profile features are helpful in interpreting the indivuality of the soil. In his paper on Marbut (in the memorial volume on the *Life and Work of Marbut*) Johnson quotes a statement by Marbut: "Forget about the names of soil types, get the characteristics.' This characterizes the broader outlook of Marbut on the classification system of the U. S. Soil Survey. He tried to limit their number and combine them within the framework of the genetic characteristics of the soils. His system of *Soil Categories* (see his monograph *Soils of the United States*) was a starting point which he was to develop later.

Marbut appreciated the importance of getting acquainted first hand with the Russian literature in pedology. To this end, he undertook, at the age of 70, to learn Russian. It was the writers good fortune to discuss with him problems in pedology at various meetings and his visits in New Jersey. At the meetings of the Third International Congress of Soil Science in 1935, at Oxford, England, Marbut had advanced far enough in his studies of Russian to conduct an ordinary conversation.

The death of Marbut cut short the rich store of knowledge that was to be ours. He died in Harbin, August 25, 1935, having contracted pneumonia while on the Trans-Siberian train on the way to China to organize the Soil Survey of that vast country. His untimely death deprived us of what would have been a new chapter in the history of pedology.

References

1. Afanasiev, Ya. N. 1922 Zonal systems of soils (Russian). Reprint from "Memoires Gorki Agr. Inst." 1-83; see also "Russian Pedological Investigations." V (1927) Acad. of Sci., U.S.S.R. (English)

2. Afanasiev, Ya. N. 1931 Fundamental Features of the Earth's Soil Surface (Russian or German). Belorussian Acad. of Science, Minsk. 1-101.

3. Berendt, G. 1877 Die Umgegend von Berlin. Allgemeine Erläuterungen zur geognostisch-agronomischen Karte derselben. I. Der nordwestern Berlins. *Abhandlung zur geol. Spezielkarte v. Preussen u. Thüringschen Staaten* 2: 68-70.

4. Berg, L. 1922 Climate and Life (Russian). Leningrad.

5. Berzelius, J. J. 1803 Lehrbuch der Chemie.

6. Braungart, R. 1876 Die Wissenschaft in der Bodenkunde. Leipzig-Berlin. (Original not seen).

7. Cotta, B. 1852 Praktische Geognosie für Land u. Forstwirte und Techniker. Dresden.

8. Cotta, B. 1858 Deutschlands Boden. I-II. Leipzig. (Original not seen).

9. Davy, Humphry. 1813 Elements of Agricultural Chemistry. London.

10. Dimo, N. 1910 Report on soil investigations in the region of the eastern part of the Golodnaya Steppe, Samarkand Province (Russian).

11. Dimo, N. and Keller, B. 1907 In the province of the semidesert (Russian). Saratov.

12. Dokuchaev, V. V. 1879 Abridged historical account and critical examination of the principal soil classifications existing (Russian). *Trans. St. Petersburg Soc. of Nat.* 10: 64-67.

13. Dokuchaev, V. V. 1879 Preliminary report on the investigation of the southeastern part of the chernozem of Russia. *Trudy Imp. Vol. Ekonom. Obshches.* (Original not seen).

14. Dokuchaev, V. V. 1879 The chernozem of European Russia (Russian). St. Petersburg.

15. Dokuchaev, V. V. 1883 Russian Chernozem (Russian). St. Petersburg.

16. Dokuchaev, V. V. 1893 The Russian steppes. Study of the soils in Russia, its past and present. Dept. Agr. Min. of Crown Domains for the World's Columbian Exposition. St. Petersburg (English). See also English bulletin in connection with the exposition: Agriculture and forestry in Russia.

17. Dranitsyn, D.   1913   The soils of western Zaangar' in the Government of Enissei.   Trudy po Issledov. Pochv. Asiat. Rossii za 1910, no. I, St. Petersburg.

18 Dranitsyn, D.   1916 A journey through Algiers.   *Trudy Dokuchaev. Pochv. Komit.,* Contribution no. 3.

19. Enculescu, P. 1928. Die Bodenkarte der steppe von Süd-Bessarabien. *Proc. and Papers. First Inter. Cong. Soil Sci.* 4 : 469-471 (Some of his earlier papers are noted in the bibliography).

20. Fallou, Fr. Alb.   1855   Die Ackererden des Königreichs Sachsen, etc.

21. Fallou, Fr. Alb.   1862   Pedologie oder allgemeine und besondere Bodenkunde.   Dresden.

22. Fallou, Fr. Alb.   1875   Die Hauptbodenarten der Nord und Ostsee-Länder deutschen Reiches naturwissenschaftlich, landwirtschaftlich betrachtet.   (Original not seen).

23. Girard, H.   1868   Grundlagen der Bodenkunde.   Halle.   On p. 276 he gives his definition of soils.

24. Glinka, K. D.   1900   Sibirtzev, his scientific activities.   *Pochvovedenie* (Pedology) 2 : 245-251.

25. Glinka, K. D.   1902   A few pages of the history of theoretical pedology.   *Pochvovedenie* (Pedology) 2 : 117-152.

26. Glinka, K. D.   1928   Dokuchaev's ideas in the development of pedology and cognate sciences.   *Proc. and Papers First Inter. Cong. Soil Sci.* 1 : 116-136; see also "Russian Pedological Investigations" I (1927), Acad. of Sci. U.S.S.R. (English).

27. Glinka, K. D.   1932   Pochvovedenie (Pedology).   Ed. 5 Moscow. See also: The Great Soil Groups of the World, translated from the German by Marbut (1927).   Edwards Bros., Ann Arbor, Mich.

28. Hausmann   1930   Lehrbuch der land- und forstwirtschaftlichen Bodenkunde.   (Original not seen).

29. Hilgard, E. W.   1893   The relation of soils to climate.   Meter. Bur. Bul. 2, U. S. Dept. Agr. Revised 1892; also Cal. Agr. Exp. Sta. Rpt. for 1892-93 and part of 1894, p. 100.   For a complete bibliography of Hilgard's work see "In Memoriam of Eugene Woldemar Hilgard."   Univ. Cal. Chron. 18, no. 2.

30. Hilgard, E. W.   1906   Soils.   Macmillan Co., New York.

31. Hopkins, G. G.   1910   Soil Fertility and Permanent Agriculture. Boston.

32. Hundeshagen, J.   1830   Forstliche Berichte und Miscellen.   (Original not seen).

33. Johnson, S. W. 1883 How crops feed: A treatise on the atmosphere and the soil as related to the nturition of agricultural plants. New York. The first edition appeared in 1870.

34. Kassatkin, V. G. and Krasyuk, A. A. 1917 Manual for Soil Investigations in the Field. Byuro po Zemled. i Pochvoved. Uchen. Komit. Minister. Zemledeliya. Contribution XXV. Petrograd.

35. King, F. H. 1901 Physics of Agriculture. Madison, Wis.

36. Kortes, S. 1818 Was ist Humus? Amelong.

37. Korzhinskii, S. 1887 Preliminary report on the soil and geobotanical investigations in the year 1886-7 in the governments of Kazan, Samara, Ufa, Perm, and Vyatka. *Trudy Obshch. Estest. Kazansk. Univer.* 16, no. 6.

38. Korzhinskii, S. 1891 The northern limits of the chernozem region of the eastern belt in European Russia from the botanical-geographic and soil standpoint. *Trudy Obshchest. Estest. pri Kazan. Univers.* XXII, Bul. 6.

39. Kossovich, P. 1910 Soil forming processes as the foundation principles of the genetic soil classification. *Zhur. Opyt. Agron.* 11 : 679-703.

40. Kossovich, P. 1911 Osnovy ucheniya o pochve (Principles of Pedology), pt. II, St. Petersburg. This title appeared in German under the name *"Schwarzerde."*

41. Kostychev, P. 1886 The soils of the chernozem region of Russia, their origin and properties. Pt. I: The formation of chernozem (Russian). St. Petersburg.

42. Krause, G. C. L. 1832 Bodenkunde and Klassifikation des Bodens nach seinen physischen, etc. Gotha.

43. Kühn, Jul. 1864 On the scientific basis of soil science. *Ztsch. des landw. Central-Vereins der Provinz Sachsen.* 21 (24?) : 13. (Original not seen).

44. Liebig, J. von 1861 Letters on Modern Agriculture. New York.

45. Marbut, C. F. 1927 A scheme for soil classification. *Proc. and Papers, First Inter. Cong. of Soil Sci.* 4 : 1-31.

46. Murgoci, G. 1903 Clasificatia naturale a solurilor, dupa Sibirtzef (from a list of references in a paper (French) on the soil zones of Rumania, 1911; in this list the earlier papers of Murgoci, Enculescu and others are given).

47. Murgoci, G. 1910 Zonale de soluri naturale ale Romaniei. *Anuarul Institutului Geologic,* v. 4 (was published in French in: Revue du Petrole IV Ann. (1911) No. 6-7, 21 pages. Abstract in *Int. Mitt. Bodenk.* I (1911), p. 176).

48. Nabokikh, A. I. 1902 The classification problem in soil science. Sel'skoe Khoz. i. Lesovod. no. 4 and no. 12. See also *Pochvovedenie* (Pedology) 4 (1902) p. 195.

49. Nabokikh, A. I. 1914 On the method of field and laboratory study of soils. *Zapiski Imper. Obshch. Sel. Khoz. Yuzh. Rossii,* No. 1-2, pp. 1-66.

50. Neustruev, S. S. 1930 Elementy Geografii Pochv. (Elements of Soil Geography). Moscow-Leningrad; see also "Russian Pedological Investigations," III. Acad. Sci., U.S.S.R. (English).

51. Nikiforov, K. K. 1916 A morphologic description of the chernozem in the northern section of the Don province. *Trudy Dokuchaev. Pochv. Komit.* no. 4, 86 p.

52. Orth, A. 1909 Die geologischen Verhältnisse des norddeutschen Schwemmlandes, u.s.w. Habilitationsschrift, Halle. (Original not seen).

53. Orth, A. 1909 Beitrag zur Kenntnis des Bodens der Umgegend von Berlin. *Landw. Jahrb.* 38, Erganzungab. 5.

54. Ototzkii, P. 1905 The ground waters, origin, activity, and distribution. (Russian). Pt. II. (Original not seen).

55. Polynov, B. B. 1927 Contributions of Russian scientists to paleopedology. (English). Russian Pedological Investigations, VIII, U. S. S. R. Acad. of Sci.

56. Polynov, B. B. 1933 From the sub-commission for the compilation of the soil map of Asia by the Inter. Soc. of Soil Science. (Russian). Contribution to the Knowledge of Soils of Asia, no. 2: 3-8. U. S. S. R. Academy of Sci., Dokuchaev Soil Sci. Institute.

57. Prasolov, L. I. 1909 The soils of the Lepsinsk County. Trudy pochv. botan. expedit. under the editorship of Glinka, no. 4.

58. Prasolov, L. I. 1925 The soils of Turkestan (Russian). Tashkhet.

59. Prasolov, L. I. 1927 The World Soil Map of Glinka. *Priroda,* no. 6:573-580; see also Russian Pedological Investigations VI. Acad. Sci. U.S.S.R. (English).

60. Ramann, E. 1905 Bodenkunde. Jul. Springer. Berlin, ed. 2.

61 Richthofen, Ferdinand Freiherr, v. 1882 China, Bd. 1 u. 2.

62. Richthofen, Ferdinand Freiherr, v. 1888 Führer für Forschungsreisende.

63. Ruprecht, F. 1866 Geobotanical Investigations on Chernozem. (Russian). St. Petersburg.

64. Saidel, T. 1928 Die Bodenkarte von Rumänien, 1:1,500,000. *Proc. and Papers, First. Int. Cong. Soil Sci.* 4: 477-478.

65. Schmalz, Fr. 1824 Versuch einer Einleitung zum Bonitiren und Klassifizieren des Bodens. Leipzig.

66. Schübler, G. 1830 Grundsätze der Agrikulturchemie in näherer Beiziehung auf Land und forstwirtschaftliche. Gewerbe. Erster und Zweiter Theil, 1-240 and 1-272. Leipzig.

67. Senft, F. 1877 Lehrbuch der Gesteins-und Bodenkunde, ed. 2. See chapter on soils, especially, pp. 384-391.

68. Shaler, N. S. 1891 The origin and nature of soils. U. S. Geol. Survey, 12th Ann. Rept. 1890-91 (pt. 1) : 213-245.

69. Sibirtzev, N. M. 1895 Genetic classification of soils. *Zap. Novo.- Aleksandr. Agr. Inst.* 9 : 1-23.

70. Sibirtzev, N. M. 1898 Chernozem in Different Countries (Russian). Public lectures.

71. Sibirtzev, N. M. 1900 Pochvovedenie (Pedology). St. Petersburg.

72. Sprengel, C. 1837 Die Bodenkunde oder Lehre vom Boden nebst einer vollständigen Einleitung zur chemischen Aanalyse der Ackererde. Leipzig.

73. Sukachev, V. 1911 On the problem of perpetual freezing in the soil. Izv. Akad. Nauk. St. Petersburg.

74. Tanfiliev, G. 1894 The limits of Forests in Southern Russia. (Russian).

75. Tanfiliev, G. 1911 The limits of Forests in Polar Russia. (Russian).

76. Thaer, Al. D. 1809, 1810, 1812 Grundsätze der rationellen Land-wirtschaft. Volumes 1, 2, 3, and 4. The quotations are from the 5th edition published in 1853.

77. Treitz, P. 1901 Die Klimatischen Bodenzonen Ungarns. *Földtani Közlöny,* v. 31, No. 10-12.

78. Treitz, P. 1910 Die Aufgabe der Agrogeologie. *Földtani Közlöny,* v. 40, No. 7-8 (Abstract in Int. Mitt. Bodenk. I (1911), p. 393).

79. Treitz, P. 1910 Les sols et les changeménts du climat. Stockholm.

80. Treitz, P. 1924 Magyarázo az orsz. átnézetes Klimazonalis talajter-kephez. (Földt. Inter. Budapest).

81. Treitz, P. 1924 Wesen and Bereich der Agrogeologie. Compt. Rend. de la Conf. extraord. agroped. a Prague 1922. Prague.

82. Tumin, G. M. 1912 A survey of the general character of soil morphology and its changes according to the zones. *Zhur. Opyt. Agron.* 13 : 321-353.

83. Vernadskii, V. I. 1937 Soil analysis from the geochemical point of view. *Pedology* (U. S. S. R.) No. 1 : 8-16.

84. Vysotskii, G. N. 1899 Hydrological and geobiological observations in Veliko-Anadol I. Illuvium. Pochvovedenie (Pedology) I: 36-44; II. Structure of soil and subsoil I: 85-97; III. Moisture in soil and subsoil I: 165-182; IV. Surface waters I: 239-254; V. Ground waters, processes of washing in and washing out, 2 (1900): 22-39; 99-113; VI. About springs and the movement of salts in the soil 2: 113-121.

85. Walther, J. 1893-1894 Einleitung in der Geologie als historische Wissenschaft. Abt. III, s. 554. (Quoted from Glinka).

86. Werner. 1818. Allgemeine Betrachtungen über den festen Erd-körper. (Quoted from Yarilov's "Pedology.")

87. Whitney, M. 1892 Some physical properties of soils in their rela-tion to moisture and crop distribution. U. S. Weather Bureau Bul. 4. See also his other publications from the U. S. D. A.

88. Whitney, M. and Cameron, F. K. 1903 The chemistry of the soil as related to crop production. U. S. Dept of Agr. Bur. of Soils, Bul. 22. See also Cameron's work on soil solution and other subjects.

89. Yarilov, A. A. 1901 Pedology, Volumes I and II. St. Petersburg.

90. Yarilov, A. A. 1904 Fallou, Fr. Alb., the founder of pedology. *Pochvovedenie* (Pedology) 6: 125-135.

91. Zakharov, S. A. 1927 Kurs Pochvovedeniya (A Course in Pedol-ogy). Moscow-Leningrad; see also: Russian Pedological In-vestigations (1927) II, Acad. Sci., U.S.S.R. (English).

CHAPTER III

SOIL DEFINED, SOIL MORPHOLOGY AND METHODS
OF STUDYING IT

A definition is a descriptive statement conveying the properties and characteristics of an object in nature, or the meaning of an idea, phenomenon, or a term. As much as possible, a definition should be scientific, i. e., true to established facts. And lastly, a definition must be brief and expressed in clear and simple language.

No well rounded definition for *soil* was possible until its properties and characteristics had been identified in nature. Soil had been defined long before Dokuchaev had discovered its place in the scheme of natural objects. However, none of the old definitions stand the tests outlined above.

In the early days, soil was defined as the upper loose layer of the earth suitable for plant growth. As late as 1917, Ramann (53, p. 1) defined soil as "the uppermost layer of the solid crust of the earth; it consists of rocks that have been reduced to small fragments and have been more or less changed chemically, together with the remains of plants and animals that live on it and use it." Such a definition does not distinguish between soil and loose rock material; it does not limit the depth of the soil; and it fails to bring out the inherent characteristics of the soil as an independent body in nature.

Hilgard (Ch. 2, 20) defined soil as "the more or less loose and friable material in which, by means of their roots, plants may or do find a foothold and nourishment, as well as other conditions of growth." This is a purely agronomic or plant physiological definition, as is that of Wahnschaffe (71, p. 3), Mitscherlich (40, 41), and other western European soil workers, which reads as follows: "Soil is a mixture of pulverized solid particles, water, and air which may serve as a carrier of available plant food materials for growth." These definitions may be summed up as the concept that the soil is just a medium for plant growth. Under these definitions, the sand and solution cultures are also soils.

Much more satisfactory than the few definitions enumerated and those implied in the preceding chapter are those proposed by Dokuchaev and his pupils. Dokuchaev defined soils as "the surface and adjoining horizons of parent material (irrespective of the kind) which have undergone, more or less, a natural change under the influence of water, air, and various species of organisms—living or dead; this change is reflected, to a certain degree, in the composition, structure, and color of the products of weathering." (Quoted from Kossovich (Ch. 2, 39). Such a definition excludes the soil from the geological system of mantle rock and gives it and independent status.

The pupils of Dokuchaev, in their zeal to escape the erroneous western European concept on soils, swung to another extreme. In the words of Marbut (Ch. 2, 45): "This (the Russian viewpoint) caused in Europe, and to a lesser extent in this country, a stampede to the Russian point of view in which the soil type is defined in terms of the climatic forces which are supposed to have brought about the development of its general characteristics. Instead of the old geologic basis of definition we adopted a climatic basis." Indeed, Dokuchaev's definition of soil designates the soil body in terms of the soil-forming processes instead of the soil body characteristics which are a result of these processes.

The Dokuchaev definition, with slight modification, has been current among the Russian workers. Occasionally, some of them have voiced criticism of this definition. Thus, Kossovich said (Ch. 3, 39): "The sum-total of the physico-chemical and biological processes which act directly in the soil and manifest themselves in various forms is the natural basis for grouping soils . . . The construction of a soil classification on the basis of coordinating individual factors of soil formation (parent material, climate, vegetation, position, age of soil, etc.) was carried out by Sibirtzev. This was a great step forward. *However, the classification of soils with any one factor as the basis does not seem to be promising. The genetic soil classification should be based on the internal properties and characteristics of the soil itself."* Kossovich, however, failed to embody his criticisms fully in his own definition which states that "the soil represnts all those surface horizons of the hard parent material in which physico-chemical processes take place under the influence of the atmospheric agencies and in the presence of vegetation and animals."

Zakharov, a pupil of Dokuchaev, defines (Ch. 2, 91, p. 4) soil as "the surface loose portion of the earth's crust, which formed under the mutual activities of plants, animals, and atmospheric agencies." Again, this is a definition in terms of the soil forming processes.

It was Marbut who made a definite step forward in defining soil in terms of soil characteristics instead of soil-forming processes: *"The soil consists of the outer layer of the earth's crust usually unconsolidated ranging in thickness from a mere film to a maximum of somewhat more than ten feet which differs from the material beneath it, also usually unconsolidated, in color, structure, texture, physical constitution, chemical composition, biological characteristics, probably chemical processes, in reaction and morphology."*

It seems, however, that any modern definition of the soil, which would place pedology on the same level with the other natural sciences, should embody the statement that the soil is "an independent natural body." A point might also be raised about the phrase: "the outer layer of the earth's crust, which conveys the earlier geological concept. Besides, the term "outer layer" may be wrongly confused with the term "surface layer." Our knowledge of *soils as a natural body* tells us that we may have soils even below the surface; for example, the buried soils which have preserved their characteristics as well-defined soil bodies.* It seems, therefore, that the phrase "the outer layer of the earth's crust" may be omitted from Marbut's definition. For the sake of brevity, the clause "ranging in thickness from a mere film to a maximum of somewhat more than ten feet" may be supplanted by the phrase "variable depth." Further, the designations "color, structure, and texture" may be omitted, since these are essentially physical and morphological properties. Such expressions as "chemical composition" and "probably chemical processes. and reaction" are included in the phrase "chemical composition and properties." And finally, any definition of soil should embody the concept of horizon formation, one of the most important characteristics of the soil body.

Soil may thus be defined as follows: *The soil is a natural body of mineral and organic constituents, differentiated into horizons, of variable depth, which differs from the material below in morphology, physical makeup, chemical properties and composition, and biological characteristics.* The introduction of the phrase "of mineral and organic constituents" in the definition deliniates the soil from peats and mucks.

Morphology of Soils

Morphology is a term introduced by Goethe (1749-1832) in 1817. In the early days of its usage, morphology was applied only to botany and zoology, but later almost all of the natural sciences adopted it. The first to apply the morphological method in the study of soil, according to Zakharov (Ch. 2, 91), was Ruprechat (Ch. 2, 63).

Morphology is not a science; it is an aid to science, one of the methods used in scientific investigations. In a way, it is an art which requires keen observation and ability to describe and record in words and drawings an object studied. The primary aim of morphology is description.

---

*Polynov (Ch. 2, 55) introduced the concept *paleopedology* a branch of pedology dealing with buried soils.

Soil morphology, therefore, means nothing more than a description of the soil body, its appearance, features, and general characteristics as expressed in the profile of a virgin soil.

In the early history of soil studies, the viewpoint prevailing at the time determined the method of studying soils. Thus, during the period of the geologic view, the petrographic and mineralogical composition of the soil was of primary importance. The chemical-agronomic point of view applied the procedures of analytical chemistry in studying the soil mass within the zone of root penetration and the availability of plant nutrients in the so-called surface soils and subsoils.

From a morphological point of view, the soil is an organized body. As expressed by Tumin (Ch. 2, 82): "A soil may be looked upon as a body with a genetic complex of horizons formed in the process of humification and humus fixation." The morphological type of a soil implies certain specific characteristics in the construction and constitution of the horizons; each type, so to speak, has a constant orderly system of relationships within the profile. Within each soil zone the particular morphological type may develop on various kinds of parent material. We may, therefore, have podzols (as a morphological term) on loess, on loams, on clays, on sands, etc. (mechanical and chemical composition and properties). And even within each morphological textural type, there may be subdivisions due to factors of micro-relief, such as a slight elevation or depression.

Studies of the soil anatomy have shown that any profile consists of three or four genetic layers: 1, humus decay-accumulative; 2, eluvial; 3, illuvial; and 4, parent material immediately below the illuvial horizon. No matter what soil one examines, as long as it is a mature virgin soil, in any climatic zone, in any geographic region, the profile characteristics as outlined hereinafter, are to be found.

Studying the morphological features of any soil profile, one must observe whether the parent material, upon which the soil formers, or factors of soil-formation, left their impressions and produced the soil body, is petrographically and mineralogically homogenous. Infrequently, the parent material through the depth of the profile consists of geologic deposits of an assortment of petrographic and mineralogic compositions. There might be, for example, a thin layer of clay at the surface, followed by a layer of silt, sand, or any other mechanical fraction. A condition of this sort is apt to occur in parent material of alluvial, lacustrine, delta, or other origin associated with transported materials. Another point to consider is whether the profile is intact, with all the component parts of the soil body in place. Under certain conditions—deforestation of mountain slopes, for example—forces of erosion remove the surface horizon, and consequently we must diagnose a crippled state of the soil body.

The successive steps in examining and describing the morphology of the soil are applicable to all profiles irrespective of the origin of the parent material or the state of the soil body.

The following characteristics are to be looked for: 1, color; 2, constitution; 3, habitus of the profile; 4, depth of profile and thickness of respective horizons; 5, texture of soil material; 6, structure; 7, concretions and foreign intrusions; and 8, miscellaneous observations. These characteristics are scrutinized first of all by four of the natural senses: sight, touch, smell, and sometimes taste.

Color.—Differences in color may serve as a means of differentiating the successive horizons in the profile. These differences are immediately apparent as the profile is exposed. In general, the surface horizon is darker in color than are those below. In some cases, the lighter horizon below the surface is followed by a darker one.

A number of soil types, like the chernozem, the gray soils, and the brown soils, have been named because of their color. Of course, the dominant color is tinged with others, and because of this we have variations in the color of the horizons. These variations are due primarily to organic matter, iron compounds, silica, and lime. Organic matter is responsible for the black to gray tinges; iron compounds impart the red, brown and yellow tinges; silica and lime give the light and light gray tinges. Gypsum, aluminum hydroxide, kaolinite, and manganese also add to the color variations in the profile. Plate 10 illustrates graphically the probable color scheme in soils.

It is well to remember that the color of the soil when wet is darker than when dry. In designating the color, it is therefore important to state the conditions at the time of examining the profile. Usually, the soil color is reported on a dry basis as determined in the laboratory. In examining the color, direct sun illumination should be avoided as the shadows obscure the true color shades. Noontime is the ideal time to note the color of the profile.

In some soils where the water table is high, the lower horizon shows mottled effects; the color is gray or light gray with a bluish, sometimes greenish blue, tinge.

A number of schemes have been proposed for the determination of soil color, but to date no satisfactory agreement has been reached as to the best method. The Ridgeway color charts, the Munsell color system, the Oswald color triangles, and a number of others have been, and still are, in use, but none has been adopted as a standard. The numerous re-

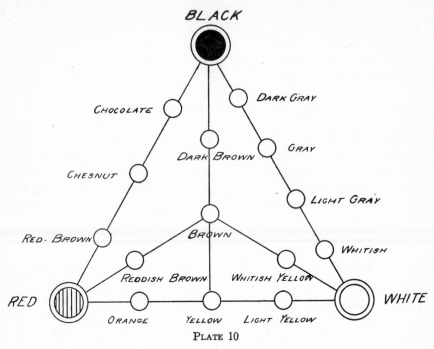

PLATE 10

Graphic presentation of the color scheme in soils
(After Zakharov)

ports of the Committee on Soil Color Standards of the American Soil Survey Association are evidence of the unsettled state of this problem. For references on soil color, besides the report of the Soil Survey Association (3), the reader is referred to the papers of Brown and O'Neal (8), O'Neal (46), Hutton (26), and Bushnell (9). A comprehensive scheme of color standards made up of soot, $CaCO_3$, Fe_2O_3, and $BaCrO_4$ has been suggested by Tyuremnov (64). These substances are mixed in various proportions and made up into small cylinders. A color scale is thus obtained which covers most of the soil colors. With this scale, Tyuremnov was able to present diagrammatically the distribution of the colors in the profile.

Constitution.—As the parent material is subjected to the influences of soil-forming processes, a profile is gradually taking on a definite build, known as the *profile constitution.* Compactness, cementation, porosity, consistency, plasticity, and stickiness are the chief attributes of the profile constitution.

Compactness.—By tapping the soil with gentle downward strokes, using a sharp, rounded, shallow hand scoop or similar instrument, along the surface of the wall of the exposed cut, one may readily detect when the scoop hits a more compact or a looser horizon. After a little practice, the various horizons may be differentiated and outlined. In the horizon of illuvation, there is a sharp rise in compactness, a fundamental constitutional characteristic of this horizon. It is more dense and firm, not because of cementation, but as a result of the reactions involved in the processes of soil formation. The antithesis of a compact constitution is a loose, mellow one, as is the case in the horizons overlying the more compact illuvial horizon.

Cementation.—Cementation is very closely related to compaction. The various structural units of the soil material become cemented together by compounds of iron, aluminum, silica, and organic colloids. The well-known hardpan or ortstein formation is a typical example. Desert pavement formation (see Index), caused by the cementation of crystallized gypsum and lime with admixtures of organic matter, is another example. In some soils, as in types of alkali soils in the semidesert zone, the cementation may produce such a compact constitution that it cannot be penetrated except with the aid of a pickax or crowbar. Cementation of the soil particles and of their aggregates diminishes the pore space of the profile constitution.

There is a fundamental difference between compaction and cementation. Compacted soil when submerged under water gradually slakes into the textural and some structural units. Cemented soil under the same conditions remains as a solid piece, stonelike, the hardness depending on the degree of cementation and type of cementing material.

Porosity.—Porosity is one of the morphological and physical attributes which is readily noted in the profile constitution. Each horizon in the profile is endowed with a porosity of its own, depending on the zonal type and texture and structure of the soil mass.

Zakharov (Ch. 2, 91) distinguished two types of porosity:

A, within the structural units of the soil mass; and *B*, between the structural units or fragments. In *A* several subdivisions may be noted:

Finely porous: the soil mass is perforated with fine pores 1 mm. in diameter. Such a condition is characteristic of the fine loess, especially in the lower horizons of chernozems and in the upper horizon of the brown soils.

Porous: the soil is perforated with pores 1 to 3 mm. in diameter. Such a constitution is typical for the loess-like materials and in the gray soil zone.

Spongy: the soil is rich in pores 3 to 5 mm. in diameter; it is usually encountered in certain podzolized horizons.

Cavernous: the soil mass contains holes 5 to 10 mm. in diameter. It is found in the illuviation horizon of the gray soil zone.

Cellular: the cavities are larger than 10 mm.; this term is used in describing the constitution of laterites.

Tubular: holes due to the channels dug out by rodents, such as moles, marmots, and others.

In *B* the following subdivisions may be noted:

Finely fissured: narrow cavities under 3 mm. in diameter, extending usually in a vertical direction; these are found in soils which have fine structural elements.

Fissured: is characterized by fissures 3 to 10 mm.; these occur in horizons of many soils with a prismatic and columnar structure.

In clefts: characterized by vertical cavities above 10 mm. in diameter; these are well expressed in soils possessing a columnar structure.

It is well to remember that a full expression of the pore space between the structural units is met with only during the dry season.

Consistency.—The degree of cohesion of the soil particles and the resistance offered to force tending to deform or rupture the aggregates is known as consistency. In the soil profile, the consistency varies with the horizons. It is closely allied to the property of compactness and is determined by the structure and texture of the soil, by the cementing materials, and by the pore space. By tapping over the surface of the profile with a scoop, as for compactness, it is easy to detect a tenacious, firm, tough, loose, or friable consistency.

Plasticity.—Resistance to rupture or breaking under stress, or susceptibility to deformation without rupture is known as *plasticity*. A plastic body has a definite measurable yielding capacity when pressure is applied. In judging the plasticity of the profile constitution, the moulding property of the material in each horizon is a very characteristic morphological feature.

Stickiness.—As the term implies, stickiness is the property of adhesiveness to other substances when wet. The clay content of the material will, to a great extent, determine the adhesive qualities of the material of each horizon. It is natural to expect that in the horizon of illuviation, which becomes enriched by mechanical movement and otherwise with clay particles, the stickiness will be greater than in the overlying horizons. The degree of dispersion, which depends on the nature of the cations and anions present, and the hydration effects on the colloids influence the stickiness and plasticity.

Habitus of the Profile.—Having established the different horizons in the profile from the constitutional and color features, one may proceed to differentiate and describe the habitus or general appearance of each horizon.*

Fundamentally, there are three horizons (see Ch. 5), since the humus-decay accumulative is not a true horizon. It consists of the undecomposed, incompletely decomposed, and completely decomposed organic re-

---

*The term *horizon* instead of *layer* has been adopted, as suggested by Glinka (Ch. 2, 27), because a layer implies a formation between two horizontal planes, whereas a horizon is not bound by any such parallel planes. The limits of the layer-like formations in the soil body are not straight lines, and, at times, one layer may penetrate the other in tongue-shaped fashion or in the form of pockets.

mains of the native flora.   In reality, it is nothing more than an organic matter accumulative surface cover which supplies the substances for the process of eluviation.   It is designated as the A_0 *layer*.

Immediately below the A_0 layer is located the horizon of eluviation proper, known as the A hoirzon.   It is subjected to the action of the percolating waters and its attendant constituents—the decomposition products of the A_0 layer, as well as the decomposition products of the organic matter within its own boundaries.

The materials that are leached and moved mechanically by the percolating waters from the A horizon are in part retained deeper in the profile, and the kind of material that accumulates there depends upon the zonal soil type.   The chief characteristics of this horizon are compactness and enrichment with the colloids of iron, aluminum, manganese, humus, clay particles, alkaline earths, and electrolytes in general.   This horizon is designated by the letter B.

Below the B horizon is the parent material, which is relatively unaffected by the soil-forming agencies that produce the soil body with its characteristic profile.   The chemical substances that are not retarded in their downward movement by the B horizon apparently do not enter into deep-seated reactions with the material through which they descend. They disappear in the ground waters, to be carried into the streams. Were this not the case, the composition of the parent material underlying the B horizon could not remain constant throughout the great depths of homogenous geologic deposits.   The layer below the B is known as the C horizon.   A few inches below the surface of this horizon, the soil profile ends. The realm of geologic deposits begins.

Depth of Profile.—Theoretically, we can very well imagine the embryonic state of a soil on the surface of a rock overgrown with mosses, lichens, algae, or similar primitive forms of biotic life.   If we were able to cut a cross-section along a vertical plane through the surface of this rock and magnify the profile view, a complete habitus of a soil body with all its morphological features would be revealed.   With age, the features develop and become more distinct; the profile deepens and attains its full depth upon maturity.   Thus, time is a factor which influences the depth of the profile.   Other important factors are the petrographic and mineralogical makeup of the parent material and its texture.   A resistant rock formation is less apt to form a deep soil body than is one which is easily decomposed under the same conditions.   In a light textured soil, the percolation effects of water extend over greater depths than in a clay soil. There is little surface runoff from sandy soils, whereas from clay soils it is appreciable.   In sandy soils, the parent material, because of its light texture, is porous and the oxidation processes are favored by good aeration. These traits tend to produce a deep profile on sandy parent material.

Relief greatly influences the depth of the profile. In hilly country, the soil as it forms is subject to erosion. On the slopes, the soil profile is, therefore, shallow, whereas at the foot of the hills the profile is deep.

In desert and semidesert regions the profile is shallow, since the biotic and climatic conditions for the processes of soil formation are not favorable. As we enter the regions of higher rainfall the depth of the profile increases, reaching its maximum in the chernozem soils of the temperate region and diminishing again as we enter the forest zone where conditions for illuviation are conducive to a relatively rapid accumulation of colloids, thereby preventing the building up of a deep profile.

Texture of Soil Material.—The fabric of the mineral component of the soil mass resulting from the relative proportion of the three particle size separates—sands, silt, and clay—is known as soil texture. In the field examination of the soil profile, the variations in texture are clearly expressed in the horizons. By the feel between the fingers, the variations in texture can easily be detected—an aid to the recognition of the horizons. Any one with some experience in field work is well qualified to do this. For an exact evaluation of the texture, the standard methods of mechanical analyses of soils are to be applied.

In examining the texture, the quality of the sand separate should be scrutinized. Frequently, the compactness of the soil is due to some very fine sand with a geometric configuration which lends itself to close packing. In such cases, the permeabiilty of the soil is impeded, preventing the normal movement of constituents in the profile and thereby causing an abnormal differentiation of horizons. Long before they were acquainted with the pedologic approach in the study of soils, the workers of the old Bureau of Soils, U. S. Department of Agriculture, now a division of the Bureau of Plant Industry, had recognized the importance of the different grades of sand in the sand separate. Accordingly, this separate has been divided into the following 5 grades: 1, fine gravel: 2.0-1.0 mm; 2, coarse sand: 1.0-0.5 mm.; 3, sand: 0.5-0.25 mm.; 4, fine sand: 0.25-0.1 mm.; 5, very fine sand: 0.1-0.05 mm. It may be well at this point to recall the particle size of the two fractions of the silt separate: coarse silt, 0.05-0.005 mm; fine silt, 0.005-0.002 mm. The clay separate consists of a grain size: < 0.002 mm .

The texture is lightest in the horizon of eluvation and becomes heavier with depth until it reaches the maximum heaviness in the horizon of illuviation. The textural properties of the soil profile, formed on homogeneous parent material, are similar for any soil in a particular climatic belt.

In transported soils with a heterogeneous parent material, the A horizon may be a layer of clay, whereas the B horizon may be a gravel. Under such conditions, the texture of the A horizon may be heavier than that of B. In examining the profile this has to be watched for and evaluated.

Soil Structure.—The aggregation of the textural units of the soil mass into variously shaped and sized soil particles forms the units constituting soil structure. The pattern of the mineralogical complexes of the soil material presents a definite type of build by itself, known as *microstructure*. The aggregation of the mineralogical complexes into larger units, as a result of cementation, is known as *macrostructure*.

It is beyond the scope of this treatise to dwell on this subject in an exhaustive manner. Those interested will find a thorough discussion of this subject in the researches of Wollny (73) and of his contemporaries and followers: Heinrich (24), Schumacher (57, 58), Schloesing (56), Amon (4), Puchner (51), and later Mitscherlich (40), and a number of others. It was Wollny who attempted to evaluate the element of structure in connection with soil productivity. He succeeded in showing that structure is one of the agencies which regulate the moisture and the air regime in the soil. He was the first to point out the advantages of the crumb structure—the German "Krumelstruktur." Hilgard (25) also contributed to the subject in Wollny's famous "Forschungen, etc." Johnson (29) was probably the first soil investigator to prove experimentally the relation of several soil properties to structure. By changing the structure from the powder to higher aggregates, he showed how a diminution in evaporation takes place.

On the basis of Schumacher's (57) work on the relation of capillary and non-capillary pore space to structure, Doyarenko (15) and his collaborators carried out a series of experiments, showing how structure affects the chemical, physical, and biological properties of the soil. Kvasnikov (34) correlated structure with the acidity of the soil, with the osmotic pressure of the soil solution, and with biological factors.

An interesting method for the study of soil structure has been presented by Pigulevskii (48). It consists in evacuating the moisture and air from a fresh clump of soil and then filling up the pores with liquid paraffin or a similar substance. Upon solidification of the fixing agent, this clump of soil can be treated like any other mineralogical specimen. Photographs from slides beautifully illustrate the structure.

Gedroiz (19) and Tyulin (63) discuss the problems of differentiating the structure in various soil zones, as well as the theoretical considerations involved in the variation of structure and methods of determining it.

Akhromeiko (2), in a monogram on "Soil Structure," summarizes and reviews the subject and presents his experimental data, part of which have been previously published (1).

A microscopic method for the study of soil structure in its natural position was developed by Kubiena (33). A special microscope, using incident light, is used in examining the soil profile in the field. He, as well as Harper and Volk (23), have followed the lead of Pigulevski in studying thin sections of structural units and debris, using various fixing agents. The Kubiena technic for the microscopic study of soil structure was modified by Redlich (54).

An excellent review of the subject up to 1940 is given by Baver (6). He tries unsuccessfully to expound the mechanism of soil structure. As yet no satisfactory explanation of this mechanism is available. As a matter of fact, not all the known facts on structure have been correlated. For example, it is generally recognized that organic matter plays an important part in structure formation. Still, no one has tried to decipher why in the case of the chernozem soils the aggregates are more stable than in other soils. It is apparent that something specific is reacting in the chernozem which makes the granules hold together, whereas similar sized granules in the soils of the forest zone slake rapidly, i. e., the cohesive forces are weaker. Is it not reasonable to assume that a different type of organic compound, or a similar compound under various conditions of hydration and desiccation, might be the cause of the difference in the stability of the structural units?

To answer the question raised, one has to evaluate the role of organic compounds in structure formation. From the point of view of soil morphology, any one dealing with soils knows that no matter how much organic matter a sandy soil may contain, no aggregation of the sand grains takes place. Reports of structure formation in soils containing as much as 90 per cent sand are misleading. Mechanical hanging together of sand grains 2mm in size has been noted by the author as a result of extensive mycelium growth of Rhizopus. This, however, is not aggregation which is the result of physico-chemical forces exhibited by the elements essential for structure, namely clay and organic compounds.

Whatever the mechanism of the physico-chemical forces are, one thing is certain: without a definite quantity of clay, from 8 to 10 per cent, no structure is possible. Moist clay, in contact with other textural units of its own and of silt and sand, will *bind* these into aggregates upon drying. This binding power of clay does not, however, insure the stability of the aggregates. When placed in water, clay bound aggregates slake into the ultimate unit size particles. However, when clay bound aggregates are leached with some soluble soil organic matter compounds, a coating is formed over the structural unit bound by the clay. This coating forms a kind of an envelope or membrane over the aggregate. Upon drying, the organic matter envelope may become stabilized, i. e., the colloidal material may become irreversible and not go into solution readily when in contact with water. In the case of the chernozem, it seems that the desiccating effects produce a very tough, and at the same time elastic membrane which is colloidally irreversible. It is probable that in the case of chernozem we are dealing with a more stable type of organic compound that resists decomposition by microbes.

Another factor in the stability of organic complexes is the type of absorbed cations. In the chernozem, calcium is the primary cation that figures in the adsorption, movement, coagulation, and stabilization of the soluble organic compounds. The Ca-humates play an important role in the stabilization of the organic membranes on the surface of the structural units. The Ca-ion reduces the swelling and contracting of the inorganic and organic membrane colloids upon intermittent wetting and drying.

A theoretical and experimental approach on the role of clay and organic matter in structure formation may be found in the work of Sideri (61). A critical review of the work of Sideri is presented by Moiseev (42). Some experimental data on the binding effects of clay are presented by Puri and Rai (52). A physico-chemical study of the problem of the binding properties of clay is presented in a monograph by Vershinin and Konstantinova (65). An interesting discussion on the problem of structure may be found in the work of Williams (72). Koposov (31) reviews investigations pertaining to structure, with special reference to structure formation by mechanical means. His work, based on the extensive treatise of Vershinin and Konstantinova, is related to the investigations of Vilenskii (67) pertaining to the effect of moisture on the stability of soil structure. Selechnik and Novoseltsev (59) report on the effectiveness of glue-like materials, such as peat or straw extracts or viscose, on stability of structure. Kanivets and Korneeva (30) report interesting data on the role of microorganisms in supplying materials for binding and stabilizing soil structure. They mention *Thricoderma lignorum,* alone, or in combination with *Aspergillus niger,* as important organisms producing these materials. Geltser (20), Mishustin (37, 38), and Mishustin and Pushkinskaya (39) discuss the more recent work on the role of microbes in structure formation.

Peterson (47) made an interesting laboratory study on the effect of kaolinite and montmorillonite on platy structure. The kaolinite is more conducive to the formation of platy structure than montmorillonitte. Because of the prevalence of kaolinite in podzols, the platy structure predominates in these soils.

Nikiforoff (45) considers soil structure as an arrangement of the soil material in which the primary particles are held together by ties stronger than the ties between adjacent aggregates. Soil structure is classified into types, classes, grades, and species. Four principal types of structure are recognized: platy, prismatic, blocky (lump and fragment), and granular. This classification is very much like that of Zakharov (Ch. 2, 91) who distinguishes three fundamental types of structure, namely: cube-like, with the vertical and horizontal axes equal; prism-like, with the vertical axis longer than the horizontal; and plate-like, with the vertical axis shorter than the horizontal. These three types encompass almost all the forms commonly used· in designating structure, e. g., cloddy, nutty, columnar, crumb, granular, platy, vesicular, and pulverulent.

Zakharov points out that the profile of every soil type has a structure of its own. Thus the upper horizon of a typical loamy chernozem has a granular structure, whereas the lower horizon has a nutty structure. In the podzolized soils, the upper horizon has a pulverized structure and the lower horizon a platy structure.

In table 1, a classification of the structural elements is presented. In

Table I

Classification of the structural elements: soil aggregates or soil fragments
(After Zakharov)

Type	Kind	Species·	Dimensions.
I. Cube-like structure — soil fragments equally developed along the three axes.	A. Faces and edges feebly manifested, soil aggregates most complex and irregular in shape.		
	1. Block structure	Large blocks	>10 cm.
		Small blocks	10–5
	2. Cloddy structure	Large clods	5–3
		Cloddy	3–1
		Small clods	1–0.5
		Pulverulent	<0.5
	B. Faces and edges more or less clearly manifested, aggregates well defined.		
	3. Nutty structure	Cuboid	>20 mm.
		Coarsely nutty	20–10
		Nutty	10–7
		Finely nutty	7–5

Table I (Continued)

Type	Kind	Species	Dimensions
	4. Granular structure	Coarsely granular (bean shaped) Granular Finely granular (powder-like)	5–3 3–1 1–0.5
II. Prism-like structure — soil fragments predominantly developed along the vertical axis.	A. Faces and edges indistinctly manifested, aggregates complex and not clearly defined.		Length of horizontal axis and cross section diameter
	5. Column-like structure	Large columns Medium columns Small columns	5 cm. 5–3 <3
	B. Faces and edges distinctly manifested, aggregates more or less well defined.		
	6. Prismatic structure, with uniform, even, often shining surfaces and sharp edges.	Large prisms Prismatic Small prisms Prismatic pencil-shaped (more than 5 cm. in length)	>5 5–3 <3 1
	7. Columnar structure— the upper base ("top") rounded, and the lower base flat	Large columns Columnar Small columns	>5 5–3 <3 Thickness
III. Plate-like structure soil aggregates predominantly developed along the two horizontal axes.	8. Platy structure — horizontal "planes of cleavage" more or less developed	Schistose Platy Laminar Foliated	>5 cm. 5–3 3–1 <1
	9. Squamous structure —horizontal faces comparatively small, partly curved.	Vesicular Coarsely squamous Finely squamous	>3 3–1 <1

Note: Large column-like fragments are sometimes called "pedestals".

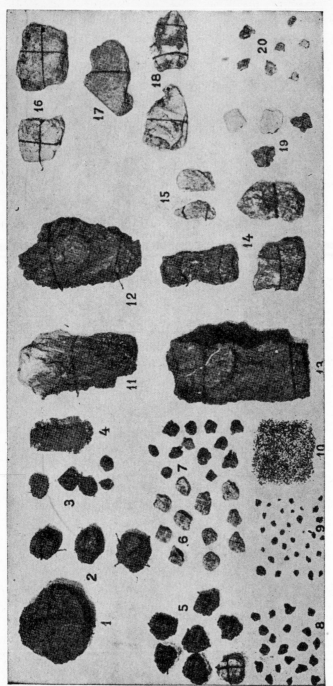

PLATE 11
Types of structure in soils
(After Zakharov)

1—large clods; 2—medium clods; 3—small clods; 4—pulverulent; 5—coarsely granular; 6—nutty; 7—finely nutty; 8—coarsely granular; 9—granular; 10—finely granular; 11—columnar; 12—column-like; 13—large prisms; 14—medium prisms; 15—small prisms; 16—schistose; 17—platy; 18—foliated; 19—coarsely squamous; 20—finely squamous.
(One-half natural size).

designating the aggregation units of soil structure in the profile, the dimensions given in the table may serve as a useful guide. Plate 11 gives a photographic view of the various types of structural elements.

Structure plays an important part in the movement of water. In a structureless soil material, with pores of capillary size, this movement is controlled primarily by the laws governing capillary rise of water. If we should allow a cube of such soil material to come in contact with a source of water from below, the water would rise along the capillaries. If water should be applied at the surface of the cube, it would move downward along the capillaries, irrespective of the forces of gravity. If water should be applied from the side, it would move horizontally. Thus, water moves through a structureless body in the direction from the source of supply, or, in terms of mechanics, the movement is caused by the difference in potential, i. e., from a higher to a lower potential. The speed of the movement is progressively decreasing and is finite, i. e., it must stop at a certain point. It is partly because of this progressively decreasing movement through capillaries that the water in lakes or ponds does not percolate and disappear.

In the arid regions, or under certain conditions even in the humid regions, we encounter a structureless condition in the soil material. We are aware of the practice in certain arid regions, as in western Kansas, of plowing only once in 3 or 4 years. The tillage operations destroy the structure and produce a dusty mass which hinders the penetration of water to any great depth. It has been calculated that on a structureless soil only 30 per cent of the rainfall becomes available; the rest is lost by surface runoff. Mulching in such areas does not improve the structure and does not, therefore, serve the purpose of conserving the moisture. This has been shown by the work of Sergeev (60) at the Saratov Experiment Station.

Anaerobic conditions prevail in a structureless soil whenever the capillaries become waterlogged. Such a condition impedes the activity of microorganisms and slows down the decomposition of organic matter. This factor and the low percolation activity impede the soil-forming processes. The time factor in producing the soil body becomes important. In a soil with good structure, percolation of moisture and formation of organic acids and minerals that react with the parent material are not impeded, and the time factor is of a lower magnitude.

New Formation and Inclusions.—In a morphologis study of the profile, careful notice should be taken of concretions, incrustations, sediments, veins, streaks, and other types of accumulation throughout the soil body, usually in the lower portion of the A and in the B horizon. All of these accumulations are known as new formations and inclusions. There are two types of new formations : of mechanical and chemical origin.

New Formation of Mechanical Origin.—Crotovinas (see Index) and nests and passageways of rodents—pocket gophers, prairie dogs, ground squirrels, badgers, field mice, and a number of others—are outstanding examples of this type of new formations. Next in importance are the burrows of earthworms, ants, wasps, beetles, crickets, grubs, other insects, and a number of other burrowing creatures (see Ch. V).

Plant roots leave certain well-marked impressions in the profile. Especially is this true for the large roots which produce channels. These channels may be located in the various horizons and are sometimes filled with material from a horizon above. They are distinguished from the nests and passageways of the rodents, since the material with which the former are filled comes only from the upper horizons, whereas within the passageway of the rodents, the material is brought from below to the upper horizons and *vice versa*.

New Formations of Chemical Origin.—These formations consist of a variety of compounds : soluble chlorides and sulfates of the alkali and alkaline earths, the relatively insoluble gypsum, insoluble carbonates of calcium and magnesium—primarily the former,—the hydroxides of aluminum and iron, the manganese oxides, silica, and humus substances.

In the profile of salinized soils, alkali and alkaline earth salts are found. In the bleached horizon of the podzols which tend to become swampy, the iron, aluminum, and manganese form dark brown smears, streaks, patches, veins, spots, and rounded and bean-shaped concretions. In the B horizon of podzols ortstein formations, which are another form of concretions, are encountered. They also consist primarily of soil particles cemented with iron, aluminum, manganese, humus substances, and sometimes titanium.

In poorly drained soils of the temperate zone, in the so-called glei (see Index) type of podzols on loess, tube-like concretions alongside the rusty brown spots on the greenish gray background of the soil material were described by Vysotskii (70). The concretions are dark iron-like in color with a concentric structure resembling knots in their cross-section. Infrequently, they are saturated with carbonates and effervesce when treated with HCl. In marshy soils, concretions of vivianite are found. In the laterites, slag-like concretions of iron and aluminum occur. In plate 12, the various forms of iron concretions occurring in a glei on loess parent material are represented.

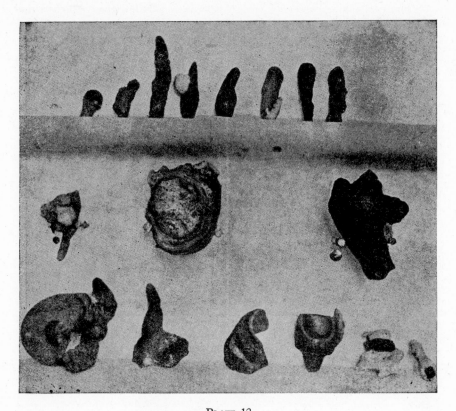

PLATE 12

Iron concretions in soils
(After Kassatkin and Krasyuk)

PLATE 13

Lime concretions in soils
(After Kassatkin and Krasyuk)

The carbonates present a variety of forms as they precipitate on the soil particles and accumulate in the non-capillary pore spaces, along tracks of roots and in hollow spaces of crotovinas.

In the slightly degraded chernozems, the lime carbonate closely resembles a network of white fungous mycelia, especially in the B horizon, giving at times the effect of snow sprinkling. In reality, these particles are needle-shaped crystals. Infrequently, the lime carbonates appear also in the form of veins, or white soft spots known among the Russian pedologists as "beloglazka," i. e., white eye spots. In the more arid regions, the lime carbonates are found in the form of solid concretions of various shapes and sizes; the well-known loess puppets are typical of this form. In plate 13, reproduced from Kassatkin and Krasyuk (Ch. 2, 34, p. 60), the various types of lime concretions are presented.

The soils of the still more arid regions also contain gypsum accumulations, usually found deeper in the profile and in a more limited variety of shapes than the lime carbonates. Large accumulations of gypsum are associated with the so-called alkali soils.

Bands of organic matter are a common occurrence in ortstein formations. Another form of accumulation is the tongue-like projections in the lighter colored horizons below the humus horizon. As a rule, these projections are darker than the humus horizon itself. A typical case of such projections is given in plate 14.

PLATE 14
Tongue-like projection of organic matter in the B horizon
(After Kassatkin and Krasyuk)

Inclusions.—Infrequently some foreign substances, playing little part in the process of soil formation, are encountered in the soil profile. Remains of animal origin, bones and shells, and remains of plant origin, petrified wood or undecayed plants, do not contribute to the processes of soil formation, but they are to be noted in any morphologic description of the profile. Neither do inclusions of geologic processes, like glacial boulders, rocks, stones, pebbles, or substances of similar character carried by water, contribute toward the processes of soil formation in any appreciable measure, but a recognition of these in the profile is important.

Such inclusions throw some light on the history of the soil. If one should find petrified wood or remnants of tree trunks in the soils of some parts of the prairie, their presence would indicate the probability of forests having been in the region. Fresh-water shells in the loess deposits of Nebraska or Mississippi would be an argument for the alluvial origin of loess. Certain mineral specimens of glacial origin might give a clue to the age of the soil. All of these observations are, therefore, important, even though the inclusions of foreign substances have no direct bearing on the processes of soil formation.

Buried Soils.—Fully developed soils existed long before the present soil cover formed. In some regions the ancient soils, covered with new materials, remained intact with all the profile features well preserved. Such soils are known as *buried soils*. A study of these is of extreme importance for the interpretation of the climatic conditions in which the soil formed. In the hands of a geologist trained in pedology, paleopedologic data might reveal much interesting geological evidence pertaining to climate as revealed in the profile of buried soils. These soils have been studied by Vysotskii (69), Nabokikh (44), Glinka (Ch. 2, 27, p. 440-453), Florov (18), and a number of others. Polynov (49) contributed a great deal to the elucidation of buried soils in the Don region. He reviewed the subject and analyzed the most important contributions. His work (Ch. 2, 55) is available in English. Plate 15 shows the lower portion of the humus horizon in a buried soil. It also shows crotovinas, lime concretions, and protruding tongue-like streamers of organic matter.

Marbut, in his guide to the transcontinental excursion in connection with the First International Congress of Soil Science (36, p. 112), points out the presence of buried soils west of the prairie region. "In eastern Nebraska there is at least one buried soil which, according to its characteristics, was developed under rainfall fully as high, if not higher, than that characteristic of the region at the present time."

Digging and Sampling the Profile.—To insure a proper morphologic study of the profile and to facilitate proper sampling, certain elementary rules in digging the profile are helpful. A trench 2.5 to 3 feet wide and as deep as required to reach into the parent material is to be dug. An 8 to 10 foot length gives sufficient room for working and enough profile exposure. Both sides and one end of the trench are cut down to form vertical walls. The other end is dug down to a slope with a step-like arrangement. This makes the trench easily accessible and affords a comfortable seat while notes are being made.

PLATE 15

The lower part of the humus (A) horizon in a buried soil with crotovinas, lime concretions, and humus tongues protruding into the B horizon
(After Vysotskii)

In laying out the trench to be dug, consideration is to be given to the topography; level, undulating areas, free from microrelief depressions or elevations are to be chosen. In digging a profile in the woods, heavy roots traversing the path of the exposed cut are to be avoided, as these obscure at times the features of the horizons and make sampling difficult.

The soil material dug out is thrown over to one side of the trench, leaving the other side and the ends free from any extraneous materials.

The fresh dead leaves, twigs, branches, and woody material in general are removed from the surface at the edges where the monolith sample is to be taken or the A_0 layer is to be sampled.

For physical and chemical analyses, samples are taken in the following manner: a spade is forced into the soil wall at the border line of each horizon, the upper 2 to 3 cm. of soil removed, and as much soil as necessary taken to a depth of 2 to 3 cm. above the surface of the spade. This insures a representative sample from each horizon.

Volume weight.—The weight of a unit volume of soil with an undisturbed structure, when dried at 105 to 110°C, is the volume weight of the soil. It is known as the apparent specific gravity and is numerically smaller than the real specific gravity because in the latter the pore space is eliminated.

In soil analyses—chemical, physical, and microbiological—the data are reported on the basis of percentage by weight, or in other words, with references to the true specific gravity of the soil material. The inadequacy of such procedure in soil analyses was recognized by Hilgard (Ch. 2, 30, p. 107), who stated: "The specific gravity of soils is, however, of little practical consequence compared with the volume weight." Indeed, the volume weight of soils varies from 1.7, that of sand, to 0.5, that of peat. A cubic foot of sand weighs 106 pounds, whereas a cubic foot of peat weighs as little as 30 pounds.

In the soil profile, the characteristic features of the soil are described with respect to the linear measurements of the horizons—a volume factor. The moisture in the soil is determined by the capillary and non-capillary pore space—also a volume factor. Plant roots feed over a definite area of the soil body, and the distribution of the available plant food ingredients takes place within a volume of the soil. To compare the number of microorganisms in a gram of peat and in a gram of loam is a fallacy which needs no explanation. Bieler-Chatelan (7) discussed the problem of volume weight of soils and pointed out the importance of this physical property of soils.

Of the methods to determine the volume weight of soils, the one by Israelsen (27) has been used successfully. It consists in digging a hole with an auger, weighing the soil excavated, and then determining the volume of the hole by inserting an elastic rubber tube and filling it with water from a graduated cylinder. When the weight of the soil and the volume occupied by it are known, the volume weight is obtained by dividing the weight by the volume. Harland and Smith (21) reviewed the subject and presented data on the volume weight of 13 soil types made by the

Israelsen method. Curry (13) compared the methods in use.

Lebedev (35) introduced a simple contrivance for determining the volume weight of soil. The sharp end of a special tube designed by Lebedev (pl. 16, fig. I) is inserted, without turning, into the wall of the soil cut at a depth of 5 to 6 cm. (pl. 16, fig. 2). With the aid of a long narrow knife, the soil from the outer end of the tube is cut off at an angle so that a heaping surface above the cutting edge of the tube remains (pl. 16, fig. 3). The tube is then freed from the soil matrix, and the surplus from the inner and outer edge is carefully removed with the sharp edge of the knife. This gives a cylinder of soil with an undisturbed structure.

The soil is placed into a tared aluminum moisture dish, weighed, dried at 105°C, and again weighed. The loss in weight gives the moisture content; the dry weight of the soil and the volume of cylinder known, the volume weight of the soil is determined. Three to four samples are taken from each horizon to eliminate individual variations.

In soils containing pebbles, the true volume of the soil is obscured, since the pebbles play no part in the chemical, physical, and biological reactions of the soil. It is important, however, to determine the active volume of the soil, in order to interpret properly the various soil phenomena. In order to surmount this difficulty, the soil upon drying is sifted through a 2 mm. sieve,* and the weight and volume of the pebbles are determined in the following way (28):

From a series of determinations on the debris of several soil types,** it was found that by taking their specific gravity as 2.6, the volume calculated checked very well with the volume obtained by the displacement method. The volume of the debris is subtracted from the volume of the sampling tube, the weight of the debris subtracted from the dry weight of the sample, the new weight divided by the new volume, and the quotient taken as the active volume weight. In table 2, data obtained by the author on some New Jersey soils illustrate the method described.

Aside from illustrating the method of obtaining the true volume weight, the figures in the table show how the volume weight increases with the depth in the soil profile. How this increase would influence the analytical figures of the physical data and their interpretation may be judged from the following example: Soil 36 contains 25.1 per cent H_2O; soil 37

---

*It is realized that the 2-mm. sieve does not eliminate all the mineralogical and petrographic elements, which play no part in the soil reactions discussed in connection with the active volume-weight relationships. The true active volume weight should be sought in the colloidal fraction of the soil and in the other fractions of the soil which react and imbibe water readily. However, the soil which passes a 2-mm. sieve approaches the true volume weight within close limits.

**Types in the sense of the U. S. Soil Survey.

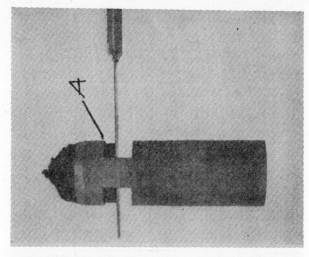

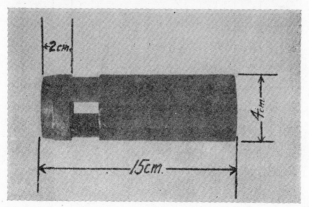

Fig. 3

Fig. 2

Fig. 1   Method of volume weight sampling (From Soil Sci. v. 28. p. 479)

Plate 16

Table 2

Volume weight of soils containing pebbles

Laboratory number of sample	Horizon in soil profile	Dry weight of soil from sampler before sifting	Weight of soil after sifting through a 2-mm. sieve	Weight of debris	Volume of debris	Volume of soil without debris*	Active volume weight of soil
		gm.	gm.	gm.	cc.	cc.	
			Gloucester gravelly loam				
35	A$_1$	22.9	22.400	0.500	0.19	27.51	0.814
35	A$_1$	26.2	24.825	1.375	0.53	27.17	0.914
35	A$_1$	24.8	24.375	0.425	0.16	27.54	0.850
36	A$_2$	30.4	29.150	1.250	0.48	27.22	1.071
36	A$_2$	32.9	31.250	1.650	0.64	27.06	1.154
36	A$_2$	33.8	32.200	1.600	0.63	27.07	1.182
37	B$_1$	37.3	32.340	4.960	1.90	25.80	1.253
37	B$_1$	35.8	34.860	0.940	0.36	27.34	1.275
37	B$_1$	36.8	35.540	1.260	0.50	27.20	1.306
38	B$_2$	40.9	37.750	3.150	1.21	26.49	1.424
38	B$_2$	38.2	36.530	1.670	0.64	27.06	1.349
38	B$_2$	39.5	36.140	3.360	1.30	26.40	1.369
			Dover loam				
42	A$_3$	40.0	35.56	4.44	1.7	26.0	1.37
42	A$_3$	39.2	34.80	4.40	1.7	26.0	1.34
42	A$_3$	36.6	34.52	2.08	0.8	26.9	1.30
43	B$_1$	39.5	36.2	3.30	1.3	26.4	1.37
43	B$_1$	42.0	37.88	4.12	1.6	26.1	1.45
43	B$_1$	43.6	36.59	7.01	2.7	25.0	1.46

*The volume of the sampling tube is equal to 27.7 cc.

contains 24.1 per cent. The average volume weight of soil 36 (the average of three samplings) is 1.136; that of soil 37, 1.278. If an area of one acre (4047 sq.m.) and a depth of 10 cm. are taken, soil 36 will have 404.7 cu. m. of soil, or 404,700,000 cc. Its volume weight being 1.136, its weight is 459,739 kgm.; its moisture content being 25.1 per cent, the total moisture in it is 115,394.5 kgm. Taking soil 37 at the same depth, we find that its weight is 517,206 kgm. and that the total moisture content is 124,646 kgm., or 7 per cent more moisture than soil 36, which has a higher percentage of moisture.

The active volume weight of soils may be represented by the following formula:

$$Va = \frac{W-W_1}{V-V_1}$$

where Va = the active volume weight, W = the weight of the dry soil as taken with the sampling tube, W_1 = weight of pebbles not passing a 2-mm. sieve, V = volume of sampling tube (27.7 cc. in our case), and V_1 = the volume of the pebbles calculated by dividing their weight by the specific gravity, which may be determined in each case, or by the value 2.6, taken as an average for the specific gravity of rock pebbles found in soils.

For soils which have no pebbles, W_1 and V_1 equal zero, i.e., the dry weight of the soil from the sampler divided by the volume of the sampler gives the active volume weight.

Miscellaneous Observations on the Soil Profile

Special attention should be given to the state of relative wetness of the respective horizons, the relation of the texture of the horizons to the moisture conditions, the imperviousness of the B horizon—whenever such is found—to percolation of the water, and any other factor pertaining to the moisture distribution in the profile. Wherever possible, an effort should be made to determine the depth of the water table, its upper limits, and its range of fluctuations in dry and wet seasons. An excellent index to determine this is the mottling effect, or the so-called glei formation (see Index).

A record of the distribution of the root systems of the native vegetation throughout the profile is to be made. It may illustrate the movement and distribution of the plant food constituents in the soil body, as well as the optimum moisture conditions for proper root development. In the genuine podzols, for instance, it is of interest to note how the roots shun the bleached A_2 horizon.

A number of simple field tests, such as determinations of the presence of carbonates and of alkali salts at any point in the soil profile and a rough estimation of the pH of a water extract, should be made. A sketch of the profile cut—if possible with colored crayons—is another valuable asset in describing it. In general, nothing is too insignificant to be noted and recorded. Every major or minor observation helps to explain the array of natural forces which are instrumental in the genesis of the soil body.

Monolith Sampling

A monolith consists of a column of soil incased in a frame or mounted on a panel, with the constitution of the profile preserved in its natural state. A monolith properly sampled becomes a permanent record of the soil under investigation and is very useful in many ways. The description of the region where the monolith has been sampled, the interpretation of the field observations, and the deductions of physical and chemical analysis are made more complete and unified by the presence of the monolith in the laboratory or in the soil museum—an invaluable aid in teaching. A series of monoliths from the various soil zones offers one an opportunity to become acquainted with the soil types without actually visiting the regions.

The first to devise apparatus and to take monolith samples was the Russian pedologist Rizpolozhenskii (55). Since his time, the methods and technique of sampling have been perfected and somewhat standardized. Still, there is no uniformity in taking monoliths and mounting them. The bulkiness of the soil column, which is usually not less than 1 m. long and occasionally much longer, depending on the depth of the profile, is a perplexing problem. In the early days of monolith sampling, a thickness of 10 cm. was not excessive, but now the tendency is toward greater thinness. An elaborate discussion of the subject was given by Kassatkin and Krasyuk (Ch. 2, 34). Vilenskii (66) presented his views on the subject in English. His paper is profusely illustrated, giving details about the taking and mounting of monoliths. This subject was treated also by Dorogov (14), primarily from the technical point of view. Polynov, Baltz, and Schokalsky (50) prepared a little booklet with instruction for collecting soil monoliths.

Monolith sampling has been practiced in recent years also in the United States. A collection of monolith soil profiles was exhibited by the Bureau of Soils, U. S. Department of Agriculture, at the First International Congress of Soil Science, held in Washington in 1927. A short description of a method developed in Hungary by Pinkert was given in the U. S. Department of Agriculture Official Record (5). This method has been further developed by Bushnell (10). It consists in "gluing cloth or other material to a soil face in the field and breaking off the sample which adheres to the glue." Chapman (11), in a note on monolithic soil profiles, outlined the technique used in North Dakota. Collison and Harlan (12) described a method of taking the rectangular monoliths which are to be used for demonstration and instruction. They also worked out a method of taking cylindrical profiles for the study of soil structure, moisture percolation, and other physical properties of the soil. Harper (22) discussed a number of methods and described and illustrated the one used in Oklahoma for mounting soil profiles.

Voigt (68) sprayed cellulose nitrate varnish diluted with 2 parts of methanol on fairly well dried surface of the exposed profile. After that, 2 or more coats of heavy lacquer are brushed on. This film can be cut and stripped off, carrying with it the adhering soil in sufficient thickness to show the characteristics of the profile in situ.

Molotkovskii (43) sprayed the face of the profile with a fine spray of 2 to 3 per cent cellulose in amyl or ethyl acetate, acetone, or some other solvent. The liquid is supposed to penetrate into the soil pore space to a depth of several millimeters. After that a more concentrated solution of cellulose is brushed on. This is repeated several times. After 20 or 30 minutes, depending on the temperature, the film is torn away from the face of the profile and mounted on a board.

Spilsbury (62) collected monoliths by forcing a metal trough into the exposed soil section through the use of a jack. The trough, open at one end, is made by attaching a strip of 22 gauge galvanized iron 2 inches wide to a board 36 x 4 x 1 inches.

General Statement on Soil Morphology

Soil morphology uncovers to the pedologist a number of facts which help to unravel many complicated problems of soil genesis. The morphological features of the soil profile are the mirror image of the processes responsible for the formation of this or the other type of soil. The differences in climate over the earth's surface leave their impression on the profile, and by these one may differentiate the soil types and classify them accordingly.

Soil morphology is the stepping stone to the thorough appreciation of the chemical, physical, and biological properties in the soil. A profile inventory of these completes the picture of soil genesis. Thus, an analysis of the anatomical features of the soil profile (morphological characteristics), supplemented by physiological and histological (chemical, physical, and biological characteristics) analyses, brings out the uniqueness of the soil body.

The morphological method has been very successfully applied by pedologists. Its validity may be proved by the fact that in numerous cases the independent description of one and the same soil by several investigators has coincided in almost every detail.

The Soil Division of the Bureau of Plant Industry, U. S. Department of Agriculture, published a "Soil Investigation Field Book" (A copy of this was presented to the author by C. C. Nikiforoff). In it are given descriptive terms used in recording the morphological characteristics of soils. These consist of horizon attributes, color, consistence, texture, coarse skeleton, and structure.

Some of the morphological features, such as color, structure, and distribution of constituents in the profile, lend themselves to experimental verification in the laboratory. An attempt in this direction has been made by Kostychev (Ch. 2, 41) in connection with his studies on Russian chernozem and by Filatov (17) and Emeis (16) in connection with ortstein formation. However, these are only a meager beginning, and more thorough investigations in experimental soil morphology are wanted.

References

1. Akhromeiko, A. 1928 Zur Frage über den Einfluss der Struktur des Bodens auf dessen Fruchtbarkeit. *Ztsh. für Pflanzen. Düng. u. Bodenkunde.* Abt. A, 2, No. 1.

2. Akhromeiko, A. 1930 Soil structure. (Russian). Leningrad-Moscow, 1-160.

3. American Soil Survey Association. 1920-1931 Reports of meetings. Bul. I-XII.

4. Amon, D. 1879 Investigations on the permeability of soils for air. *Forschungen auf d. Geb. der Agr. Phys.* 224-230.

5. Anonymous. 1927 U. S. Dept. of Agr. Official Rec. (38), 3.

6. Baver, L. D. 1940 Soil Physics. John Wiley & Sons. New York.

7. Bieler-Chatelan, Th. 1926 Constitution volumétrique des sols en place. *4th Inter. Con. of Pedology* 1st Commission, Section A. Societe Internat. de la Science du sol, Rome. 1-22.

8. Brown, P. E. and O'Neal, A. M. 1923 The color of soils in relation to organic matter content. Iowa Agr. Exp. Station Research Bul. 75.

9. Bushnell, T. M. 1928 The soil color field. *Proc. and Papers, First Inter. Cong. of Soil Sci.* 4 : 429-434.

10. Bushnell, T. M. 1930 The Purdue technique for taking and mounting monolithic soil profile samples. *Soil Sci.* 29 : 395-399.

11. Chapman, J. E. 1928 Monolithic soil profiles. *Science* 68 (1761): 299.

12. Collison, R. C. and Harlan, J. D. 1930 Preparation of soil profiles for exhibition and soil study. N. Y. State Agr. Exp. Sta. Bul. 173.

13. Curry, A. S. 1931 A comparison of methods for determining the volume-weight of soils. *Jour. Agr. Res.* 42 : 765-72.

14. Dorogov, A. A. 1928 An apparatus for monolith sampling. *Byuletin Pochvoveda,* No. 3-7 : 64-66.

15. Doyarenko, A. G. 1924 Soil structure in relation to capillary and non-capillary pore space and its significance to soil productivity. *Nauchno-Agron. Zhur.* I : 451-474.

16. Emeis, C. 1908 Die Ursachen der Ortsteinbildung und ihr Einfluss auf die Landeskultur in Schleswig-Holstein. Vereinsblatt des Heidekultur-Vereins für Schl.-Holstein, 9-20. Quoted from Zakharov.

17. Filatov, M. 1922 On the problem of the genesis of ortsand. *Russkii Pochvoved,* No. 1-3.

18. Florov, N. 1928 Uber Lössprofile in den Steppen am Schwarzen Meer. *Proc. and Papers, First Inter. Cong. Soil Sci.* 4 : 391-420.

19. Gedroiz, K. K. 1926 The problem of soil structure and its agricultural significance. *Izv. Gosud. Inst. Opyt. Agron.* 4, No. 3 : 117-127.

20. Geltser, F. Yu. 1940 The significance of microorganisms in the formation of manure and the stability of soil structure (Russian). Selkhozgiz.

21. Harland, M. B. and Smith, R. S. 1928 Volume weight of certain field soils. *Jour. Amer. Soc. Agron.* 20 : 533-41.

22. Harper, H. J. 1932 A study of methods for the preparation of permanent soil profiles. Oklahoma Agr. Expt. Sta. Bul. 201.

23. Harper, H. J. and Volk, G. W. 1936 A method for the microscopic examination of the natural structure and pore space in soil. *Proc. Soil Sci. Soc. Amer.* 1 : 39-42.

24. Heinrich, R. 1886 Uber Prüfunge der Bodenarten auf Wasser-Kapacität und Durchluftbarkeit. *Forsch. auf. dem. Geb. Agr. Phys.* Bd. IX.

25. Hilgard, E. 1879 On the flocculation of small particles and the technical and physical relations of this phenomenon. *Forsch. auf. d. Geb. der Agr. Phys.* 441-454.

26. Hutton, J. G. 1928 Soil colors, their nomenclature and description. *Proc. and Papers, First Inter. Cong. Soil Sci.* 4 : 164-172.

27. Israelsen, O. W. 1918 Studies on capacities of soils for irrigation water and on a new method of determining volume weight. *Jour. Agr. Res.* 13 : 1-36.

28. Joffe, J. S. and Lee, L. L. 1928 A note on the determination of the volume weight of different soils in the soil profile. *Soil Sci.* 26 : 217- 219.

29. Johnson, S. W. 1877 Studies on the relation of soils to water. Conn. Agr. Exp. Station Annual Report.

30. Kanivets, I. I. and Korneeva, N. P. 1938 Inoculation of soils with microorganisms for the improvement of the cultural character- istics of soils (Russian). *Mikrobiologiya* 7, No. 3 : 273-302; see also their paper in *Pedology* (1937) No. 10 : 1429-1441.

31. Koposov, I. P. 1937 The chances for artificial structure formation in chernozem. *Pedology* (U.S.S.R.) No. 2 : 184-221.

32. Kossovich, P. 1911 Osnovy Ucheniya o Pochve (Principles of Pedology), pt. II, St. Petersburg.

33. Kubiena, W. L. 1938 Micropedology. Collegiate Press, Ames, Iowa.

34. Kvasnikov, V. V. 1927 The influence of soil structure on the phys- ical, chemical and biological properties of soil (Russian). *Con- tributions from the Samara Agr. Inst.* 4 : 1043.

35. Lebedev, A. F. 1928 The volume weight of soils as a physical char- acteristic of soil profile. *Soil Sci.* 25 : 207-211.

36. Marbut, C. F. 1927 The transcontinental excursion. *First Inter. Cong. Soil Sci.* Washington, D. C.

37. Mishustin, E. N. 1941 The microbiological factor in the formation of soil structure (Russian). *Mikrobiologiya* 10, No. 3 : 341-356.

38. Mishustin, E. N. 1945 The labile part of the macrostructure of soils. *Pedology* (U.S.S.R.) No. 2 : 122-130.

39. Mishustin, E. N. and Pushkinskaya, O. I. 1942 The microbiological factor in the formation of soil structure. *Mikrobiologiya* 11, No. 3 : 92-103.

40. Mitscherlich, A. 1901 Untersuchungen über dis physikalischen Bodeneigenschaften. *Landw. Jahrbüch.* 30 : 361-445.

41. Mitscherlich, Eilh. Alfred 1920 Bodenkunde für Land und Forst- wirte, 3rd ed. Paul Parey, Berlin.

42. Moiseev, I. G. 1938 On the new theory of structure formation. *Khimisatsiya Sotsial. Zemled.* No. 3 : 109-110.

43. Molotkovskii, G. Kh. 1939 A new method for taking soil mono- liths. *Pedology* (U.S.S.R.) No. 3 : 100-101.

44. Nabokikh, A. I. 1914 On the method of field and laboratory study of soils. *Zap. Imper. Obshch. Sel'sk. Khoz. Yuzh. Ross.* No. 1-2, pp. 1-66.

45. Nikiforoff, C. C. 1941 Morphological classification of soil structure. *Soil Sci.* 52: 193-211.

46. O'Neal, A. M. 1923 The effect of moisture on soil color. *Soil Sci.* 16: 275-278.

47. Peterson, J. B. 1944 The effect of montmorillonitic and kaolinitic clays on the formation of platy structure. *Proc. Soil Sci. Soc. Amer.* 9: 37-48.

48. Pigulevskii, M. Kh. 1927 Problems of agro-physics and agronomy in judging soil tillage implements. *Izv. Otdela Mashinoved. Gosud. Inst. Opyt. Agron.* 2 (2nd ser.) : 97-128.

49. Polynov, B. B. 1926-1927 The sands of the Don region (Russian). Pt. I and II. Academy of Science, U.S.S.R.

50 Polynov, B. B., Baltz, V. A. and Z. J. Schokalsky. 1929 Instructions for collecting soil monoliths and soil samples for laboratory investigations. (In English). Academy of Science, U.S.S.R. Dokuchaev Institute of Soil Science.

51. Puchner, H. 1889 Investigations on the coherence property of soil types. *Forschungen auf d. Geb. der Agr. Physik,* 12: 195-241.

52. Puri, A. N. and Rai, Balwant. 1944 Physical characteristics of soils. VIII: State of aggregation. *Soil Sci.* 57: 391-396.

53. Ramann, E. 1928 The Evolution and Classification of Soils. English translation by C. L. Whittles. Cambridge, W. Heffer and Sons.

54. Redlich, G. C. 1940 Determination of soil structure by microscopic investigation. *Soil Sci.* 50: 3-13.

55. Rizpolozenskii, R. V. 1897 A collection of instruments and other equipment necessary and handy in making soil collections. (Russian). Derevnya, No. 18: 435-439.

56. Schloesing, Th. 1888 Chimie agricole.

57. Schumacher, W. 1864 Die Physik des Bodens in Ihren theoretischen und praktischen Beziehungen, etc.

58. Schumacher, W. 1874 Die Ackererde. Wien.

59. Selechnik, N. Ya. and Novosel'tsev, N. D. 1935 Structure formation binders (Russian). *Trudy sektora fiziki pochv. fiziko-agron. inst.* No. 1. VASKHNIL, pp. 37-43.

60. Sergeev, S. F. 1931 The influence of mulching on the moisture of the soil and yield of crops. *Zhur. Opyt. Agron. Yugo-Vostoka* (Saratov) 11: 35-57.

61. Sideri, D. I. 1936 I. The structure of soil colloids. *Soil Sci.* 42: 281-393; II. Synthesis of aggregates: on the bonds uniting clay with sand and clay with humus. *Soil Sci.* 42: 461-481.

62. Spilsbury, R. H. 1940 A method for taking soil monoliths. *Sci. Agr.* 20, No. 5: 297-300.

63. Tyulin, A. F. 1928 Problems of soil structure. III. Aggregate analysis as a supplementary method in determining the true soil structure. Reprint from *Resultaty Rabot Agrokhim. Otdela Perm. Sel.-Khoz. Opyt. Stantzii,* No. 2, pp. 77-122.

64. Tyuremnov, S. I. 1927 Soil colors. Reprints from *Trudy Kuban. Sel'sko-Khoz. Inst.* 5: 1-59.

65. Vershinin, P. V. and Konstantinova, V. P. 1935 Physico-chemical basis of artificial structure of soils (Russian). Physico-Agronom. Inst. No. 1 WASKHNIL. Izdanie Kolkhoz.-sovkhoz. 'literat. See also their paper in *Pedology* (1937) No. 2: 176-183.

66. Vilenskii, D. G. 1927 The desirability of organizing an exchange of monoliths and the necessity of introducing some changes in the technique of taking and mounting monoliths. *Pedology* (U.S.S.R.) No. 2: 59-66.

67. Vilenskii, D. G. 1936 The effect of moisture on stability of soil structure. Soil Physics in U.S.S.R., Trans. MAP, Selkhozgiz.

68. Voigt, Eh. 1936 A new procedure for the conservation of soil profiles. *Ztsch. Pflanzenernähr, Düng. u. Bodenkunde* 45: 111-115.

69. Vysotskii, G. N. 1901 Steppe illuvium and the structure of steppe soils. *Pochvovedenie,* (Pedology) 3: 137-156, 237-252.

70. Vysotskii, G. N. 1905 Gley. *Pochvovodenie* (Pedology) 7: 291-327.

71. Wahnschaffe, F. 1887 Anleitung zur wissenschaftl. Bodenuntersuchung. Berlin.

72. Williams, V. R. 1930 Osnovy obshchego zemledeliya (Fundamentals of general agronomy—Russian) Novy Agronom—Moscow.

73. Wollny, E. 1886 Forschungen auf dem Geb. Agr. Phys. Bd. IX; also the volumes as early as 1880 and as late as v. 16 (1893).

74. Zakharov, S. A. 1927 Achievements of Russian science in morphology of soils (English). Russian pedological investigations. II. Academy of Science, Leningrad, 1-47.

CHAPTER IV

SOIL GENESIS: THE PROCESS OF WEATHERING

Introduction.—Soil genesis is the evolution of the soil body in the geochemical cyclic process operating in the crust of the belt of weathering. Any cyclic process consists of a series of consecutive changes or equilibrium states through which a system may be taken, finally returning to its original position or state. The system is physically and chemically identical at the beginning and at the end of the cycle. At the Fourth International Conference of Soil Science held in Rome in 1924, Vernadskii (91) demonstrated this fundamental principle with the soil system as a state in a geochemical cycle:

$$\text{Soil} \longrightarrow \text{fresh water} \longrightarrow \text{ocean water} \longrightarrow \text{ocean botton sediments}$$
$$\uparrow \qquad\qquad\qquad\qquad\qquad\qquad\qquad\qquad \downarrow$$
$$\text{clastic rock} \qquad\qquad\qquad\qquad\qquad\qquad \text{clastic rock}$$

One need not limit this schematic presentation to the geochemical cycle of clastic rocks. It will also hold true for igneous or metamorphic rocks. Any of the deposits on the bottom of the ocean may become a part of the zone of metamorphism or magmatic zone and appear on the surface as igneous rock.

To appreciate fully the sequence of events in soil genesis, we must turn our attention to the consecutive changes or equilibrium states in geochemical reactions. Specifically, we are to look into the cyclic process involved in the geologic history in the crust of the belt of weathering.

An analysis of the cyclic process in which the soil system appears as one of the equilibrium states reveals two distinct phases. First, the preparation of the raw material (rocks and minerals), the mass of the soil body. Second, the conversion of this material into a soil body. The first phase represents the process of weathering, the *disintegration and decomposition of rocks and minerals,* whereby energy is liberated, many of the reactions being exothermic. Long before life appeared on this earth, disintegration (physical weathering) and decomposition (chemical weathering) had been active. With the advent of life the second phase in the genesis of the soil found expression. The biosphere and climate, acting on the products of weathering as well as on the native rocks and minerals, are primarily responsible for the creation of the soil body.

73

The Earth's Crust*

Clarke (8) confines the term "crust" to the surface sheath of the earth extending from the top of the mountains to 10 miles below sea level. In the more modern version, the earth's crust embraces the outer sheaths of our planet which are spheres, the planet itself being one. These outer spheres comprise the atmosphere, hydrosphere, and lithosphere.

The inner part of our planet, the barysphere, is known to consist of high specific gravity material. Geophysicists generally agree that the barysphere is at present a solid metallic core surrounded by concentric layers, of less and less dense materials.

The lithosphere varies in composition from place to place, depending on the factors of temperature and pressure prevailing at any one place. On the basis of these factors, the lithosphere is divided into three thermodynamic belts. As presented by Polynov (62), below a depth of 10 to 12 miles lies the magmatic region, under pressures exceeding 5000 atmospheres, with temperatures around 1000° C. Above that is the zone of metamorphism, with a unilateral pressure measured in thousands of atmospheres and a temperature fluctuating widely above and below the critical temperature of water (374° C.). Overlying the zone of metamorphism is the belt of weathering with the temperature of the surface of the earth and pressures varying from atmospheric to that of the bottom of oceans.

A comprehensive presentation of the alterations in the earth's crust is to be found in the classical monograph on the subject by Van Hise (89). One may recognize in his *zones of metamorphism and anamorphism* the modern classification of the earth's crust into three thermodynamic belts. In the zone of anamorphism, alteration of rocks takes place with simple compounds combining into more complex compounds in a medium of high temperature, pressures, and vapors of all kinds. This is, in a sense, the zone of true metamorphism, corresponding to the magmatic region. Overlying the zone of anamorphism is the one of katamorphism, which is divided into: (a), *belt of weathering,* extending from the surface to the level of the ground waters; and (b), *belt of cementation,* extending from the level of the ground waters to the zone of anamorphism.

Fersman (15, pp. 286-9) also holds the view that the belt of weathering is limited by the level of the ground waters. He concedes the possibility of some weathering in the region below the water table, providing

---

*The concept of crust stems from the idea that our planet was originally molten and, in cooling, crusted over at the surface. The gaseous hypothesis on the origin of the earth is in line with this idea, but not the planetesimal. Neither of the hypotheses exclude the possibility of the inner core having been or capable of being at times in a molten stage.

there is some source of CO_2 and O_2 entering the water table. Below the belt of weathering, Fersman recognizes the zone of cementation.

The hydrosphere covers more than two thirds of the lithosphere. In depth, the hydrosphere approaches 7 miles as the highest value, with an average of little more than 2 miles.

Over the lithosphere and hydrosphere is the blanket of air, the atmosphere. In it we recognize the troposphere, or the nitrogen-oxygen zone, 10 miles * above sea level, and the stratosphere.

Belt of Weathering.—Accepting the modern concept on the belt of weathering, as presented by Polynov, it is necessary to examine more closely the outer sheath of the lithosphere. It is obvious that some riddles of soil genesis are hidden in this belt.

Physically, the change of primary igneous or metamorphic rocks to sedimentary deposits involves an increase in surface and hence greater reactivity with the media surrounding them. The chemical transformations taking place lead to a simplification of the residual products. In other words, the tendency is for the products of weathering in the outer sheath of the belt of weathering to be reduced to compounds of a lower molecular order. Thus, the sesquioxides formed in laterite weathering can not decompose any further under conditions of temperature and pressures existing on the surface of the belt of weathering. It should be remembered that the chemical reactions involved in the weathering of the surface of the lithosphere are exothermic. Using a portion of the cycle of sulfur in nature, Polynov (62, p. 15) illustrates very vividly the reactions just discussed.

Juvenile sulfur is ejected by volcanoes in the form of vapor. As the sulfur loses heat, it liquifies and then solidifies. Exposed to the air, sulfur is oxidized (chemically and biologically), with the evolution of heat:

$$S + 3O \rightarrow SO_3 + 102,160 \text{ calories}$$
$$SO_3 + H_2O \rightarrow H_2SO_4 + 20,470 \text{ calories}$$

In contact with some products of weathering, such as K_2CO_3, more heat is liberated:

$$H_2SO_4 + K_2CO_3 \rightarrow K_2SO_4 + H_2O + CO_2 + 195,500 \text{ calories}$$

*This figure is given by Polynov. He points out that "other determinations give figures of another order: 40-55 miles (diffraction of sunlight by particles in the air), 100 miles (observations on falling stars which flame up on entering the atmosphere)."

The products of the reaction are carried to the ocean where the more stable calcium sulfate is formed:

$$K_2SO_4 + CaCl_2 + 2H_2O \rightarrow CaSO_4.2H_2O + 2KCl + 13,570 \text{ calories}$$

The surface sheath of the belt of weathering, where the physical and chemical transformations described take place, has been designated by Polynov (62, p. 14) as the *crust of weathering*. It is defined as *"that upper part of the lithosphere which consists of the loose products of the disintegration of igneous and metamorphic rocks."*

Besides the crust of weathering, Polynov (62, p. 20) recognizes a *region or zone of weathering,* i.e., "that upper part of the lithosphere which in different places and at different times may consist of various materials such as igneous and metamorphic masses, and loose sedimentary rocks, *but within which the processes are directed towards the disintegration and comminution of rocks and the formation of the crust of weathering."*

Mention has been made of the exothermic reactions taking place in the crust of weathering. Some of the energy dissipated by these reactions has been recovered ever since the advent of life on this planet. The primitive forms of life, on the order of the autotrophic organisms (such as Thiobacillus thiooxidans which utilizes heat evolved in the oxidation of sulfur), began to accumulate energy in the crust of weathering. This process has been stepped up with the evolution of the fauna and flora. Through the medium of photosynthesis, cosmic energy has been pouring in into the crust of weathering. In the cycle of weathering a portion of this energy accumulation finds expression in the creation of the soil body, a constructive process in association with the reactions of the crust of weathering, as shown in the next chapter.

The accumulation of energy in the crust of weathering extends to the depths of root penetration and distribution of microorganisms. Some of the accumulated energy moves, in the form of soluble organic compounds, to depths greater than root penetration, in some cases perhaps through the zone of weathering. Some of the energy finds its way into hydrosphere and atmosphere. In the final analysis, the domain of the biosphere includes the crust of weathering of the lithosphere, the hydrosphere, and the lower parts of the atmosphere.

In summarizing the broad aspects of the process in the belt of weathering in relation to soil genesis, it may be well to emphasize once again that weathering of rocks and minerals has been in operation in the geochemical cycle independent of the biosphere. It is well known, as pointed out in the excellent treatise of Schuchert and Dunbar (80), that the Pre-Cambrian age, which occupies three quarters of geologic time in the history of our earth as revealed in the rocks, was one of great erosion cycles (weathering) with very little of living matter participating in these. There was very little life on the earth except for some algae, sponge spicules, and some forms of worms in the seas. As a matter of fact, there is no record of terrestrial life even in Cambrian rocks.

Kinds of Rocks

No discussion on weathering of rocks and minerals would be complete without mentioning the principal rocks and noting certain characteristics of some and simply mentioning others.

On the basis of genesis and structure, three groups of rocks are generally recognized: 1, *igneous;* 2, *sedimentary or clastic;* 3, *metamorphic.*

Igneous Rocks.—These are divided into three kinds, on the basis of SiO_2 content: *a, acid,* containing 65 to 75 per cent; *b, intermediate,* 55 to 65 per cent; *c, basic,* 40 to 55 per cent SiO_2.

Examples of igneous acid rocks are: *granites*—representatives of intrusive, or plutonic rocks; *rhyolites*—a representative of effusive, or volcanic.

Examples of igneous intermediate rocks are: *syenites, nepheline syenites,* and *diorites*—intrusive, or plutonic; quartz—*phonolites, porphyrites, trachytes,* and *andesites*—effusive, or volcanic.

Examples of basic rocks are: *gabbros, norites, diabases, theralites, peridotites* (these are spoken of sometime as ultra basic, because they carry less than 40 per cent SiO_2), *pyroxenites*—intrusive, or plutonic; *basalts, augite porphyrites, leucite rocks, nepheline rocks,* and *melilite rocks*—effusive, or volcanic.

Sedimentary and/or Clastic Rocks:—These two designations are used interchangeably by some; others make a distinction between the two. Sedimentary rocks are those formed through chemical reactions, primarily precipitation from aqueous solution. Clastic rocks are those formed as a result of mechanical sedimentation reactions; clastic rocks are usually fragmental in structure.

Examples of sedimentary rocks are the oxides, silicates, sulfate, carbonates, phosphates, and chlorides. Representative oxides are: *hematite* (Fe_2O_3); *limonite* (brown iron ore, $Fe_2O_3 3H_2O$); *pyrolusite,* a form of manganese oxide usually MnO_2; *bauxite,* Al_2O_3; *silica,* SiO_2. Representative silicate rocks are: *serpentine,* a metasomatic (substitution and replacement) product of magnesium and silica; *pyrophillite,* a hydrous silicate of aluminum; *clay* mineral rocks. Sulfate rock, *gypsum.* Representative carbonate rocks are calcitic limestone, dolomitic limestone, *shell* and *coral* limestone, and lime *marls*. Phosphate rock, *phosphorite*. Chloride rock, *rock salt*.

Examples of clastic rocks are: *sandstone, conglomerate, breccia, unconsolidated silt, shale, clayey marl, clay, argillite, phosphatic sandstone, limestone* (glacial origin) ; *tuffs, sand and ashes, pumice-dust, diatomaceous earth, marl, peat, lignite,* and *coal.*

It is generally accepted that 75 per cent of the earth's land surface is occupied by sedimentary and clastic rocks.

Metamorphic Rocks.—They are a group of either igneous or sedimentary rocks which have undergone transformations in structural features and sometime also in composition induced by heat or pressure, or both. Among the prominent examples of these rocks are *marble, slate, gneiss,* and *schists.*

General Facts.—At this point some general facts on the relation of weathering to the three types of rocks may be cited:

All rocks are subject to losses and gains in the process of weathering, the net effect being a loss. Without it, our mountains would not have been peneplained. Not all rocks lose equally, even under similar environmental conditions. Thus, siliceous rocks rarely lose more than 60 per cent of their mass whereas calcareous rocks may lose as much as 90 or more per cent.

Not all rocks weather equally. The more complex the mineral composition of the rock, the more easily it weathers. Therefore, igneous and metamorphosed igneous rocks weather much more readily than limestone, marble, quartzite, or conglomerate. Igneous rocks containing R_2O_3 minerals in association with calcium minerals weather much faster than those consisting exclusively of aluminum or aluminum and magnesium silicates. Basic rocks carrying biotite retain this mineral in the residual products of weathering. Acid rocks give up biotite very readily and it does not appear in the residual products of weathering.

Sedimentary and clastic rocks, by and large, do not weather as readily as igneous or metamorphosed igneous rocks, since many of their constituents consist of the end-products of an earlier cycle of weathering.

Clastic rocks contain more potassium than sodium, and the reverse is true for primary rocks. The ratio of alkali and alkaline earth bases to alumina is lower than in igneous rocks. Clastic rocks retain more magnesium than calcium, whereas the reverse is true for igneous rocks.

As a general rule, sedimentary and clastic deposits are richer in SiO_2 and such elements as sulfur, chlorine, phosphorus, titanium, and barium.

In addition to the general facts on rocks, it is important to bear in mind the relation of the abundance of the elements in rocks. In table 3,

Table 3

*Percentage composition of lithosphere**

(After Clarke)

Oxygen	47.33	Titanium	0.46
Silicon	27.74	Carbon	0.19
Aluminum	7.85	Chlorine	0.06
Iron	4.50	Phosphorus	0.12
Calcium	3.47	Sulfur	0.12
Magnesium	2.24	Barium	0.08
Sodium	2.46	Manganese	0.08
Potassium	2.46	Strontium	0.02
Hydrogen	0.22	Fluorine	0.10

All other elements 0.50

*The lithosphere comprises 93 per cent of the known terrestrial matter.

the relative percentages of the elements in the lithosphere, as given by Clarke (8), are noted. The figures show that Al, Fe, Mg, Na, and K are the only metallic elements in sizable quantities. Of the non-metallic elements, O and Si are present in abundance, comprising 75 per cent of the lithosphere. According to Emerson (13, p. 5), the Si and the O together with eighteen other elements comprise nearly 99 per cent of the rocks.

Agents of Weathering

In the cycle of weathering, a series of physical and chemical agents are responsible for the transformations that take place in the rocks and minerals. Those interested in tracing the cycle of the individual elements and the agents involved in the reactions are referred to the extensive treatise of Van Hise (89). A simplified and more up-to-date summary is presented in a most interesting and original manner by Polynov (62). In some measure his ideas and deductions are based on the scholarly work of the world famous mineralogists, Vernadskii and Fersman, whose original views on geochemistry and biogeochemistry are most fascinating and instructive.

Physical Agents.—Expansion and contraction, due to the changes of day and night temperatures and seasonal variations, are the most vital forces of disintegration. All kinds of stresses come into play as a result of the differential expansion and contraction of the rocks. The more complex the rock is mineralogically, the more variable are the coefficients of expansion and contraction and the more easily is it subject to disintegration. The southern exposures of mountains usually abound with talus much more than do the northern exposures. There is more thermal absorption and radiation over the southern exposures, hence more stresses and more disintegration.

In the regions where the temperature drops to the freezing point and below, the force exerted by water frozen in rock crevices is one of the most potent factors in rock disintegration. Water, as it solidifies, expands about 9 per cent of its bulk with a force of 150 tons to the square foot. This form of weathering is hydrothermal since it engages the action of both moisture and temperature. Intermittent freezing and thawing is an effective force in hydrothermal weathering.

The disintegrated rock material does not differ from the original bed rock, except in form. Instead of being massive solid rock, it is loose rock. All other properties, petrographic and mineralogic, remain the same.

Water is one of the most potent weathering agents extant and undoubtedly has been ever since the temperature relations allowed the formation of water basins and water sheds in the geological history of the earth. In the words of Hilgard (Ch. 2, 30, p. 5): "From the sculpturing of the original simple forms in which geological agencies left the earth's surface into the complex ones of modern mountain chains, to the formation of valleys, plains and basins out of the materials so carried away, its effects are prodigious. The torrents and streams in carrying silt, sand, gravel, and boulders, according to velocity and volume, do not merely displace these materials; the rock fragments of all sizes not only scour and abrade the bed of the rill or stream, but by their mutual attrition produce more or less fine powder similar to that formed by glacier action . . . In the United States the stupendous gorges of the Columbia and Colorado rivers, the former cut to a depth of over 2000 feet into hard basalt rock, the latter to over 5000 feet, partly into softer materials, partly into granite, are perhaps the most striking example of the power of water." The erosive force of water as a physical agent is a well-known phenomenon. Its transport capacity increases to the sixth power of the velocity of the currents, i.e., the motor power is increased 64 times by doubling the velocity.

Wind by itself does not act on the native rock, but its abrasive powers are important. The sands, and even gravels carried by the wind, grind away the bed rock surface and move it. The winds also move the cleavage talus from the bed rock, exposing new surfaces to further action by the hydrothermal and purely thermal forces. The stony deserts are an example of the sweeping capacity of the wind. The grotesque forms of mushroom-like rocks in Wyoming indicate remnants of resistant strata, the softer parts of which have been blown away.

Glaciers are an important physical agent of weathering. The ice sheets take up, in the course of their slow movement, a large number of rocks, boulders, and stones, and with them do the cutting, scouring, grinding, and crushing of the bed rock over which they make their overbearing advance.

Chemical Agents.—The decomposition of the rock, while still in the massive form or as loose material, is known as *chemical weathering*. It produces changes in the nature and composition of the body, as distinguished from physical weathering—disintegration—which produces a change only in the form of the body. Chemical weathering may be considered either from the standpoint of the processes that are instrumental in the alteration of the chemical makeup of the rocks or from the standpoint of the composition of the petrographic elements of the rocks and the resulting products. The former approach leads to an understanding of the general aspects of chemical weathering, whereas the latter tends to stress the possible end-products resulting from the change in the nature of the materials that comprise the lithosphere. Each approach involves the elucidation of the transformation that are implemented by chemical agents in rocks and minerals.

In chemical weathering five principal agents are involved: oxidation, hydration, carbonation, solution, and deposition.

Oxidation.—Oxygen is the most energetic oxidizing agent in nature, and there are few minerals that are not subject to oxidation reactions. Active oxidation is conditioned by the presence of moisture, but even in the deserts there is sufficient moisture to promote this reaction. Of course, in the humid region this reaction is more active.

Iron minerals that undergo oxidation more generally than other minerals are common constituents of rocks of all ages. Some of the important iron ores, such as hematite (Fe_2O_3) and limonite ($2Fe_2O_3.3H_2O$), are products of the ferruginous silicates, sulfides, and anhydrous oxides. As stated by Van Hise (89, p. 467): "Ferrous oxide occurs in the following classes of minerals: oxides, carbonates, and silicates. Of the oxides, magnetite ($FeO.Fe_2O_3$) is the most important. It may be oxidized without hydration into hematite. This change is very well illustrated by martite ores of the Lake Superior region and by the pseudomorphs of hematite after magnetite in the martite bearing schists. Simultaneously with the oxidation of magnetite hydration may take place and thus produce hydrated hematite, limonite, or the other hydrated oxides of iron."

Pyrite, marcasite, and pyrrhotite are the most important iron ore minerals to undergo oxidation. The end products, depending on the hydration effects, are either the oxides—in pure oxidation—or iron sulfate, where hydration takes place in the reaction. In the latter case sulfur is separated and, in turn, oxidized into sulfuric acid. The lower oxides of manganese and partly of chromium are other minerals subject to oxidation.

The products of oxidation of course are split off and some are washed out. The residual altered minerals are further subjected to the action of other forces of weathering, and the resultant is the mantle rock, or, as Van Hise calls it, "the belt of weathering."

Hydration.—Hydration is the process by which water combines with other constituents. It is more extensive in the humid than in the arid regions. In general, hydration plays a very important part in chemical weathering, being considered by some geologists as the dominant reaction of the belt of weathering. A large number of silicates, oxides, carbonates, and even sulfates form hydrous compounds. The kaolins, the serpentines, and the so-called zeolites are examples of the silicate minerals which become hydrated. Gibbsite is the hydrated mineral of aluminum oxide; limonite is the hydrated compound of iron oxide. Some of the rock minerals become hydrated while still in the rock matrix under pressure. Such rocks when brought to the surface become still more hydrated and in some instances break up so fast that the term *slaking* is applied.

Merrill (49, p. 188) points out how "granitic rocks in the District of Columbia have been shown to have become disintegrated for a depth of many feet with loss of but comparatively small quantities of their chemical constituents and with apparently but little change in their form of combination. . . . Natural joint blocks of the rock brought up from shafts were, on casual inspection, sound and fresh. It was noted, however, that on exposure to the atmosphere such shortly fell away to the condition of sand. Closer inspection revealed the fact that the blocks when brought to the surface were in a hydrated condition." According to Vernadskii the water of the lithosphere amounts to less than 50 per cent of that in the hydrosphere.

Merrill quotes Alexander Johnstone (37) who showed experimentally that normal muscovites, when submitted to the action of pure and carbonated waters for the space of a year, underwent very little change other than hydration and a diminution in luster, hardness, and elasticity. They seemed to be converted merely into hydromuscovites. Anhydrous mica becomes hydrated and increases in bulk. It retains the original crystal structure, but takes on different optical constants.

The phenomenon of increase in volume by hydration is well known. Van Hise (89, p. 483) states: "Whether hydration occurs alone or combined with other processes, there is an increase in volume. In simple hydration the volume increase ranges from a very small per cent to as high as 160 per cent, as in the alteration of corundum to gibbsite. Commonly the increase in volume is less than 50 per cent."

In the semiarid and arid regions where the temperature, during the dry summer season, rises very high, there is a chance for dehydration. As pointed out by Van Hise (89, p. 482) : "Ferric iron in the belt of weathering is ordinarily hydrous, and this gives a yellow color. In regions of high temperature where the humidity is low for at least a portion of the year, the soil is likely to be red, the iron being in the form of hematite . . . It is highly probable that, under the same conditions in which dehydration of iron occurs, dehydration of aluminum hydroxide also takes place to some extent."

Carbonation.—Carbonic acid is a weak acid, but as an agent of chemical weathering is of tremendous importance, because of the large quantities present in rainwater. Though the air contains not more than 0.03 per cent of CO_2 by volume, rainwater might contain as high as 0.45 per cent. In regions of high rainfall the action of CO_2 on the decomposition of rocks is of considerable moment.

Merrill (49, p. 192) quotes the work of Müller (52), who has ascertained experimentally the capacity of CO_2 in water to dissolve various minerals under ordinary conditions of temperature and pressure. In table 4, the solubility of various silicates and other minerals in carbonated water is presented.

Adularia, the orthoclase potash feldspar mineral, proved to be more resistant than oligoclase, the plagioclase-Na-feldspar. Hornblende was attacked more readily than the feldspars. In the feldspars, in general, the decomposition seemed to have taken place by a process of substitution. Some SiO_2 was released and the alkali and alkaline earth carbonates were formed. Aluminum was dissolved in appreciable quantities. The liberated silica partly went into solution but also appeared as quartz. It is of interest to note that apatite is just as soluble as the more soluble silicates.

The solvent action of CO_2 merits mention here. Van Hise (89, p. 487) points out that "where vegetable matter is abundant it has also been observed that the amount of dissolved silica contained in underground water is much greater than where vegetation is sparse or absent."

The process of carbonation with desilication is accompanied by hydration, since CO_2 acts in solution, and according to Van Hise (p. 479) "it is one of paramount importance in the belt of weathering. Although the process is not so extensive as hydration, if one were to pick out a single chemical process especially characteristic of this belt and of great significance in geology, it would be carbonation. Carbonation has continued through all geological time since land areas first arose above the sea."

Any brief presentation of carbonation in the process of chemical weathering would be incomplete without mention of the effect of CO_2 on

Table 4

Percent of total constituents dissolved by carbonated water from various minerals

(After Merrill)

Mineral	SiO_2	Al_2O_3	K_2O	Na_2O	MgO	CaO	P_2O_5	FeO	Total
Adular	0.1552	0.1368	......	......	......	......	......	Trace	0.328
Oligoclase...	0.237	9.1717	......	2.367	......	3.213	......	Trace	0.533
Hornblende.	0.419	Trace	......	......	t......	8.528	......	4.829	1.536
Magnetite...	Trace	......	......	......	......	......	......	0.942	0.307
Apatite	......	......	......	......	......	2.168	1.822	......	2.018
Olivine	0.873	Trace	......	......	1.291	Trace	......	8.733	2.111
Serpentine..	0.354	......	......	......	2.649	......	......	1.527	1.211

limestone. Merrill (49, p. 194) cites the estimate of Ewing "that some 275 tons of calcium carbonate are annually removed from each square mile of calciferous limestone exposed in the Appalachian region alone." Of course it is through the formation of the bicarbonate that most of the limestone is being leached away.

Solution.—Water is the universal solvent, and its role is closely connected with the other agents of chemical weathering: carbonation, oxidation, and hydration. The solvent action of water by itself is slow, but with some salts or acids in solution, the solubility effects increase tremendously. Mention has been made of how rainwater when charged with CO_2—and it always is—acts on the various silicates. The oxidation of sulfur and its compounds gives rise to H_2SO_4, which, in turn, increases the solvent effect of the water, even more so than carbonated water. However, the large mass of CO_2 in water gives to this weak acid major importance in the solvent action of acids in solution. There is no mineral which will not be affected by the solvent action of water, and in the belt of weathering, water is one of the most potent factors in the decomposition of the rocks. Merrill (49, p. 194) quotes the data of Reade (66), who calculated that throughout the entire globe there is removed annually in solution 96 tons of material per square mile, which he divides as follows: calcium carbonate, 50 tons; calcium sulfate, 20 tons; sodium chloride, 8 tons; silica, 7 tons; alkaline carbonates and sulfates, 6 tons; magnesium carbonate, 4 tons; oxide of iron, 1 ton. In England, with 32 inches of rainfall, which percolates to a depth of 18.3 inches, there is a removal of 143.5 tons of constituents per square mile. The earlier work of Beyer (5), Lemberg (40), and Johnston (37) and the more recent work of Zemyatchenskii (99) abound with evidence on chemical weathering by solution reactions.

Deposition.—If we accept the classification of Van Hise on the metamorphism of the earth's crust, as already mentioned, it would seem that most of the deposition reactions take place in the belt of cementation. However, it is known that in the belt of weathering precipitation takes place alongside of the solution reactions. The movement of iron and aluminum as colloids, which coagulate because of the presence of electrolytes at a certain point in the path of their movement, because of intermittent heating and drying, or because of certain electrokinetic conditions, is one of the phenomena of deposition. The decomposition of the silicates and the separation of silica are another illustration. As stated, the deposition reactions are more active in the belt of cementation, where the reactions in the ground waters play their part.

Summary Statement on Chemical Weathering.—The five principal processes of chemical weathering are not at work independently. All of them usually complement one another, reacting in variable combination. It is important to remember that the *oxygen, carbon dioxide, and water are added to the lithosphere from the hydrosphere and the atmosphere; in the process of solution and deposition, most of the materials involved in these reactions find their origin in the lithosphere.*

Factors Influencing Weathering

Climate.—It has been generally recognized that the climate influences the type of weathering. The efficiency of either of the two most potent manifestations of weathering—disintegration and decomposition—is, in a large measure, determined by the climate. Thus, in the desert and arctic regions, especially in the former, disintegration predominates. In recent years evidence has been accumulated showing that decomposition also is active in the desert regions, especially on the surface. Reference to this revised view may be found in the papers of Blank and Passarge (2) and Fersman (14). Of course, the products removed and those which remain behind in the process of weathering vary in accordance with the climate.

In the humid tropics physical weathering, as a rule, is subordinate to chemical weathering. The most potent factor in physical weathering, sharp fluctuations in temperature, are non-existent in the humid tropics. On the other hand, the high temperature and abundance of water are conducive to vigorous chemical weathering.

From the geologic point of view on soil formation, the variations in the products of weathering due to climate seem to complicate the problem of correlating the relation between the geologic formation and the type of soil. Pedology, however, finds in these variations another link in the chain of evidence that the climate is the primary force of soil formation. Unfortunately, the data available on the composition of the products of weathering under varied climatic conditions are meager.

Comparative analyses of the weathered material, in situ, and of the massive rock underlying it, give us an idea of the quantity of products removed. Merrill (49, pp. 207-209) presents data on the composition of the original and partly decomposed granite rock of the District of Columbia with calculations on the losses of the various constituents. Table 5 gives the analyses of the fresh and altered granite.

The figures indicate that this particular rock, even though it is located in a climatic zone where the forces of weathering are very prominent, is not decomposed much. Undoubtedly the age of the weathering process, the composition of the rock, and other minor factors are responsible for the slow decomposition. As pointed out by Merrill (p. 213) : "We have to do

Table 5

Analyses of fresh and altered granite from the District of Columbia

(After Merrill)

Constituent	Composition of fresh granite material	Composition of decomposed granite	Loss of each constituent
	per cent	*per cent*	*per cent*
SiO$_2$	69.33	65.69	14.89
Al$_2$O$_3$	14.33	15.23	3.23
Fe$_2$O$_3$ and FeO as Fe$_2$O$_3$	4.00	4.39	0.00*
CaO	3.21	2.63	25.21
MgO	2.44	2.64	1.49
Na$_2$O	2.70	2.12	28.62
K$_2$O	2.67	2.00	31.98
P$_2$O$_5$	0.10	0.06	40.00
Ignition loss	1.22	4.70	0.0

* Any absolute lowering of the percentage composition of an element in weathered material, in comparison with the parent rock, is not always a loss, nor is any absolute increase a gain. The point is that the change in percentage composition of any element does not depend on the accumulation or removal of this element only. This change is conditioned also by the translocation, removal, and accumulation of other elements in the process of weathering.

In calculating the loss or gain of elements, the most common method is to assume that the element or radical whose relative percentage composition has increased considerably in the weathered material has not moved in any perceptible quantity, whereas other elements or radicals did move and have been leached. With this assumption of the immobility of one element it is possible to figure out the per cent of constituents left behind out of the original 100 units of the original parent rock. The values obtained are subtracted from the percentage composition of the same elements in the original rock. An example illustrating the above is given, using the figures of this table and the reasoning of Kossovich (Ch.2, 40, p. 119).

Let us assume that the Fe$_2$O$_3$ and Fe as Fe$_2$O$_3$ did not move as the granite was subjected to weathering. In 100 units of the granite under consideration we have 4.0 units of Fe$_2$O$_3$ in the fresh granite and 4.39 units in the decomposed granite. In order to determine the true percentage of the other compounds in the decomposed granite, in comparison with the composition of the original 100 units of fresh granite, we must decrease proportionally the percentage composition of these compounds by the ratio of 4.0/4.39 = 0.9111. Thus, for K$_2$O we have 2.0 per cent in the decomposed granite, then 2.0 x 0.9111 which equals 1.822 has to be subtracted from the K$_2$O percentage of the original granite, or 2.67 -- 1.822 = 0.848. The per cent loss of K$_2$O is then: 0.848 x 100/2.67 = 31.98.

Merril presented the calculations given in the form of the following formula:

A/B x C = X, and 100 -- X = Y. A = the percentage of any constituent of the residual material; B = percentage of the same constituent in the fresh rock, and C = the quotient obtained by dividing the percentage of alumina (or iron sesquioxide, whichever is taken as a constant factor) of the residual material by that in the fresh rock, the final quotient being multiplied by 100; X then equals the percentage of the original constituent saved in the residue, and Y the percentage of the same constituent lost.

Polynov (63) points out that the methods used in calculating the translocation of elements based on the immobility of one of these are erroneous. There is no such a thing as absolute immobility. Marshall (44) discusses the use of heavy minerals, especially the zircon minerals, for the evaluation of the movement of constituents. Haseman and

(*Continued on next Page*)

here with but the preliminary stages of granitic weathering; the process is more one of disintegration than decomposition."

Analyses of rocks in a more advanced stage of weathering will indicate how decomposition is effective in this climatic belt. Table 6 gives the analyses of biotite gneiss or gneissoid granite near North Garden in

Table 6

Analyses of fresh and altered gneiss from Virginia
(After Merrill)

Constituent	Composition of fresh gneiss	Composition of decomposed gneiss	Loss of each constituent
	per cent	*per cent*	*per cent*
SiO₂	60.69	45.31	52.45
Al₂O₃	16.89	26.55	0.0*
Fe₂O₃	9.06	12.18	14.35
CaO	4.44	Trace	100.00
MgO	1.06	0.4	74.70
K₂O	4.25	1.10	83.52
Na₂O	2.82	0.22	95.03
P₂O₅	.25	0.47	0.0
Ignition loss	.62	13.75	....

*These analyses are based on the aluminum remaining intact.

Albermarle County, Virginia. It is interesting to note that desilication has gone on to the extent of 52.45 per cent loss of silica, and that lime and the other bases are extensively attacked and lost. On the other hand, the alumina and the bulk of the iron—85.65 per cent of the iron and most of the aluminum—remain behind. With the remaining silica the aluminum makes up the potential source of the kaolin portion of the residual products.

If we take similar analyses of rocks and weathered products from a more northern region, Massachusetts (table 7), the proportions of the chemical substances removed and those left behind are somewhat different from those in the Virginia rocks and their weathered products.

A comparison of the climatological data of Virginia and Massachusetts, as compiled in table 8 (88), shows that the precipitation in these two sections of the country is the same, whereas the temperature differs, being almost 9° F. higher in Virginia.

The climatic differences in the respective regions apparently are re-

(footnote from p. 87, continued)

Marshall (27) review the entire subject on the use of an immobile indicator for calculating changes taking place in profile development of soils. They present a method based on zircon as the immobile element. It would seem that the choice of an immobile indicator would depend on the climate. For the zone of podzolization titanium could be used; for the chernozem — SiO₂ could be suggested. An excellent review of the methods used in calculating the mobility of elemnts is givn by Reiche (67, p. 46).

sponsible for the variations in the mode of weathering. In Massachusetts we have a relatively smaller decrease of SiO_2 and a far greater decrease of sesquixides than in Virginia, which is in line with the facts as far as the soil proper is concerned. We have less SiO_2 and a higher sesquioxide content in the soils which develop under the climatic conditions approaching the humid subtropics (Virginia), whereas in the cool temperate regions, the reverse is true; i.e., we have a relatively greater decrease of sesquioxides and a small decrease of SiO_2, sometimes even a relative increase. Of course, the data presented are not strictly comparable for several reasons. First, the rocks in the two regions under consideration are not of the same mineralogic and petrographic constitution. Secondly, from the standpoint of geologic age, we do not know the exact stage of decomposition of the materials compared.

Table 7

Analyses of fresh and altered diabase from Medford, Massachusetts

(After Merrill)

Constituent	Composition of fresh diabase material	Composition of altered diabase material	Loss of each constituent
	per cent	*per cent*	*per cent*
Silica	47.28	44.44	18.03*
Al_2O_3	20.22	23.19	0.00
Fe_2O_3	3.66	12.70	18.10
FeO	8.89	.....	...
CaO	7.09	6.03	25.89
MgO	3.17	2.82	21.70
MnO	0.77	0.52	41.57
K_2O	2.16	1.75	29.15
Na_2O	3.94	3.93	12.83
P_2O_5	0.68	0.70	11.39
Loss on ignition	2.73	3.73	

*Calculation based on Al_2O_3 being constant.

Table 8

Climatological data of sections mentioned in tables 5, 6, and 7

Section	Mean annual precipitation	Mean annual temperature
	inches	*degrees F.*
District of Columbia	38.40	54.9
Virginia (Albemarle County)	44.83	55.8
Massachusetts (Middlesex County)	45.00	47.0 *

* The temperature data are those for Boston, which are probably slightly higher than those for Medford.

An interesting study on the composition of fresh rock and its weathered material has been presented by Palmer (57). Table 9 illustrates

Table 9

*Analyses of fresh and altered basalts from the Hawaiian Islands**

(After Palmer)

Constituent	Composition of fresh basalt material	Composition of decomposed basalt	Loss of each constituent
	per cent	*per cent*	*per cent*
SiO₂	52.13	25.77	80.2
Al₂O₃	13.96	34.90	0.0
Fe₂O₃	3.40	14.49	70.3**
FeO	6.62	2.77	83.2
MnO	0.58	0.18	87.9
MgO	5.95	0.14	99.0
CaO	9.47	0.24	98.9
K₂O	0.89	0.31	86.5
Na₂O	2.61	0.44	93.1
SO₃	0.46	0.63	45.7
P₂O₅	0.25	0.20	68.0
TiO₂	2.79	3.47	50.2
H₂O	0.89	16.46	640.0**

*Palmer discusses the method of calculating the values given in the table.
**This sign indicates gain instead of loss. In the case of the Fe_2O_3 the gain is due to the oxygen.

this. It will be noted that the subtropical climate of the Hawaiian Islands is conducive to a leaching of the SiO_2 and a retention of the iron and aluminum, a phenomenon which is very important in connection with the laterite process of soil formation.

An interesting angle on the relation of climate to weathering has been brought out by Merrill (p. 284). The loads of the Yukon River in Alaska, a subarctic region, and the Nile, an arid tropical region, are primarily the products of disintegration. The soluble products in the Nile are a result, not of the materials brought in, but of the high evaporation. Otherwise, the soluble load in the rivers of the two extreme climatic zones is the same.

Warth (96) presents comparative data on the decomposition of dolerite in England and India. There is a very sharp contrast in the composition of the fresh and weathered dolerite in the two respective regions, as shown in table 10.

Salminen (78) presents some instructive observations on the influence of exposure upon the temperature, and hence, on the weathering efficiency of rocks.

Robinson and Richardson (69) suggest a method

whereby an approximate estimate may be obtained of the extent to which chemical weathering has proceeded in a given soil. Assuming that the clay fraction separated in mechanical analysis of soils represents that portion of the soil which has resulted from processes of chemical weathering—the so-called weathering complex—and that the remainder of the soil consists of unweathered minerals, such as feldspars, and unweatherable minerals, such as quartz, the proportion of the total alumina of the soil present in the clay fraction should give a rough measure of the degree to which chemical weathering has proceeded. Since the principal clay forming minerals are complex alumino-silicates, a soil which has reached the endpoint of weathering will contain no alumina in its non-clay fraction. On the other hand a soil in the early stages of chemical weathering will contain considerable amounts of alumina as unweathered alumino-silicates, in the non-clay fraction. We therefore propose as a measure of the degree of weathering the amount of alumina in the clay fraction calculated as a per-centage of the total alumina of the soil. For example, if a certain soil contains 20.5 per cent of alumina, of which 16.4 per cent is in the clay fraction, the degree of weathering is 80 per cent.

Table 10

Composition of rocks and weathered products in different climatic regions
(After Warth)

Constituents	Dolerite from Rowley-Regis (England)		Dolerite from West Ghats (India)	
	Fresh	Weathered	Fresh	Weathered
	per cent	*per cent*	*per cent*	*per cent*
SiO_2	49.3	47.0	50.4	0.7
TiO_2	0.4	1.8	0.9	0.4
Al_2O_3	17.4	18.5	22.2	50.5
Fe_2O_3	2.7	14.6	9.9	23.4
FeO	8.3	....	3.6	....
MgO	4.7	5.2	1.5	....
CaO	8.7	1.5	8.4	....
Na_2O	4.0	0.3	0.9	....
K_2O	1.8	2.5	1.8	....
P_2O_5	0.2	0.7	....	....
H_2O	2.9	7.2	0.9	25.0

Type of Rock.—The process of weathering is influenced by the type of rock; its capacity for heat absorption, which depends upon the color and composition of the rock, and its structure and constitution. Bartlett (3), as early as 1832, pointed out that granites will expand 268×10^{-8} of an inch per foot for one degree C.; marble will expand 3149×10^{-9} of an inch; and sandstone, 5295×10^{-9} of an inch. Glinka (p. 86) points out that on the high plateaus of Armenia no snow remains during the summer and the vegetation is luxuriant simply because the rocks are a dark colored volcanic tuff.

The heat conductance of rocks is low and variable. Thus, gray small-grained marble has a conductance equivalent to 3.48; white large-grained marble, 2.78; and gypsum, 0.33 to 0.52, which in comparison with copper, which is 69.0, is very small (cited from Glinka).

In a dry climatic region, the heat effect is greater than that in a humid region, since a large share of the heat in the humid region is dissipated in evaporating the larger amounts of water present in the rock.

It is well known that in the desert the high absorption of heat during the hot day and the rapid cooling at night are much more effective in disintegrating the rocks than are thermal conditions in the humid region. The peculiar sounds heard at night in a mountainous desert region have been traced to the cracking of the rocks due to the sharp changes in temperature between day and night.

Glinka (p. 87) analyzes the character of rock disintegration in relation to the constitution and structure of the parent rock as follows: "Compact or finely grained rocks, such as certain limestones, quartzite, felsite, and porphyry (which consist of a homogenous ground mass), basalt, finely grained granites, and diorites, break at the surface along cracks barely noticeable with the naked eye. A blow with a hammer over apparently fresh rock surface will crumble it easily. Talus accumulation at the bases of slopes is the product of natural crumbling. The stratified rocks, such as shales, finely grained gneiss, shaly sandstone, and limestone fall apart into flat plates. The soft and homogenous rocks, such as clays and marls, disintegrate into sharp-edged pieces, frequently cubical in shape and sometimes into nutty-shaped forms or into grains and dust."

Polynov (62) presents a rather interesting point that the general direction of the process of weathering is independent of climate, but the latter has a *substantial influence on the intensity of the process*. Fundamentally the products of weathering are removed from the native igneous rocks and redistributed in the crust of weathering according to the "varying mobility of the compounds of which the products consist. The degree of mobility, i.e., the ability to be transported, coincides to a great extent with the ease of dispersion. It is evident that the most mobile compounds are those which appear in the highest state of dispersion, i.e., molecular solution in water."

From a comparative study of the composition of primary (igneous) rocks and the minerals in river waters (table 11), Polynov draws a series of logical conclusions on the mobility of the products of weathering and their eventual distribution in the crust of weathering.

It is apparent that the quantitative composition of the minerals in river waters is fundamentally different from that of the igneous rocks which are the source of supply of these minerals. It is also apparent that chlorine may be taken as one of the most easily leached elements. Its relative mobility is therefore taken as 100 per cent. If the sulfur of the rocks had the same mobility as cholrine, the amount of $SO_4^=$ in river

water would have to be 3 times as great, as indicated by the simple calculation: 0.15 (per cent $SO_4^=$ in original rock) : 0.05 (per cent of CI^-) = 3.
In other words, the sulfur should make up 20.25 per cent of the mineral
residue.   Actually, it is only 11.6 per cent, which means that only 57 per
cent of the sulfur in the original rock has dissolved.

Table II

*Data on composition of igneous rocks, minerals in solution in river waters,
and relative mobility of constituents.*

(After Polynov*)

Constituents	Composition (average of 30 analyses):		Relative mobility of constituents
	Of igneous rocks	Of minerals in river water	
	per cent	*per cent*	*per cent*
SiO_2	59.09	12.80	0.20
Al_2O_3	15.35	0.90	0.20
Fe_2O_3	7.29	0.40	0.04
Ca	3.60	14.70	3.00
Mg	2.11	4.90	1.30
Na	2.97	9.50	2.40
K	2.57	4.40	1.25
Cl	0.05	6.75	100.00
SO_4	0.15	11.60	57.00
CO_3	—	36.50	—

* Compiled from the data of Clarke (8).

By the method just described, Polynov calculated the figures in the
third column.   Rearranging these figures in the decreasing order of their
relative mobility, Polynov obtains the successive phases of the removal
of constituents from the primary rocks.   In terms of the usual concept,
these phases represent the ease of the removal of constituents in the process
of weathering:

Phase   I: CI .... 100.00 per cent
Phase   I: SO_4 .... 57.00 per cent
Phase   II: Ca .... 3.00 per cent
Phase   II: Na .... 2.40 per cent
Phase   II: Mg .... 1.30 per cent

Phase   II: K .... 1.25 per cent
Phase III: SiO_2 .... 0.20 per cent
Phase   IV: Fe_2O_3 .... 0.04 per cent
Phase   IV: Al_2O_3 .... 0.02 per cent

The order of the relative mobility of the elements shows that Ca is ahead of Na and that Mg and K are on a par. It should, however, be pointed out that the order does not always hold true, since the climate is a disturbing factor in the sequence of the phases as given by Polynov. In the tropics, more than 50 per cent of the minerals in solution of river waters may consist of SiO_2. This, of course, will throw off the order of the phases.

To justify any questioning of the wisdom of abandoning the school of thought (as attempted by Polynov) that there exists a constant relationship between the products of weathering and the climate, one would have to present the elaborate and scholastic discussion of Polynov's scheme. As a matter of fact, he admits some departures in the succession of phases. He strives, however, to belittle the factor of climate in determining the type of weathered products one might expect.

It should be added that the scheme of phases in the mobility of weathered products has been advanced by Polynov in connection with the so-called geologic profile, or belt of weathering. The soil profile as an expression of the processes of soil formation is another segment of the geochemical cycle. In it, the mobility of constituents follow still less the order given by Polynov. In the reactions responsible for the creation of the soil body there is an overlapping of the geologic and soil forming processes and the relationship between the latter and the climate is more apparent. This will be pointed out as we develop the discussion on the specificity of the genesis of the various soil zones.

Biological Weathering

Strictly speaking there is no biological weathering. Essentially it is physical and chemical weathering by biological agencies. Plant roots are potent agents of physical weathering. Tree roots penetrating into crevices and cracks of rocks exert tremendous pressures which cause the rocks to split. Lichens, mosses and similar forms of plant life growing on bare rock penetrate into minute cracks and fractures with their thalli in search of a foothold and food. They exert a powerful force in the disintegration of rocks. Fry (17) has demonstrated that the gelatinous mass of lichens adhering to a rock is capable of tearing its surface in the same manner as gelatin films sticking to the surface of a glass plate do it.

The chemical effects of the biosphere are by far more important in the process of weathering than are the physical effects. The roots of all plants secrete carbonic acid and other acids which act upon the rocks and minerals. An examination of rocks over which roots have formed a network of organic material reveal marks produced by the solvent action of root secretions. Reference to these phenomena may be found as early as in the work of Liebig (41) and Sachs (76). Doyarenko (12) has demonstrated the formation of the calcium oxalate mineral *tirshite* by lichens sium from nepheline and mica than does an extract of carbonated water. A detailed review of this subject may be found in the work of Czapek (10).

Glinka (p. 101) cites the case of a polished marble column in Tyrol attacked by lichens. Not only did the polish disappear, but the marble was pitted and full of holes, in some of which rhombohedral crystals of calcite could be seen. He also cites the work of Shkatelov, who demonstrated the formation of the calcium oxalate mineral *tirshite* by lichens growing on limestone in southern Crimea. Oxalic acid excretions by lichens were also noted by Senft (82).

Various groups of microorganisms are active in the decomposition of rocks and minerals. Especially is this true for the autotrophic organisms, which derive their carbon from the CO_2 of the atmosphere and their energy from the decomposition reactions of the inorganic constituents upon which they thrive. An example of the autotrophic process is the oxidation of ammonia in the soil. Another interesting example of strictly autotrophic reactions is the cycle of sulfur in the biosphere. A summary of this problem is to be found in the work of Joffe (36). A specific organism —*Thiobacillus thiooxidans*—has been isolated which is very active in the process of sulfur oxidation. This organism has been found everywhere about the sulfur mines, and it is probably one of the early forms of life.

Müntz (53) was among the early investigators to point out the role of microorganisms in the decomposition of minerals. He demonstrated the presence of nitrifying organisms on bare rocks. Bassalik (4) investigated the power of bacteria to decompose silicates. With mixed cultures on powdered orthoclase he obtained a decomposition equal to 0.91 per cent. Potassium and SiO_2 were found in the filtrates. *Bacillus extorquens* was especially reactive. It decomposed as high as 3.5 per cent of the feldspars. Bassalik attributed the decomposition to respiration activity as well as to the other products of metabolism; namely, organic acids, ammonia, nitrous, and nitric acids. The B. *extorquens* forms around the silicate particles a film which seems to aid in the decomposition. Ravich-Shcherbo (65) conducted a series of experiments on the decomposition of carbonates and other minerals by various groups of microorganisms—*laxinobacteria,* bacteria decomposing fatty acids, nitrogen fixing organisms, and others. Omelyanskii (56) discussed extentively the role of microorganisms in weathering and presented data on the power of microbes to decompose rocks and minerals. Sackett, Patten, and Brown (77) demonstrated the solvent action of a number of soil bacteria on rock phosphate. Both the CO_2 and the organic acids formed by bacteria have been instrumental in dissolving insoluble phosphates. Remezev (68) reported the release of Al_2O_3 and SiO_2 from microcline, olivine, kaolinite, and biotite when incubated with a soil infusion from the A_2 horizon of a podzol in a solution culture medium of sugar, asparagin, and ammonium phosphate. An infusion from a solodi was not as active in releasing Al_2O_3 and SiO_2, and one from a chernozem was practically inactive.

Microorganisms are also responsible for the synthesis of new minerals. Nadson (54) cites the formation of limestone as a result of bacterial activities. Pure cultures of B. *vulgare,* when grown on media containing both calcium and magnesium, were instrumental in the formation of dolomite. The decomposition of iron compounds and the deposition of iron carbonates and silicates by *iron bacteria* have been discussed by Winogradsky (98), Molisch (50), Harder (26), and others. A critical review of this subject has been presented by Halvorsen and Starkey (25) and by Starkey and Halvorsen (85). A monograph on the aluminum cycle in nature in relation to microorganisms was published by Stoklasa (86). A most comprehensive contribution on the biogeochemistry of aluminum and related elements in nature was made by Hutchinson (34). Vinogradov and Boichenko (95) observed nacrite being decomposed by *Navicula* and *Nitzschia* (diatoms) separating SiO_2 and Al_2O_3. These reactions have been accomplished by a viscous mass consisting of pectic substances.

Another phase of biological weathering which deserves consideration is the effect of humus on minerals. Glinka (Ch. 2, 27) points out that the subject has not been studied adequately and, in reviewing the work done, he notes the shortcomings. The difficulty involved in such a study lies in the scant knowledge about the humus complexes. Besides, the reactions involved are associated with the metabolic activities of microbes.

Glinka (p. 110) conducted a series of experiments on natrolite, hydrothomsonite, and pseudomorphs of kaolinite from biotite, with humic acid of the alkalies and alkaline earths, and his conclusions are as follows: 1. Alkali solutions of the humic acid group are very active reagents. 2. These alkali etxracts partly decompose the aluminum silicates. In addition, an exchange takes place between the insoluble constituents of the complex and the mineral complexes of the extract. 3. In solution we find, besides the alkalies and alkaline earths, some sesquioxides. 4. When the extract becomes saturated with the sesquioxides and clay, an amorphous gelatin-like precipitate appears which adsorbs bases and is hydrophylic.

An approach to the study of the effects of organic matter—as it is found in nature—on minerals has been made by Niklas and Nikiforov, whose work was summarized by Glinka.

Niklas mixed powdered feldspar, agate, hornblende, mica, and labradorite with peat. These mixtures, as well as the individual materials, were kept moist in glass containers for several years, extracted with water, and extracts analyzed. Very little of the mineral substances entered into solution as a result of their contact with the peat. On the other hand, electrolysis experiments on the mixtures and on the peat showed that, in the case of the mixtures, appreciable quantities of bases and sesquioxides accumulated at the cathode. These constituents, of course, are the split products of the minerals as a result of the action of the peat on them.

Nikiforov obtained samples of gneiss from a boulder exposed in a swamp near München, Germany, and of gneiss and diorite buried about 4 feet deep in the swamp. He also had a sample of gneiss from the collection of the München University. Analyses were made on fresh and weathered portions of the samples. The results, as quoted by Glinka, are not very striking, although definite differences were apparent. As Glinka remarks: "Such differences might be found in the different parts of the same piece of gneiss or diorite."

From the point of view of soil genesis and the reactions involved in the constitution of the soil body, the migration of elements in the geochemical cycle is of paramount importance. Outstanding sources of material for this phase of the subject of weathering are to be found in the monumental work of Van Hise (89). Vernadskii (90, 92, 93), Fersman (15, 16), and Goldschmidt (19, 20, 21). In the course of development of this esubject, the importance of the biosphere element became evident. Vernadskii (93) has advanced original ideas on geobiochemical or biogeochemical reactions that gradually take over the role in all transformations on our planet and extend their domain deeper and deeper into the belt of weathering, the lithosphere, hydrosphere, and atmosphere. The biosphere is becoming the focal point of all transformations in nature. The viewpoint of biogeochemical reactions has been followed up and simultaneously developed and furthered by Fersman. Polynov, in his monograph (62), interprets and applies the theories of Vernadskii and Fersman in his discussions on the cycle of weathering. In another contribution (64) he analyzes the effects of lichens and mosses on crystalline rocks as viewed from the point of view of migration of elements in the belt of weathering. Under his direction Lazarev (39) has worked on the migration of phosphorus. For the pedologist, data of this kind are highly instructive. The work of Vinogradov (94) has a bearing on this subject.

TYPES OF MINERALS AND THE PROCESS
OF WEATHERING

Minerals are divided into two principal groups: *essential* and *accessory*. Most silicates belong to the essential group and they comprise the bulk of primary rocks. Clarke (8) gives the following analyses of igneous (primary) rocks: *feldspars*—60 per cent; *quartz*—12 per cent; *amphiboles* and *pyroxenes* (augite)—18 per cent; *micas,* primarily *biotites*—4 per cent. The remaining 6 per cent is made up of the accessory minerals: *ilmenite, zircon, titanite, apatite, pyrite, magnetite, rutile,* and sometime *vivianite* and a few others.

Minerals are also classified on the basis of their specific gravity: *light* and *heavy*. The light minerals include those of a density less than 2.85, such as quartz, calcite, feldspars, clay minerals, and mica. Minerals having a density greater than 2.85 belong to the heavy group. The accessory minerals belong to this group. The weathered products of igneous rocks consist of 98 per cent light minerals and 2 per cent heavy minerals.

In an attempt to arrange the minerals in the order of their resistance to weathering, Pettijohn (61) has compared the minerals of sedimentary rocks of increasing geologic age with those of recent sediments. The order of persistence gives the following series: zircon, tourmaline, monazite, quartz, garnet, biotite, apatite, microcline, ilmenite, magnetite, stauroilte, kyanite (cyanite), epidote, hornblende, andalusite, topaz, titanite, zoisite, and olivine. The minerals anatase, muscovite, and rutile were found to be more abundant in ancient sediments than in recent ones. This is due to the fact that these minerals are frequently secondary as well as primary. Smithson (84) and Goldrich (18) have suggested different groupings.

According to Van Hise (p. 518), the order of decomposability of the silicates is as follows: "Nepheline—leucite minerals are the most readily decomposed. Second in order are the olivines and similar minerals. The third group is the pyroxene and amphiboles. Fourth is the biotite-muscovite group. The fifth and most difficultly decomposable important group is the feldspars. Still more difficultly decomposable are some of the subordinate silicates. Of these garnet, staurolite, tourmaline, andalusite, fibrolite, cyanite, and zircon are probably the most important."

"While the above statements hold in a general way, besides the constituent elements another very important factor enters into the rate of decomposition, viz. the acidity of the mineral. Thus the feldspars vary from orthhosilicates to trisilicates. On this account, the orthosilicate anorthite decomposes more readily than the trisilicate albite and orthoclase, notwithstanding the fact that alkalies are absent in the first and abundant in the second. For the same reason some of the basic feldspars decompose under some circumstances more readily than certain of the more acid pyroxene-amphibole and biotite-muscovite groups." It is worth noting that here we have a case where a primary sodium mineral is more resistant to weathering than a primary calcium mineral.

Silicate Minerals

Silicates are generally considered salts of three groups of silicic acids: 1, orthosilicic acid, H_4SiO_4; 2, metasilicic acid, H_2SiO_3; 3, aluminosilicic acid, $H_2Al_2SiO_6$ or $H_2O.Al_2O_3.SiO_2$. There can also be an orthodisilicic and orthotrisilicic as well as metadisilicic and metatrisilicic acids. As to the aluminosilicic acid form, there are 4 others: aluminodisilicic, aluminotrisilicic, aluminotetrasilicic, and aluminohexasilicic acids.

Not all the silicic acids enumerated have been isolated and some of these are therefore hypothetical, but the salts corresponding to these have been accounted for. It was Vernadskii who proposed and expounded the alumino and other sesquioxide silicates based on the 5 groups of aluminosilicic acids.

Examples of the first group of silicic acid (H_4SiO_4) are the minerals olivine, Mg_2SiO_4, and muscovite, $KAl_3H_2(SiO_4)_3$. Examples of the second group (H_2SiO_3) are the minerals enstatite, $MgSiO_3$, and tremolite, $Ca,Mg_3(SiO_3)_4$. Examples of the third group, the aluminosilicates, are the mineral orthoclase, $K_2O.Al_2O_3.6SiO_2$, a potassium salt of aluminohexasilicic acid, and kaolinite, $2H_2O.Al_2O_3.2SiO_2$, an aluminodisilicic acid.

Silicate and other minerals associate with some selectivity. Thus, nephelite and quartz do not coexist; muscovite and hornblende seldom occur together, unless biotite is present; muscovite and pyroxene are almost never found in the same rock; muscovite and olivine do not seem to like each other; neither does quartz frequently associate with olivine.

The Feldspars.—On the basis of the difference in cleavage angles, the feldspars are divided into two groups: *orthoclase*, breaking at right angles; and *plagioclase*, breaking at oblique angles. In rocks it is difficult to distinguish orthoclase from plagioclase. Still, besides the difference in cleavage planes, the pink or flesh color of orthoclase differentiates it from plagioclase.

In the orthoclase group, the potassium mineral *orthoclase*, $K_2O.Al_2O_3.6SiO_2$ is most prominent. Upon weathering, it becomes soft and crumbly, loses its potassium by solution and carbonation, giving rise to kaolinite, silica, and potassium carbonate, as shown in the following equations:

$$K_2Al_2Si_6O_{16} + CO_2 + 2H_2O = H_2Al_2Si_2O_8.H_2O \text{ (or}$$
$$2H_2O.Al_2O_3.2SiO_2 - \text{Kaolinite)} + K_2CO_3 + 4SiO_2$$

Other minerals of less importance in this group are: *soda-orthoclase* in which albite molecules ($Na_2O.Al_2O_3.6SiO_2$) replace some of the orthoclase molecules; *hyalophane* (K_2,Ba) $Al_2(SiO_3)_4$, a rare feldspar in which barium replaces a part of the potassium; *sanidine,* a clear glassy orthoclase found in acidic lavas, such as trachyte and some rhyolites.

In the plagioclase group, the sodium mineral *albite,* $Na_2O.Al_2O_3.6SiO_2$, is an important member. It is rarely found in pure form and occurs in rocks usually in association with anorthite (a calcium plagioclase), orthoclase, hornblende, quartz, and micas. Like the K-feldspar, albite weathers under the influence of solution and carbonation to kaolinite, silica, and sodium carbonate. Muscovite or sericite is sometime formed.

Another important mineral of the plagioclase group is *oligoclase,* a sodium-calcium-aluminum silicate, or a mixture of albite and anorthite. Similar to this mineral are *andesine* and *labradorite.* The first two are found in granites, syenites, and diorites; the last one is associated with gabbros, basalts, and other basic rocks.

Anorthite is the pure calcium plagioclase, $CaO.Al_2O_3.2SiO_2$, associated with the same rocks as labradorite.

In the plagioclase group we also find two potash-soda minerals, *microcline* and *anorthoclase.* They are similar to orthoclase in composition, but they belong to the triclinic crystal system whereas orthoclase is in the monoclinic system. The difference between microcline and anorthoclase lies in the sodium content, the former containing only small quantities and the latter large quantities, and because of that it is known also as soda-microcline.

Feldspathoids.—Closely related to the feldspars are the *feldspathoid* minerals. They resemble the feldspars in composition, but they differ in the percentages of the contained oxides. They are lower in silica and higher in other oxides. The more common minerals of this group are:

Leucite, $K_2O.Al_2O_3.4SiO_2$(21.5 per cent K_2O), a metasilicate, is associated with recent lava flows. It loses potassium readily. Lemberg (40) has demonstrated that all of the K may be replaced by washing it with NaCl and thus convert it to analcite, the Na-feldspathoid. Leucite may alter to potash feldspars, nephelite and muscovite. According to Glinka (p. 123), leucite may also alter to kaolinite.

Nephelite, $3Na_2O.K_2O.4Al_2O_3.9SiO_2$, is an orthosilicate, associated with orthoclase, augite, hornblende, and other minerals. It alters into sodalite, analcite, and other minerals. The name *elaeolite* is given to the massive, opaque, or coarsely crystalline nephelite of older rocks.

It is worth noting that as far back as 1851 Sellem and in 1865 Fritsch (quoted from Glinka) demonstrated the formation of kaolinite from hauynite and similar feldspathoids under the influence of water and CO_2. Thugutt (see Glinka) has shown experimentally the possibility of the formation of potassium mica from nephelite.

In table 12, data are reproduced from an investigation made by Beyer (5) in 1866 on the solubility of feldspar in pure water and various solutions. He placed one kilogram of ground feldspar into 2.5 liters of pure water and in a series of solutions. After 4 months the supernatant liquid was analyzed. It is to be noted that more Na went into solution than K,

Table 12

Solubility of feldspar; grams in 2.5 liters of solution *

(After Beyer)

No.	Treatment: Distilled water +	K_2O	Na_2O	CaO	MgO	SiO_2
I	O	0.051	0.078	0.058	0.006	0.049
2	Aeration	0.037	0.064	0.044	0.005	——
3	CO_2	0.071	0.114	0.076	0.004	0.069
4	CaO	0.209	0.174	0.067	0.003	0.061
5	$CaCO_3$	0.042	0.073	0.112	0.009	0.019
6	$CaCo_3 + CO_2$	0.067	0.094	0.273	0.018	0.034
7	Gypsum	0.053	0.074	——	0.016	0.033
8	Gypsum + CO_2	0.068	0.097	——	0.016	0.062
9	$Ca(NO_3)_2$	0.041	0.062	——	0.016	0.036
10	$Ca(NO_3)_2 + CO_2$	——	——	——	0.017	0.045
11	$(NH_4)_2SO_4$	0.161	0.094	0.122	0.035	0.066
12	$(NH_4)_2SO_4 + CO_2$	0.162	0.107	0.147	0.015	0.056
13	MgO	0.359	0.315	0.013	0.004	0.159
14	MgO + CO_2	0.312	0.255	Tr.	7.569	0.048
15	K_2CO_3	——	——	Tr.	Tr.	0.026
16	$K_2CO_3 + CO_2$	——	——	0.029	0.007	0.029
17	$NaNO_3$	0.089	——	0.049	0.003	0.060
18	$NaNO_3 + CO_2$	0.096	——	0.120	0.008	0.032
19	NaCl	0.163	——	0.091	0.008	0.032
20	NaCl + CO_2	0.183	——	0.123	0.006	0.057

* The Al_2O_3 and Fe_2O_3 data are not included since these are given for just a few of the solutions.

in spite of the fact that this feldspar contained 8.51 per cent K_2O and only 3.37 per cent Na_2O. The effect of CO_2 is, of course, very marked. One can also read in these data the effect of cation exchange. One would also have to evaluate the effect of microbial activity in some of the products obtained. As yet we do not have fundamental data on the solubility of the various minerals.

Pyroxenes and Amphiboles.—The minerals of the groups under the names *pyroxenes* and *amphiboles* are closely related chemically. Tourmaline, epidote, and vesuvianite also resemble the pyroxenes and amphiboles. The pyroxenes are more common in the heavy basic rocks in which quartz, orthoclase, and muscovite rarely occur. Amphiboles are found in the more acidic rocks, with quartz and orthoclase present. Amphiboles have a more brilliant luster and retain it better than pyroxenes. Both of these groups belong to the heavy minerals, most of them having a specific gravity more than 3, with augite as high as 3.6.

The pyroxene group takes in *enstatite*, $MgO.SiO_2$; *bronzite*, $(Mg,Fe)O.SiO_2$; *diopside*, $CaO.MgO.2SiO_2$; *pyroxene*, $Ca(Mg.Fe)SiO_6$ or $CaO.(Mg,Fe)O.2SiO_2$; *hedenbergite*, $CaFe(SiO_3)_2$, occasionally with manganese; *augite*, $CaO.MgO.2SiO_2$ with $(Mg,Fe)O.(Al,Fe)_2O_3.SiO_2$.

The amphibole group includes *tremolite*, $CaO.3MgO.4SiO_2$; *actinolite*, $CaO.3(Mg,Fe)O.4SiO_2$; *hornblende*, chiefly a calcium-iron-magnesium silicate, with some sodium and aluminum, $CaO.3(Mg,Fe)O.4SiO_2$ with $Na_2O.Al_2O_3.4SiO_2$ and $2(Mg,Fe)O.2(Al,Fe)_2O_3.2SiO_2$; *olivine*, a ferromagnesian silicate, $2(Mg,Fe)O.SiO_2$; some rocks like dunite consist primarily of olivine, commonly of a light green color.

Because of the more basic character of the pyroxenes, they weather much faster than the amphiboles. According to Glinka (p. 124) augite weathers to a certain type of clay-like substance. In the subtropics of the Caucasus (Chakva) the same mineral changes completely into clay.

The Micas.—In most cases micas are orthosilicates of aluminum, with potassium and hydrogen, and often magnesium, ferrous iron, and in some cases ferric iron, sodium, lithium, and a host of other elements. Micas occur both as primary (in igneous rocks) and as secondary minerals (alteration products of feldspars and other minerals). The two most important varieties of mica are: *muscovite*, the white mica, and *biotite*, the black mica.

Muscovite is a potassium aluminum silicate, $K_2O.2H_2O.3Al_2O_3.6SiO_2$. It is found abundantly as a primary constituent of granites, syenites and gneisses; sometime also in porphyries and felsites. Secondary muscovite, frequently in the form of *sericite* (a silvery white variety of muscovite in contrast to the colorless, gray, brown, yellow, pale green and other colors of the primary muscovite), is found in altered feldspathic and in metamorphic rocks, such as schists and gneisses.

Biotite is a potassium-aluminum-magnesium-iron silicate, approximately: $H_2K(Mg,Fe)_3Al(SiO_4)_3$. It is green to black in color, in contrast to the generally light colored muscovite with which it is often found in association, as well as with orthoclase, plagioclase, hornblende, augite, and others. Biotite is most common in granites, syenites, diorites, gneisses, and pegmatites. It may also appear in lavas.

Phlogopite, also known as amber mica or magnesium mica, is a magnesium-aluminum silicate, with potassium and fluorine, $R_3Mg_3Al(SiO_4)_3$, where R = H, K, Mg, or F. It is not common in igneous rocks, but occurs mainly in crystalline calcium and magnesium limestones.

Lepidolite, also known as lithium mica, is chiefly: $(OH,F)_2KLiAl_2 Si_3O_{10}$. It is associated with other lithium minerals, with tourmaline and beryl.

Several other micas, more rare than those mentioned are known. These are: *paragonite,* a sodium mica; *zinnwaldite,* a lithium-iron mica; *lepidomelane,* a variety of biotite, rich in ferric iron and poor in magnesium. There is also a vanadium mica, known as *roscoelite.*

According to Glinka (p. 121):

micas weather much easier than orthoclase. Laboratory experiments show that muscovite splits off its bases much more energetically than orthoclase. The biotites decompose very rapidly. The products of biotite weathering are: 1, efflorescence which in the end turns into kaolinite. Usually, this kaolinite retains the appearance of biotite and several of its properties. In the course of the reactions secondary quartz is formed. This is primarily a product of the final decomposition of the olivine nucleus of biotite. Usually, kaolinite formed from biotite retains some oxides of iron. Most of the ferrosilicates of biotite decompose. Efflorescence is a very widespread type of biotite weathering. The factors involved are water and CO_2.

In table 13, data are presented on the analyses of the successive products in the efflorescence of biotite. A good example of the formation of kaolinite from biotite is cited by Kerr (38). In general, muscovite is much more resistant to weathering.

Table 13

Successive steps in the decomposition of biotite

(After Glinka)

Constituent	Fresh biotite; sp. gr. 3.11	Dark, golden biotite; sp. gr. 2.83	Silvery biotite sp. gr. 2.80	White flakes, with a hardey noticeable greenish tinge
	per cent	*per cent*	*per cent*	*per cent*
H_2O	2.37	5.05	5.44	12.76
SiO_2	36.63	34.71	40.93	43.36
TiO_2	1.28	3.19	0.46	—
Al_2O_3	17.37	15.46	19.43	34.31
Fe_2O_3	6.75	12.56	8.92	3.98
FeO	15.41	2.80	1.94	—
MnO	1.04	0.80	—	—
MgO	9.73	15.77	13.80	2.43
CaO	0.23	1.89	0.50	—
K_2O	8.15	7.32	7.52	2.67
Na_2O	0.94	0.68	0.87	0.33
Total	99.90	100.2	99.81	99.84

Other Minerals

A number of primary and secondary minerals of minor importance and many secondary minerals of greater importance merit brief mention in a discussion on alterations as a result of weathering. It is to be noted that our knowledge on the minor minerals is at present not helpful in elucidating problems of pedogenesis. However, a study of these minerals is important. After all is said and done, any information on the mass of the soil body (and this consists primarily of mineral matter) is helpful in clarifying the genesis of the soil and its constitution in the various geographic-climatic positions of the crust of weathering.

Quartz is very widespread. It occurs as a primary mineral and as a product of alteration of a great many primary and secondary silicate rocks. Being one of the final residual products of weathering, quartz is stable and can not, under natural conditions of temperature and pressure, undergo further chemical changes. It is, however, subject to leaching in solution, in spite of its relative resistance to chemical reagents. Glinka (p. 115) cites the "studies of Karpinskii on the Hebrewstone of Murzinki from which quartz was leached and feldspars remained intact; the early work (in 1848) of Delesse on the solubility of crystalline rocks in water; and the observations of Hayes (28) on the solubility of siliceous concretions in carboniferous limestone." Conclusive evidence of the solubility of quartz is its presence in river waters.

Alkali carbonates and alkali soluble organic complexes attack quartz quite readily. The solubility rate of quartz depends on its mode of formation, such as crystallization temperature (cristobalite forming at temperatures above 1470° C. is the most resistant type) and physico-chemical state, i.e., amorphous or crystalline.

A few nonsilicate primary rocks and minerals play an important part in the genesis and constitution of various soils.

Calcite, known in very pure form as Iceland spar, is nothing more than $CaCO_3$; it is the mineral of most limestones, marble, chalk and marls. It may be considered as a primary (essential) mineral when associated with igneous rocks where it is formed by the alteration of feldspars and other lime-bearing minerals.

Most calcite is associated with secondary limestones as sedimentary rocks of organic origin.

Aragonite is in composition the same as calcite, namely $CaCO_3$. Occasionally a little strontium, lead, or zinc are associated with this mineral. It differs from calcite by its crystallization pattern being orthorhombic whereas calcite is hexagonal and remarkably varied. Goldschmidt claims over twenty six hundred calcite crystals.

Aragonite is very common in gypsum beds and in iron ores. It is often found in basic lavas, such as basalt.

Magnesite is the carbonate of magnesium, $MgCO_3$. The crystalline magnesite forms in magnesia limestones by the action of hot waters. In the weathering of rocks rich in Mg, the CO_2 in solution unites with the oxide of magnesium, forming an amorphous carbonate.

Dolomite in pure form is a mixed crystal of calcite and magnesite, $CaCO_3.MgCO_3$ which is equivalent to 54.3 per cent $CaCO_3$ and 45.65 per cent of $MgCO_3$. It occurs in igneous rocks as a secondary mineral derived from the alteration of minerals containing Ca and Mg. In sedimentary rocks it is common in dolomitic limestone, which is a magnesium limestone having the two carbonates in any proportion up to true dolomite. Dolomite is not as soluble as calcite. It is generally conceded that nearly all of the dolomite is the result of the action of $MgCl_2$ on $CaCO_3$ in the sea.

Gypsum is a hydrous calcium sulfate, $CaSO_4.2H_2O$. It occurs in beds and seams in sedimentary rocks and occasionally in igneous rocks. It is fairly soluble in water and under anaerobic conditions it may be reduced to sulfides.

Of other minor minerals mention is to be made of *zircon,* a silicate of zirconium, ZrO_2SiO_2, which is very resistant to alterations (see p. 87 on the use of zircon as a mineral in tracing the relative losses and gains in the process of weathering). *Tourmaline,* a complex silicate of boron and aluminum, is associated with the minerals of granite, gneiss, and schist.

A number of iron minerals, primarily oxides, is associated with many of the processes of alterations in the crust of weathering. Prominent among these are *magnetite,* $FeO.Fe_2O_3$; *hematite,* Fe_2O_3; *pyrite,* FeS_2; *ilmenite,* $FeO.TiO_2$.

Of the more prominent secondary (accessory) minerals which deserve attention are the so-called zeolites and related minerals. These include the minerals *chabazite,* a hydrous silicate of calcium, sodium, aluminum, and sometime potassium. Its usual composition is $(Ca,Na_2)O.Al_2O_3.$ $4SiO_2.6H_2O$; *analcite,* a hydrous silicate of sodium and aluminum, $Na_2O.Al_2O_3.4SiO_2.2H_2O$; *natrolite,* $Na_2O.Al_2O_3.4SiO_2.2H_2O$, is similar to analcite, but differs in crystallization; *scolecite,* a hydrous silicate of calcium and almuinum, $CaO.Al_2O_33SiO_2.3H_2O$; *thomsonite,* a hydrous silicate of sodium, calcium, and aluminum, $(Ca, Na_2)O.Al_2O_3.2SiO_2.$ $5/2H_2O$; *apophyllite,* a hydrous silicate of potassium and calcium, $K_2O.-8CaO.16SiO_2.16H_2O$, is not strictly a zeolite, but is closely related to it.

The zeolites are closely related to the feldspars and feldspathoids. They are associated with low silica igneous rocks of volcanic origin, such as basalts and diabases.

Some minerals occur more frequently as secondary products. To these belongs *serpentine,* a hydrous magnesium silicate, $2H_2O.3MgO.SiO_2$. The fibrous form of serpentine is known as *crysotile,* or asbestos.

The chlorite group includes a series of secondary minerals derived mainly from ferromagnesian minerals bearing aluminum. They are similar to micas, inasmuch as they have basal cleavage. Members of this group are: *clinochlore,* $Al_2O_3.5MgO.3SiO_2.4H_2O$; *penninite,* $Al_2O_3.5(Mg,Fe)O.3SiO_2.4H_2O$; *epidote,* $H_2O.4Ca_3(Al,Fe)_2O_3.6SiO_2$. Talc, soapstone, and steatite are related to this group; they are hydrous magnesium silicate, $H_2O.3MgO.4SiO_2$.

There is a group of minerals which is characteristic of metamorphic rocks. These minerals are rarely found in other rocks. Prominent members of this group are: *garnets,* orthosilicates of calcium and aluminum; iron and aluminum; calcium, magnesium, and iron; calcium and chromium. They are associated with schists and gneisses. They are very resistant to weathering, but alter into serpentine, hornblende, epidote, and feldspars. *Sillimanite,* an aluminum silicate, $Al_2O_3.SiO_2$, found in association with quartz, garnet, corundum, and micas; it is very resistant to weathering. Of similar composition are the minerals *andalusite, chiastolite, kyanite,* and *disthene.*

A number of other complex silicates is known in this group: *dumortierite,* an aluminum borosilicate, usually of the following composition: $8Al_2O_3.B_2O_3.6SiO_2.H_2O$; *vesuvianite,* a silicate of indefinite formula; it is given as: $H_4Ca_{12}(Al,Fe)_6Si_{10}O_{43}$; *cordierite,* a silicate of aluminum, iron, and magnesium, $(Mg,Fe)_4Al_8(OH)_2(Si_2O_7)_5$, or $4(Mg,Fe)O.4Al_2O_3.10SiO_2.H_2O$; *chondrorite,* a fluo-silicate of magnesium, usually with iron replacing a part of the magnesium, $[(Mg(F,OH)]_2Mg_3(SiO_4)_2$; *scapolite,* a group of silicates of aluminum, with calcium and sodium in varying amounts; chlorine is frequently present; *staurolite,* a hydrous silicate of aluminum and iron, $5Al_2O_3.2FeO.H_2O.4SiO_2$, with magnesium replacing some of the iron; *wollastonite,* a calcium silicate, $CaO.SiO_2$, found in granular limestone as a result of contact metamorphism.

An outstanding feature of practically all the minerals associated with metamorphic rocks is *hardness;* very few minerals of this group show a hardness lower than 5.

Clay Minerals

Of the many minerals in the soil, none are as conspicuous and as important as the clay minerals. There is hardly a chemical, physical, and morphological property of the soil body that is not influenced by these minerals. One may venture to state that there is not a problem of soil science that is not in one way or another associated with the reactions exhibited by clay minerals.

In the foregoing brief review on the various minerals, mention has been made on the formation of clay from primary and secondary silicates and their alteration products. The process of clay formation has been known as *kaolinization* and the term *kaolin* has been used synonymously with clay. Among chemists, mineralogists, ceramists, and soils men the term clay has attained several shades of meaning.

Clay as a separate in mechanical analysis of soils represents a particle size unit, to wit, particles of 0.002 mm. (2μ) and less. Clay in the terminology of the mineralogist connotes a group of minerals. Naturally, the clay separate and the clay minerals are not one and the same. The clay separate may include quartz silica of a particle size as small as 0.1 μ and smaller, as the case is in cristobalite, as reported by von Moos (51) and Marshall (44). Organic matter of particle size smaller than 0.1 μ and appreciable quantities of R_2O_3 may also contribute to the makeup of clay separate. Pure clay minerals contain no such admixtures. As a rule, they are of a particle-size less than 0.002 mm., even though they are coarser in crude state. According to Ardenne, Endell, and Hofmann (1) "certain of the clay minerals can exist in particles approaching their unit cell height, that is about 1 mμ."

The term *clay,* as designated by the Committee on Sedimentation of the National Research Council and by a committee of the American Ceramic Society, carries with it three implications: "1, a natural material with plastic properties; 2, an essential composition of particles of very fine size grades; and 3, an essential composition of crystalline fragments of minerals that are essentially hydrous aluminum silicates, or occasionally hydrous magnesium silicates."

According to Grim (22), clay minerals "are hydrous aluminum silicates, frequently with some replacement of the aluminum by iron and magnesium and with small amounts of alkalies and alkali-earths. In rare instances, magnesium and iron completely replace the aluminum."

Clay minerals, like many other residual products of weathering, are colloidal in nature, the colloid state being the more stable one, which most substances tend to acquire. By virtue of their colloidal nature, clay minerals perform a series of functions which mould the constitution of the soil body and impart to it specific properties, such as retention of water, adsorption of cations, structure formation, and to a large degree, texture.

Clay minerals, except allophane, are crystalline, another indication of stability. Most freshly formed clay and clay-like minerals are for a time amorphous, but gradually they become crystalline.

Classification of Clay Minerals

Kaolin or Kaolinite.—This group consists of several minerals. *Kaolinite,* $Al_2O_3.2SiO_2.2H_2O$, or as written by Ross and Kerr (73) $(OH)_8Al_4Si_4O_{10}$. The latter formula attempts to give an idea of the lattice structure of this mineral. *Dickite* and *nacrite* are of the same composition as kaolinite, but of slightly different crystallographic forms.

The lattice structure of kaolinite has been variously presented. As worked out by Gruner (24), kaolinite is composed of a gibbsite sheet with a single tetrahedral silica sheet. This lattice does not expand with varying amounts of water and because of that kaolinite has a low cation exchange capacity. The lattice structure for kaolinite is on the order of the generalization of Pauling (59) on the broader features of the structure of the clay minerals.

Montmorillonite.—The name stands for a group of minerals with a probable composition of $(OH)_4Al_4Si_8O_{20}.XH_2O$, suggested by Hofmann, Endell, and Wilm (31). The aluminum is usually partly replaced by magnesium and ferric iron. When substitution is complete with magnesium, the mineral is known as *saponite;* with iron—*nontronite.* For a thorough discussion of these two minerals the reader is referred to the extensive investigations of Caldwell and Marshall (6).

According to Hofmann and associates, the montmorillonite structure consists of units of one gibbsite sheet between two sheets of silica tetrahedral groups. The mineral is said to have an expanding lattice and because of that has a high cation exchange capacity. The amount of expansion is related to the character of the exchangeable cation. In general, lithium and sodium induce the highest swelling, whereas calcium, magnesium, hydrogen, and potassium do not. For a discussion of the behavior of montmorillonite in relation to cation sorption and other properties, the reader is referred to the paper by Grim (22). In this paper one may find a selected bibliography on the various clay minerals. For a detailed study and thorough discussion of the minerals of the montmorillonite group, their origin and relation to soils and clays the reader is referred to the monograph by Ross and Hendricks (71). An extensive well selected bibliography is a valuable asset of this monograph.

Beidellite has been placed in the montmorillonite group and defined as differing from it by having a molar silicate-alumina ratio of 3:1 instead of 4:1, as shown by Ross and Kerr (72). Ross and Shannon were among the first to use X-ray methods in the study of bentonite and related minerals.

Illite.—Grim, Bray, and Bradley (23) suggested this group name for clay materials that are similar to, but not identical to, white micas. They are known under the name "mica-clay minerals," discussed by Maegdefrau and Hofmann (42) and "potash-bearing clay mineral," discussed by Ross and Kerr (72). The general formula of illite has been suggested by Grim and his associates as $(OH)_4K_y (Al_4.Fe_4.Mg_4.Mg_6)$ $(Si_{8-y}.Al_yO_{20})$ with y varying from 1 to 1.5. According to Hendricks and Alexander (30), glauconite (a hydrous mica-like mineral), the mineral found abundantly in greensand marl, is closely similar in structure to illite. Grim and associates state that "the illite structure is similar to that of montmorillonite, except that 15 per cent of Si^{++++} positions are replaced by Al^{+++}, and the resulting excess charges are satisfied chiefly by K^+ ions between the silica sheets of two successive units."

Other less important clay minerals are halloysite and attapulgite. According to Hofmann and associates (31), *halloysite* is $Al_2O_3.2SiO_2.4H_2O$ $[(OH)_{16}.Al_4.Si_4.O_6]$. At 50° C., it loses $2H_2O$ and changes to kaolinite. In its adsorptive properties halloysite resembles montmorillonite. *Attapulgite* is related to the amphiboles. It has been identified with some deposits of fuller's earth in Georgia and Florida. An extensive study of this mineral has been made by Caldwell and Marshall (6).

Related Studies on Clay Minerals.—Shaw and Humbert (83) have investigated the structure of the various groups of clay minerals with the electron microscope. Jackson and Helman (35) have probed the possibility of differentiating montmorillonite from hydrous mica by X-ray diffraction procedures.

Schachtschabel (79) differentiates clay minerals by their sorption selectivity of cations. Montmorillonite adsorbs preferentially Ca ions from a solution containing equivalent concentrations of Ca and K. The opposite is true for muscovite. Hendricks and Alexander (29) followed up the work of Schachtschabel. They saturated bentonites, mica-like materials, such as sericite and glauconite, kaolinites, and mixtures of these with various cations. By the differential sorption of cations, they have been able to estimate the amount of montmorillonite in the mixtures.

Peterson (Ch. 3, 47) investigated the differential behavior of clay minerals on structure. Kaolinite gives rise to anisotropic platy structure and montmorillonite an isotropic structural pattern.

In connection with the effects of climate on the type of weathering and resulting end-products, it is of interest to note the researches of Mattson (45) on the electrokinetic and chemical behavior of the aluminum silicates and the mechanism of the reactions responsible for the variation in the $SiO_2:R_2O_3$ ratio in clay colloids.

According to Mattson, in the absence of bases colloids must contain a low proportion of SiO_2, provided the pH is high. "At a pH near 7.0 and in the practical absence of bases the gel would consist of almost pure sesquioxides." It is logical to infer that in the regions of the humid, temperate climate (the podzol zone of the pedologist) where the pH is low, there should be a high proportion of SiO_2 in the colloid. On the other hand, in the arid regions with a prevailing high pH, the SiO_2 proportion in the colloid is high, because of the high base content. Both the pH and the base content—primarily the divalent cations which stabilize the colloid—are therefore responsible for the respective $SiO_2:R_2O_3$ ratios; and these in turn are controlled by the climatic factors. In the arid regions, with a low precipitation and a high temperature, we have a high base content and, hence a high pH, whereas in the humid, temperate regions, we have a low base content and a low pH. In the tropics the base content is low, but the turnover of bases is high because of the abundance of vegetation and the rapid decompoistion. As a result of this, there is no accumulation of acids and the pH value is intermediate. Thus with a low base content and an intermediate pH, the conditions are favorable for a low proportion of SiO_2 in the colloid. Mattson (47) cites the analysis of a Nipe colloid from a Cuban soil with a $SiO_2:R_2O_3$ ratio of 0.31.

A very interesting and most important fact about the climatic effects on the colloids formed in the process of weathering may be inferred from the work of Robinson and Holmes (70). Their analyses show that in the humid temperate regions the silica-sesquioxide ratio is higher than in the humid warm regions. Thus, the colloids from the Cecil series of soils in Maryland have a $SiO_2:R_2O_3$ ratio of 1.55, whereas the Cecil series from Georgia has a ratio of 1.20. These differences are not so marked, however, as the differences in the silica-sesquioxide ratio of the humid temperate region and that of the arid regions. The colloids of the Fallou series from Nevada have a ratio of 3.82, whereas the colloids of the Cecil series from Maryland have a ratio of 1.55.

A thorough review of the subject of mineralogy in relation to soils and clays is presented by Sedletskii (81). In his monograph, one may find the more important and latest references on clay minerals. He dwells primarily on the colloids of the clastic rocks which do not readily show crystal formations. He justly credits Cornu (9), the brilliant Austrian mineralogist whom death claimed at the age of 25, as one among the first to bring out the idea of the colloidal nature of the products of surface weathering. In the words of Fersman, the savant Russian mineralogist, "the monograph takes us into a sphere of entirely new concepts . . . It gives new ideas on the specific world of chemical and physico-chemical equilibria which are established in the soil cover as a result of complex chemical and biochemical reactions."

Sedletskii associates the minerals of the crust of weathering with the biosphere and considers these as a specific formation. He designates these minerals as colloidally dispersed. He recognizes three types of these; 1, *mutabillites*, amorphous colloidally dispersed minerals which are transitional; 2, *metastabillites*, incompletely crystallized; 3, *stabillites*, fully crystallized. In these three groups, one can recognize the evolutionary process of the colloidally dispersed minerals.

Sedletskii presents his ideas in a concise and somewhat categorical manner, reserving a more thorough discussion and the presentation of factual data for a more elaborate treatise. Unfortunately, we can not review even in part this most stimulating presentation. To get a glimpse into his views, one may study the work of Cornu which is available in German and of Fersman and Vernadskii whose works are in part available in French and German. Sedletskii considers his novel ideas as an elaboration of the views and theories advanced by these investigators.

For an up-to-date brief review of mineral weathering based almost exclusively on selected data published in English, the reader is referred to the paper by Reiche (67). For an extensive discussion of clays, their origin and properties, the reader is to consult the book of Parmelee (58).

Weathering of Minerals in the Soil Profile

Very little has been done on the mode of weathering of minerals in different soil types and in the soil profile. Most of the analyses on weathering of minerals have been made on minerals isolated from the native rocks with no direct reference to the soil. Denison, Fry, and Gile (11) reviewed the investigations on the weathering of muscovite and biotite in connection with their own investigations on these minerals isolated from the soil. They isolated the mica from each horizon of a number of soil profiles in the Piedmont plateau, from such diverse soil series as the Cecil, of the southern Piedmont, and the Manor and Chester, of the northern Piedmont.

A comparison of the chemical composition of the isolated soil micas with those of average fresh muscovite and biotite shows, that the average soil muscovite differs from fresh muscovite in being much lower in potash and higher in water, and that the average soil biotite differs from fresh biotite in containing higher percentages of alumina, silica, and water, lower percentages of magnesia, potash, and iron, and in almost complete oxidation of iron.

Apparently neither in the case of muscovite nor of biotite is the alteration a simple replacement of basic elements by hydrogen. Evidence is presented to show that muscovite and biotite tend to be altered to a material of the composition of kaolinite and it is suggested that altered particles of soil mica are isomorphous mixtures of muscovite and biotite wth kaolinite.

The mica of any one profile varies little in composition in horizons above the lowest C horizon. Mica in the hard rock, however, may have a quite different composition from that in the upper C or A horizons.

In all soil profiles biotite seems to be altered to about the same extent, the potash content of the material usually approximating 4 per cent. Muscovite, on the other hand, in some profiles may contain less than 1 per cent K_2O and in other profiles as high as 9 per cent K_2O. This variability is attributed to the possibility of two forms of muscovite being present, primary and secondary, the secondary form being more readily altered.

A study of the mineralogic composition of podzol profiles in the northern part of European Russia is reported by Trutnev (87). He points out that

the parent material is made up of Precambrian rocks. The 0.25-0.01 mm. fraction consists primarily, up to 99 per cent, of the light minerals, such as quartz, feldspars, biotite, muscovite, and a few others. In podzol soils formed on glacial drift the mineralogical composition is as follows: the eluvial (A) horizons are relatively richer in quartz and poorer in feldspars, biotite, and muscovite than the illuvial (B) horizons and the parent material. The A_1 and A_2 horizons are poorer in ore minerals than horizons B and C.

In podzol soils formed on ancient lake deposits (clay lenses), the light minerals are present in small quantities. The basic mass consists of clay particles, stained with iron oxide or some weathered minerals of undetermined composition. There are cases where in some horizons the light minerals make up to 96 per cent of the mass.

In soils on loess-like loams, the eluvial horizons are richer in quartz. Among the heavy metals in these horizons there is an increase in limonite, magnetite, and ilmenite, as well as zoisite and epidote.

The soil series studied by Denison and his associates belong to the podzols and very little difference in the mode of weathering should be expected in the region under consideration. Undoubtedly the biotite and muscovite alteration would be different in a different zonal soil type. Of course, the forms of the mica, as pointed out by the authors, influence the mode of weathering. As a matter of fact, the mica percentages varied at times within the same series more than between the profiles of the different series, showing again that we are dealing here with various forms of the mineral.

Investigations on the mineralogical makeup of a number of soils in Australia were reported by Carroll, (7). Rozanov and Shukevich (74) reported on the mineralogical composition of the loess-like parent material of Central Asia. Hendricks and Alexander (29) made a study of the minerals present in the soil. Hosking (33) points out that in Australia, under conditions of abundant rainfall and active leaching, kaolinite soils form on basic igneous rocks, whereas under conditions of low rainfall and poor leaching montmorillonite soils form from the same igneous rock. According to Nagelschmidt (55), kaolinite and montmorillonite may form from the same parent rock under different environmental conditions. Studies of clay minerals in Iowa soils by Peterson (60) show that the proportion of montmorillonite to kaolinite varies in the profile. In areas of greater rainfall more montmorillonite is found in the B horizon and more kaolinite in the A horizon. The clay minerals were studied by differential thermal analyses, X-ray diffraction pictures, and base-exchange capacity determinations. Somewhat similar studies were reported by Whiteside and Marshall (97) on the minerals of the Putnam silt loam soils of Missouri. Haseman and Marshall (27) made use of the heavy minerals in studies on the origin and development of soils.

Tables 14-15, compiled by Sedletskii (81), give the mineralogic composition of the products of weathering of various rocks in various soil zones, and the paragenetic associations of the minerals of the principal soil types. One can readily see from the data how important the mineralogic composition of soils is becoming in pedologic studies.

Table 14

Paragenetic association of the minerals of the principal soil types

(After Sedletskii)

Depth of sampling	Minerals in fraction < 0.2 μ	Depth of sampling	Minerals in fraction < 0.2 μ
cm.		cm.	III. CHERNOZEMS
	I. GRAY SOILS (SEROZEM)		*Degraded chernozem on porphyry eluvium (Crimea)*
	Light colored gray soils on granite porphyry	0- 10	Montmorillonite, illite
0- 10	Beidellite, illite	20- 26	Montmorillonite, illite
15- 20	Beidellite, illite		*Medium-humus cherno-*
30- 40	Beidellite, illite		*zem on granite eluvium*
50- 60	Beidellite, illite		*(Southern Ural)*
	II. CHESTNUT BROWN SOILS	5- 10	Montmorillonite
		15- 20	Montmorillonite, illite
	Light colored chestnut brown soils on quartz porphyry	30- 40	Montmorillonite, illite
		70- 80	Montmorillonite-Muscovite-sericite
0- 6	Montmorillonite Muscovite-sericite		Illite
15- 20	Montmorillonite, illite		*Degraded chernozem on andesite eluvium (Armenia)*
	Light colored chestnut brown soils on granites	0- 13	Montmorillonite
0- 7	Montmorillonite, illite	13- 36	Montmorillonite, illite
15- 55	Montmorillonite, illite	35- 65	Montmorillonite, illite
55- 65	Montmorillonite, illite	65-100	Montmorillonite

Table 14 (*continued*)

Paragenetic association of the minerals of the principal soil types

(After Sedletskii)

Depth of sampling	Minerals in fraction $< 0.2\,\mu$	Depth of sampling	Minerals in fraction $< 0.2\,\mu$
	IV. PODZOLIZED SOILS		**VI. YELLOW EARTHS**
	Podzol on granite eluvium (Southern Ural)		*Yellow-brown, weakly podzolic clay soil on sandstone eluvium*
A 13- 20 (A₂)	Forest floor Quartz Kaolinite Hydrous muscovite	0- 5 (A₁)	Halloysite Hydrous gothite
20- 90 B	Quartz Kaolinite Gothite Hydrous muscovite	15- 20 (A₂)	Halloysite Hydrous gothite
50- 60	Quartz Kaolinite Hydrous muscovite	25- 30	Halloysite
		40- 50 (B)	Hydrous hematite Hydrous hematite
	Podzol on serpentine alluvium (Southern Ural)	50- 55	Halloysite Hydrous gothite
5- 7 (A₁)	Quartz Kaolinite	80- 85	Nontronite
10- 15 (A₂)	Quartz Kaolinite	140-180 (C)	Kaolinite
30- 40	Kaolinite Nontronite		**VII. RED LOAMS (KRASNOZEM)**
55- 65 B	Quartz Kaolinite Nontronite		*Red loam deposit of augite-porphyry eluvium*
	V. PODZOLIZED SOILS OF THE SUB-TROPIC	3- 10	Halloysite
		10- 15	Halloysite Hydrous gothite
	Strongly podzolic, sub-tropical soil of Talysh	20- 25	Halloysite Gothite
0- 5 (A₁)	Quartz Halloysite	60- 65	Halloysite Gothite
10- 15 (A₂)	Quartz Halloysite	110-115	Halloysite Gothite
25- 30 (A₂ B)	Halloysite Hydrous gothite (little)	285-290	Halloysite Hydrous hematite
60- 65 B	Halloysite Quartz Nontronite Hydrous gothite	495-500	Halloysite
			VIII. LATERITES
			Lateritic deposit of andesitic eluvium
100-105 (C)	Halloysite Quartz	Surface horizon	Metahalloysite Gibbsite
		Red horizon	Metahalloysite Gibbsite
		Mottled horizon	Metahalloysite Gibbsite
		Laterite	Gibbsite Metahalloysite

Table 14 (*continued*)

Paragenetic association of the minerals of the principal soil types

(After Sedletskii)

Depth of sampling	Minerals in fraction $< 0.2\ \mu$	Depth of sampling	Minerals in fraction $< 0.2\ \mu$
	IX. SOLONETZ		X. OTHER SOIL TYPES (*continued*)
	Sodium salonchakous solonetz (Hinter-Volga)	0- 10	Montmorillonite Muscovite-sericite Halloysite (little)
0- 3	Montmorillonite		*Red loam (krasnozem) in Erythrea* (Prasolov and Sedletskii, 1940)
5- 10	Montmorillonite		
10- 15	Montmorillonite (beidellite)		
20- 25	Montmorillonite (beidellite)	0- 10	Halloysite Bemite
40- 50	Montmorillonite (beidellite)		*Red earth (krasnozem) in Abyssinia* (*terra rossa type*)
195-200	Beidellite (Montmorillonite)		
	X. OTHER SOIL TYPES	0- 10	Halloysite Gothite Hematite
	Chernozem-like soil in Erythrea (Regur type) (Prasolov & Sedletskii, 1940)		*Red loam in India* (Nagelschmidt and associates, 1940)
0- 10	Montmorillonite Muscovite-sericite	0- 10	Halloysite Hydrous gothite Hydrous hematite Montmorillonite (little)
	Chernozem-like soil in India (regur type) (Nagelschmidt and associates, 1940)		

Table 15

The minerals of the products of weathering

(After Sedletskii)

Products of weatthering	Minerals
Granites and gneisses on the Kola peninsula	Quartz Hydrous mica Kaolinite (little)
Granites and gneisses in Southern Ural (a) zone of podzolization	Quartz Kaolinite Hydrous muscovite
(b) zone of chernozem	Montmorillonite Illite
Serpentinites in Southern Ural, in zone of podzolization	Quartz Kaolinite Nontronite Hydrous gothite
Granites and porphyry in Crimea, in zone of chernozems	Montmorillonite Illite
Granites in Uzbekistan, in zone of gray semidesert soils	Beidellite Illite
Andesitic basalts in Armenia, in zone of chernozems	Montmorillonite Illite
Augite porphyry in the Caucasus, in the region of red loam (krasnozem)	Halloysite Hydrous hematite Hydrous gothite
Granites and gneisses in India, in the region of red loam (krasnozem)	Halloysite Hydrous hematite Hydrous gothite
Andesitic-basalts in India, in the region of laterites	Metahalloysite Hematite Gibbsite

References

1. Ardenne, M. K., Endell, K., and Hofmann, U. 1940 Investigations of the finest fractions of bentonite and clay soils with the universal electron microscope. *Ber. Deut. Keram. Geselsch.* 21: 209-227.

2. Blanck, E., and Passarge, S. 1925 Die chemische Verwitterung in der Agyptischen Wüste. Berlin.

3. Bartlett, William H. C. 1832 Experiments on the expansion and contraction of building stones by variations of temperature. *Amer. Jour. Sci. and Arts* 22:136-140.

4. Bassalik, K. 1912 Uber Silikatzersetzung durch Bodenbakterien. *Zeitsch. Garungsphysiol.* 2:1-32; see also 3:15-42 (1913).

5. Beyer, A. 1871 Uber die Zersetzung des Feldspathes unter dem Einfluss von Salzlösungen und einigen anderen Agentien. *Land. Ver. Stat.* 14:314-322.

6. Caldwell, O. G. and Marshall, C. E. 1942 A study of some chemical and physical properties of the clay minerals, nontronite, attapulgite, and saponite. Missouri Agr. Expt. Sta., Res. Bul. 354, pp. 1-51.

7. Carroll, D. 1944 Mineralogic examination of some soils from South-Western Australia. *West-Australian Dept. Agr. J.* (2nd ser.) 21:83-93; see also 21:313-319; *Soil Sci.* 60:413-426 (1945).

8. Clarke, F. W. 1924 The Data of Geochemistry. United States Geol. Survey Bul. 770.

9. Cornu, F. 1909 Die heutige Verwitterungslehre im Lichte der Kolloidchemie. *Comp. Rendus de la Premiere Conf. Internat. Agrogeol.* (Budapest).

10. Czapek, Fr. 1920 Biochemie der Pflanzen. II. Jena.

11. Denison, I. A., Fry, William H., and Gile, P. L. 1929 Alteration of muscovite and biotite in the soil. U. S. Dept. of Agr. Tech. Bul. 128.

12. Doyarenko, A. G. 1909 On the problem of root excretions. *Trudy I Mendeleev. Sezda.* (Transac. of the 1st Mendeleev Meetings), p. 455-464. Reprinted in the "Collection of Doyarenko's Work." (Russian). I:140-146. (1926).

13. Emerson, Frederick V. 1920 Agricultural Geology. John Wiley and Sons, New York.

14. Fersman, A. E. 1926 Sulfur (Russian). *Materialy po izunchen. estest, proizvodit. sil soyuza.* No. 59. p. 133.

15. Fersman, A. E.   1936   Geochemistry (Russian), v. II., p. 296, Leningrad (Quoted from Yarilov, *Pedology* (U.S.S.R.) No. 8 (1938), p. 1103.

16. Fersman, A. E.   1944   New Paths in the Chemistry of the Earth (Russian). Moscow.

17. Fry, E. J.   1924   A suggested explanation of the mechanical action of lichens. *Annals of Botany* 38:175-196.

18. Goldrich, S. S.   1938   A study in rock weathering. *Jour. Geol.* 46:17-58.

19. Goldschmidt, V. M.   1922-1927   Geochemische Verteilungsgesetze der Elemente. I-VIII. Shriften Videnskaps Akad. Math.-Phys., Oslo.

20. Goldschmidt, V. M.   1934   Drei Vorträge über Geochemie. Geol. För. Stockholm., pp. 385.

21. Goldschmidt, V. M.   1937   The principles of distribution of chemical elements in minerals and rocks. *J. Chem. Soc.* England, pt. 1: 655-673.

22. Grim, R. E.   1942   Modern concepts of clay minerals. *Jour. Geol.* L:225-275.

23. Grim, R. E., Bray, R. H., and Bradley, W. F.   1937   The mica in argillaceous sediments. *Amer. Miner.* 22:813-829.

24. Gruner, J. W.   1932   The crystal structure of kaolinite. *Ztsch. Krist.* 83:75-88; see his publications in the *American Mineralogist,* volumes 19, 20, 25 (1934, 1935, 1940).

25. Halvorson, H. O. and Starkey, R. L.   1927   Studies on the transformation of iron in nature. I. Theoretical considerations. *Jour. Phys. Chem.* 31:626-631.

26. Harder, E. C.   1919   Iron depositing bacteria and their geologic relations. Prof. Paper. 113, U. S. Geol. Survey.

27. Haseman, J. F. and Marshall, C. E.   1945   The use of heavy minerals in studies of the origin and development of soils. Univ. of Missouri Agr. Expt. Sta. Res. Bul. 387.

28. Hayes, G. W.   1897   Solution of silica under atmospheric conditions. *Bul. Geol. Soc. Amer.* 8:213-220.

29. Hendricks, S. B. and Alexander, L. T.   1939   Minerals present in soil colloids. *Soil Sci.* 48:257-271.

30. Hendricks, S. B. and Alexander, L. T.   1940   Semiquantitative estimation of montmorillonite in clays. *Proc. Soil Sci. Soc. Amer.* 5:95-99.

31. Hofmann, U. Endell, K., and Wilm, D. 1933 Crystal structure and swelling of montmorillonite. *Ztsch. Krist.* 86:340-348.

32. Holmes, R. S., and Edgington, G. 1930 Variations of the colloidal material extracted from the soils of the Miami, Chester, and Cecil Series. U. S. Dept. Agr. Tech. Bul. 229.

33. Hosking, J. S. 1941 The soil clay mineralogy of some Australian soils developed on basaltic and granitic parent material. *Jour. Coun. Sci. and Ind. Res.* 13:206-211.

34. Hutchinson, Evelyn. 1943 The biogeochemistry of aluminum and certain related elements. *The Quart. Rev. of Biology* 18:1-29; 128-153; 242-262; 331-363.

35. Jackson, M. L. and Hellman, N. N. 1941 X-ray diffraction procedure for positive differentiation of montmorillonite from hydrous mica. *Proc. Soil Sci. Soc. Amer.* 6:133-145.

36. Joffe, J. S. 1922 Biochemical oxidation of sulfur and its significance to agriculture. New Jersey Agr. Exp. Sta. Bul. 374.

37. Johnstone, A. 1887 Trans. Edinb. Geol. Soc. 5:282; also *Quart. Jour. Geol. Soc. London* 45 (1889); 363-368; *Proceed. Royal Soc. of Edinb.* 15 (1888), Nos. 127 and 128.

38. Kerr, P. F. 1930 Kaolinite from a Brooklyn subway tunnel. *Jour. Miner. Soc. Amer.* (Amer. Miner.) 15:144-158.

39. Lazarev, A. A. 1945 The accumulation and transformation of P in miaskites and gneissoid granite in the first stages of soil formation. *Pedology* (U.S.S.R.) No. 7:340-347.

40. Lemberg, J. 1876 On the transformation of silicates. *Ztsch. Deut. Geol. Gesell.* 28. pp. 519-562; also 22 (1870), p. 335, 803; 24 (1872), p. 187; 29 (1877), p. 483.

41. Liebig, Justus, v. 1851 Familiar Letters on Chemistry, ed. 3.

42. Maegdefrau, E. and Hofmann, U. 1937 The mica-clay minerals. *Ztsch. Krist.* 98:31-59; on montmorillonite, pp. 299-323.

43. Marshall, C. E. 1935 Layer lattice and the base exchange clays. *Ztsch. Krist.* 91:433-439.

44. Marshall, C. E. 1940 A petrographic method for the study of soil formation processes. *Proc. Soil Sci. Soc. Amer.* 5:100-103.

45. Mattson, S. 1928 The electrokinetic and chemical behavior of the alumino-silicates. *Soil Sci.* 25:289-311.

46. Mattson, S. 1930 The laws of soil colloidal behavior: III. Isoelectric precipitates. *Soil Sci.* 30:459-495; IV. (1931) *Soil Sci.* 31:55-77.

47. Mattson, S. 1931 The laws of soil colloidal behavior: V. Ion adsorption and exchange. *Soil Sci.* 31:311-331; VI. Amphoteric behavior. *Soil Sci.* 32:343-365.

48. Mattson, S. 1932 The laws of soil colloidal behavior: IX. Amphoteric reactions and isoelectric weathering. *Soil Sci.* 34:209-240.

49. Merrill, G. P. 1897 A Treatise on Rocks, Rock Weathering, and Soils. Macmillan Co., London, New York.

50. Molisch, H. 1910 Die Eisenbakterien. Jena.

51. von Moos, A. 1938 Unconsolidated sediments and soil mechanics. *Geol. Run.* 29:368-381.

52. Müller, Richard. 1877 Untersuchungen über die Einwirkung des Kohlensaurhaltigen Wassers auf einige Mineralien und Gesteine. *Tschermak's Mineral. Mitteil.* 7:25-48.

53. Müntz, A. 1890 Chimie agricloe. Sur la decomposition des roches et la formation de la terre arable. *Comp. Rend. Acad. Sci.* 110:1370-72.

54. Nadson, G. 1903 Microorganisms as Geological Agents. (Russian). St. Petersburg.

55. Nagelschmidt, G. 1939 The identification of minerals in soil colloids. *Jour. Agr. Sci.* pt. 4, 29:478-501

56. Omelianskii, V. L. 1927 The role of microorganisms in weathering of rocks. Yubil. Magaz. imeni I. P. Borodin. January. See also his book: "Microbiology."

57. Palmer, Harold S. 1931 Soil forming processes in the Hawaiian Islands from the chemical and mineralogical points of view. *Soil Sci.* 31:253-265.

58. Parmelee, C. W. 1939 Clays and some other ceramic materials. Edward Bros., Ann Arbor, Mich.

59. Pauling, L. 1930 The structure of mica and related minerals. *Proc. Nat. Acad. Sci.* 16:123-129.

60. Peterson, J. B. 1946 Relation of parent material to the clay minerals in Iowa soils. *Soil Sci.* 61:465-475. See also: Proc. Soil Sci. Soc. Amer. 9 (1944): 37-48.

61. Pettijohn, F. J. 1941 Persistency of heavy minerals and geologic age. *Jour Geol.* 49:610-625.

62. Polynov, B. B. 1937 Cycle of Weathering. Thomas Murby & Co. London.

63. Polynov, B. B. 1944 Total analyses of soils and their interpretation. *Pedology* (U.S.S.R.) No. 10: 482-490. See English summary in Pedology No. 1 (1945), p. 61.

64. Polynov, B. B. 1945 The first stages of soil formation on massive crystalline rocks. *Pedology* (U.S.S.R.) No. 7:327-339.

65. Ravich-Shcherbo, U. 1923 On the role of microorganisms in weathering of parent rock. *Arch. Biologic. Nauk.* 26, no. 3.

66. Reade, T. Mellard ? Chemical denudation in relation to geological time. (Quoted from Merrill).

67. Reiche, Parry. 1945 A survey of weathering processes and products. Univ. of New Mexico Publications in Geology, No. 1:1-87.

68. Remezev, N. P. 1947 On the process of the formation of the podzolized horizon. *Pedology* (U.S.S.R.) No. 5: 265-276.

69. Robinson, G. W., and Richardson, M. 1932 Degrees of weathering of soils. *Nature.* April.

70. Robinson, W. O., and Holmes, R. S. 1924 The chemical composition of soil colloids. U. S. Dept. of Agr. Bul. 1311.

71. Ross, C. S. and Hendricks, S. B. 1945 Minerals of the montmorillonite group. Professional Paper 205B. Geol. Sur., U. S. Dept. Interior, pp. 23-79.

72. Ross, C. S. and Kerr, P. F. 1931 The clay minerals and their identity. *Jour. Sed. Petr.* 1:55-65.

73. Ross, C. S. and Kerr, P. F. 1931 The kaolin minerals. U. S. Geol. Surv. Prof. Paper 165-E.

74. Rozanov, A. N. and Shukevich, M. M. 1943 On the mineralogic composition of loess-like rocks of Central Asia. *Pedology* (U.S.S.R.) No. 9-10:37-43.

75. Russell, M. B. and Haddock, J. L. 1940 The identification of clay minerals in five Iowa soils by the thermal method. *Proc. Soil Sci. Soc. Amer.* 5:90-94.

76. Sachs, J. 1860 Auflösung des Marmores durch Mais-Pflanzen. *Bot. Zeitung* 18, No. 13:117-119.

77. Sackett, W. G., Patten, A. J., and Brown, C. W. 1908 The solvent action of soil bacteria upon the insoluble phosphates, etc. *Centbl. Bakt.* II, 20:688-703.

78. Salminen, A. 1932 The influence of exposure upon temperature differences in rocks. Bul. of the Agrogeolog. Inst. of Finland No. 32.

79. Schachtschabel, P. 1940 Untersuchungen über die sorption der Tonmineralien und organischen Bodenkolloide, und die Bestimmung des Anteils dieser Kolloide an der Sorption im Boden. *Koll. Beihef.* 51:199-276.

80. Schuchert, Ch. and Dunbar, Carl O.. 1941 A Textbook of Geology, pt. II: Historical Geology. John Wiley and Sons, New York.

81. Sedletskii, I. D. 1945 Colloid-dispersoid mineralogy (Russian) Acad. of Sci., U.S.S.R., pp. 114. Moscow-Leningrad.

82. Senft, F. 1862 Die Humus, Marsch, Torf und Limonitbildungen.

83. Shaw, B. T. and Humbert, R. P. 1941 Electron micrographs of clay minerals. *Proc. Soil Sci. Soc. Amer.* 6:146-149.

84. Smithson, F. 1941 Alteration of detrital minerals in Mesozoic rocks of Yorkshire. *Geol. Mag.* 68:97-112.

85. Starkey, R. L. and Halvorson, H. O. 1927 Studies on the transformation of iron in nature. II. Concerning the importance of microorganisms in the solution and precipitation of iron. *Soil Sci.* 26:381-402.

86. Stoklasa, J. 1922 Uber die Verbreitung des Aluminiums in der Natur, etc. Jena.

87. Trutnev, A. G. 1938 Mineralogic composition of the soil profile of podzol soils. *Pedolgy* (U.S.S.R.) No. 5:695-707.

88. United States Department of Agriculture. 1926 Ed. 2. Summary of the climatological data for the United States by sections. Sections 93, 94, and 105. Weather Bureau Bul. W.

89. Van Hise, Ch. R. 1904 A treatise on metamorphism. Monographs of the U. S. Geol. Survey v. 47.

90. Vernadskii, V. I. 1926 The Biosphere (Russian) Leningrad. (French and German translations available).

91. Vernadskii, V. I. 1926 Sur l'analyse des sols an point de vue geochimique. *Actes de la IV Conference Inter. de Pedologic.,* 2:570-577. See also *Pedology* (U.S.S.R.) No. 1 (1936): 8-16.

92. Vernadskii, V. I. 1927 Geochemistry (Russian). Leningrad. (German and French translations available).

93. Vernadskii, V. I. 1940 Biogeochemical Essays (Russian). Academy of Sci. Leningrad-Moscow.

94. Vinogradov, A. P. 1945 On the chemistry of the biosphere. *Pedology.* (U.S.S.R.) No. 7:348-354.

95. Vinogradov, A. P. and Biochenko, A. E. 1942 Decmposition of kaolin by diatoms. (English). *Compt. Rend. (Doklady) de l'Acad. de l'SRSS.* 37:135-138.

96. Warth, H. 1905 Geological Magazine. (Quoted from Blanck's *Handbuch der Bodenlehre* 3, p. II).

97. Whiteside, E. P. and Marshall C. E. 1944 Mineralogical and chemical studies of the Putnam silt loam soil. Missouir Agr. Exp. Sta. Res. Bul. 386.
98. Winogradsky, S. 1888 Uber Eisenbakterien. *Bot Ztg.* 46:262-270.
99. Zemyatchenskii, P. 1923 Otchety o deyatel'nosti Keps'a pri Akadem. Nauk. No. 8:93-108.

CHAPTER V

SOIL GENESIS: SOIL FORMERS OR FACTORS OF SOIL FORMATION

Weathering and Soil Formation.—In the final analysis, soil genesis is linked with the reactions of the biosphere on the products of weathering. In other words, the energy releasing elements of living matter acting on the mass of inanimate mineral matter serve as agents in the formation of the soil body. In the evolution of the cyclic process which includes the soil system, other factors besides the biosphere had been operating and had also contributed to the formation of the soil body.

According to Dokuchaev, "the soil is the result of the combined activity and reciprocal influence of parent material, plant and animal organisms, climate, age of the land, and topography." These were named by Dokuchaev *soil formers.* In the words of Zakharov (Ch. 2, 91), "the soil is the derivative or function of the soil formers or factors of soil formation enumerated by Dokuchaev." In mathematical form, the Dokuchaev proposition was expressed as follows:

$$S = f(pm, c, b, a, and t),$$

where S=soil, f=function, pm=parent material, c=climate, b=biosphere, a=age of land (time factor), and t=topography.

In the evolution of the soil body, *from the moment life appeared on this earth,* some of the enumerated factors of soil formation have made themselves felt. It is not imperative to trace which of these was first, and what, if any, was the sequence or parallel activity of these in the process of soil formation at the dawn of life. It is, however, important to realize that there existed products of weathering, a mantle of clastic or sedimentary rocks. These rocks, being, as a rule, more suitable for plant life than solid rocks, have served as parent material for the aboriginal soil body. In those remote days, geochemical reactions alone had implemented a change of state in the cyclic process. With the advent of life, biogeochemical reactions came into play. In terms of soil genesis, this meant that the parent material as a factor of soil formation was supplemented with the biosphere, the energy element, acting on the apparently inert mass of mineral matter. But ever since the formation of the aboriginal soil body, the succession of the individual geochemical and biogeochemical reactions have been running parallel to each other and have acted in unison in the cyclic process. Whether it is possible now to separate the purely geo-chemical from the biogeochemical reactions is a moot question. *It might be well to mention areas, such as the desert or the polar regions, where geochemical rather than biogeochemical reactions are the rule even in our own days.*

One should not imply from what has been said that loose clastic rock is the only recipient of biogeochemical reactions. Any student of geology is aware of the activity of primitive forms of life on primary rocks. This form of activity is generally known as biological weathering.

As pointed out in Chapter IV, the process of weathering, its rate and type, is largely controlled by the climate. Still, there is no climatic zone inhibiting the process. On the other hand, the process of soil formation, although also being dependent in a large measure on the climate, is in-hibited in certain climatic zones.

The process of soil formation, with the soil body as an end-product, tends to protect the rocks from further weathering. Whereas the process of weathering is destructive in nature, the process of soil formation is creative. In a way, the process of soil formation may be looked upon as the counter-reaction to weathering.

From the point of view of transformations, the process of weathering is analytical, whereas that of soil formation is synthetic. Weathering tends toward simplification of substances, the final products of weathering being simple compounds. Soil formation leads to the equilibrium state of a system beginning with the simple and ending with the complex.

Under existing conditions in nature, the reactions involved in the processes of weathering and soil formation act simultaneously on the soil mass. The tendency is, therefore, to identify these processes as one and the same. It should be noted, however, that although there is now no hard and fast line of demarcation between the two processes, they should be examined in their historical sequence, namely, weathering as the first phase followed by soil formation as the second phase.

In the process of soil formation, the factors involved may be divided into *active* and *passive*. The passive factors (or soil formers) represent the constituents which serve as the source of the mass (mineral matter) and some environmental conditions which affect it. They comprise the parent material, the topography, and the age of the land (the time factor). The active factors of soil formation are represented by agents supplying the energy that acts upon the mass and furnish reagents for the process of soil formation.* The elements of the biosphere, the atmosphere, and the hydrosphere are representative of this class of factors.

To isolate the individual factors of soil formation and follow through the bonds between them, from the viewpoint of the relations of matter and energy, would involve a thorough analysis of the cyclic process of which the soil system is just an equilibrium state. This would lead to a consideration of the law of conservation of energy and other phases of theoretical physics. As yet, no studies in this direction have been made and no treatises on the subject are available.

PASSIVE FACTORS OF SOIL FORMATION
Parent Material

In chapter III, parent material was defined as material underlying the B horizon. At the same time, the C horizon was defined as the layer below the B horizon, indicating the relation of the parent material to the C horizon. Such definitions convey geomorphological attributes of the soil profile. From the point of view of soil formation, the concept of parent material must stem from the internal characteristics of the raw material which makes up the mass of the soil body in relation to the other factors of soil formation. Focusing our analysis of soil genesis to the distant past of aboriginal soils, it is fair to conjecture that the mineral material of whatever origin—igneous, metamorphic, or clastic rocks or their products of weathering—has served as parent material.

Whether the parent material was mechanically homogenous, such as products of weathering of igneous rocks resting on bed rock, or a heterogenous mixture of sedimentary deposits, matters little. For soil genesis, as exhibited in the soil profile, any deposit may be looked upon as parent material. Any mass of eroded soil material subjected to the factors of soil formation in its new position is to be considered as parent material. Of course, in analyzing the genetic relations of the horizon to the parent material, certain sedimentary deposits present some difficulties. It is therefore, as a rule, much simpler to study the process of soil formation on homogeneous parent material.

The passive character of parent material may be inferred from the fact that various parent materials (the conditions for the activities of the other factors of soil formation being similar) give rise to the same

---

*It should be stated that the above is a rather simplified form of differentiating between the two types of factors of soil formation. Actually, the energy of the organic substances activates the parent material which in itself is not devoid of energy forces. With the activities of the biosphere, exo- and endothermic reactions of the mineral complexes are set off and play their part in the energy levels of the processes of soil formation.

type of soil. On the other hand, where the conditions for the activities of
the other factors of soil formation are dissimilar, similar parent materials
give rise to entirely different types of soil. As Marbut (Ch. 2, 45) notes:
". . . although the geological formations of Piedmont, Maryland, for
example, and those of Georgia are closely similar in all respects, the soils
are widely different; that soils in Georgia overlying granite rocks and
undoubtedly developed from their disintegrated product have no single
element of similarity to soils on and derived from granite in Los Angeles
County, California; that soils on limestone glacial drift in South Dakota
and those on limestone glacial drift in Indiana have no single important
characteristic in common except texture; that soils derived from loess in
Saunders County, Nebraska, Grenada County, Mississippi, or Clermont
County, Ohio (often identified as loess) are different in every important
respect from soils derived from loess in Spokane County, Washington."
Chernozem, podzol, or chestnut brown soils may be found on such variable
parent material as loess, glacial drift, marine and lake sands, clays, limestone, marl, shale, and sandstone.

There are departures from the passive behavior of parent material.
As Neustruev (Ch. 2, 50) expresses it: "Parent materials are far from
being a blank sheet of paper on which the climate may write anything it
desires." And Glinka (p. 299) points out that there are groups of soils
"where the composition of the parent material subdues the effects of the
climate. These soils we call *endodynamomorphic* in contrast to *ectodyna-
momorphic*. The endodynamomorphic soils are often a temporary formation, which may persist until the chemical composition of the parent material has changed. After such a change these are converted into soils
characteristic of their zonal position; thus rendzina in the podzol zone is
gradually converted into a podzolized soil." On mountain slopes, endodynamomorphic soils are more apparent, since erosion washes out considerable amounts of the fine materials and the parent material becomes
very much more in evidence in the soil body. Young soils have a similar
constitution and might be classed with the endodynamomorphic soils.
Morphological and chemical observations and analyses on the Hagerstown
series (in New Jersey) present little evidence of podzolization, a characteristic feature of the soils in the state. The cause of the specific behavior of the Hagerstown series is a resistant parent material, dolomitic
limestone. Its properties predominate over other soil formers, and hence
we have an endodynamomorphic soil.

Mechanical Composition.—The process of soil formation finds its
greatest expression in parent material consisting of residual products of
weathering. It is obvious that variations in the physical and chemical

properties of parent materials may modify the process of soil formation. Residual products of weathering are mechanically a mixture of particles (exclusively mineral before life came, and primarily mineral at present) varying in size from large boulders through stones, gravel, sand, silt, and down to clay of colloidal dimensions. It is clear that the predominance of any one, or combination of groups of particle size fractions, in the mechanical mixture of the parent material must influence the other factors in the process of soil formation and hence the constitutional development of the soil profile. In other words, the texture (the relative proportion of arbitrarily accepted particle size fractions, or separates) of the parent material is an important element in the process of soil formation. The procedure determining texture is known as *mechanical analysis*. In designating texture of parent material or soils, we speak of their mechanical composition.

In making a mechanical analysis of parent material or soil, it is customary to take the mineral mass below a certain particle size. Some European investigators restrict the mechanical composition of soil to the mass of 0.25 mm. and below. All materials above 0.25 mm. are considered as the "soil skeleton," indicating thereby that these mechanical elements are the shell of the soil mass which takes no direct part in the life processes of the soil. In the United States, any material above 2 mm. in diameter is usually excluded in mechanical analysis procedures. The official method of the International Society of Soil Science recognizes the following fractions: coarse sand, 2.0 to 0.2 mm.; fine sand, 0.2 to 0.02 mm.; silt, 0.02 to 0.002 mm.; clay $<$ 0.002 mm.

In evaluating the parent material as a factor of soil formation, the capacity and rate of reaction are in a large measure related to particle size, i.e., to the mechanical composition of the parent material. The greater the bulk of the fine fractions and their subdivisions, the greater is the surface energy. It may be shown that the more complex the parent material (physically and chemically), the greater is its free energy resources. It is to be noted that energy relations are also involved in the passive parent material. However, its passive character may be defended on the basis that to activate these energy resources in the direction of soil formation an outside source of energy, through the medium of the biosphre, is essential. It is clear that for the reactions engendered in the parent material as a factor of soil formation, one may invoke the second law of thermodynamics. This law calls for external energy for a self-acting machine to convey heat from a body at a low temperature to one of a higher temperature.

The texture of the parent material determines, in a large measure, the depth of the soil profile.   It is deeper on light than on heavy textured parent materials.   It is to be noted at this point that over the wide geographic regions of soil distribution, the depth of the profile varies with the climate.   Thus, in the arctic and in the desert the profile is shallow because of the lack of the elements essential for profile development, such as percolation of water, mobilization of reagents, and translocation of the reaction products in the profile.   The zonal soil types the world over vary in depth, with the chernozem generally the deepest soil.

Composition of Rocks and Minerals.—The composition of the petrographic and mineralogic elements exerts a profound influence on the process of soil formation.   Quartz, orthoclase, microcline, biotite, and muscovite are the more prominent minerals that persist much longer in the products of weathering than do other minerals.

Oxides of iron, variously hydrated, serve as a protective coating for other minerals against further decomposition.   They also impart the red, orange, and yellow tinges to the soil.   The oxides of manganese impart black to dark brown color to the mass of mineral material.   •

The red shales of the Piedmont physiographic-geologic region in the United States are the result of an erosion cycle depositing residual products of lateritic weathering.   The sesquioxides have protected the residual primary minerals in the shale from further weathering and from entering into reactions with the elements of the biosphere.   Because of this, there is little horizon differentiation in soils developing on shales.

An interesting case of the effect of parent material on soil formation was noted by the author on the Baltic sea coast in Estonia.   An area extending over several square miles has a xerophytic type of vegetation cover, edged off on the horizon by forests.   The reason for the grass cover is the *glint,* a deposit of limestone which has not the type of impurities which would leave behind products of weathering.

A comprehensive discussion is presented by Polynov (83) on the effects of the composition of the parent material, in general, and of the composition of the minerals in particular on soil formation.

In the podzol type of soil formation, limestone parent material resists the reactions leading to podzolization.   On the other hand, the paucity of calcium in parent material in the zone of chernozem prevents the formation of this type of soil.

Topography Factor

In geomorphology, the term *relief* denotes "the form and distribution of the continents and oceans (31, p. 9)."   In pedologic literature, the term *topography* is used synonymously with relief; its meaning is generally restricted to land features.

Topography as a factor of soil formation is an arbitrary designation. Actually, it is a condition influencing in many important ways the other factors of soil formation. In the words of Zakharov (Ch. 2, 91, p. 246), "whereas parent material, biosphere, and atmosphere participate in soil formation by their mass, or energy, relief only conditions the redistribution of matter and energy without contributing anything new."

Zakharov considers two types of topography, macro- and microtopography. Under macrotopography he includes the large elements of the earth's surface features, such as mountains, plains, hills, plateaus, and valleys. Under microtopography he embraces local depressions, hillocks, mounds, hollows, and minor low spots.

The importance of topography in soil formation had been recognized long before the principles of pedology had been advanced by Dokuchaev and his pupils. Its effects on the soil profile have been utilized as evidence of the soundness of pedologic principles.

Dokuchaev (22), in his studies of the chernozems of Russia, noted the differences in depth of profile due to undulating topography even in the plains. Later he established "the law of constant relations between the surface forms and the character of the soil." Vysotskii (109) made a comprehensive study of the effects of topography on soil moisture and water table which in turn influence the process of soil formation. A low spot in the plains of the semidesert will accumulate soluble salts which cause solonchak formation. In the chernozem, a similar condition will produce a meadow soil with a high calcium carbonate content. In the podzol zone, bog-iron accumulation and the formation of semi-marshy soils will result.

The most pronounced influence of topography on soil formation is encountered in mountainous country. Normal geologic erosion removes from slopes some products of weathering which, under conditions of level topography, would contribute to the development of the soil profile. As a result, the depth of the profile is generally shallow on the upper regions of slopes. Norton and Smith (75) correlated slope measurements with depth of the A horizon. They established a parabolic relationship between degree of slope, in per cent, and depth of horizons, in inches.

Ellis and Shafer (30) contributed to the problem on the relation of moisture conditions and slope to profile development. They have shown how the soils on the knolls and steep slopes receive less water for percolation. In effect, microclimatic elements enter into the play of forces and cause departures from the normal development of the profile as noted above. These microclimatic elements are associated with the microrelief (microtopographic) features, introducing different plant associations and thereby giving rise to specific types of soil within the generally prevailing soil cover of the area.

On the sandy soils of the Costal Plain in New Jersey (Lakewood and Sassafras soil series), microtopographic features are very much in evidence. Within distances of a few feet, one may find well developed A_0 layers in local depressions (sometime as small as 2 to 3 feet square) alongside large and small areas, with no A_0 layer, on the higher elevations. The difference between the higher elevations and the depression may amount to not more than a few inches.

Slope exposure is another distinctive feature of the effect of topography on soil formation. In general, southern exposures are warmer and drier and sustain marked fluctuations in temperature and moisture. Northern exposures are the converse—colder and sustain less fluctuations. Western and eastern exposures occupy an intermediate position. Zakharov (Ch. 2, 91, p. 249) points out that "on the southern exposure of Mount Hood, in the main mountain chain of the Caucasus, there are chernozem-like soils, whereas on the northern exposure podzolized soils prevail. In the Armenian mountains, with a drier climate, the chernozem-like soils appear on the northern exposure, whereas on the southern exposure gray soils predominate, often enriched with carbonates." Similar observations were made by Thorp (100) while investigating the soils in the Big Horn Basin, Wyoming. An interesting paper on the relation of topography to ecologic differences has been presented by Albright and Stoker (3).

The Time Factor

Time is one of the most important factors in all processes, natural or man-made. Soil formation is, therefore, also intimately related to the time factor. Dokuchaev formulated the relation of soil formation to time in terms of the age of the soil. This age is ostensibly to be measured from the moment the parent material has emerged, either from under water, glacier, or some other condition, to be subjected to the other factors of soil formation until it has attained the status of a soil.

In an attempt to decipher the time it takes to develop a soil, Dokuchaev (22, p. 343) made a study of the ruins of the Staro-Ladoga fortress in 1880. It was built in 1116 of slabs of Silurian limestone and granitic boulders. At the time of the examination, the age of the soil was 870 years. It was a brownish gray, sod-covered soil, 10 to 12 cm. deep.

Ruprecht (Ch. 2, 63) observed the formation of chernozem on the mounds built by the Tartars in the European steppe of Russia. When

Ruprecht examined the soil it was about 600 years old, 15 to 28 cm. deep. The depth of the normal chernozem profile in the neighborhood was 60 to 150 cm. Assuming that the development of the normal profile had progressed at the same rate as that of the profile on the mounds (this assumption is not fully justified because of the difference in the type of parent material of the 2 profiles), it was 2400 to 4000 years old at the time Ruprecht made his observations.

Akimtsev (2) investigated the soils formed on top of the walls of the Kamenets fortress in Ukraine, U.S.S.R., built by a Russian-Lithuanian princess, Koriatovich in 1362, of calcareous slabs. He compared the soil material of the fortress with that of nearby soils formed on Silurian limestone. In table 16 the data are self-explanatory. It is pointed out by Akimtsev that a thickness of 30 cm. has been reached in 230 years.

Table 16

Composition of natural soil and of soil formed on Dennaya tower of the fortress at Kamenets, U. S. S. R.

(After Akimtzev)

Units of comparison: composition data on A horizon only	Soil on fortress	Natural soil nearby
		(for A horizon only)
Depth of profile, cm	30.0*	8.0
Humus, per cent	3.5	3.8
CaCO$_3$, per cent	5.0	5.0+
Physical clay, per cent	50.5	53.3
Skeletal elements, per cent	2.0 (11 in B)	1.03
Cation exchange capacity, per cent (?)	1.14	0.91
Exchangeable Ca, per cent	0.89	0.89
pH	7.68	7.67

*—At another point of the fortress the profile was 55 cm deep. In general, the depth of the profiles examined varied from 10 to 90 cm.

It is problematic whether the time factor in the process of soil formation, or the age of the soil, can be determined in terms of years. Soil formation is associated with other factors which may retard or accelerate the growth of the soil. As expressed by Zakharov (Ch. 2, 91, p. 252), "a soil lives for a time with all its characteristic attributes. Then it begins gradually to change, or degrade. Each soil goes through a process of evolution. Like organisms, the soil goes through stages of youth, maturity, and senility. We do speak, for example, of undeveloped chernozem, deep chernozem, and degraded chernozem."

Byers, Kellogg, Anderson, and Thorp (7, p. 969) speak of soils which date back, as such, to the ancient geologic times of "the Tertiary period, variously estimated at from 1 to 6 million years." They speak of these soils as being in a "senile stage of development." These authors do not define the terms youth, maturity, and senility. To them, these stages in the development of the profile have a meaning primarily with reference to the fertility of the soil. It is clear that soils which date back 1 to 6 million years are pedologically speaking an absurdity, unless we refer to buried soils. Chandler (13) studied the time factor in relation to podzolization.

Jenny (48, p. 11) defines soil formation as "the transformation of rock into soil." He considers the soil as mature when the transformation of the rock, the process of soil formation, has been completed and reached an equilibrium state. Incidentally, Jenny speaks of weathering as "one of the processes of soil formation;" he mentions no other processes of soil formation. No reference is made by Jenny on the condition of the profile in equilibrium state; he does not define maturity.

To the author, the terms youth, maturity, and senility, indicate stages in the development of the profile in relation to the factors of soil formation. As the parent material is subjected to the activities of the other factors of soil formation, the growth stages (to use an analogy with living objects) become apparent. They are expressed in the form of horizon differentiation, or profile development; they are effects which are additive and accumulative until the equilibrium state is achieved. When this point is reached, the profile is mature, i.e., the profile features remain constant, as long as the climate remains the same. The prevailng features of the profile are then recognized as normal for the climatic zone. We have no distinct criteria for the other stages in the development of the profile; we can not, therefore, characterize these by being embryonic, infantile, youthful, or any other designation which we may borrow from terminology in botany or zoology.

In the light of the aforesaid, it seems reasonable to speak of the age of soil in terms of state of maturity rather than of years. We have mature soils with fully developed profiles, and young soils showing only indications of horizon differentiation independent of the geologic age of the land or the years it took to reach the state of development of the soil profile. Mature soils, as a rule, have been acted upon by the principal soil factors for a longer period of time than young soils. Sometimes, however, a soil has been acted upon for a longer period of time than a mature soil in the same region and has remained young. In other words, the time factor is to be related to maturity and not to age of the soil, and still less to age

of the land, which is related to the geologic history of the land. The Penn
soils in the Piedmont physiographic-geologic region, formed on parent
material of an earlier geologic age than the soils of the Coastal Plain, are
younger, in the sense of maturity, than any of the soils of the Coastal
Plain. The fact is that the Penn soils have little horizon differentiation,
whereas the soils of the Coastal Plain have fully developed mature profiles.

The Human Factor

Like the time factor, the human factor introduced conditioning elements which affect the other factors of soil formation. Ever since homo-
sapiens took to settled agriculture he interfered with the factors of soil
formation. He has changed the flora, accepting and developing some plant
species and subduing or exterminating others. With the aid of metal and
fire he has accomplished his ends. Burning the sod in the grass country,
resorting to the system of assartage in the tropics, felling the forests with
saw and ax, and finally turning the furrow with the plow, the farmers of
the world have brought into cultivation about 800 million square miles of
land. Perhaps half as many more square miles are in pasture and meadow;
and the exploitation of these had a definite effect on the features of the
profile.

In the northern parts of the world, deforestation turned cut-over land
into swamps and marshes. Denuded hillsides had their soils washed away
to bury the soils in the valleys, change the water table, clog stream beds,
and leave behind the scars of erosion. Everywhere in the world, the herds
of the nomads contributed to the destruction of the forests. The goats
in the Mediterranean region left only memories of the remarkable beech
forests of Montonegro. The Bedouins of desert Arabia "took care" of
the Cedars of Lebanon and laid waste the entire Middle East. The rivers
of the world carry annually 8 to 12 cubic miles of dry matter to the seas
and oceans. In the United States, Davis (16) estimated that 870 million
tons of suspended material are carried yearly into the ocean by the streams.
A large share of these sediments consists of material of the A horizon, removed from the cultivated land. Due credit for the sediments and constituents in solution should be given to geologic erosion. If not for that
we would still have mountains towering miles and miles high. The process
of peneplanation shapes the geomorphological features of the land.

Irrigation has invariably introduced modifying effects on the soil.
Besides the direct effects on the moisture regime of the soil, the change in
the flora and quantity of dry matter produced as a result of irrigation have
a bearing on the changes in the soil profile. The pumping of water for

irrigation and for modern living has an influence on the depth of the ground waters and these in turn affect the soil. For a discussion on the effects of irrigation on desert soils, the reader is referred to the paper by Shires (90).

There are many other deleterious and beneficial effects resulting from the entry of the human as a tiller of the soil. These effects are more prominent in the realm of soil productivity which is beyond the scope of this treatise.

ACTIVE FACTORS OF SOIL FORMATION

The climate, through its component elements (precipitation, temperature, humidity, and wind) and the biosphere are the two in one factors of soil formation which activate the passive factors of soil formation in creating the soil body.

Precipitation

Moisture is one of the primary elements of climate that is responsible for the features of the soil body. The rainwater and the thawing waters of the snow act directly and indirectly in many ways on the formation of the soil body. As in the process of weathering, moisture does its work through solution and hydration on mineral matter (and in this respect the activity of moisture can not be seperated from that as an agent of weathering) and on the newly formed substances of organic nature, living and dead, supplied by the biosphere.

Moisture acts directly in translocating substances in solution and in colloidal state from one point in the soil body to another, depriving one part of some constituent and enriching another part. The movement may be either downward or upward, as well as horizontal. Large particles of soil material are transported mechanically, both vertically and horizontally, from one place to another within the soil body, or out of its bounds into the subsoil and ground waters. It is the movement and translocation of the various reagents, made available through the biosphere, that mould the morphological, chemical and physical features of the soil profile.

The quantitative aspect of the movement of constituents is controlled by the amount of moisture available. Under conditions of excessive precipitation, some of the constituents move away from the soil profile into the rivers and oceans. In regions of low rainfall, large quantities of the products of the reaction are retained in the profile and thereby impart definite characteristics to the soil body. In short, it is the amount of available percolating waters that controls the qualitative and quantitative distribution of the substances through the profile. In rainless desert regions no percolation is possible, and hence no soil can form. In contrast to the rainless regions we might consider districts in Eastern India, in ancient Kolkhidia, where the rainfall is 120 inches or more annually. In some sections of Java the rainfall reaches a figure of 300 inches and at Mount Waialele, Kanai, Hawaiian Islands, an average of 476 inches is recorded. Of course, not all of this water passes through the soil, and the percolation effects are therefore reduced. The amount of percolation also affects the level of the ground waters which in turn have an effect on the movement of salts into and from the profile. The level of the water table determines the accumulation of organic matter and hence the type of soil.

In evaluating precipitation data, consideration is to be given to type of moisture—rain, snow, hail, or dew—, seasonal distributions, intensity, topography of the land, and texture and structure of parent material.

Besides the direct effects of moisture in soil formation, there are indirect effects. Moisture is one of the determining factors in plant growth which in turn harnesses the energy of the sun to act on the mineral matter. It is the biosphere variations that have such an important bearing on the reactions which contribute to the specificity of the different soil types.

Temperature

Temperature is the next important element of the climate. With the same precipitation in two different isothermal belts, different soil profiles will develop. In the arctic and subarctic regions temperature is of little significance. The long winter season, the extremely low temperatures, and the short summer season with comparatively little total heat accumulation keep the soil in a condition unfavorable for percolation. We have in these regions the perpetually frozen layer which modifies the activity of the factors of soil formation. In the hot arid regions, the high evaporation ratio impedes the leaching effects and causes an upward movement of some soluble salts which modify the effects of the other factors of soil formation.

Another aspect is the relation of temperature to organic matter formation and decomposition. In the cold regions, because of the low temperatures, an accumulation of organic matter, peat formation, takes place. The processes of decomposition are slow because of the unfavorable condition for microbial activity; moreover, freezing favors the irreversible state of the organic colloidal complexes, rendering them resistant to decomposition. The resulting accumulated organic matter naturally has a very pronounced effect on the characteristics of the soil profile.

In the humid tropics and subtropics, because of the favorable temperature relations, there is a luxuriant vegetation. On the other hand, these regions offer optimum conditions for a rapid decomposition of organic matter by microbes. This phenomenon is conducive to the accumulation of iron in the surface horizons, imparting to laterites the characteristic brick-red color.

In recent years, the attention of pedologists has been called to certain elements in the soil climate, to wit, moisture, temperature, and diffusion of gases. Undoubtedly there are certain aspects of the soil climate which are of considerable moment in the reactions and processes that go on in the soil. Not much has been done with reference to these.

In the northern temperate climate, the heaving property of frost may exert considerable mechanical activity. An excellent example of this is cited by Merrill (Ch. 4, 49, p. 393) : "Every farmer boy who has been condemned to pick the drift boulders from a field knows through bitter experience that, however well he may do his work in the fall, however clean the surface may be when winter sets in, the following spring, after the frost is out of the ground, will find a new crop in no way distinguishable from the old, and which, for all that he can see, may have rained down during the winters' storms. The fact is, however, that they have been actually thrown up, 'heaved out,' the farmer will say, from below the surface by the frost which here (in New England) penetrates not infrequently to a depth of two or more feet. . . . In wet boggy lands this heaving action of frost as exerted on partially buried boulders of small size, is sometimes exemplified in a peculiarly striking manner. The surface of the ground will be dotted here and there with small hummocks, each with a comparatively large crater-like opening at the top. Investigations reveal the fact that at a distance of but a few inches at most below the surface of this crater-like opening is a rounded boulder." In the tundra zone, the hummocky topography and crater-like openings through which soil material from the lower horizons oozes out to the surface are in a large measure the result of the heaving action of frost.

Subordinate Elements of Climate

Evaporation, transpiration, and humidity are designated as subordinate elements because they are not as important as the primary elements of climate, precipitation and temperature, as factors of soil formation. These subordinate elements may become primary from the point of view of public health, production of crops, development of industries, colonization, and similar aspects of the life of organized society.

Evaporation and Humidity.—These elements of climate modify the effects of precipitation by either reducing or increasing the quantity of moisture available for percolation. Moisture evaporates from the surface of the soil at various rates, depending chiefly on temperature and humidity. The free-water surface method used in measuring evaporation, or the atmometer method, are not adequate for soils. Type of vegetation and texture, structure, composition (chemical and mineralogical), moisture content, and color of soil introduce variables in the quantity and rate of evaporation from soils. A glance at the evaporation map of the United States, prepared by Kincer (52), shows that during the warm season (April-September) evaporation varies from 25 to 88 inches in the different parts of the country.

Another loss of water by surface evaporation is the moisture intercepted by the plant cover. From 30 to 40 per cent of the total precipitation may be evaporated from a forest canopy and from 13 to 43 per cent by grass sod, a stand of wheat, corn, or alfalfa.

An excellent study on evaporation may be found in the work of Meyer (67). An extensive review of the subject on evaporation, with a list of 181 references, is presented by Thornthwaite and Holzman (99).

In the greater part of the United States where precipitation is light, the annual evaporation from a water surface is greater than the annual rainfall. In parts of Arizona it has been found to be more than 9 times the rainfall. Of course, under such conditions percolation is greatly impeded.

Evaporation-precipitation ratios have figured in classifying and charting climates and soil groups. Transeau (103) constructed a precipitation-evaporation ratio map of Eastern United States. In Europe, Penk (82) has used the same method for classifying climates into three groups. First, the arid region where E (evaporation) exceeds P (precipitation); second, arid-humid boundary where E equals P; third, humid region where E is smaller than P. As pointed out by Jenny (48), "the main advantage of a precipitation-evaporation ratio map over a rainfall map lies in the possibility of comparing conditions of soil moisture of regions having different temperatures and different air humidities. For instance, St. Paul, Minn. and San Antonio, Texas, have about the same mean annual precipitation, 27.4 and 27.7 inches respectively. Yet the effective moisture conditions in regard to plant growth and soil formation are by no means alike. Actually, San Antonia's climate is much drier than that of Minnesota's capital. This difference is clearly indicated by the Transeau ratio, which is 0.51 for San Antonio and 1.02 for St. Paul. In accordance with these values, the climatic soil profile features of the two localities exhibit marked differences."

In 1915, Lang (59, 60) proposed the *rain factor,* a ratio of annual precipitation (P) in millimeters to the mean annual temperature (T), as a means of characterizing the soil groups of the world as outlined by Ramann (Ch. 2, 6o). For a time Lang's work* had attracted considerable attention. Hirth (43) published a map of rain factors for the world, and Jenny (47) published a more detailed one for the United States. Attempts to correlate these maps with soil features failed.

Lang cites a series of "black soil formations" in widely different latitudes having practically the same rain factor. The black soils of Kazan (Russia) are associated with a P:T ratio (rain factor) of 133 to 167, the mean annual temperature being 3° C. and the annual rainfall from 400 to 500 millimeters. The black soils of Württemberg (Germany) are associated with a P:T ratio of 167-183, the mean annual temperature being 6° C. and precipitation—1000 to 1100 millimeters. The black soils of Penandjáan (Dutch East Indies) are associated with a rain factor of 180, the mean temperature being 12° C. and the precipitation 1800 millimeters. The black soils of T'joeroeb (India) are associated with a slightly higher rain factor, from 175 to 200, the mean temperature being 20° C. and precipitation from 3500 to 4000 millimeters. In spite of the close similarity of the rain factors for the four soils cited by Lang, they are not related except for color.

Lang disregarded completely the element of humidity, evaporation rates, runoff, seasonal distribution, type of precipitation (rain or snow), and intensity of rainfall. He failed to appreciate the principles of pedology so clearly enunciated by Glinka whom he quoted.

Meyer (66) appreciated the shortcomings of the Lang factor and emphasized the importance of humidity as a regulator of evaporation rates. He, therefore, suggested a humidity factor, the ratio of precipitation (in mm.) to the absolute saturation deficit of the air (in mm. mercury). This saturation deficit was named by Wiegner (112) the N-S coefficient.

The saturation deficit is calculated by multiplying the vapor tension corresponding to the mean annual temperature by the relative deficit of saturation calculated on the basis of the local meteorological data ($100 =$ mean relative moisture). Under saturation deficit is understood the difference between the vapor pressure of the air when saturated and the vapor pressure actually found. The formula used to calculate this is E-e, where $E =$ the vapor pressure at saturation and $e =$ the actual pressure.

Jenny (48) prepared an N-S quotient map for the United States. He illustrated the method of calculating the N-S quotient by taking the

---

*In this connection it may be of interest to note the attempt of Vysotskii (111) to establish the relation of soil formation to climate in terms of ratios of annual precipitation to evaporation from a water surface. For peat and glei formations he used the ratio of 1⅓; for meadow-sod, podzolic-glei, and leached soils—a ratio of 1; for chernozem—a ratio of 2:3; and for the arid steppe a ratio of 1:3.

meteorological data of Sheridan, Wyoming. The mean annual temperature of 6.17° C. corresponds to a vapor tension of 7.06 mm. mercury. The relative humidity at Sheridan is 67.5 per cent. This makes the annual relative saturation deficit of moisture 100-67.5 = 32.5 per cent. Multiplying this figure by the vapor tension and dividing by 100 we get $\frac{32.5 \times 7.06}{100} = 2.29$ millimeters of mercury corresponding to the mean absolute deficit of moisture. Dividing 367 (mm. precipitation at Sheridan) by 2.29 we get a N-S quotient equal to 160.

Whereas the N-S quotient is an improvement over the Lang rain factor, it does not bring out its relation to one of the *fundamental factors of soil formation, the percolation effect.*

In constructing his so-called climatic soil classification, Meyer ignored the pedologic principles even though he was acquainted with the work of Glinka and Kossovich whom he quoted in his monograph. Meyer adhered to the geologic viewpoint of Ramann whose definition of soil ("the soil is the weathered layer of the earth's crust") he heralded as a great contribution to science.

The shortcomings of the attempts to correlate climatic elements with the distribution of soil types lie in the failure to appreciate the factors of soil formation in terms of moisture available for percolation. Crowther's (14) *percolation factor* comes nearest in name to the one laid down by the principles of pedology. Unfortunately Crowther used the lysimeter data of Rothamsted for his calculations. These lysimeters do not represent natural conditions for the movement of moisture and translocation of constituents, as pointed out elsewhere (49). It might have been, perhaps, better to introduce the author's concept of effective precipitation (49), the rainfall responsible for leaching effects which, in the final analyses, are the reactions associated with the other factors of soil formation in moulding the soil body.

Transpiration.—In evaluating the quantity of moisture available for percolation, the amount of water transpired by plants has to be considered. Transpiration is in a large measure controlled by temperature and humidity. Its effects on the moisture available for percolation is, therefore, indirect.

Wind

As a factor of soil formation, winds are indirectly of importance in connection with the moisture component; they influence the evaporation rate. To a certain extent, however, they act directly. Thus, fine particles of soil material are carried off by the winds, thereby impoverishing the A horizon. In the semideserts, the movement of sand prevents the formation of horizons. Winds are to be reckoned more as a soil destroyer in certain regions than as a soil former.

Biosphere as a Factor of Soil Formation

The biosphere as an active factor of soil formation consists of two main divisions, phytosphere and zoosphere.

Phytosphere

Plants act directly and indirectly as a factor of soil formation. Their direct activity consists of their roots penetrating into the lithosphere, where they act mechanically on the rock and mineral material and serve as channels for drainage and sometime for deposition of suspended material. Roots excrete a number of acid substances of which CO_2 is of considerable moment. These act on the rocks and minerals, bringing into solution certain constituents. At the same time, roots absorb mineral substances in solution and translocate them to the stems and leaves. These metabolic functions, together with the photosynthetic processes, are responsible for the growth of plants.

With the death of plants, the processes of humification and mineralization give rise to organic and inorganic acids and to the release of minerals. In their movement through the soil profile, some minerals are fixed in the exchange complex of the soil, others are leached out and escape with the ground waters, and still others are tied up with the humus complexes and become an integral part of the so-called organo-mineral gels. The manner in which the enumerated reactions take place differs with the climate, thereby influencing the detailed features of the profile constitution. The type of vegetation—grassland or timber—and the physiological functions of the plants and their composition also influence the profile constitution.

The indirect participation of the phytosphere as a factor of soil formation makes itself evident in its effects on the elements of climate. It is well known that forests tend to make the climate milder. Forests cut down the sweep of the winds, thereby regulating to a certain extent the evaporation rate during the summer and the thickness and uniformity of the snow cover during the winter. Because of the snow blanket, the soils in the forests are warmer than in the open country.

Shelter Belts.—In an attempt to study the effect of forests on the soil and on climatic changes, Dokuchaev established strips of forest plantings in the steppe. Records have been kept of the moisture and temperature regime of the soil and air, of the open steppe, of the strips of steppe between the forest strips, and of the forest strips themselves. The results up to 1930 for a period of about 50 years, summarized by Tumin (104), show that even in the arid steppe hydrothermal changes may be brought about with as low as 3 to 4 per cent of the area in forests plantings. Furthermore, the soils in the forest strips were shown to have degraded, with the organic matter content at first having increased and later decreased.

Tumin pointed out that 3 to 4 per cent forest plantings might be sufficient as protection against excessive blowing. To induce more marked ameliorative effects, a larger per cent of the area has to be in forest strips. Only then can one hope to temper the winds sufficiently to take on moisture as they pass the strips of forest and thereby reduce surface evaporation. Tumin proposed a system of forest plantings for best results. On areas of 2500 to 10,000 acres the strips should make up 10 to 12 per cent of the area; on areas from 10,000 to 25,000 acres 8 to 10 per cent of the area is to be in forest strips; and on areas up to 80,000 acres 6 to 8 per cent is sufficient. For a more detailed discussion on the effects of forest plantings on the soil and the methods of laying these out, the original paper of Tumin is to be consulted.

Remezov and Smaragdov (86) discuss the expediency of forest plantings in the steppe region in connection with problems of soil erosion. They point out that an extensive system of forest plantings, covering an entire watershed may reduce the flow of water in rivers. This may imperil the quantity of water available for irrigation, raise havoc with the natural forests adjoining the river banks, reduce the fishing capacity of rivers and ponds and endanger the water supply in wells and municipal waterworks. They also discuss measures of averting the perils enumerated by regulating the seasonal flow of water in the rivers and by constructing dams and spillways.

Long before the inauguration of systematic projects of planting forest strips as a measure of affecting the soil, the planting of trees as windbreaks was a common practice. They are commonplace on American farms in the prairie and plains country. A systematic program of planting forest strips, known in the United States as shelter belts, was started in 1935. The project extended through 6 states, from the Canadian border in North Dakota south to the Texas Panhandle, at a width of 100 miles. A total of 16,105 miles of belts has been planted, the rows varying from 7 to 17 trees wide. A record of the shelter belts and their successful operation in the United States is given by Guthrie (40). An extensive discussion on the effects of the shelter belts on winds, evaporation, and temperature may be found in the papers by Bates (4).

Forests and Precipitation.—Conflicting ideas are in vogue on the effects of forests on precipitation, moisture content of the soil, and ground waters. There is more clarity about the humidity and temperature of the air in forests. Investigations have fairly well established that the temperature of the soil and air is lowered by forests, whereas the humidity is increased.

Matthieu (64) showed that the temperature of the air in forests differs with the type of vegetation. A 10 year record in the region of Nancy, France, has shown that the mean annual temperature in the forest was 8.19°C against 8.65°C in the adjacent open field. According to Nördlinger, as quoted by Glinka, the air temperature in coniferous forests, as compared with open areas, is lower by 1.3°C and in the deciduous forests by 0.9° C.

Ebermayer (26-28) figured that a beech forest produced, on the average, 7057 kgm. of dry matter per hectare and used 2,187,670 kgm. of water, whereas a crop of clover produced on the average 4500 kgm. of dry matter and used 1,395,000 kgm. of water. He also showed that a conifer stand withholds from the soil in its crown 40 to 50 per cent of the rainfall, whereas a deciduous stand withholds 10 to 25 per cent. During the winter the deciduous forests retain more snow, but during the summer they transpire more water than conifers. On the whole, however, the soil under conifers gets less moisture.

According to Ebermayer (27), the moisture evaporated from the soil surface in forests is less than one half of the moisture evaporated from a similar area in the open. The transpiration losses are higher in forests than in the open country and more than offset the gains made by the low surface evaporation in forests. Large amount of water are pumped by the roots from the lower horizons, which, therefore, usually contain less moisture than the upper ones.

Ototzkii (77-79) studied the fluctuations in the level of the ground waters in forests and adjacent cultivated plots and he concluded that the water table is always lower in the forests. This was confirmed later by a number of other investigators. Henry (42), somewhat skeptical of the results of Ototzkii, made a study of this problem in the forests of northeastern France. His findings, however, merely confirmed Ototzkii's conclusions. Pearson (80) in India made a similar study; his results also substantiate the findings of Ototzkii. A summary of this problem may be found in the works of Zon (115) and of Glinka (Ch. 2, 27).

Another aspect of the effect of forests on the moisture relationships is the general belief that forests prevent floods or, at least, are a factor in flood control. Williams (Ch. 3, 72) suggested an explanation on the mitigation of floods by forests, based on the property of soil structure, which is highly developed in the A horizon of forests, immediately below the A_0 layer. This results in a high capacity of non-capillary pore space, which is conducive to effective percolation of water and its gradual seepage to the rivers. In other words, the rush of rainwater to the rivers is retarded and an occasional increase in flow is easily accommodated by the stream channel. In the open cultivated country, the surface horizons are of poor structure, giving rise to capillary pore space which prevents rapid percolation of water. Most of the precipitation, therefore, leaves the soil as surface runoff, carries sediment, rushes in large quantities to the river channels, fills them rapidly, and causes floods. Another benefit of the forest is that vast amounts of water are temporarily arrested in the pore spaces because of the coalescence and swelling of the structural aggregates. The forest litter also takes care of large quantities of water by absorption.

Forests retard erosion which infrequently removes from the soil body its A horizon. In this connection a word of warning must be given concerning the study of the profile in the regions of erosion. Frequently the B or even C horizon outcrops to the surface; in some places where the A horizon is differentiated into A_1 and A_2, the A_1 is eroded. This seems to be the case in the Alabama soils studied by Baver and Scarseth (5). In this region one might expect, as suggested by Marbut (63), an eluviation, or partial washing out, of the finer fractions of the surface layer instead of a subsidence of the fine material to lower horizons.

Another effect of the plant cover as a factor of soil formation is its protective action against the forces of weathering. It is well known that the sod of a virgin soil is the shield which protects it from destruction. Simultaneously, the soil prevents the forces of weathering from acting on the bed rock. The protective action of the plant cover against weathering is very much in evidence in mountainous country where xerophytes cling to the rocks and prevent the washing away of whatever soil has formed. Merrill (p. 202) points out that "in the glaciated regions it is often the case that the striated and polished surfaces of the rocks have been preserved only where protected from the disintegrating action of the sun and atmosphere by a thin layer of turf or moss."

An excellent review on the influence of higher plants on soils is presented by Lundegardh (62). It is, however, more a discussion of the effect of higher plants on soil properties than on the plant as a factor of soil formation.

MICROORGANISMS

The cycle of the mineral substances, which are pumped by the roots from the lower horizons to the plants and then given up again to the surface horizons, is intimately related to the activities of microbes. Many of these are determined by the reciprocal relation of plant life to climate. For instance, the conditions prevailing in the chernozem belt reduce the activities of microbes and are partly responsible for the accumulation of organic matter in these soils. In the northern belt of the podzol zone, the anaerobic conditions and short summers are the factors responsible for the slow decomposition of organic matter, which in turn results in the characteristic formation of peat. Similarly, we can trace the influence of climate on the decomposition activities of microorganisms in other soil belts.

The role of microorganisms as a factor of soil formation has not received the attention it deserves in the light of pedogenesis. The so-called standard texts on soil microbiology show little appreciation of pedologic principles. The subject of microbes as a factor of soil formation is either ignored or poorly presented. Very little is known about the relation of climate to the distribution and differential behavior of microbes in the profile. Unquestionably, each climatic soil zone has its specific microbial activities, a knowledge of which would help to complete the picture of the processes of soil formation. A beginning in this direction has been made by Kostychev (58) and his pupils, Sheloumova, Shulgina, Ryskalchuk and Shvetsova, Korsakova and Lopatina (56), Korsakova and Bylinkina (55), and by others. The first of this series of investigations dealt with the nitrogen problem in the soils of Crimea and the northern podzol region. Subsequent contributions covered other soil zones. Similar investigations have been undertaken by Uspenskii (106) and his associates. Of these, the most interesting are the contributions of Yashnova (114) on nitrification in podzol soils, of Potapov (84) on the distribution of denitrifiers in the genetic horizons and on the mutual relations between Azotobacter and denitrifiers, and of Vinogradova (108) on the depth of penetration of bacteria in the soil. An interesting discussion of the relation of climate to bacterial activities is given by Mishustin (68). Domracheva (24, 25) studied the flora of rendzina soils and the role of microorganisms in the processes of soil formation in general; Nikitina (74) investigated the biodynamic conditions of the various horizons of podzol and peat soils of the Moscow region. Kardo-Sysoeva (50) made a similar investigation on deep chernozems at the Tambov Experiment Station; Kononova (54) studied the vertical distribution of Azotobacter and nitrifying organisms in the soils of Middle Asia; Kholkin (51) investigated the biodynamics of peat soils; Harder (41) contributed to the study of the biodynamics of humus-carbonate soils; Lopatina (61) reported on microbiological characteristics of several mountain soils; Bobko, Bielkin, and Ostshchepkov (9) investigated the process of nitrification in a solonetz-chernozem profile;

Shvetsova (94) investigated the microbiological activities of red soils; Korsakova and Shvetsova (57) studied the microbiological characteristics of chernozem soils; Shturm (91) and Shturm and Simakova (92) studied the distribution of various physiological groups of bacteria in the profile of a number of soils; Raillo (85) investigated the distribution of fungi in the soil profile.

Timonin (101) recorded the number of bacteria, actinomyces, fungi, anaerobic bacteria and fungi, algae, and protozoa on 12 profiles of virgin soils in Manitoba, Canada. It is brought out that algae and protozoa are limited to the A horizon. Bisby, Timonin, and James (8) made a study on the fungi of the profiles reported on by Timonin. Except for the C horizon there was no difference in the fungus flora in A and B horizons. Gray and associates (35-37) studied the flora of a number of podzol profiles in Canada. Newman and Norman (72) followed the evolution of CO_2 at various depths in the profile as an index of microbial activity in two prairie soils and three podzolized soils. Vandecaveye and Moodie (107), reporting on the occurrence of Azotobacter in different rainfall belts of the semiarid region of Washington, stated that "no difference in Azotobacter population was observed between cultivated and virgin non-irrigated soils. It was present dominantly in the irrigated soils in the rainfall belt of less than 10 inches annually, frequently in the non-irrigated soils of the rainfall belt of 15-20 inches, and rarely in the non-irrigated soils of the two belts." An extensive survey on the distribution of Azotobacter in the soils of Russia was made by Shushkina (93). She has examined 1500 soil samples covering most of the zonal and subordinate soil types. Soils subject to the processes of podzolization, solodization, reversion of meadow to chernozem, chestnut brown, brown, and serozem (grayearths) are not conducive to the development of Azotobacter. On the other hand, the processes of sod-meadow, salinization, and marsh formation do not seem to hinder the development of Azotobacter. Caster, Martin, and Buehrer (12) made a study on the microbiological oxidation of ammonia in desert soils with special reference to the threshold pH values for nitrification. Yakubov (113) reported on the microbial flora of the sands and sandy soils of the desert and semidesert regions of Russia. Novogrudskii (76), in a study of the microbiological processes in the soils of the semidesert, has shown that soil microbes cease their activities at hygroscopic moisture. A few fungi and actinomyces can thrive even at 50 to 85 per cent hygroscopic moisture. In the review of Isachenko (45) on microbiological investigations in the U.S.S.R. for the 25 years from 1917 to 1942, very little may be found on the relation of soil microbes to soil formation.

In recent years, a number of papers appeared on the functions of microorganisms in the formation of water-stable aggregates. For a bibliography on the subject and as a typical example of the line of work done, one may consult the papers by Browning and Milam (11) and Peele and Beale (81). In reviewing the published data on the subject, one can not help but note that some confusion exists with reference to the concept of soil structure. Mishustin and Gromyko (68) have shown that the slimy substances credited with the cementing of soil aggregates are readily decomposed chemically and biologically. They are pseudo-stabilizing agents and simply serve as temporary gluing agents. Similar findings are reported by McCalla (65).

A field method for studying the profile flora has been advanced by Kubiena (Ch. 3, 33). As yet, this direct microscopic method has not been tested sufficiently to warrant the optimistic views held by Kubiena; more studies are wanted. In the same category of studies belong those on the microbrial flora in the rhizosphere. There is promise in this method for the pedologist-microbiologist. Thus far this type of microbiologist has not appeared on the horizon of soil science. Those interested in studies of the microflora in the rhizosphere will find the work of Starkey (95) helpful. He used the technic of buried slides in determining the nature of development of microorganisms about plant roots.

Zoosphere

In contrast to the phytosphere, the zoosphere does not always aid in differentiating the horizon of the soil profile. The different animals harboring the soil dig into the soil body, mix the material of the different horizons, and thus disturb the soil profile. Only a few investigations on the role of the zoosphere in soil formation are reported.

The scholarly work of Müller (70) on humus may be cited as an example of the earlier investigations dealing with the distribution of animal life in the soil. A summary, with an extensive bibliography on the subject, may be found in the treatise by Hoffman (44). Among the other investigations on this subject, the work of Thompson (98), Edwards (29), Bornebusch (10), Jacot (46), and Baweja (6) deal with the type of fauna found in cultivated soils, methods of counting these, and other phases pertaining to animal life in soils.

Gilyarov (32) reviews the functions of the fauna in the soil. He enumerates the various species involved and estimates the numbers found. In the temperate regions of Europe, Asia, and America the average number of invertebrates per hectare varies from 12.5 millions to 2 billions.

A list of 34 references is appended. A method of evaluating the soil fauna is given by Grigor'eva (38).

Gilyarov (33, 34) cites data showing that in the dark colored cultivated soils the average number of the mesafauna per square meter is 100; in the sod of these soils the number goes up to 270. In podzolized soils the figures are 37 and 148 respectively. The number of the microfauna in the two soils is: 30 to 40 thousands for the dark colored soils and 4 to 5 thousands in podzolized soils. Table 17 shows that the type of animal life and the numbers in the soil differ from forest to forest, depending on the type of flora and soil conditions.

Table 17

Animal life per square meter in the forests of Denmark

(After Bornebusch)

Animal life	Oak, with a cover of *Mercurialis*		Beech, with a cover of *Melica*		Pine, with a cover of *Hylocomium*	
	Number	Weight	Number	Weight	Number	Weight
		gms.		gms.		gms.
I. Earthworms (Lumbricidae)	122	61.00	93	27.20	18	0.90
II. Herbedora (a total of 2675 in number) 1. Gastropoda	68	5.32	66	3.98	2	0.15
2. Diplopoda	110	4.70	67	1.87	2	0.10
3. Acarina	967	0.06	1919	0.17	7828	0.62
4. Diptera	271	3.10	349	1.03	336	4.31
5. Elateridae	12	0.18	12	0.58	249	3.71
6. All others	1247	1.61	1751	1.72	2046	1.33
III. Carniverous	181	0.84	167	0.51	231	1.10
Total	2978	78.81	4424	37.76	10712	12.22

Worms

Zakharov (Ch. 2, 91, p. 241) points out that in the chernozem belt, the steppe rodents and earthworms are the most active representatives of the zoosphere. The small worms penetrate the soil to a depth not more than 1 to 1.5 m.; the large ones go deeper. Kassatkin and Krasyuk (Ch. 2, 34, p. 63) note that earthworms generally do not penetrate the soil beyond a depth of 2 m. Vysotskii (109) observed that the passageways of the large *Allolobophora marinpoliensis* may be found in the subsoil as deep as 8 m. He points out that the large roots of plants follow the abandoned tunnel borings of the rodents, worms, and insects. Over an area of 1 sq. m. to a depth of 1 m. he counted 525 easily discernible burrows of earthworms. A similar observation on the relation of root penetration to borings of animals in the soil was made by Tkachenko (102).

In chernozem soils earthworms are very active. They are considered as a factor in the formation of the typical granular structure of these soils (39 a). In the podzol soils, dark gray channels of earthworms may be noted on the light bleached background of the A_2 horizon. The color is due to the organic matter which the earthworms bring down from the humus accumulative horizon. Tamm (97) reports the absence of earthworms in the podzols of northern Sweden. Salisbury (87) points out that "earthworms are only frequent in soils where the subsoil at least is well supplied with $CaCO_3$." On the heavily limed experimental plots at the New Jersey Experiment Station, the author observed passageways of large earthworms lined with dolomitic limestone (added to neutralize soil acidity) mixed with organic matter at a depth of 30 inches. The walls of these holes were somewhat cemented and rigid.

It is known that earthworms are very active in decomposing forest litter. About 250 kgm. of leaves per hectare, or 10 per cent of the yearly growth, are worked over by the earthworms. Darwin (15) calls attention to the fact that in certain parts of England earthworms bring to the surface every year, as excreta, more than 10 tons per acre of fine dry mould, "so that the whole superficial bed of vegetable mould passes through their bodies in the course of a few years." Darwin collected and weighed the excretions deposited by earthworms on a small area during a given time interval. He calculated that the rate of accumulation of the excreted material would amount to one inch in five years. It is of interest that the earthworms do their work at night, dragging down into their burrows leaves and grass from the surface and thereby mixing the material of the horizons. Another point to be noted is that the excrements of earthworms contain more lime than the surrounding soil. Their channels serve as routes for percolation of water and for aeration.

According to Henry (42) each worm consumes 0.61 grams of dry matter per month. Tyurin (105, p. 43) estimates that "with 30 worms per square meter about 1000 kgms. of organic matter may be worked over in 6 months. This amounts to ¼-⅕ of the annual forest floor receipts. In soils with a larger worm population, all of the organic material reaching the surface may be consumed. Under hardwoods or even mixed forests, the forest floor does not accumulate much debris and the surface soil is mellow (mull). In the coniferous forests, where the earthworm activities are subdued, a mat of forest floor gives rise to raw humus."

According to Dimo's (21) report on the earthworms in the soils of vertical zonation in Central Asia, the desert soils (not more than 100 mm. precipitation) harbor no earthworms. In the light colored soils of the desert steppe (500 meters above sea level, with 250 to 500 mm. precipitation), earthworms are found in the surface soil in the spring. As the dry season advances, they dig in deeper into the soil profile, 30 to 90 cm. and even deeper. There they hibernate until the fall rains come. From then on, until next summer, they are active. In the chestnut brown soils (at a still higher altitude and more abundant precipitation), the earthworms are still more active. In the higher altitudes, in the pine forest zone, no earthworms could be found. Neither have earthworms been noted in the alpine and subalpine regions. This observation does not necessarily mean that no earthworms are present in all regions with a similar climate. Dimo cites data from Darwin and others on the presence of earthworms in the subarctic region. According to Seton (88), the earthworm is non-existent in the arid region between the Rocky Mountains and the immediate Pacific Coast, from Manitoba to Texas.

Dimo (20) describes the types of worms, the diameter of the holes they make, the passageways, the type of excreta, the number of worms (he digs around a column of 1 cubic meter and then dissects it inch by inch and obtains the information desired), the strength of the walls of the worm holes, and the distribution of the worms in the profile. In the spring, most of the earthworms are concentrated in the first 5 cm. and are not present beyond the 18 cm. depth. From 610,000 to 740,000 worms per hectare have been counted. The worms are most active at 60-70 per cent of the moisture holding capacity of the soil. In alfalfa sods, as many as 14,780,000 holes per hectare have been counted in the spring. In the non-saline soils of the semidesert, Dimo counted 375,000 earthworms. They disappear whenever the salt concentration reaches the 0.5 to 1.0 per cent mark. The author observed a tremendous increase in earthworms when a podzolic soil in New Jersey was heavily limed, raising the pH from 5.6 to 7.1.

Ants and Termites

Ants penetrate the soil and subsoil, carry material from lower to higher levels, build galleries and underground passageways, throw out a great deal of material to the surface, and frequently form ant hills and mounds. Shaler (89, p. 278) calculated that over a certain field in Cambridge, Massachusetts, the ants make an average transfer of soil material from below to the surface sufficient to form each year a layer of at least a fifth of an inch over the entire four acres under observation. He pointed out:

. . . in general it may be said that the several species of ants dwell only where the soil is of tolerable depth and fertility and where it is at the same time of a somewhat sandy nature. They avoid the tough clay because it holds so much water as to menace the growing of a colony.

One of the most curious effects arising from the interference of the ants with the original conditions of the soil consists in the separation of the finer detritis from the coarse mineral elements of the detrited layer. I long ago had the occasion to observe that in certain parts of New England, where the sandy soils had not for a long time been exposed to the plow or agents of tillage, certain fields were covered to the depth of some inches by a fine sand without pebbles larger than the head of a pin, while the deeper parts of the section, say below the level of a foot in depth, were for a foot or so further down mainly composed of pebbles of various sizes with little finer material among them. This distribution of materials was not to be explained by the supposition that the original deposition led to the peculiar arrangement. It was easy to see that the ancient order of the deposits must have been distributed by tillage, but it was clearly accounted for by the action of the ants.

Shaler further (p. 277) mentions an interesting species of social ants, the *Myrmica barbata* of Texas, commonly known as the "agricultural ant." It has "the remarkable habit of clearing away the natural vegetation, or at least the slight annual undergrowth, from a bit of ground near its habitation. On this surface it plants particular species which afford nutritious grains. If the conclusions of the observers are correct, this creature is the solitary animal besides man which has invented any kind of agriculture."

Merrill (Ch. 4, 49, p. 391) cites the observations of Branner on a species of ants in the Amazon valley locally known as *saubas* or *sauvas*. "The species excavate and build galleries which are frequently from 50 to 100 feet long, from 10 to 20 feet across, and from 1 to 4 feet high, and contain tons of earth."

The white ants or termites, like the true ants, burrow extensive channels in the ground and build huge nests upon the surface. Such nests vary in size from 1 to 12 feet in height and from 1 to 10 feet in diameter. Especialy large are the termite nests in the tropical forests, where termites live primarily in earthy structures or in the trunks of trees.

Zakharov (Ch. 2, 91, p. 242) cites the presence in Turkestan of other species of termites which are subterranean dwellers. Their nests and tunnels go down deep to the moist layers. In the zone of the gray soils in the semidesert and arid regions, these termites are the most active burrowing animals. They bring to the surface, from the lower horizons and subsoil, materials rich in soluble salts. As a result of this, the small ant hills, 5 to 15 cm. in height and about 4.5 sq. m. in area, are salinized and contain a prevailing alkali soil flora.

Hilgard (Ch. 2, 30, p. 160) points out, "The work of ants is in some regions on so large a scale as to attract the attention of the most casual observer. Especially is this the case in portions of the arid regions, from Texas to Montana, where at times large areas are so thickly studded with hills from three to twelve feet in diameter and one to two feet high, that it is difficult to pass without being attacked by the insects. The mounds studding a large portion of the prairie country of Louisiana, although not inhabited at present, seem to be due to the work of ants."

Dimo (18) studied the activities of termites in the arid regions of Turkestan. They form hills as large as 4.4 m. in area and 5 to 15 cm. high. Their passageways are filled with material from various depths and penetrate to the ground waters. In a later publication, Dimo (21) reported on the role of *Hemilepistus* (Percellio) in the formation of soils in the desert. The number of adult specimens in typical cases is on the order of 1,260,000 to 1,440,000 per hectare during the summer. They live predominantly in takyr soils, preferring the salinized gypsum bearing sites. They do not thrive in non-salinized soils. As many as 630,000 to 720,000 holes and passageways per hectare, extending to a depth of 0.8 to 1.0 meter, have been counted. During the period of highest activity—in midsummer—as much as 5 to 6 tons of earth is being brought to the surface.

Adamson (1) discussed the role of termites in humus formation under humid conditions of tropical Trinidad. These termites also increase the lime content of soils. The influence of ants upon soil reaction is discussed by Grinfeld (39). He shows that ant hills have a higher pH than the soil surrounding them.

Rodents

In the treeless arid regions, a large number of vertebrates—birds, mammals, and reptiles—are forced to choose the soil as their habitation. All of them contribute to the processes of soil formation. Among them, the rodents are by far the most active soil disturbers. Next to the earthworms, these animals have been studied most. The Russian term "crotovina," which has been adopted as a pedological term in most of the western European languages, literally means the nest of a "krot," the Russian name for a mole.

In the United States, according to Shaler, "the larger part of the burrowing animals belong to the moles and rodents or gnawing animals." The moles, as a rule, are not deeply burrowing creatures. They live mostly below the surface of the plant roots, forming a network of ridges which mark the paths they follow. The majority of the rodent family dwell underground, where they make deep burrows with a complicated system of tunnels and passageways. Hilgard (Ch. 2, 30, p. 160) cites the claim of Seton that "the pocket gophers (*Tomomys*) in a great degree replace the activity of the earthworms in the arid regions where they together with the voles (commonly known there as field mice) exist in great numbers."

Besides the gophers we find prairie dogs, ground squirrels, badgers, and other genera contributing their share in distributing the soil profile. No studies, to the best knowledge of the author, have been made in the United States on the relation of these animals to the soil profile. In the chernozem belt of soils in European Russia, the most important gnawing animals associated with crotovinas are the ground squirrel (*Epermophillus guttatus*) and the blind mole rat (*Spalax typhlus*).

In the humid regions, field mice are of considerable interest with respect to their work in the soil. Shaler (89, p. 284) points out the following: "In certain parts of the country, notably in regions where weasels and other small predaceous mammals are absent or rare, the species of field mice exist in amazing plenty. Thus, on the island of Marthas Vineyard, Massachusetts, the wild mice are so abundant that brushwood areas, often acres in extent, are completely honeycombed by their burrows, and many species of plants whose bark affords nutritious food in winter are almost extirpated by their attacks." None of the rodents in the humid regions, however, can compare in their activity with those in the arid regions, where the crotovinas have been investigated more extensively. Norton and Smith (75) cite examples of the activity of burrowing animals in southern Illinois.

Dimo (21) gives interesting data on the mice population in the soils of the solonetz-solonchak complex. Mice form mounds 10 to 15 cm. high, 1 to 2 meters wide, occupying at times as much as 40 per cent of the area. On the average, the number of mice per hectare was 60,000 with 31,264 passageway openings. In the fall, 0.07 per cent of the area was covered with these openings, and the material thrown out amounted to 24 tons per hectare. For the entire year, 50 tons of material was thrown out. Tables are given showing an increase in salt content of the surface soil and even throughout the profile wherever mice have been active.

According to Kossovich (Ch. 2, 40, p. 176), the first one to describe crotovinas was Kupriyanov in 1854. Sukachev (96) claimed that it was Levakovskii who first called attention to the crotovinas and their significance. He considered them as abandoned passageways and nests of rodents filled in with soil material. This view was contested by other observers who claimed that crotovinas were tracks of decayed roots. They cited this as evidence in support of a theory that the steppe was forested at some prehistorical period. Dokuchaev (23) refuted the theory of the root origin of crotovinas. He pointed out that the presence of crotovinas in the southern limits of the forest steppe as evidence that in prehistoric times the treeless steppe extended further north.

Sukachev (96) made an exhaustive study of crotovinas. In his work, he reviewed the controversy on the origin of crotovinas. He took up the arguments of Taliev who, as an exponent of the root origin of crotovinas, criticized Dokuchaev's view on the animal origin of crotovinas. Sukachev presented extensive evidence in support of the theory of the animal origin of crotovinas. His descriptions of crotovinas, which were very thorough, have been quoted by the leading pedologists.

PLATE 17
Crotovinas in a chernozem profile from Ufa
(After Kassatkin)

He classified crotovinas into the following four main types:

1. *Continuous.* These are made up of a more or less homogenous material and appear in the soil cut as continuous circles or ellipses of various shades of color. In the humus horizons of the chernozem, they show up as light spots on a dark background; in the subsoil, as dark spots on a light background. In loess underlain by sands, the crotovinas are noted for their color. These crotovinas that are found in the humus layers are filled with a dark colored material, which makes recognition difficult but does not obscure the characteristic core-like structure evident upon a close examination.

2. *Edged-off Crotovinas.*—The entire crotovina consists of two cylinders, one fitting within the other. In cross-section, it represents a somewhat circular outline with a more or less heavily edged rim which is either darker or lighter—usually darker—than the inner section of the crotovina. In loess material the rim is thin, not thicker than I cm., and continuous, whereas in other materials it is from 2 to 5 cm. thick and stratified. Generally, the rim is more compact and harder than the surrounding soil

material or the material within the cylindrical crotovina. In some cases the rim is rich in lime, which gives it a hard consistency. Some crotovinas of this type are not edged off with a complete rim; only a crescent-shaped rim may be noted.

3. *Concentric or Eccentric Stratified Crotovinas.*—On a cross-sectional cut, this type of crotovina appears in the form of concentric circles or ellipses with concentric striations in the ground mass. These are encountered in the subsoil only. Crotovinas of this type are compact, as distinguished from the two preceding types, which are loose. They are quite as compact as the surrounding material. Their color does not differ much from the color of the surrounding soil.

In reality there are no eccentric forms of crotovinas; they only appear as such whenever the soil cut is not exactly perpendicular to the long axis of the crotovina. This also explains the elliptic and oval-shaped forms of crotovinas.

4. *Complex Crotovinas.*—This type of crotovina is a product of the first two types mentioned. A cross-section reveals a complex form, with one kind of crotovina intersecting other kinds. Infrequently a thinner crotovina is found within a thicker one, in which case it resembles the edged type.

On a level topography, a soil profile shows not only transverse cuts of crotovinas but also longitudinal cuts along the long axis. If the soil profile is exposed on a rolling topography, following the angle of the dip, both transverse and longitudinal forms will be found, with the longitudinal predominating. However, if the soil cut is made perpendicular to the angle of the dip, only transverse forms will be found.

Distribution and Size of Crotovinas.—Sukachev estimated the distribution of crotovinas in the respective horizons of the profile by measuring their areas. He found most of the crotovinas at a depth of 1 to 1.5 m. in the B and C horizons. Infrequently, however, they were found as deep as 3 or 4 m. below the surface and even at depths of 5 and 7.5 m. Vysotskii considered such deep crotovinas as indications of buried soils. While on the soil trip with the Second International Congress of Soil Science, the writer examined a number of crotovinas in a buried soil near Kharkov, Ukraine, at a depth 5 to 6 meters below the surface of the overlying present soil. The crotovinas were located in the B horizon.

The diameter of crotovinas varies within narrow limits. Sukachev made measurements on 192 crotovinas. The results are summarized in table 18. The largest number of crotovinas have a diameter of 8 cm. and the general average is about 7.5 cm. In sandy parent material, the crotovinas are large, and in loess and limestone, somewhat smaller. Sukachev described crotovinas going down vertically to a depth of 2.4 meters and then turning at a sharp angle and running horizontally. The horizontal passageways are usually larger than the vertical ones. Frequently, one could find the branching type of crotovinas in which the angles are not sharp and the diameter of the various branches is the same. This uniformity in diameter is another bit of evidence against the "root origin" theory, which would necessarily postulate a narrowing of the diameter with increase in depth. Sukachev also pointed out that roots of trees very seldom extend to the depth of the crotovinas.

Table 18
Diameter of crotovinas
(After Sukachev)

Region	4 cm.	5 cm.	6 cm.	7 cm.	8 cm.	9 cm.	10 cm.	11 cm.	12 cm.
Kursk		5	16	33	43	23	˙10	4	2
Voronezh	1	2	5	9	8	12	3	1	1
Don				2	4	2			
Kharkov					6				
Total	1	7	21	44	61	37	13	5	3

*The diameter has been measured on cuts made perpendicular to the long axis of the crotovinas.

According to Sukachev the diameters of the channels and nests of the several species of burrowing animals responsible for the formation of crotovinas are as follows: Woodchuck (*Arctomys Bobac*): channels—18 to 21 cm.,

$$nest \frac{22\text{-}31}{18\text{-}22} cm;**$$

ground squirrel (*Spermophyllus guttatus*): channel—4 to 7 cm.,

$$nest \frac{18\text{-}22}{13\text{-}18} cm;$$

blind mole rat of Europe (*Spalax-typhlus*): channel—8 to 11 cm.,

$$nest \frac{20\text{-}28}{18\text{-}24} cm;$$

**The numerator represents the limits of the large diameter; the denominator, the small diameter.

hamster (*Cricetus frumentarius*) : channel 8—12 cm., nest—similar to that of the mole. It is apparent that most of the crotovinas are made by the mole rat, ground squirrel, and hamster.

Not much is known about the age of crotovinas, and no reliable method has yet been offered for its determination. On cuts made in a "kurgan"—a mound in the steppe either used as a burial ground for the chiefs or prepared by the invading Asiatic hordes as orientation points in their travels—Sukachev found just as many crotovinas as he found in cuts made on natural soils in the neighborhood. He points out this fact as an argument against the theory that crotovinas are of ancient origin, but he does not offer any data as to the possible age of the crotovinas or the relative age of the various types. It is a problem still awaiting solution.

References

1. Adamson, A. M. 1943 Termites and the fertility of the soil. *Trop. Agr.* 20:107-112.

2. Akimtzev, V. V. 1932 Historical soils of the Kamenetz-Podolsk fortress. *Proc. and Papers Second Inter. Cong. Soil Sci.* 5: 132-140.

3. Albright, W. D. and Stoker, J. G. 1944 Topography and minimum temperatures. *Sci. Agr.* (Canada) 25, No. 3: 146-155.

4. Bates, C. G. 1945 Shelterbelt influences: I, *Jour. of Forest.* 43: 88-92; II; 176-196.

5. Baver, L. D. and Scarseth, G. D. 1931 Subtropical weathering in Alabama as evidenced in the Susquehanna fine sandy profile. *Soil Research* (Inter. Soc. Soil Sci.) 2:288-307.

6. Baweja, K. D. 1937 The calculation of soil population figures. *Jour. Anim. Ecology* 6 (2) : 366-367.

7. Beyers, H. G., Kellogg, Ch. F., Anderson, M. S., and Thorp, J. 1938 Formation of soil. *Soils and Men*: Yearbook of Agr., U. S. Department of Agriculture, pp. 948-978.

8. Bisby, G. R., Timonin, M. I., and James N. 1935 Fungi isolated from soil profiles in Manitoba. *Canad. Jour. Res.*, C. 13: 47-65.

9. Bobko, E. W., Bielkin, N. J. and Ostshchepkov, N. 1928 Nitrification in a solonetz-chernozem soil complex. *Trudy Sibir. Inst. Sel'shokhoz.* i Lesovod., *X.* Omsk.

10. Bornebusch, C. H. 1930 The fauna of forest soils. Det Forstlige Forsogsvaesen I Danmark 11 (1), pp. 224: see also Das Tierleben der Waldboden. *Forstwiss Centralbl.* 54: 266 (1932).

11. Browning, G. and Milam, F. 1944 Effect of different types of organic matter and lime on soil aggregation. *Soil Sci.* 57: 91-107.

12. Caster, A. B., Martin, W. P., and Buehrer, T. F. 1942 The microbiological oxidation of ammonia in desert soils. I. Threshold pH values for nitrification. Ariz. Agr. Expt. Sta. Tech. Bul. 96, 475-510.

13. Chandler, R. F. 1942 The time required for podzol profile formation as evidenced by the Mendenhall glacial deposits, near Juneau, Alaska. *Proc. Soil Sci. Soc. Amer.* 7: 454-459.

14. Crowther, E. M. 1930 The relationship of climate and geological factors to the composition of soil clay and the distribution of soil types. *Proc. Roy. Soc.*, B. 107: 1-30.

15. Darwin, Charles. 1881 Earthworms and vegetable mould. *Trans. Geol. Soc.* (1837) v. 5: 505; or: The formation of Vegetable Mould Through the Action of Worms, 1-326. London (1881).

16. Davis, R. O. E. 1913 Economic waste from soil erosion. Yearbook of Agriculture. U. S. Dept. of Agriculture, p. 213.

17. Dimo, N. A. 1903 Observations on ants (pedozoological notes). Paper delivered at the *Saratov. Obshch. Estestvoisp.* 4, No. 2, 1-17.

18. Dimo, N. A. 1916 The role and significance of termites in the life of the soil in Turkestan (Russia). *Russkii Pochvoved* 2: 1-38.

19. Dimo, N. A. 1938 Earthworms in the soils of Middle Asia. *Pedology* (U.S.S.R.) No. 4: 494-526.

20. Dimo, N. A. 1941 Activity of animals in soils of the Alazan Valley, Caucasus. *Pedology* U.S.S.R.) No. 6: 12-20.

21. Dimo, N. A. 1945 Hemilepistus and their role in soil formation in the desert. *Pedology* (U.S.S.R.) No. 2: 115-121.

22. Dokuchaev, V. V. 1883 Russkii Chernozem (Russian Chernozem). St. Petersburg.

23. Dokuchaev, V. V. 1889 On the theory of natural zones (Russian). St. Petersburg.

24. Domracheva, E. A. 1927 On the microbiological characteristics of the rendzina soils in the Leningrad government. *Nauch.-Agron. zhur.* 4, No.11: 762-767.

25. Domracheva, E. A. 1930 The role of microorganisms in the processes of soil formation. *Pedology* (U.S.S.R.) No. 5: 142-160.

26. Ebermayer, E. 1889 Einfluss des Waldes und der Bestanedsdichte auf die Bodenfeuchtigkeit und auf die Sickerwassermenge. *Forst. u. Jagad-ztg.* n. s. 65: 1-13.

27. Ebermayer, E.   1897   Untersuchungs-Ergebnisse über die Menge und Verteilung der Niederschlage in den Wäldern.   *Forstlichna-turwissenschaft Ztschr.* 6: 283-291.

28. Ebermayer, E.   900   Einfluss der Wälder auf die Bodenfeuchtig-keit, auf das Sickerwasser, auf das Grundwasser, und die Ergie-bigkeit der Quellen.   Stuttgart.

29. Edwards, E.   1929   A survey of the insect and other invertebrate fauna in permanent pasture and other land of certain soil types at Aberzstwyth.   *Ann. Appl. Biol.* 16: 299-323.

30. Ellis, J. H. and Shafer, W. H.   1940-1943   Soil Survey of South-Western Canada, Soil Rpt. No. 3, pp. 1-104; Soil Survey of South-Central Manitoba, Soil Rpt. No. 4, pp. 1-146. Manitoba Soil Survey, Univ. of Manitoba.

31. Engeln, von O. D.   1942   Geomorpholgy.   The Macmillan Co., New York.

32. Gilyarov, M. S.   1939   The soil fauna and the life of the soil. *Pedology* (U.S.S.R.) No. 6: 3-15.

33. Gilyarov, M. S.   1941   Methods of quantitative enumeration of the soil fauna.   *Pedology* (U.S.S.R.) No. 4: 48-77; bibliography of 77 titles.

34. Gilyarov, M. S.   1942   A comparative study of the animal popula-tion in the dark colored and podzolic soils.   *Pedology* (U.S.S.R.) No. 9-10: 3-15.

35. Gray, P. H. H.   1935   A microbiological study of podzol soil pro-files: 3.. Bacteria found in separate horizons.   *Canad. Jour. Res.* C, 13: 256-262.

36. Gray, P. H. H. and McMaster, N. B.   1933   A microbiological study of podzol soil profiles.   *Canad. Jour. Res.* C, 8: 375-378.

37. Gray, P. H. H. and Taylor, C. B.   1935   A microbiological study of podzol profiles.   *Canad. Jour. Res.* C, 13: 251-255.

38. Grigorieva, T. G.   1938   On the methods of evaluating the soil fauna (Russian). *Zashchita Rastenii* 17: 97-110.

39. Grinfeld, E. K.   1941 Influence of ants upon soil reaction. *Zool. Zhur.* (U.S.S.R.) 20, No. 1, p. 100.

39a. Gur'yanova, O. Z.   1940   The influence of earthworms and organic manures on the structure of chernozem.   *Pedology* (U.S.S.R.) No. 4: 99-107.

40. Guthrie, J. D.   1942   Trees, peoples, and foresters.   *Jour. of Forest.* 40: 477-480.

41. Harder, L.   1930   Investigations on the biodynamics of humus-carbonate soils.   *Trudy Otdela Sel'skokhoz. Mikrobiol.* 4: 119-132.

42. Henry, E. 1903 The forests in the plains and the ground waters. *Pochvovedenie* (Pedology) 5: 1-30; see also Les sols forestiers (1908) Paris.

43. Hirth, P . 1926 Die Isonotiden. *Ref. Petterm. Mitt.* 72: 145-149.

44. Hoffman, R. W. 1931 Die Tiere: Leben und Wirken der für den Boden wichtigen Tiere. Blanck's *"Handbuch der Bodenlehre,"* v. 7: 381-437.

45. Isachenko, B. L. 1942 Microbiology in the U.S.S.R. for 25 years, 1917-1942. *Mikrobiologiya* (U.S.S.R.) v. II, No. 506, I-XVI.

46. Jacot, A. P. 1937 Soil structure and soil biology. *Ecology* 17: 359-379. References to his earlier contribution are listed in bibliography.

47. Jenny, H. 1929 Klima und Klimabodentypen in Europa und in den Vereiningten Staaten. *Soil Research* (Int. Soc. Soil Sci.), I: 139-189. See also Missouri Agr. Expt. Sta. Res. Bul. (1930) No. 152.

48. Jenny, H. F. 1941 Factors of Soil Formation. McGraw Hill and Co., New York.

49. Joffe, J. S. 1932-1940 Lysimeter studies. I, *Soil Sci.* 34: 123-143. II, *Soil Sci.* 35: 239-257. III, *Soil Sci.* 35: 401-411. IV, *Soil Sci.* 50: 57-63. V, *Proc. Soil Sci. Soc. Amer.* 5: 187-190.

50. Kardo-Sysoeva, E. K. 1938 The biodynamics of a deep chernozem at the Tambov Agr. Exp. Sta. *Trudy Otdela Sel'skokhoz. Mikrobiol.* 3: 95-102.

51. Kholkin, I. S. 1928 Investigations on the biodynamics of peat soils. *Trudy Otdela Sel'skokhoz. Mikrobiol.* 3: 131-152; see also v. 4 (1930): 83-90.

52. Kincer, J. B. 1922 Precipitation and humidity. Atlas Amer. Agr. Pt. II. Climate, Sec. A. Advance Sheets no. 5, U. S. D. A.

53. Kiryanova, E. S. 1936 The vertical and horizontal distribution of invertebrates in the soils around Tashkent. *Trudy Zool. Inst. Akad. Nauk* (U.S.S.R.) v. III (Quoted from Grigorieva).

54. Kononova, M. M. 1930 The vertical distribution of Azotobacter and nitrifying organisms in the soils around Tashkent. *Trudy Sredne-Aziat. Opyt. Issledovat. Inst. Vodnogo Khozyaistva.* Bul. 7: 53-67.

55. Korsakova, M., and Bylinkina, V. 1926 Microbiological characteristics of soils in the podzol zone. I. Nitrogen fixation. *Trudy Otdela Sel'skokhoz. Mikrobiol.* I: 47-72.

56. Korsakova, M., and Lopatina, G. 1926 Microbiological characteristics of soils in the podzol zone. II. The energy of microbiolog-

ical activity in the soil. *Trudy Otdela Sel'skokhoz. Mikrobiol.* I: 73-84; see also v. 2. (1927): 37-64.

57. Korsakova, M., and Shvetsova, O. 1927 The microbiological characteristics of the soils in the chernozem zone. *Trudy Otdela Sel'skokhoz. Mikrobiol.* 2: 65-76.

58. Kostychev, S., Sheloumova, A., and Shulgina, O. 1926 Microbiological characteristics of southern soils. *Trudy Otdela Sel'-skokhoz. Mikrobiol.* I: 5-45.

59. Lang, R. 1915 Versuch einer exakten Klassifikation der Böden in Klimatischer u. geologischer Hinsicht. *Inter. Mitt. fur Bodenkunde* 5: 312-346.

60. Lang, R. 1920 Verwitterung und Bodenbildung als Einführung in die Bodenkunde. Stutgart.

61. Lopatina, G. 1930 The microbiological characteristics of several mountain soils. *Trudy Otdela Sel'skokhoz. Mikrobiol.* 4: 149-162.

62. Lundegardh, H. 1925 Klima und Boden in ihrer Wirkung auf das Pflanzenleben. G. Fischer. Jena.

63. Marbut, C. F. 1928 Lectures on soil genesis and classifications before graduate school of the United States Department of Agriculture. Quoted from Baver and Scarseth (5).

64. Matthieu, A. 1878 Meteorologie comparee agricole et forestiére. Paris.

65. McCalla, T. M. 1945 Influence of microorganisms and some organic substances on soil structure. *Soil Sci.* 59: 287-297.

66. Meyer, A. 1926 Uber einige Zusammenhänge zwischen Klima und Boden in Europa. *Chemie der Erde* 2: 209-347.

67. Meyer, A. F. 1942 Evaporation from lakes and reservoirs. St. Paul, Minn. Resources Committee, pp. III+56.

68. Mishustin, B. 1926 Adaptation of bacteria to the prevailing soil temperature. *Centralbl. Bakt.* 2 Abt. 66: 328-344. See also *Pedology* (U.S.S.R.) (1925) No. 1-2: 43-67.

70. Müller, P. E. 1887 Studien über die natürlichen Humusformen. Berlin. (A typewritten English translation available in the private library of the author: J. S. J.).

71. Neustruev, S. S. 1927 Genesis of soils. Russian Pedological Investigations III. Academy of Science of the U. S. S. R. 1-98. (In English).

72. Newman, A. S. and Norman, A. G. 1941 The activity of the microflora in various horizons of several soil types. *Proc. Soil Sci. Soc. Amer.* 6: 187-194.

73. Newman, A. S. and Norman, A. G. 1943 The activity of sub-surface soil population. *Soil Sci.* 55: 377-391.

74. Nikitina, E. A. 1928 Investigations on the biodynamics of various genetic horizons of podzol and peat soils in the Moscow government. *Trudy Otleda Sel'skokhoz. Mikrobiol.* 3: 115-130.

75. Norton, E. A., and Smith, R. S. 1930 The influence of topography on soil profile character. *Jour. Amer. Soc. Agron.* 22: 251-262.

76. Novogrudskii, D. M. 1946 Microbiological processes in semi-desert soils: I. Soil microbes and hygroscopic moisture. *Mikrobiologiya* (U.S.S.R.) 15 (3): 177-186.

77. Ototzkii, P. 1896 Hydrological excursion in 1895 in the steppe forests. In Trudy Imper. Vol'nogo Obshchest. no. 5. This report has been published in French; Annales de la Sci. Agron. Franc. et Etrang. Par L'Grandeau, Tom III, 1897. Translated into German and published in Zeitschrift für Gewässerkunde (1898, no. 4 and 5).

78. Ototzkii, P. 1899 On the influence of forests on the ground waters. *Pochvovedenie* (Pedology) 1: 101-116.

79. Ototzkii, P. 1905 I. Ground waters, their origin, behavior, and distribution. II. Ground waters, and forests, primarily in the valleys of the temperate latitude. Trudy Opyt. Lesnichestva. See also *Pochvovedenie* (Pedology), No. 3 (1915), nos. 3-4 (1916).

80. Pearson, R. S. 1907 The level of subsoil waters with regard to forest. *Indian Forester* 33: 57-69.

81. Peele, T. C., and Beale, O. W. 1941 Effect of runoff on erosion of improved aggregation resulting from the stimulation of microbial activity. *Proc. Soil Sci. Soc. Amer.* 6: 176-182.

82. Penk, A. 1910 Versuch eines Klimaklassifikation auf physiogeographischer Grundlage. Sitzber. Preuss. Akad. Wiss. physik. math. Klasse. Berlin, 236.

83. Polynov, B. B. 1930 Das Muttergestein als Faktor der Bodenbildung und als Kriterium für die Bodenklassifikation. *Soil Research* (Int. Soc. Soil Sci.) 2: 165-177.

84. Potapov, N. G. 1930 On the distribution of denitrifiers in the genetic horizons. *Trudy Nauch. Inst. po Udobreniyam,* no. 76: 92-96, 97-111.

85. Raillo, A. I. 1928 Contribution to the study of soil fungi. Bul. Otdela Zemled. GIKA, no. 6.

86. Remezev, N. P., and Smaragdov, D. G. 1943 The complex problems involved in forest plantings in the steppe. *Pedology* (U.S.S.R.), No. 3: 34-40.

87. Salisbury, E. J. 1935 Soil structure in relation to vegetation. *Sci. Progress* 29 : 409-425.

88. Seton, E. T. 1904 The master plowman of the world. *Century Magaz.* 68 : 300-308.

89. Shaler, N. S. 1891 The origin and nature of soils. U. S. Geol. Survey 12th Ann. Rpt. 1890-1891 (pt. 1) : 213-345.

90. Shires, L. B. 1939 The effect of irrigation and cropping on desert soils. New Mexico Station Bul. 263, p. 39.

91. Shturm, L. 1928 On the distribution of various physiological groups of bacteria in the upper and deeper lawers of several soils. *Trudy Otdela Sel'skokhoz. Mikrobiol.* 3 : 189-202.

92. Shturm, L., and Simakova, T. 1928 The distribution of a number of physiological groups of bacteria in the genetic horizons of several soils of the Black Sea coast in Transcaucasia. Trudy *Mikrobiol.* 3 : 171-189. See also v. 4, no. 3 (1931) : 11-28.

93. Shushkina, N. N. 1942. The regularity in the distribution of Azotobacter in the soils of U. S. S. R. *Pedology* (U.S.S.R.) No. 9-10 : 25-35.

94. Shvetsova, O. 1930 On the microbiological characteristics of several soils of the Black Sea coast in Transcaucasia. *Trudy Otdela Sel'skokhoz. Mikrobiol.* 4 : 133-148. (German summary : 279-300).

95. Starkey, R. L. 1938 Some influences on the development of higher plants upon the microorganisms in the soil VI. Microscopic examination of the rhizosphere. *Soil Sci.* 45 : 207-249.

96. Sukachev, V. N. 1902 On the problem of crotovinas. *Pochvovedenia* (Pedology) 4 : 397-423.

97. Tamm, O. 1920 Soil studies in the coniferous forest of N. Sweden. *Meddel. Sta. Skogsförsöksanst.* 17 : 49-300.

98. Thompson, M. 1924. The soil population; an investigation of the biology of the soil of certain districts of Aberystwyth. *Ann. Appl. Biol.* 11 : 349-394.

99. Thorntwaite, C. W. and Holzman, B. 1942 Measurement of evaporation from land and water surfaces. Tech. Bul. No. 817, U. S. Dept. of Agr., pp. 43.

100. Thorp, James 1931 The effect of vegetation and climate upon soil profiles in northern and northwestern Wyoming. *Soil Sci.* 32 : 283-301.

101. Timonin, M. I. 1935 The microorganisms in profiles of certain virgin soils in Manitoba. *Canad. Jour. Res.* 13 : 32-45.

102. Tkachenko, M. E. 1908 On the role of forests in soil formation. *Izves. Lesnogo Inst.* 18: 1-114.

103. Transeau, E. N. 1905 Forest centers of eastern America. *Amer. Naturalist* 39: 875-889.

104. Tumin, G. M. 1930 The influence of forest strips on the soils of Kamennaya Steppe. Kamenno-Stepnaya Opyt. Stan. imeni Dokuchaeva (Lenin Acad. Agr. Sci.), Voronezh, pp. 1-40.

105. Tyurin, I. V. 1937 Organicheskoe veshchestvo pochv (Soil Organic Matter) Selkhozgiz. Leningrad.

106. Uspenskii, E. E. 1930 The fundamental trends in the work of the microbiological section of the Scientific Inst. for Fertilizers. *Trudy Nauch. Inst. po Udobreniyam,* no. 76: 3-13.

107. Vandecaveye, S. C. and Moodie, C. D. 1942 Occurrence and activity of Azotobacter in the semiarid soils of Washington. *Proc. Soil Sci. Soc. of America* 7: 229-236.

108. Vinogradova, O. S. 1930 The depth of penetration by bacteria into the subsoil. *Trudy Nauch. Inst. po Udobreniyam,* No. 76: 112-115.

109. Vysotskii, G. 1899 Hydrological and geo-biological observations in Veliko-Anadol. *Pochvovedenie* (Pedology) 1: 85-97.

110. Vysotskii, G. 1901 Steppe illuvium and the structure of steppe soils. *Pochvovedenie* (Pedology) 3: 137-156, 349-354.

111. Vysotskii, G. 1906 An oro-climatogenic basis for classifying soils. *Pochvovedenie* (Pedology) 8: 1-17.

112. Wiegner, G. 1927 Neuere Bodenuntersuchungen in der Schweiz. Schweiz. Landw. *Monatshefte, S. Yahrgang,* 193: 207-239, 247-256.

113. Yakubov, T. F. 1942 Microbiological characteristics of sands and sandy soils of semideserts and deserts of U. S. S. R. Sbornik Pamyati Williams. Acad. of Sci. U. S. S. R., Dokuchaev Soil Inst., 247-266.

114. Yashnova, N. V. 1930 Nitrification in a podzolized soil. *Trudy Nauch. Inst. po Udobreniyam,* No. 76: 50-68.

115. Zon, R. 1927 Forests and water in the light of scientific investigation. Reprint from Appendix V of the Final Report of the National Waterways Commission (1912). Senate Document No. 469, 62nd Congress, 2nd Session, pp. 1-106.

CHAPTER VI

SOIL GENESIS: SOIL-FORMING PROCESSES

In soil genesis, the interaction of the factors of soil formation may be expressed by a series of physical, chemical, and biological reactions. Collectively, these represent soil-forming processes which lead to the moulding of the soil body. A pedologic scrutiny of soil profiles the world over reveals two outstanding characteristics. First, all profiles, irrespective of their geographic position, are endowed with a series of fundamental features. Second, there are specific profile features which differentiate one soil group from another. Accordingly, we have the broad fundamental and specific soil-forming processes.

The relationship between the two sets of processes and the physical, chemical, and biological reactions involved are schematically outlined, with modifications, after Zakharov (Ch. II, 91, p. 256).

Fundamental processes	*Specific processes*	*Physical, chemical, and biological reactions*
I. Accumulation of humus decay material on surface of soil, the formation of the A_0 layer	Humus formation Grass vegetation Forest vegetation Peat formation Solonchak Organo-mineral gels	A. *Physical* Permeability Translocation (Mechanical) Texture Structure
II. Eluviation, the formation of the A horizon	Leaching of bases Podzolization Humus accumulation Laterization	B. *Chemical* Colloid state Solution Precipitation Hydration Oxidation Reduction Carbonation Silication Desilication Sorption Ion exchange
III. Illuviation, the formation of the B horizon	Lime, clay and iron and aluminum accumulations Solonetz	
IV. Differentiation of the mass in the respective horizons	Soil solution Depth of profile Soil maturity Aeration Temperature	C. *Biological* Groups of microbes Humification Mineralization Ammonification Nitrification Dentrification Nitrogen fixation Other reactions

The A_0 Layer

The materials that make up the humus decay accumulative layer, designated as A_0, are not confined to their position on the surface of the soil. Some organic matter is scattered throughout the entire profile. We find roots, microorganisms, and relics of the zoosphere in the A and B horizons. However, the initial source of reagents of biosphere origin is associated with the A_0 layer.

Plants began their active cycle on the surface of the mantle rock or bed rock, drawing their nutrients from the lithosphere, the hydrosphere, and the atmosphere. For our present discussion, it matters little which of the forms of plant life appeared first. In all probability, the nitrifying organisms and, in general, the autotrophic organisms, were among the first. No heterotrophic organisms or chlorophyll-bearing plants of any significance were possible until combined nitrogen was deposited with the residues of the autotrophic organisms. In our own time, we have the recorded phenomena of nitrifying organisms thriving on apparently bare rock and sulfur oxidizing organisms obtaining their energy from the oxidation of sulfur. With the evolution of life, other forms of plant life developed: algae, lichens, mosses, fungi, and finally the higher plants. With the death of plants, creative forces come into play. The energy released and the reactions resulting in the processes of organic matter decomposition bring forth the processes of soil formation. It is from this point that the system of soil begins in the geochemical cycle.

Soil genesis is associated with the origin and development of the biosphere. A logical inference would be that soil age corresponds to that of life on our planet. Although this is true, it does not imply that the soils we see now have their origin in those remote days. It is very probable that all of the aboriginal soils have been destroyed and recreated again several times during the geological history of our earth. The existing soils are the result of the present day climate.

Humification.—The process of decomposition of organic matter and the synthesis of new organic complexes is known as *humification*. On the surface of virgin soils, there is an accumulation of materials to be humified and some products of humification. In the forests, the raw materials available for the creative reactions—the building of the soil body—consist of dead leaves, twigs, branches, tree trunks, herbaceous vegetation, and remnants of animal life. In the meadow, prairie, and steppe, it is the grass cover that furnishes the raw materials. In the process of humification, a large portion of the minerals is set free. Some are utilized by the microbial flora, others are absorbed by the newly synthesized humus complexes, and the rest are leached downward. A residual product of the various reactions is the humus.

The rate of accumulation of organic residues, the reactions that take place in the A_0 layer, and the general characteristics of this layer vary with the climate. Within each climatic belt, the type of vegetation puts its mark on the character of the A_0.

In the humid tropics and subtropics, conditions are ideal for microbial activities and the consequent breakdown of the natural organic matter and of the synthesized humus complexes. We have in these regions a rapid "burning up" of organic matter.

In the cool temperate regions, the process of humification slows down. The seasons for favorable microbial activities are not as long; the lower temperatures are not conducive to oxidation. All in all, the organic matter residues remain intact much longer than in the humid tropics, and there is a greater accumulation of forest floor debris, even though the quantity factor of growth is not as high as in the tropics.

The further north we go, the less intense become the processes of decay. Anaerobic conditions are widespread, temperatures are low, and the rate of humification is, therefore, slow. The result is a deep A_0 layer, and peat formation is a common occurrence.

In the grasslands, the humus-decay accumulative layer blends in with the horizon of eluviation, but the partly decomposed and completely humified substances are very much in evidence. The true A_0 layer is represented by a mat of dead vegetation on the sod of the meadow in the humid regions and of the prairie in the less humid and partly arid regions. In this connection, it is of interest to note the differences in conditions under which the layer of accumulation is formed in meadow and prairie regions respectively. In the meadow, the death of the plants comes as a result of low temperature, usually with no lack of moisture. In the steppe, and in a large measure also in prairie, the grass dies primarily as a result of high temperature and low moisture supply. The difference in mode of formation of the A_0 layer undoubtedly influences the composition of the accumulated materials, but no studies in this direction have been made. It is possible that the change in the state of the colloidal organic complexes in the two grass associations, due to the differences in moisture and temperature, affect the aging of the colloids and hence their decomposition.

The type of vegetation, forest or grass, markedly influences the humification process. Woody plants contain large quantities of lignins, waxes, and resins which are highly resistant to decomposition; they are also rich in tannins and other acid-producing substances which tend to subdue the activities of bacteria and stimulate fungous development. In the hardwood forests, the earthworms destroy large quantities of the A_0 material. In the grasslands, humification is intense, but mineralization is slow; the result is, therefore, an accumulation of organic matter.

Müller (Ch. 5, 70) was the first to study humification. His monograph on organic matter is a classic. Of the later investigations, those of Kravkov (19), Hesselman (14), Nemec (24), Glomme (13), and Zaitsev (52) may be cited. The 3 last named investigators used the Robinson and Jones (34) method—6 per cent H_2O_2 extraction—for determining degree of humification. Nemec reports 44 per cent humified litter in a pure stand of conifers; in a pure stand of hardwoods—67 per cent; and in a mixed stand—55 per cent. Zaitsev shows that the higher the N content of the litter, the higher the degree of humification. He reports a certain relation between N:Ca ratio and the degree of humification. Meyer (23) and Kubiena (21) have contributed to the problem of humification in relation to the soil fauna.

Foresters recognize the F (from the Swedish Förna—the unaltered residues and by-products of the plant and animal kingdom) and H layers—the Hesselman designations—in the A_0, the former referring to the unaltered (physically) litter and the latter—the humus-like material. Some investigators differentiate several F layers, the uppermost with the latest leaf fall, followed by a layer of leaf fall of previous years, somewhat decomposed but still indentifiable as to source of origin. Variations in the humification of the A_0 layer have been noted by foresters in studies of forest litter—the mull and duff (mor). Notable investigations are those of Hesselman (14), Romell (36), and Romell and Heiberg (37) who give extensive bibliographies on the subject. A new wrinkle on the problem of mull and duff has been presented by Plice (27, 28) and Heiberg (15). Broadfoot and Pierre (3) present valuable data on the acid-base balance of different forest species. For recent data on forest litter, the papers by Chandler (6) are to be consulted.

The information made available on mull and duff may help to interpret the behavior of the reaction products in moulding the profile constitution. The reagents furnished by the respective types of forest litter have their effects on the profile.

Mattson, one of the very few original thinkers and students of physico-chemical reactions of the acidoid-basoid complexes of the soil, has contributed in collaboration with Koutler-Anderson (Ch. 6, 39) a series of 8 papers on the acid base condition in vegetation, litter, and humus. These studies have a bearing on the reactions taking place in the course of humification. They come to the conclusion (paper IV) "that the amphoteric humus complex is directly derived from the litter (including microbial litter) and represents a digestive residue produced by enzymatic action but modified also by purely chemical reactions." This conclusion differs in no way from an earlier statement that humus is not only a product of decomposition (the "digestive residue") but also of synthesis inasmuch as it contains the living and dead bodies of microbes and it enters into chemical and physico-chemical reactions with the products of decomposition. The novel feature of the conclusion is the way in which the authors come to it, namely by following through the reactions of the acidoid-basoid complexes that take place in the course of organic matter decomposition.

Under conditions of a high water table, the A_0 layer becomes deeper and deeper as the age of the land advances. If the water table persists for any length of time at the surface, the decomposition reactions do not keep up with the source of supply of litter. This condition causes the formation of peat (see also chapter XV) which may extend to depths of 10 to 30 and more feet.

In the arid and semiarid regions, high evaporation may cause a rise of salts and accumulation of these on the surface of the soil. The results are a destruction of the vegetation common to normal non-saline soils and the appearance of a selected group of saline plants. Such an accumulation of salts represents one type of solonchak (see chapter XIV).

Mineralization.—The decomposition of organic matter to its fundamental composition, i.e., to CO_2, and other gases, water, and minerals is known as *mineralization*. This process proceeds simultaneously with humification in the A_0 layer and at any point in the profile where organic matter appears. Whereas humification increases the organic acids and acidoid content of the humus complex, mineralization tends to decrease these acids and to increase the basoid content. In the final analysis, the residue should be alkaline. However, leaching of bases determines the reaction in the A_0 layer.

In the grass country of the arid and semiarid regions, the paucity of rainfall prevents the immediate removal of the bases released from the mat of dead grass vegetation, the A_0 layer. As a matter of fact, the A_0 layer of the regions under consideration is not humified and hence not mineralized to any great extent. The desiccating temperatures and winds impede the activities of microbes. Wind and water erosion remove large quantities of the A_0. A minor portion of the A_0 layer, closer to the mineral constituents of the A horizon and imbedded in the sod undergoes decomposition. The dead grass does give up, by solution, the alkalies, with the K subject to fixation at the surface of the mineral layer. Some Ca and Mg is translocated, and in their downward movement react with the humus constituents, forming humates of calcium which upon drying become insoluble and are thus fixed in place.

Levakovsky (22) has shown that extracts of partly decomposed woody substance of *Corylus avellana,* when treated with salts of iron or aluminum, yielded an insoluble residue. This was considered by Levakovsky of prime importance in explaining the phenomenon of humus fixation. The water soluble organic compounds, in their downward movement through the soil profile, encounter iron and aluminum ions and precipitate. According to Zakharov (Ch. 2, 91, p. 268), "such a supposition finds corroboration in the findings of Dokuchaev that an abundance of organic matter in chernozem is related to the abundance of iron and aluminum oxides in that soil."

Slezkin (40) repeated the work of Levakovsky, percolating soluble organic substances through soils of various textures. Zakharov (p. 268) cites the experiments of Slezkin as follows:

> In the first series of experiments, Slezkin used coarse sand, medium sand, loam, and kaolin. He was convinced that the dark organic substances from the decomposing hay gradually penetrate the fine grained mass by osmotic forces. Fungous mycelium also penetrates the mass. In another series of experiments, conducted in shallow glass vessels, he was able to observe the process micrococically and to follow closely the organic matter penetration and its fixation in the soil. As the organic substances have distributed themselves through the soil, they were attacked by fungi, but the lime in the loess loam hindered the organic matter from becoming mouldy. The effervescence observed indicated chemical reaction between the soluble decomposable organic substances and the lime. At the same time, a change in the state of the organic compounds took place: the soluble and colloidal organic compounds coagulated, coated the particles of lime, gradually oxidized, and took on the appearance and composition of humus.

In the semiarid-subhumid region of the grass country, microbial activity and chemical decomposition release somewhat more bases from the A_0 layer. It is to be remembered, however, that the bulk of the reagents responsible for the reactions in grass country comes from the extensive root system. As a result of the slow movement of bases and the abundance of these in grasses, the A_0 layer of the soils in the grass country is neutral or even slightly alkaline.

In the humid regions, the A_0 layer consists of forest litter. No wind nor water remove any of the debris accumulating on the surface after the growing season is over. Thanks to the favorable moisture conditions and shade, the organic matter is subjected to humification and mineralization whenever the temperature is favorable. This condition prevails all year around in the humid tropics and subtropics, most of the year in the southern belt of the humid temperate climate, and a few months less in the northern belt of the humid temperate climate. Of course, in the extreme northern belt of the forest zone, the period of microbial dormancy is long. Because of this we have a deeper A_0 in these regions.

Long before decomposition commences, practically all of the K and the bulk of the Ca is leached from the leaves. Lysimeter studies (Ch. 5, 49) show how the pH rises in the fall soon after the leaf fall. The K and Ca content also increases in the leachings during that period. As decomposition ensues, large quantities of organic and some inorganic acids appear and impart an acid reaction to the medium. A series of reactions take place. The H-ions replace whatever bases enter into circulation as a result of mineralization. The acidity is higher in the A_0 of the coniferous than in deciduous forests, since the ash content of the latter is higher.

The microbiological picture of the A_0 layer is still obscure. It has been studied primarily by foresters. In their studies, any one interested may find references on this subject. In general, bacteria appear first, followed by fungi as the acidity increases.

The Horizon of Eluviation

The decomposition products of the A_0 layer are translocated through the underlying mineral material by the percolating waters. In their downward movement, the acids and bases react with the rock and mineral constituents. The reactions involved are: solution, hydrolysis, adsorption and replacement of ions, recombination with residual mineral products, and substitution within the lattice structure of the primary minerals to form secondary clay minerals. The reagents of the A_0 are reinforced with those produced by the humification and mineralization of organic matter of the dead subsurface vegetation, microflora, and various animal bodies.

In the exchange reactions, Na is first to be replaced, usually by H. Since Na forms no insoluble compounds under conditions existing in the soil, and is loosely held in adsorbed state because of its hydration envelope, the sodium compounds are carried in the form of nitrates, sulfates, bicarbonates, and humates by the percolating waters into the ground waters, to the streams, and finally to the ocean.

Following the fate of Na, the K, Ca, Mg, Mn, Al, Fe and any other base attached to the minerals are split off. The series of cations given represent the usual descending order of the ease with which the elements are released by replacement reactions. It may be of interest to note that K seems to be refixed in the soils of the semiarid and semiarid-subhumid regions, and in the order of loss from the A horizon, K may be lower than Ca and Mg. Another point to remember is that percolating waters invariably carry the alkali and alkaline earth bases simultaneously. The sesquioxides enter into circulation only after the medium has reached a pH below the neutral point. The amphoteric behavior of these elements makes it possible for them to move even at pH levels higher than the neutrality point.

In the arid, semiarid, and semiarid-subhumid regions (the natural geographic habitat of the gray and red semidesert soils, the brown, chestnut brown, and chernozem soils), there is generally speaking no movement of R_2O_3. The quantity of alkali and alkaline earth bases removed varies with the respective zonal soils. This phase will be discussed in the chapters devoted to an analysis of these soils.

In the humid tropics and subtropics and humid temperate regions (the natural geographic habitat of laterites, red and yellow soils of the subtropics, and podzolized soils), the alkali and alkaline earth bases are removed in large quantities. In the tropics and subtropics, the sesquioxides are released, but only part of them are removed. On the other hand, in the humid temperate climate less sesquioxides are split off, but more is removed from this horizon.

A great disparity exists in the type and quantity of organic matter retained in and removed from the A horizon of the soils of different climates. In the humid regions, appreciable quantities of soluble organic matter is removed by the percolating waters and still more is decomposed. In the grasslands, the organic matter tends to accumulate even though some moves out. These points of difference are discussed at length in chapters VIII and IX.

A characteristic feature resulting from the removal of constituents from the A horizon is a coarser texture. The A horizon has less clay and silt than the underlying horizon. Because of the textural property and because of the presence of organic matter in this horizon, the structure is fairly open and its consistency more mellow and friable than in the underlying horizon.

Because of the removal of constituents from the A horizon and the distribution of organic matter in it, the A horizon is divided into subhorizons, such as A_1 and A_2.

From the discussion presented, it is evident that the net result of the reactions in the A_0 and the A horizon is the removal of certain constituents by percolation. This horizon is, therefore, known as the *horizon of eluviation* (washing out).

Biologically, the horizon of eluviation has been only slightly investigated. Most studies have been made on soils sampled at arbitrary depths, and for that reason, the true picture of the distribution of microbes in the profile has been obscured. Only within the last few years have any investigations been made from the genetic point of view.

The distribution of Azotobacter in the profile has been studied by Keller and Karel'skaya (16) and by Sabanin and Henkel (38). The latter came to the conclusion that the distribution of Azotobacter in the soil is very closely related to the genetic horizons irrespective of their position below the surface. Brown and Benton (4) made a study of the distribution of bacteria, actinomyces ,and fungi in some Iowa soils. Their division of the horizons, especially with respect to the horizon of illuviation, is morphologically not exact, and their results are, therefore, not very significant.

Studies on the vertical distribution of Azotobacter and nitrifying organisms in soils in the vicinity of Tashkent (Middle Asia) have been made by Kononova (Ch. 5, 54). In the same soils, the distribution of protozoa has been studied by Belyaeva (2), who found them in abundance in the surface horizon only. With cultivation, the depth of the penetration of protozoa has increased very considerably. A more thorough investigation into the distribution of microorganisms in the profile has been made by Razumov and Remezev (33) on podzol soils. They found a sharp decline in the various forms of microorganisms in the A_2 horizon. In the B horizon, the microorganisms were concentrated on the surface of the structural units, but the whitish spots—material from the A_2 horizon distributed through the B_1 horizon—were very low in microbe content. Orlovskii (26) reports on the process of nitrification in the profile of a chestnut soil showing signs of solonetz formation. He also found variation in the nitrification power of the various horizons.

The depth of the A horizon varies with the zonal soil type. The depth also varies within the soil type depending on the origin and composition of the parent material and texture. In general, the deepest A horizon is encountered in the chernozem soils, extending to depths of 4 to 6 feet and even more, although depths of 2 feet and even less are not uncommon. In the forest zone, the depth of the A horizon rarely exceeds 2 feet. These facts, as well as many others pertaining to the horizon of eluviation will be elaborated upon in part II, Soil Systematics.

The Horizon of Illuviation

The eluviated products move into the new physico-chemical environment of the B horizon. At that point in their movement, the products are less acid than while in the A horizon. As a matter of fact, variable quantities of bases and very few acid salts reach the B horizon. Of course, the composition of these products is determined by the climate.

Very few elements of the biosphere are generated in the B horizon. Whatever energy releasing substances, in the form of organic matter, are found in it originate in the A horizon. The B horizon is receiving substances and is entering into reactions with them, with very few of its own substances being activated to react with the parent material. This horizon is gaining instead of losing, as is the case of the A horizon. The B horizon is therefore known as the *horizon of illuviation* (washing in) or horizon of accumulation.

The B horizon is built up from the bottom upwards. As a layer of clay and other colloidal substances is formed at some point in the column of parent material and the pore space is diminishing to capillary size, very little of the colloid gels pass beyond this layer. Another layer of these colloids must form on top of the other. In this manner the "growth" of the B horizon takes place. This growth ceases with the maturity of the soil body. Replacement of colloids goes for repair work only, i.e., as some colloids become dispersed or reacted upon and succeed in moving into the ground waters, other colloids enter into circulation and repair the "tissues" of the soil body.

An outstanding physical characteristic of the B horizon is compactness, which is brought about primarily by the lodging of the fine particles carried mechanically from A into the pore syaces between the textural units. This gives to the soil material in the B horizon its finer texture as compared with the A or the parent material. Besides the fine particles brought down mechanically, we have in this horizon an accumulation of one or a combination of precipitates (the kind depending on the climate), such as carbonates of calcium (sometime also of magnesium), gypsum, sesquioxides with more or less organic matter, silica gels, and other colloidal complexes. Some of these substances serve as binding materials for building various structural units, which, as a rule, are larger in the B horizon than in A or in C. Some of these chemical compounds are responsible for the ortstein and orterde (types of hardpan), gypsum, and lime concretions, and bands or layers of these in this horizon. Which of the cementing materials should occur in the B horizon depends on the products of eluviation which in turn are controlled by the climatic factors. A logical inference of the aforesaid is that within each soil zonal type there should be a variation in the compactness, structure, permeability, and other physical properties of the horizon of illuviation.

Chemically, the horizon of illuviation may be characterized as the arena of an array of reactions which give rise to the so-called "new formations." These are formed in the process of the accumulation of fine particles and bases removed from the A horizon. The pH environment shifts toward more alkalinity, as compared with the A horizon. This shift, as well as the variation in electrolyte content, influences the isoelectric point of precipitation of the sesquioxides and of other soil colloidal complexes, organic and inorganic. A redistribution of the components of the acidoid-basoid ratio takes place. The increased alkalinity increases the basoid part which in the organic colloids consists of the protein. For this reason, perhaps, we find in some soil types a higher nitrogen content in the organic matter of the B horizon than of the A horizon.

In regions where the ground waters contain a high salt content and the evaporation is high, the B horizon becomes enriched with soluble salts from below. Such soils are called "disguised saline soils," for the salts do not rise to the surface.

Biologically, the horizon of illuviation has not been investigated to any extent. Some data on the microbiological conditions in the B horizon may be found in the discussion on the horizon of eluviation. The composition and position of the B horizon bring about partial anaerobic conditions whereby the oxygen tension is low because of the active utilization of this element by the decomposition processes in the horizon of eluviation. Besides, the compacted condition (primarily in the humid regions) of the B horizon causes frequent waterlogging which favors reduction reactions. Biological activities are, therefore, subdued in the B horizon.

There is a wide variation in the thickness of the B horizon in the different zonal types depending on the depth of the soil profile. But even within each zonal type the thickness of the B horizon varies, depending on the composition and texture of the parent material. In light textured parent materials, the products of eluviation move deeper, and under such conditions the B horizon, as a rule, is deep. Of course, the development of the B horizon depends also on the supply of materials from the A horizon and on the time period from the embryonic state of the soil body to the point where equilibrium between the outgo and the return of materials in the profile has been reached.

Differentiation Within the Horizons

As a result of the processes of eluviation and illuviation, a differentiation of the materials within the profile and within each horizon of the profile takes place. Morphological features, physical, chemical, and biological makeup (like color, structure, type of chemical constituents, mineral and organic), are criteria by which these differentiations are recognized. Within each horizon, a set of these criteria is established. We have quantitative and qualitative variations in the organic matter, in the type of the new formations, in the clay-like substances formed in the process of decomposition of minerals and rocks, in the humates of the various cations, in the absorption complexes, and in the other components of the respective horizons in the profile. These variations reflect the activity of the soil-forming processes and serve as a basis for the classification of soils.

One of the chief agencies responsible for the differentiation of the materials within the horizon is the soil solution. It is the "blood stream" of the soil body, carrying the substances back and forth, taking some constituents from one part and adding other constituents to another part of the soil body.

The literature on "soil solution" is voluminous. No systematic efforts, however, have been made to investigate the soil solution and its dynamics according to soil zones and their genetically related horizons. Unquestionably, a study of this nature would yield valuable data in the elucidation of the soil-forming processes and in providing an insight into the nutrients carried in the profile of the various soil zones.

Trofimov (42) referred to the soil solution as the medium which reflects the tendency of the dynamic processes of the soil. Zakharov (53) discussed the significance of the soil solution for the processes of soil formation and established its characteristic properties for the various soil types. The soil solution of the podzols has been studied by Sobolev (40) and Trofimov (42) ; that of the chernozem, by Gedroiz (9) and Kravkov (20).

Classification of Soil-Forming Processes

From the point of view of pedogenesis, the classification of the soil-forming processes, in their broad aspects, should hinge on the elements of climate: soils develop certain typical zonal characteristics because of the climatic conditions in the particular zone. To be sure, we do have a number of zonal soil types. But the continuity of the climatic soil zone is at times broken because of local factors such as topography, moisture conditions, composition of parent material, local climate, each one of which leaves a definite impression on the processes of soil formation. These circumstances give rise to the formation of soils not typical of the climatic belts geographically. Such soils are known as climatogenically subdued, of which more is to be said in Part III. For the present, we shall confine our discussion to an outline of the soil-forming processes of the broad zonal types, mentioning the others only incidentally. Of the several attempts to classify the chief soil-forming processes, those of Kossovich (Ch. 2, 40), Neustruev (Ch. 2, 50), Vilenskii (43, 44), and Glinka (Ch. 2, 27) are most interesting. Fundamentally, all of these systems of classification hinge on the one proposed by Dokuchaev and Sibirtsev. Table 19 gives the classification system of Vilenskii.

Kossovich looked upon the process of soil formation as a series of physico-chemical transformations specific for a definite physico-geographic region. The following types of soil formation were recognized by him:

1. **Desert Type.**—Extremely low rainfall, dry and hot, with very little vegetation and animal life (biosphere), meager eluviation, and infrequent rise of salts with the typical hard desert pavement and soft salt accumulation.

2. **Desert or Arid Steppe Type.**—Rainfall is low, but enough to produce an almost closed surface vegetation cover, and eluviation is more marked than in the desert. This process of soil formation goes on under conditions of an alkaline medum.

3. **Steppe Type.**—An increased precipitation, fairly luxuriant grass vegetation, more energetic eluviation, and some loss of bases which accumulate at a certain depth of the profile. This process of soil formation goes on under conditions of a slightly alkaline or neutral medium.

4. **Humid Cool Temperature Forest and Meadow Types.**—Abundance or even excess of rainfall with a vegetation cover, usually forests, controlled in a large measure by the plant-food resources, rapid leaching of bases, acid reaction, release of silica in the process of decomposition of minerals, removal of sesquioxides, and their accumulation in the form of ortstein, orterde, and concretions.

5. **Polar Region Type.**—Low temperature, relatively low precipitation, and scant vegetation. Because of slow decomposition, organic matter accumulates at the surface giving it a peat-like character. Leaching goes on, but not to any great depth, and is somewhat similar to the process mentioned in 4.

6. **Humid Tropic and Subtropic Type.**—Abundance of rainfall, a high temperature, and luxuriant vegetation. Because of favorable conditions of temperature and moisture, rapid decomposition continues to the CO_2 stage, thus leaving behind little humus. Leaching is high, causing a loss of bases and silica from the surface layers with a simultaneous accumulation of sesquioxides.

Kossovich placed the aforementioned types of soil formation in a class known as genetically independent. These follow definite climatic belts. Within the borders of the respective soil zones, local types of soil formation are found, designated by Kossovich as "genetically subdued." A further step in developing the genetic classification of soils was made by Gedroiz (10, 11). He suggested the base exchange capacity of soils as a criterion for classifying soil forming processes.

Neustruev, the great Russian pedologist geographer, established two broad divisions of soil-forming processes: automorphic (normal moisture) and hydromorphic (excessive moisture). The former embraces the zonal soils, and the latter, the intrazonal. He further subdivided the soil-forming processes, on the basis of their effects on the state of decomposition of the mineral constituents of the soil material, into the following three groups:

1. The mineral mass decomposes to a point where the sesquioxides, silica, and alumino-silicic acids are split off and set free, resulting in lateritic, podzol, and solonetz and solonetzic types of soil formation. These soils include the soils of the tropics, subtropics, deciduous forests of the temperate warm zone, deciduous and coniferous forests, and forest steppe and steppe zones.

One might question the zonal character of the solonetz, which belongs to the climatogenically subdued soils; but, from the standpoint of the state of decomposition of the mineral complex, the solonetz and the solodi,

Table 19

Systems of soils (After Vilenskii)

Climatic conditions of soil formation		Soil divisions (Humidity regions)	Soil types				
Temperature zones	Zonality		Arid A	Semiarid SA	Feebly arid FA	Semihumid SH	Humid H
Polar	Zonal Soils	Hydrogenic H	Tundra HA	Semi-bog HSA	Bog HFA	—	Concealed podzol, podzolized bog HH
Cold		Phytohydrogenic PH	Sward PHA	—	Black meadow PHFA	Degraded meadow PHSH	Podzolized PHH
Temperate		Phytogenic P	Gray PA	Chestnut brown PSA	Chernozem (Black soils) PFA	Degraded (Gray-forest) soils PSH	Podzolized PH
Subtropic		Thermophytogenic TP	—	Yellow soils of arid steppe TPSA	Yellow TPFA	Degraded yellow soils TPSH	Podzolized yellow soils TPH
Tropic		Thermogenic T	Red soils of semi-deserts TA	Red soils TSA	Laterite TPA	Degraded red soils TSH	Podzolized red soils TH
Temperate		Halogenic G	Dry salines GA	Columnar alkali soils GSA	Black columnar alkali soils GFA	Degraded alkali soils GSH	Podzol-like alkali soils GH

Table 19

Systems of soils (After Vilenskii)

Temperature zones	Zonality	Soil divisions	Soil types				
			Gray alka-line soils PGA	Chestnut alkaline soils PGSA	Black alkaline soils PGFA	Degraded alkaline soils PGSH	Podzol-like alkaline soils PGH
Temperate	Intrazonal Soils	Phytohalogenic PG					
All zones		Hydrohalogenic HG	Salines containing chlorides and sulfates; salines containing calcium carbonate, and salines containing sodium carbonate.				
Subtropic and tropic		Thermohalogenic TG	Alkaii soils of the subtropical and tropical zones.				
Subtropic and tropic		Thermohydrogenic TH	Bog soils of the subtropical and tropical zones.				
Mountain region	Soils of vertical zones	Orogenic O	Soils of high mountain regions				

to which Neustruev (Ch. 2, 50) is specifically referring, are true representatives of this subdivision.

2. The mineral mass decomposes without the separation of free sesquioxides and alumino-silicic acids, forming intermediary products of decomposition (the acid salts of the alumino-silicic acids) and products of the mutual coagulation of the sols of the sesquioxides and silica-clays. The result is the chernozem, the dark chestnut, and the light chestnut (brown) types of soil formation. These include the true steppe soils of the arid and subarid zones.

3. The mineral mass decomposes slightly. The products of mechanical disintegration (physical weathering) of the soil constituents—a silty fraction primarily of allochtonic origin—predominate, resulting in gray and red soils of the semidesert and desert and primitive soils of the dry tundra. These soils include those of the extremely arid zone, the arctic, and those of the high mountain tundra zone.

In his hydromorphic (intrazonal) division, Neustreuev included the solonchak, peat, and bog types of soil formation.

Vilenskii, one of the younger representatives of the Dokuchaev school of pedology, criticizes the terminology of "automorphism" used by Neustruev. He points out that the soil is an exogenous and not an autogenous or ontogenous body, as is the case with a mineral or living body. "Soil is a product of *the factors of soil formation* and can neither arise nor exist by itself. In a similar way, the evolution of the soil is not the result of the processes which occur within the soil, but of the changes in the conditions of soil formation."

Vilenskii's system is very similar to those already mentioned except that the various factors of soil formation—temperature, moisture, vegetation, and parent material (active and passive soil formers)—are more vividly brought into the scheme of soil classification and genetically correlated.

Taking Köppen's (18) zonal temperature classification of climatic conditions—polar, cold, temperate, subtropic, and tropic—, on the one hand, and Wiegner's (49) regions of humidity—arid, semiarid, feebly arid, semihumid, and humid—, on the other, Vilenskii constructs a system of five principal zonal soil divisions and a number of intrazonal divisions. These are clearly brought out in table 19.

Ramann's system of soil classification contain some elements of Vilenskii's system. But Ramann (Ch. 3, 53) did not recognize clearly the Dokuchaev viewpoint of soil formation. He followed the Hilgard system of two large climatogenic divisions: arid and humid.

Kardos and Bowlsby (15a) reviewed the work done on the chemical properties of soils in relation to the genetic soil classification and have advanced the problem a step farther. They followed the line of investigations initiated by Mattson on characterizing the genesis of the profile by studying the neutralization curves and the equionic pH (the pH of exchange neutrality) of the soil colloids. They have shown that this method may be used in characterizing the different soil groups. Discrepancies noted by Kardos and Bowlsby in the neutralization curves have been explained by the nature of other indices used in characterizing the soil colloids. For example, they found that "the C:N ratio of organic matter in the clay fraction of the pedocal grays is much narrower in general, than that of the pedalfer group."

Glinka distinguished five fundamental types of soil formation: laterite; podzol, primary and secondary; steppe, the gray chestnut-brown and chernozem; alkali; the bog.

Summarizing the various classification systems of the Russian pedologists, Zakharov (Ch. 2, 91) presents the fundamental types of soil formation as follows:

1. Desert Type:—This type occurs under conditions of extremely low rainfall, in the almost complete absence of the higher forms of plant life. Chemical weathering is subdued, the biosphere is of little consequence, and an alkaline reaction is favored. Eluviation is limited because of low rainfall. Infrequently, soluble salts such as $NaCl$ and Na_2SO_4 accumulate on the surface because of high evaporation. Some of these salts may be blown away by strong winds prevailing in these regions. Everything considered, one may speak of primitive or embryonic soils in the desert.

2. Dry Steppe Type.—Rainfall is generally deficient, but sufficient to support a scant grass cover and to facilitate the process of eluviation. The soil solution carries an abundance of bases and sodium salts—carbonates, silicates, and humates. The process of soil formation goes on in an alkaline medium. Notwithstanding the scant percolation, most of the soluble salts and even some alkaline earth carbonates are washed out from the surface horizon. Under certain conditions even some sesquioxides are removed. Because of these reactions the surface becomes somewhat lighter in color. The surface horizon also loses some silt and attains a laminar structure, while the lower horizon, where the fine particles and some sesquioxides accumulate ,becomes more compact and attains a columnar or prismatic structure. In the lower horizons, gypsum and soluble salts are encountered.

3. Chernozem Type.—This type occurs under more humid conditions than 1 or 2, with a heavy grass stand which gives to the soil a high organic matter content. There is considerable eluviation; the easily soluble salts are removed from the soil, whereas the alkaline earths are washed out from the surface and accumulate at some point in the profile. The process of soil formation goes on in a slightly alkaline or neutral medium thereby favoring the accumulation of humates of calcium and other cations.

4. Podzol Type.—This type forms under conditions of the humid temperate regions, under forest and meadow, with an abundance and sometimes an excess of precipitation. Eluviation is pronounced, causing the loss of soluble salts and even of alkaline earth bases. The sesquioxides are washed out from the surface and accumulate in the horizon of illuviation. This movement is associated with the movement of some of the humus substances. Because of the favorable moisture conditions, a large portion of the organic matter is mineralized, with the formation of crenic and apocrenic acids. Since the medium is acid, some of the mineral complexes are disrupted, leaving behind silica, which appears in the profile as a coating over the soil particles.

5. Polar Region Type.—This region has scarcely been investigated. The process of soil formation takes place under conditions of a low temperature, comparatively low precipitation, and scant vegetation of the tundra. Because of the low evaporation, the process of eluviation goes on notwithstanding the low precipitation. The process of soil formation should, therefore, approach the podzol and bog type.

6. **High Mountain Type.**—This type is instrumental in the formation of mountain-meadow soils under conditions of strong eluviation, considerable fluctuations in temperature and humidity, a short vegetation period, and a usually acid medium. Since the type of vegetation is grass, there is a considerable accumulation of organic matter. The characteristic features of the mountain meadow type of soil formation are a meager leaching of bases and almost total absence of illuviation of sesquioxides.

7. **Laterite Type.**—This is the process of soil formation in the humid subtropical and tropical regions. It takes place under conditions of high temperatures and abundance of precipitation. Organic matter does not accumulate, except at the surface, and is rapidly mineralized. Leaching is very energetic, and, except for the sesquioxides, most of the constituents are washed out from the surface. And yet there is no well-expressed horizon of illuviation. The red or orange color is due to the accumulation of iron in the surface horizon.

8. **Bog Type.**—This process includes the true bogs, semi-bogs, and meadow bogs. It occurs under conditions of excessive moisture. Anaerobic conditions prevail, and decomposition is slow. Reduction reactions are common in the mineral mass, and this gives rise to the process of gleiing.

9. **Solonchak Type.**—This type forms in regions of a relatively smooth topography with a rising water table which sends up soluble salts. The result is an accumulation of the easily soluble chlorides and sulfates and the formation of the so-called "saline horizon" which is mellow and fluffy in structure. Because of the excess of salts, the vegetation is scant and the humus is, therefore, low. Sometimes there are signs of gleiing due to the rise of the water table.

10. **Solonetz Type.**—This type occurs under conditions of temporary surface excess of moisture in an alkaline medium in the presence of sodium carbonate. The high alkalinity is conducive to a disruption of the alumino-silicate complex with the separation of SiO_2 and R_2O_3. The latter move downward with the fine particles and produce a compact constitution and columnar structure. The upper horizon becomes enriched with SiO_2 and somewhat resembles a podzol. In the horizon of accumulation, carbonates and soluble salts are usually found.

An examination of Zakharov's classification system shows that it embraces the salient features of the more important classification systems of soil-forming processes discussed, save that of Vilenskii. In general, there are no sharp differences between the various systems, but that of Zakharov offers a more tangible outline, a more workable plan, for the survey of the great soil types of the world.

Marbut (Ch. 2, 45) differentiates two broad divisions of soil formations: (a) Shifting and accumulation of the sesquioxides in the profile, with no higher percentage of lime carbonate at any point in the profile than in the parent material. (b) An accumulation of lime carbonate at some point in the profile, with or without the presence of other salts. "The lime carbonate is present in higher percentages than in the parent material and is found there regardless of the character of the parent rock." The first group of soils is designated by Marbut as "pedalfers" (Ped-Al-Fe-r) and the second as "pedocals" (Ped-o-Ca-ls). These names suggest the nature of the soil-forming processes. The pedalfers represent the podzol and laterite types of soil formation, and the pedocals, the chernozem, chestnut-brown, and gray types of soil formation.

SOME FUNDAMENTALS OF PEDOLOGY
UNDER REVISION

The orthodox tenets of the Dokuchaev genetic school of soil formation have been questioned from time to time. Most of the criticisms leveled against this school have not stood the test of time and are of historical interest only. A good review of these criticisms may be found in the work of Yarilov (51), the most prominent historian of soil science in general and of pedology in particular. Of the critics of Dokuchaev and his school, Williams (50) stands out, not so much for disproving the theories of Dokuchaev as for advancing novel ideas on soil formation that are at variance with those of Dokuchaev. Instead of the climate as the primary factor of soil formation, Williams stressed the biosphere, or rather the succession of plant associations as the factor responsible for the zonal characteristics of soils. Williams was also one of the first to apply the dialectics of Marx and Engels (the fathers of the modern philosophy of socialism) in the study of the evolution of soils as a body in nature. As an outgrowth of this scholasticism, the concepts of fertility and state of productivity had to be recognized as fundamental elements in the genesis of soils. Yarilov, the astute disciple of Dokuchaev, has lent his ear to this heresy and has tried to reconcile the views of Williams with those of Dokuchaev. Even Vilenskii (45, p. 797) has agreed in some measure to the views of Williams as may be judged from the following: "Soil formation begins from the moment organisms had settled on rocks and biological processes had ensued. In this relationship lies a fundamental qualitative difference between soil and rock, the latter being lifeless whereas the former is teeming with life. Through the mutual relations of organisms and rocks, a new natural body develops—the soil. It acquires a new property not possessed by rocks—*fertility.*"

Without entering into the controversy of the meaning of the concepts *soil fertility, productivity,* and *state of productivity,* we may agree on the point that these elements of the soil are simply manifestations of the reactions that take place in the fundamental and specific soil forming processes. By themselves, these elements do not impart to the soil such characteristics or properties that would identify it as a type. One of the outstanding differences between the Western-European geologic-agronomic viewpoint on soils and that of the Dokuchaev school is the following: The genetic school searches the facts about the soil and from these it is ready to evolve a soil management program to induce the highest productivity; the geologic-agronomic approach is a purely empirical, inasmuch as it tries to exploit the soil, or force it into productivity without knowing it. Soil fertility and productivity are technologic applications of knowledge acquired about the soil as a body in nature.

Volobuev (47), speaking of the rebellious currents among some Russian pedologists against the orthodox Dokuchaev concepts, makes the following statement:

Of late, the doctrines on the zonality of soils have been subjected to drastic criticism and revision. For a while, the idea of soil zonation has become an odious concept. More time was required and additional data were wanting to corroborate anew the regularity of the zonal distribution of soils. On the basis of comparative studies, primarily during the last decade, showing the repetition of the fundamental types of soil throughout the world, Prasolov (30) states: It is therefore possible to accept the bioclimatic soil zones as absolutely real. This general conclusion has been substantiated in recent general regional investigations. The soils of Western Siberia have been considered as departing from the true type of the European zonality of soils because of local geomorphological and historical causes. Gerasimov and Rozov have concluded, after a thorough investigation, that 'the zonal distribution system of these soils is in principle fully analogous to the system of Eastern European zones.' However, the soil zone in Siberia is considered as a soil complex with certain features of its own.

Thus, the law of the natural relation between climate and soil formation is embodied in the basic idea of Dokuchaev on the zonal distribution of soils. With that, it is of interest to note the possibility of expressing the dependence of soil formation on climatic conditions in the form of certain definite indices.

Some of the rebels questioning the validity of the Dokuchaev concepts, or those who want to pin on him a pet concept of their own, take only those excerpts from the writings of Dokuchaev which serve their purpose. Sokolov (41, p. 368), for example, quotes Dokuchaev to prove that he considered the factor of plant growth as primary in determining the process of soil formation. "Dokuchaev," states Sokolov, "in reporting on the depth of soil profiles, gives the average depth of chernozem as 65 cm.; of northern light gray soils—18 to 20 cm.; and of southern chestnut-brown—20 to 23 cm. In other words, the surface layers of the soil profile which are agronomically most important are considered by Dokuchaev as the soil." Quotations of this kind are misleading, inasmuch as they eliminate the more important utterances of the writings which lay stress on other points. As a matter of fact, Dokuchaev did not isolate any one factor in presenting his fundamental principle of the zonality of soils. To him, the zonality has been the result of the interdependence of a series of factors. Gerasimov (12) analyzes Dokuchaev's views and quotes from his monograph on zones in nature (8): "All of the most important soil formers are distributed on the earth's surface in belts or zones. These belts stretch out more or less parallel with the latitudinal lines. Because of that, it is unavoidable for the soils—our chernozems, podzols, etc.—to be distributed zonally on the surface of the earth, following closely the climate, vegetation, etc."

Some of the orthodox disciples of Dokuchaev have, in recent years, uncovered in the writings of the master some contradictory statements which are not in line with the facts discovered later. Of course, the evidence in support of the revolutionary ideas of Dokuchaev on the soil as an independent body in nature could not have been furnished by him in the manner we know it now. For the 60 years since the pronouncements of Dokuchaev, a great many facts on the processes of soil formation have been discovered. The newer knowledge on the distribution of the climatic and biosphere elements on the surface of the earth and the more advanced ideas on the biogeochemical cycle in the crust of weathering have been applied in interpreting the processes of soil formation, the evolutionary character of the soil types, and their stages of development. Rode (35), one of the second generation illustrious set of Dokuchaev's disciples, has summarized the neo-pedologic interpretations in 19 theses. The first of these is the cornerstone on which the others rest; it reads: "The idea of the evolution of soils—an idea of their eternal change with time—was upheld by all prominent repreesntatives of the Russian school of pedology, beginning with Dokuchaev. This idea was laid down by Dokuchaev as the basis of pedology, as one of its most prominent concepts."

Thesis 4 reads: "The soil forming process represents the combination of phenomena of transformation and translocation of substances and energy which go on in the surface layers of the earth's crust. Within these layers, the more characteristic and essential are the phenomena of the interaction (exchange of substances and energy) between the layers which form the soil and the living organisms (primarily plants)."

Anyone indoctrinated in the principles of pedology will recognize in the aforesaid, in capsule form, the essence of the reactions in the processes of eluviation and illuviation.

Theses 5 reads: "The soil forming process is cyclic in nature, subject to rhythmic fluctuations, in accordance with the manner in which the sun's rays reach the earth. Most important are the diurnal and annual cycles. Besides, there is also the effect of the irregular periodic fluctuations associated with the change in the meteorologic conditions and, perhaps, also with more extensive cycles such as the 11 and 5 year cycles related to the activity of the sun, the 35 year Brickner cycle, etc."

In this thesis, the variations in the elements of climate are presented in a manner more pointed than hitherto. It remains to be seen, however, how Rode will indicate the effects of these cycles on the constitution of the soil profile. Will it be possible to single out the features in this or the other zonal soil due to any one of these cycles?

Thesis 9 reads: "The five factors of soil formation established by Dokuchaev (parent material, topography, climate, plant and animal kingdom, and time) have to be augmented by three more: gravitation, waters (surface, soil, and ground), and production activity of the human."

It is not clear why water has been singled out as a factor of soil formation. In any discussion of soil formation, the hydrologic elements are featured as one of the outstanding factors associated with the climate (Ototskii, Vysotskii, Lebedev, and many others).

As to the human activities, this factor has been discussed in the earlier literature, especially by Zakharov (Ch. 2, 91, p. 243).

How the force of gravitation affects the processes of soil formation is not clear, except that it represents, in the interpretation of Rode (thesis 10), "a source of energy."

The few theses quoted and those that have not been (to save space and to give those interested a chance to consult the original) illustrate the running commentary of the neo-pedologists. Further elaboration of the concepts of Dokuchaev, in terms of modern knowledge, may also be found in the papers of the old and new disciples of Dokuchaev, such as Prasolov (30-32), Polynov (29), Vilenskii (46), Zakharov (54), Afanasiev (1), and Dimo (7).

Before closing the sketchy review of the appraisals of the theories of Dokuchaev on the processes of soil formation, it will be worth while to look into the paper of Nikiforoff (25) on the subject of soil formation. At present, Nikiforoff is undoubtedly the most prominent disciple of Dokuchaev in the United States. His pedologic investigations on the soils of the United States have not been fully appreciated. In the rapidly accumulating pedologic reports on the soils of the United States, those of Nikiforoff stand out as the most thorough.

In the paper referred to, Nikiforoff adheres to the viewpoint that "the soil is a product of a continuous, endless, and universal process and that all varieties of existing soils are nothing more than temporary stages." He speaks of soil maturity as being in a state of dynamic equilibrium. In other words, the soil as we know it is at equilibrium as long as the factors of soil formation remain constant. This equilibrium may be shifted with any change in climate.

Nikiforoff discusses the effect of climate on soil formation and makes the statement that "the climate of the soil which is instrumental in soil formation, however, is to a large extent the function of the soil." Now, what is *soil climate?* If the conditions of moisture and temperature in the soil represent the soil climate, which is supposed to be instrumental in soil formation, would not one expect to find different soil types in the different textural classes under conditions of the same climatic belt? Actually, the differences in texture of parent material represent only variations in percolation and in temperature fluctuations (of minor significance in the processes of soil formation as compared with percolation effects) which either retard or speed up the process of soil formation. Variations in profile constitution due to texture are caused by the composition of the parent material, as shown by Nikiforoff (Ch. 2, 51) in his studies of the Don sands.

Koloskov (17) speaks of soil climatology in manner presented by Demolon (Annals Agronomiques, No. 5, 1937): "the soil climate is the sum total of the diurnal and annual cyclic phenomena prevailing in the soil. These phenomena influence the life and productivity of the soil and they are dependent on the outside climate, soil substratum and the effect of the human on the soil and its cover." It seems that these studies are nothing more than studies on soil temperature, moisture, and aeration.

Thus far, the critical revision to which the tenets of Dokuchaev have been subjected has found expression primarily in modifying the classification charts of soils. There is a tendency not to stress the principle of intrazonality, since any soil may be fitted into the scheme of the evolution of soils and stages of their development (see Part III).

References

1. Afanasiev, E. A. 1946 On the problem of the origin and evolution of chernozem. *Pedology* (U.S.S.R.) No. 6:379-384.

2. Belyaeva, K. V. 1930 The vertical distribution of protozoa in the soils around Tashkent. Trudy Sredne-Aziat. Opyt. Issledovat. Inst. Vodnogo Khozyaistva, Bul. 7.

3. Broadfoot, W. M. and Pierre, W. H. 1939 Forest soil studies: I. Relation of rate of decomposition of tree leaves to their acid-base balance and other chemical properties. *Soil Sci.* 48:329-348.

4. Brown, P. E. and Benton, T. H. 1928 Microorganisms in some soil profiles in Iowa. *Proc. and Papers, First Inter. Cong. Soil. Sci.* 3:100-106.

5. Chandler, R. F. 1939 The calcium content of the foliage of forest trees. Cornell Univ. Agr. Exp. Sta. Mem. No. 228.

6. Chandler, R. F. 1941 The amount and mineral nutrient content of freshly fallen leaf litter in the hardwood forests of Central New York. *J. Am. Soc. Agr.* 33:859-871; see also: The amount and mineral nutrient content of freshly fallen needle litter of some north-eastern conifers. *Proc. Soil Soc. Amer.* 8:409-411 (1943).

7. Dimo, N. A. 1946 Dokuchaev the founder of institutions of higher learning. *Pedology* (U.S.S.R.) No. 6:377-378.

8. Dokuchaev, V. V. 1889 On the study of zones in nature (Russian) St. Petersburg. (Quoted from Gerasimov).

9. Gedroiz, K. K. 1906 On the variability of the concentration of the soil solution and the soluble salt content of the soil as influenced by external conditions. *Zhur. Opyt. Agron.* 7:521.

10. Gedroiz, K. K. 1925 The soil absorbing complex and the adsorbed cations as a basis for the genetic soil classification (Russian). Nosovka Agr. Expt. Sta. Bul. No. 38, 1-25.

11. Gedroiz, K. K. 1926 The movement of soil components and the influence of Ca on it. Nosovka Agr. Expt. Sta. Bul. No. 43, 1-18.

12. Gerasimov, I. P. 1946 The Dokuchaev doctrines on zones in nature. *Pedology* (U.S.S.R.) No. 6:354-360; see also his paper: The World Soil map and general laws of soil geography. No. 3-4: 152-161.

13. Glomme, H. 1928 Soil of the forest areas of E. Norway, etc. Medd. fra Det. Norska Skogfors., 3, No. 10. Quoted from *Proc. Inter. Soil Sci. Soc.* 4:97-99 (1929).

14. Hesselman, H. 1936 Studies of the humus layers of coniferous forests, their peculiarities and their dependence upon silviculture. *Med. Statens Skogsforsoksanst.* 22:169-552.

15. Heiberg, S. O. 1937 Nomenclature of forest humus layers. *Jour. Forest.* 35:36-39.

15a. Kardos, L. T. and Bowlsby, Clyde C. 1941 Chemical properties of some representative soil samples of certain great soil groups and their relation to genetic soil classification. *Soil Sci.* 52:335-349.

16. Keller, B. K. and Karel'skaya, A. F. 1926 Investigations in the realm of the geography and ecology of soil microorganisms. Sel'skoe Khoz. Zasush. Pustyn. Oblast. U. S. S. R. *Priroda,* No. 1-2.

17. Koloskov, P. I. 1946 Soil climatology. *Pedology* (U.S.S.R.) No. 3:159-163.

18. Köppen, V. 1900 Haupsätze über die Temperaturvertheilung in der Erdatmosphere. *Meteor. Ztschr.* 17:182-186; see also: v. 1 (1894): 215-226; on the observation of periodic phenomena in nature (Russian). *St. Peterb. Soc. Russe Georg. Mem.* 6, pt I (1875): 255-276.

19. Kravkov, S. P. 1911 Investigations on the role of the dead plant cover in soil formation (Russian). St. Petersburg.

20. Kravkov, S. P. 1937 Pochvovedenie (A text-book). Moscow-Leningrad.

21. Kubiena, W. 1943 L'investigation microscopique de l'humus. *Ztschr. Weltforstw.* 10:387-396 (England and German version: 396-410).

22. Levakovskii, S. 1888 Some supplementary facts on chernozem research. *Trudy Obshchest. Ispyt. Prir. pri Kharkov. Univers.*, 22. (Quoted from Zakharov).

23. Meyer, L. 1943 Experimentaller Beitrag zur macrobiologischen Wirkungen auf Humus und Bodenbildung. *Bodenk. u. Pflanzenernährung* 29:119-140.

24. Nemec, A. 1926 On the degree of humification of the dead covering of forest soils. *Proc. Int. Soc. Soil Sci.* 2:255-257; see also *Compt. Rend.* 185 (1927):1154-1155.

25. Nikiforoff, C. C. 1942 Fundamental formula of soil formation. *Amer. Jour. Sci* 240:847-866.

26. Orlovskii, N. V. 1930 The natural fertility factors of a solonetzic chestnut soil. Zapadno-Kazakhstan. Sel.-Khoz. Opyt. Stan. Bul. 4:1-110.

27. Plice, M. J. 1934 Acidity, antiacid, buffering, and nutrient content of forest litter in relation to humus and soil. Cornell Agr. Expt. Sta. Mem. 166.

28. Plice, M. J. 1945 What is a mull? *Proc. Soil Sci. Soc. Amer.* 10:410-413.

29. Polynov, B. B. 1946 The role of Dokuchaev in the development of the natural sciences. *Pedology* (U.S.S.R.) No. 6:341-342.

30. Prasolov, L. I. 1940 The roads leading to the solution of current problems of pedology. *Problemy Sov. Pochvovedeniya*, v. 11. (Quoted from Volobuev).

31. Prasolov, L. I. 1945 Geography of soil types and their distribution. *Pedology* (U.S.S.R.) No. 3-4:146-151.

32. Prasolov, L. I. 1946 Dokuchaev, his life and work. *Pedology* (U.S.S.R.) No. 6:333-340.

33. Razumov, A. S. and Remezev, H. P. 1929 The distribution of microorganisms in the profile of podzol soils. *Pedology* (U.S.S.R.) No. 1-2:137-159.

34. Robinson, G. W. and Jones, J. O. 1925 A method for determining the degree of humification of soil organic matter. *J. Agr. Sci.* 15:26-29; see also the volume by Robinson: Soils. p. 167 (1936).

35. Rode, A. A. 1946 The process of soil formation and the evolution of soils. *Pedology* (U.S.S.R.) No. 7: 400-402.

36. Romell, L. G. 1935 Ecological problems of the humus layer in the forest. Cornell Univ. Agr. Expt. Sta. Memoir 170, p. 28; see also: *Soil Sci.* (1932) 34:161-188.

37. Romell, L. G. and Heiberg, S. O. 1931 Types of humus layers in the forest of eastern United States. *Ecology* 12:567-608.

38. Sabanin, D. A. and Henkel, P. A. 1928 On the distribution of Azotobacter in the soils of the Troitsk district in the Ural region (Russian). Rept. of the All-Russian Conference of Botanists in Leningrad.

39. Slezkin, P. 1900 Etyudy o Gumuse (Studies on Humus). Kiev, Russia.

40. Sobolev, D. 1925 On the relation between the nitrification process and phosphorus mobilization in podzols. *Nauch. Agron. Zhur.* 2:186-198.

41. Sokolov, A. V. 1946 The role of plants in the teachings of Dokuchaev on soils. *Pedology* (U.S.S.R.) No. 6:366-373.

42. Trofimov, A. V. 1924 Some observations on the changes of the soil solution in fallow soils during the growing season. *Nauch.-Agron. Zhur.* 1:587-613.

43. Vilenskii, D. G. 1925 Classification of soils on the basis of analogous series in soil formation. *Proc. Inter. Soil Sci. Soc.,* n.s. 1, No. 4:224-241.

44. Vilenskii, D. G. 1927 Concerning the principles of a genetic soil classification. Contributions to the study of the soils of Ukraine, No. 6. Report to the First Inter. Cong. Soil Sci., pp. 129-151.

45. Vilenskii, D. G. 1937 Some regularities in the development of the soil forming processes. *Pedology* (U.S.S.R.) No. 6:792-809.

46. Vilenskii, D. G. 1946 The role and importance of Dokuchaev in soil science. *Pedology* (U.S.S.R.) No. 6:343-352.

47. Volobuev, V. R. 1945 On the soil climatic areals. *Pedology* (U.S.S.R.) No. 1:3-16.

48. Volobuev, V. R. 1946 Soil climatic laws in the U. S. S. R. *Pedology* (U.S.S.R.) No. 10:645-648.

49. Wiegner, G. 1926 Boden und Bodenbildung in Kolloidchemischer Betrachtung. Dresden-Leipzig.

50. Williams, V. P. 1927 Obshchee Zemledelie s Osnovami Pochvovedeniya (Agriculture and the Fundamentals of Pedology). Moscow.

51. Yarilov, A. A. 1946 Dokuchaev and his teachings. *Pedology* (U.S.S.R.) No. 6:374-376.

52. Zaitsev, B. D. 1937 The N content and degree of humification of organic substances of a forest podzol. *Pedology* (U.S.S.R.) No. 10:1442-1453.

53. Zakharov, S. A. 1906 Soil solution, its role in soil formation, methods of study, and its significance for the characterization of soil types. *Zhur: Opyt. Agron.* 7:388-477.

54. Zakharov, S. A. 1946 Dokuchaev as the founder and organizer of the new science of genetic soil science (Pedology). *Pedology* (U.S.S.R.) No. 6:361-365.

CHAPTER VII

SOIL ORGANIC MATTER

Introduction.—Ever since the days of Pasteur, microbiologists have explored the domain of soil organic matter and made important contributions. The fundamental work on the carbon and nitrogen cycle, the processes of ammonification, nitrification, nitrogen fixation, the isolation of the different groups of organisms, their relative importance in the soil as a medium, and the studies on the physiology of these organisms, all of these discoveries have been accomplished in rapid succession during the last decades of the 19th century and the first decade of the 20th century. Subsequent studies have in the main, with few exceptions, simply repeated the fundamental work. Soil microbiology got into a rut, limiting its studies to test tubes, flasks, and tumblers. Little effort has been made by microbiologists to integrate the findings on soil microbes with their natural habitat in the soil profile. Neither have they coordinated their findings with the investigations on soil organic matter by the chemists. On the other hand, the chemists have not appreciated some of the truths in the vociferous claims of soil microbiologists. Tyurin (74, p. 12) ascribes "the essential difficulty in deciphering the riddles of soil organic matter to the lack of coordination between the various scientific disciplines engaged in the studies."

Historical Background.—Ever since man tilled the soil, he has been pondering over the dark brown to black in color earthy material, which in modern times has been popularily known as humus. Systematic studies on the chemical nature of the dark substance date back to Berzelius (4), one of the founders of quantitative chemistry. He prepared humus substances from sugar and isolated crenic and apocrenic acids from springs and brooks. de Saussare (52), who clarified the process of photosynthesis, presented analyses on the elemental composition of a great many sources of organic matter. Sprengel (61), who overthrew the so-called humus theory, analyzed humus and described carefully "humus acids" which may accumulate in the soil or combine with the soil bases and form "neutral humus." Mulder (42) systematized the information on the subject, differentiating humus substances insoluble (indifferent) and those soluble in alkali. Mulder even determined the elemental composition of crenic ($C_{24}H_{24}O_{16}$) and apocrenic ($C_{24}H_{12}O_{12}$) acids. The early investigators appreciated the fact that humus was a decomposition product of organic matter, but the role of microbes in this process was not understood until

191

Pasteur clarified the puzzling phenomena of fermentation. Investigations on the chemical and some microbiological aspects of soil organic matter followed. Of these, more important are those reported by Müller (Ch. 5, 70), Hope-Seyler (22), Detmer (6), Berthelot and Andre (2), and others. They repeated the work of their predecessors, but have not advanced the problem much. Glinka (Ch. 2, 27) and Zakharov (Ch. 2, 91) quote von Ollech stating that the problem of organic matter at that time was *chemicorum crux et scandalum* (the misfortune and shame of the chemists). The point is that these investigators have not, as may be judged by their contributions, advanced the subject much beyond the sound position established by Mulder in 1839. Their work was of a corroboratory nature and deserves scrutiny in any historical review of the subject.

Deherain (5), Berthelot and Andre (2), Doyarenko (7), and others dealt with the character of the nitrogen compounds of soil organic matter. Gustavson (20), Grandeau (19), Slezkin (60), and others investigated the ash constituents of soil organic matter. Still others have subjected the soil organic matter to fractionation procedures of organic chemistry. One of the most extensive investigations in this direction was carried out by Schreiner and Shorey (55). They fractionated the humic, crenic, and apocrenic acids (obtained by the methods of Sprengel, Berzelius, Mulder, and others) of 23 soils and isolated about two dozen nitrogen free hydrocarbons and related compounds and a dozen nitrogenous compounds. These investigators have noted the variability of organic matter of different soils. Gortners' work (16) should not be overlooked.

Khainskii (26) followed the experimental procedure of Schreiner and Shorey, introducing improvements in the technique and modifying some of the experimental methods. He used the differential precipitation activity of various acids on the alkali extracts of organic matter to detect differences in the composition of organic matter from various soil types. Thus, the sulfuric acid reprecipitation of organic matter from an original nitric acid precipitation gave a highly colored supernatant solution from a podzol soil, a less colored solution from a chernozem, and only a trace of color from a chestnut-brown soil. Khainskii also tested the behavior of organic matter of the different zonal types toward alkali. Six successive extractions of chernozem with a 2 per cent sodium carbonate solution at 80° C gave a definite amount of organic matter. When the sample was subsequently treated with a 2 per cent sodium hydroxide solution, more organic matter was extracted. After four extractions, no more organic matter was given off, and the quantity extracted with the sodium hydroxide was the same as with sodium carbonate. In podzols, the soda alone extracts about 80 per cent of the total organic matter and caustic alkali extracts about 20 per cent of the amount extracted with the soda. In chestnut soils, only 10 per cent of the organic matter extracted with soda is extracted with alkali. The combined soda and caustic treatment extracted 77.13 per cent of the total organic matter from the chernozem, 87.34 per cent from the podzol, and almost 100 per cent from the chestnut soils. The subsequent treatment of the various organic matter fractions showed very clearly the differences in the organic matter from the various soil types. "The facts that the chief components of chernozem are the insoluble humic and slightly soluble ulmin acids, and that the chief components of the podzols are crenic and apocrenic acids may serve as important evidence that there are variations in the composition of the organic matter from the different soil types." A similar viewpoint has been expressed by Grachev (18).

A critical analysis of the work of Schreiner and Shorey is presented by Tyurin (70). He points out that "the relatively low quantity of humin and humic acid in the organic matter of the soils investigated by Schreiner and Shorey are characteristic for the soils of the humid and arid regions that are poor in organic matter. . . The composition of the humin and humic acid insoluble in alcohol (it represents 40 per cent of the total organic matter) remained unexplored in the work of Schreiner and Shorey."

For a comprehensive critical review and discussion of the problem of soil organic matter, the book by Tyurin (70) has no rival. It has a list of 776 references. An excellent supplement to it is the recent series of papers by him and his collaborators (75). A more comprehensive list of references is to be found in the compilation by Waksman (79), who treats the subject of soil organic matter from the point of view of the conventional soil microbiologist, with no appreciation of pedologic principles. For an appraisal of Waksman's work, the reader is referred to the papers of Tyurin (70), Sedletskii (56), and Rode (48).

Humus.—In the literature on soil organic matter, the terms *humus* and *soil organic matter* have been used synonymously. Actually, there is a fundamental difference between these two terms. Soil organic matter consists of any substance of organic origin, living or dead, encountered in the soil. Humus, on the other hand, is only a portion of the soil organic matter. *Humus is the dark brown-black organic matter that has undergone decomposition to such an extent that one can no longer determine by inspection the nature of the material from which it was derived.* The plant or animal substance of today is the humus of tomorrow.

It is clear that the definition expresses merely the morphologic characteristics of a complex or complexes of organic compounds, the nature and composition of which has not been determined as yet. The only method in use for the separation of the humus fraction from the bulk of soil organic matter is the one used by Karrer (25). It is based on the stability of the humified fraction of soil organic matter to treatment with acetyl bromide. Springer used this method in his early work, but later (63) he turned to a mixture of acetic acid, acetic anhydride, and sulfuric acid. Springer found that the humus content varied from 46 to 49 per cent of the total organic matter in peat-bog soils; in genuine podzols, from 46 to 52 per cent; in brown forest soils, from 50 to 70 per cent; in rendzina, from 57 to 65 per cent; in meadow bog, from 81 to 82 per cent; and in chernozem, from 71 to 91 per cent.

Information of this kind does not tell much on the nature and composition of humus. There is, however, an opportunity for the organic chemist to take this fraction as a starting point in studying it with methods at his disposal. The quantitative variations of the humus fraction in the different soil types are by themselves of importance. They serve as identification marks for the soil types.

A distinctive property of humus is a high N content which is ascribed to the microbial cells, dead and living, that are a part of the humus. Because of this property, soil organic matter contains a percentage of N higher than the average plant residue that enters the soil.

One fundamental error that still prevails in the literature is the designation of humus as a decomposition product. Chemically speaking, decomposition implies a simplification of the substance, the resulting products being of a lower molecular order than the original substance. This is, however, not the case in the process of organic matter decomposition and humus formation. The residual humus products are of a higher molecular order, and some investigators attribute to them a constitution far more complex than of the original organic matter. Humus is the resultant of the decomposition and synthetic reactions of the process of humification, and it is endowed with a definite colloidal behavior. The colloidal properties of the end-products of mineral decomposition and of the newly formed substances serve to stabilize and preserve these in the soil body. Similarly, the humus colloidal complexes, newly synthesized in the process of organic matter decomposition, tend to become stable and contribute to the stability of the organic matter fraction of the soil.

Views on Nature of Soil Organic Matter

Any organic matter entering the soil is subjected to an array of chemical and microbiological reactions. Because of the latter's obvious prominence, and the almost practical monopolization of the field by soil microbiologists, the chemical and physico-chemical reactions involved in the decomposition of organic matter have been frequently overlooked and neglected.

Most plants and their fruit when subjected to freezing turn brown and black. They also change color upon injury. All of these color changes involve chemical reactions. As pointed out by Tyurin (70, p. 37), the color change is due to "the oxidation of various aromatic compounds under the influence of oxidizing enzymes, or oxydase. . . Tannins are subject to browning, the result of the formation of condensation products known as tannin red or phlobaphene. . . The enzymatic oxidation of the tannins of tea into dark colored substances may be accelerated by the addition of peptone. . . Plant residues turn black because of the oxidation of tyrosine and other aromatic amino-acids by tyrosinase. As a result, we get black or dark brown condensation products (melanins) that resemble humus substances." Tyurin quotes the investigation of Zolcinski (80), who contended that humus formation is a physico-chemical and not a biological process. Microbes play only an indirect role in the formation of humus. They are responsible for the aromatic compounds which upon oxidation give rise to the dark colored substances.

Trusov (67) conducted a series of investigations on the interaction of carbohydrates and amino-acids and came to the conclusion that the formation of humic substances takes place by the interaction of sugars with the amide group. Similar humic substances are formed by the action of small quantities of ammonia on sugar.

An outstanding contribution on the problem of soil organic matter is the one by Oden (46). His physico-chemical researches have led him to accept as fundamentally correct the viewpoint of Berzelius and Mulder on organic matter. Oden investigated soil organic matter by means of definite physico-chemical indices, such as ion exchange and valance reactions. He recognized 4 component groups: 1, *humus coal,* insoluble in alkali (the humin or ulmin of Berzelius and Mulder); 2, *humic acid,* soluble in alkali and insoluble in alcohol; 3, *hematomelanic acid,* soluble in alcohol; and 4, *fulvic acids,* soluble in water (similar to the crenic and apocrenic acid of Berzelius). Oden's preparations of humic acid from various sources of organic matter showed a cation exchange capacity as high as 300 milliequivalents per 100 grams. He concluded that humic acid is quadribasic, is a compound endowed with definite properties, in spite of the impurities that always accompany it, has an equivalent weight of 350, and its separation in pure form is difficult. Tyurin (71) reports the following composition of fulvic acid from podzolized and chernozem soils respectively: C-44.82 and 44.32; H-5.77 and 5.94; 0-43.66 and 44.2; N-5.75 and 5.52 per cent.

Mattson (Ch. 4, 47) has shown that the anionic portion of humic acid is capable of replacing silicate ions of the alumino-silicates and to some extent the phosphate ions of Fe and Al-phosphates. His original researches on acidoid-basoid ratios and other physico-chemical properties of soil colloids have also covered the realm of soil organic matter. He followed up (38) the work of Oden and contributed very important data illuminating the conditions in the chemical system of proteins and humic acid. He clarified the electrokinetic behavior and the amphoteric nature of the protein-humic acid complex which contains either high or a low quantity of protein or humic acid, depending on the pH and the electrolyte content of the medium. These reactions may afford the pedologist an opportunity to account for the variations in the nitrogen content of the organic matter in the different genetic soil types.

Trusov (67) applied the methods of plant analyses (determining the principal organic compounds, carbohydrates, proteins, fats, waxes, etc.) in studying the transformation of plant materials in the soil. He also investigated the chemical and biological factors involved in the formation of soil organic matter. According to him, most component parts of higher plants, as well as fungi and bacteria, may serve as a source of soil organic matter. Carbohydrates, on decomposition give no humic acid. *"The amount of humic acid formed in the decomposition of proteins is proportional to the number of phenol groups in them.* Soil organic matter forms from lignins, whose hydroquinone and polyphenol groups are oxidized into condensation products with an oxyquinone character."

The shortcomings of plant analyses methods in analyzing soil organic matter were pointed out by Norman (44) : "It is premature yet to describe the components of soil organic matter in terms of specific plant constituents, though it may in part be correct. What in fact is being said is that X per cent of the total is dissolved by, or is resistant to, a particular reagent, which under the same conditions identifies a certain plant contstituent. The development of an adequate system of analysis is perhaps the major problem that confronts us." Norman also reviews the question on the relation of lignin to soil organic matter.

According to Tyurin (70, p. 39), the mutual precipitation of lignins and proteins and their significance in the formation of soil organic matter was advanced for the first time by Deherain (5). Hobson and Page (21) also called attention to this reaction. The lignin-protein nature of soil organic matter was revived by Waksman and Iyer (79) in their empirical studies on the resistance of combinations of lignin and proteins to decomposition by microorganisms. A comprehensive study on soil organic matter, as related to newer concepts of lignin chemistry, is presented by Gottlieb and Hendricks (17).

Lein (33) subjected the work of Waksman and Iyer to a critical analysis after having repeated their experiments on the lignin-protein complexes as the humus nuclei. He uncovered some fundamental errors in their work. He stated: "the assumption made by Waksman and Iyer of new exchange properties appearing in the lignin-protein complex was due to an error in the method of investigation. These authors did not take into consideration the fact that the exchange capacity of lignin is many times increased by a treatment with weak alkali." Lein, therefore concluded that, "from the point of view of exchange reactions the ligno-protein complex is not to be considered as the nucleus of humus. Rather, the humic acid and its complexes with other substances should be considered as the nucleus."

Shmuk (58, 59) investigated the chemical composition of organic matter, not so much the organic compounds that can be isolated from it, but rather from the bulk of organic matter obtained in the form of "humic acid" by extraction with alkali and precipitation with acid. A significant statement on the status of the researches on soil organic matter was made by Shmuk: "The chemical composition of soil organic matter should be investigated with no reference to the problem of its origin. In general, rather than to attempt to gain a knowledge of the chemistry of organic matter from its genesis, it should be easier to understand the processes of its formation from an insight into its chemical structure. To choose the former avenue of approach means to seek an unknown, whose single indisputable property is the dark color. It means the same as if one would try to synthesize a substance, the composition of which is unknown. Not excluding the independent value of such investigations (genesis of organic matter), I am inclined to think they will hardly offer any data clarifying the chemical character of soil organic matter. The problem of the constitution of organic matter could be solved only by methods of general chemical investigations."

A summary of Shmuk's ideas on soil organic matter follows:

1. The soil organic matter represents a complex mixture of various organic compounds, the latter frequently depending on the crop grown.

2. Among the products of the soil organic matter, the proteins are to be noted. They are always found in the soil and are to be recognized as a specific soil substance. The character of these proteins is not clearly understood; it is questionable whether they are present in the free state or in combination with other substances.

3. Outside of a few organic compounds of plant or animal origin, the bulk of the organic matter in the soil is identified with a distinct dark-colored substance or substances with specific characteristic properties.

4. A large portion of the soil organic matter—humic acid—may be obtained by extraction with alkali and precipitation with acid. Some of its original properties undergo a chemical change during the process of extraction and precipitation.

5. In its chemical properties, humus represents a nitrogenous substance with an acid character.

6. The bulk of the soil proteins separates out with the humic acid, but no chemical relationship has been established between the nitrogenous and other parts of the humic acid.

7. The nitrogenous fraction of humic acid contains typical decomposition products of the protein chain. However, the absence of glucose-amine indicates that this protein is not of microbial origin.

8. The acid character of humic acid is determined by the adsorption phenomena that are characteristic of the colloidal properties of the humic acid as well as by the presence of carboxyl groups.

9. Humic acid does combine with salts stoichiometrically, but forms complex adsorption compounds.

10. The solubility of humic acid in water is associated with a change of state, from gel to sol, and depends on the presence of protective colloids. Under favorable conditions, one could prepare a stable colloid solution that shows all the properties of stable emulsoids, such as cataphoresis, reversibility, Brownian movement, and Tyndall effect.

11. The presence of carboxyl groups in humic acid can be demonstrated by the formation of esters, as well as by conductivity.

12. There are benzol nuclei with side chain compounds (tri-substitution) in humic acid; this chemical structure brings it close to the tannins.

13. The hydroxyl groups are found in humic acid, apparently as side chains of the benzol nuclei.

14. The unsaturated character of humic acid is indicated by its oxidation with permanganate in alkaline medium, as well as from its direct combinations with the halides.

15. The ash content of humic acid has been studied but little; it might be assumed that the ash of the humic acid is primarily that of the protein.

16. The compounds formed with humic acid offer a wealth of material for the elucidation of the chemical structure of the humic acid.

17. The humic substances of the soil are similar in composition to the substances that are obtained artificially from proteins, carbohydrates, and other substances .They are also similar to the natural melanins of the animal kingdom.

DIGEST OF AND EXCERPTS FROM TYRUIN'S PRESENTATION ON SOIL ORGANIC MATTER

In his book *Soil Organic Matter,* Tyurin recognizes the difference between soil organic matter and humus. For convenience, he uses these terms interchangeably in the text, and occasionally it is puzzling as to which is which. In general, the terminology on soil organic matter has been greatly confused, but gradually, with the advance in our knowledge on the character and nature of the different fractions of soil organic matter, an understanding is being reached on the meaning of the terms. To this end, Tyurin has contributed a great deal. It was, therefore, deemed appropriate to give, within the limited space available, some parts of his presentation and ideas on soil organic matter.

Chief Groups of Compounds in the Makeup of Soil Organic Matter

From the point of view of the origin of soil organic matter, its complex and dynamic chemical makeup may be reduced to the following groups:

1. Organic compounds present in undecomposed organic residues of plant and small part, animal origin.

2. Substances of microbial synthesis, living and dead microorganisms, not fully decomposed.

3. Intermediate products of decomposition of complex organic compounds of the two groups enumerated and of the one that follows.

4. Humin substances (and partly bitumens), as a product of unique processes of physico-chemical and extracellular enzymatic synthesis. Only a portion of the organic matter substances differing in origin and chemical nature is in the form of a physical mixture or a mechanical admixture with the soil. The larger portion of these substances forms complexes of a physico-chemical and chemical character, combining among themselves as well as with the mineral portion of the soil, its bases, and the clay fraction. This circumstance is the cause of the thus far insurmountable difficulties of separating the soil organic matter from the bulk of the soil and to study its composition.

Present day concepts on the chemical composition of organic matter are nothing more than approximations that are determined by the analytical methods. Thus far, these methods could distinguish a relatively small number of substances. They actually represent more or less large groups of substances, the chemical nature of which and uniformity still raise many doubts.

Substances Soluble in Organic Solvents (Bitumens).—In fuel chemistry, bitumens represent a group of substances extractable with organic solvents (a mixture of alcohol and benzol). These bitumens are a "mixture of hydrocarbons and their derivatives formed by the transformation of waxes, resins, and fatty acids in the course of geologic periods (70, p. 106)." In soil organic matter, which represents a younger and contemporary formation, the bitumen content should be small. A considerable portion of the substances soluble in organic solvents is made up of the waxes, resins, fatty acids, and glycerides of the fatty acids that are inherent constituents or plant residues and microbial cells. These constituents are poor in oxygen and rich in carbon, and under aerobic conditions, in well aerated soils, there is little of these substances, usually not more than 5 per cent of the total organic matter, as shown in table 20, reproduced from Tyurin and Ponomarova (70, p. 107). In peats, the quantity of the bitumens goes up to 15-20 per cent.

Humin Substances.—Humin substances are characterized by Tyurin as a constituent part of soil organic matter as well as of peat and brown coal. They are dark colored substances partly soluble and partly insoluble in alkali. They consist of high molecular hydroxycarboxylic acids with strongly expressed colloidal properties, as shown by Fuchs (12). Stability to acid hydrolysis and insolubility in acetyl bromide are properties common to all of these substances. The insolubility in acetyl bromide differentiates them sharply from the majority of substances of plant origin, including the liguins which like the humic sbustances are stable to acid hydrolysis. Maiwald (35) and Springer (62) have identified the humin substances with *humus substances* or *genuine humus substances.* In Tyurin's interpretation, the term *humin substances* stands for "something

Table 20

Substances soluble in organic solvents in different soils.
(After Tyurin and Ponomarova)

Soil	Hori-zon	Total organic matter in soil	Soluble in ether	Soluble in alcohol	Soluble in alcohol -benzole	Total
				per cent of organic matter		
		per cent			—	3.8
					—	2.4
Gray semidesert	A₁	1.10	1.9	1.9	3.7	4.2
Chestnut brown	A₁	2.35	1.2	1.2	1.9	2.2
Chestnut brown solonetz	A₁	6.12	0.5	—	2.6	2.6
Chernozem	A₁	10.58	0.3	—	6.7	9.6
Gray forest	A₁	4.1	—	—	12.2	12.2
Podzolized	A₁	10.65	2.9	—	7.9	7.9
Peat (Sedge)	0.5 m				13.8	13.8
" "	1.0 m				21.7	21.7
Sphagnum — peat	0.5 m				24.4	24.4
" "	1.0 m					
" "	2.0 m					

definite, originating from the names *humic acid* and *humin* which, unlike the term humus with its broad applications, are restricted in their meaning."

Summing up the status of humin substances, Tyurin considers as probable that they make up 40 to 50 per cent of the total organic matter in podzols and 80 to 90 per cent in chernozem and meadow-bog (neutral) soils. In the soils of the more arid regions, the content of humin substances decreases. In a later publication, Tyurin and Gutkina (75) define humins (of chernozem) as "the organic matter soluble in alkali after decalcifying the soil . . . The humin complex is characterized by a stable bond between the humic acid and suggested fulvic acids." These acids are considered by Tyurin as a type of ester having lost a considerable part of its acid functions when highly polymerized and condensed.

Humic Acids.—The group of substances extracted from soil organic matter with alkali and precipitated with acid is known under the general name *humic acid*.

The methods of separating humic acids vary. The variations consist in strength of alkali used, temperature gradient, time of extraction, and other factors. Because of these, the quantity of humic acid extracted varies, depending on the impurities associated with it and the adsorption constituents. Fundamentally, however, the quality of the humic acid is practically the same, but not the quantity. Tyurin obtained by one and the same method of extraction a series of values for humic acid in different soil types. The data are presented in table 21.

Table 21

Humic acid content of a number of soils in the U.S.S.R., per cent
(After Tyurin)

Soil Type	Horizon	Organic matter in soil	Humic acid	
			In soil	In organic matter
Tundra (Khibin)	A_0	73.10	8.24	11.3
Podzolized (Leningrad)	A_1	10.65	1.20	11.3
Gray forest	A_1	3.48	0.84	24.1
Chernozem (leached)	A_1	8.00	3.20	40.0
Chernozem	A_1	10.58	3.80	35.9
Chestnut brown	A_1	4.16	1.19	22.7
Sononetz	A_1	6.12	1.19	28.6
Podzolized soil (Abkhazia)	A_1	6.20	0.84	12.6
Podzolized soil (Abkhazia)	A_1	3.10	0.32	10.1
Dark brown soil (rendzina-like)	A_1	10.60	3.27	30.8

It is clear that chernozem has the highest quantity of humic acid, and podzols—the lowest.

The residual soil organic matter of a podzol, after acetyl bromide treatment, may be completely recovered with the reagents used for the extraction of humic acid. For chernozem, only 80 per cent of the residual organic matter may be recovered.

In table 22, the data of Tishchenko and Rydalevskaya are cited by Tyurin. They found that with the transition from podzolized soils to chernozem and chestnut brown soils, the carbon content decreases. The ratio of O:H increases with the transition listed. This indicates that the podzols are more hydrated and less oxidized.

The humic acid from soils and several peats shows a fairly constant N content, 3.5—4 per cent. There are, however, in nature considerable accumulations of humic acid of a low N content, such as in brown coal and sphagnum peat. There are observations on the lowering of the N content in humic acid preparations when reprecipitated, especially when $NaHCO_3$ is used as the solvent and H_3PO_4 as the precipitant. These facts give credence to the view that humic acid per se as a specific compound is a N free substance. The presence of N may be explained by the inevitable admixture of N compounds (proteins). However, at present it may be accepted as an established fact that along with the N free humic acids that have formed from lignin and other N free substances, humification of nitrogenous substances in the soil may form humic acids containing N. These considerations are based on the work of Standnikov, Orlov, Fuchs, and others. Besides, it may be stated without a doubt that N free humic acids are easily transformed into N containing substances by reacting with the proteins and their split-products of decomposition.

The term *humic acid* represents an entire group of high molecular compounds that differ somewhat in composition, but possess a series of common properties and a general type of structure.

Haematomelanic Acid.—The alcohol soluble fraction of raw humic acid that precipitates upon acidifying the alkali extracts was named by Hoppe-Seyler *haemato-*

Table 22

Elementary composition of humic acid in different soils of the U. S. S. R.
per cent of ash-free substance

(After Tishchenko and Rydalevskaya)

Soils	C	H	O	N	$\dfrac{C}{N}$ ratio	$\dfrac{C}{H}$ ratio	$\dfrac{O}{H}$ ratio
Podzolized (Leningrad region)	52.39	4.82	39.05	3.74	14.0:1	11.0:1	8.1:1
Peat-bog	54.29	4.53	37.34	3.84	14.0:1	12.0:1	8.2:1
Rendzina loam (Leningrad region)	54.90	4.36	36.34	4.07	13.5:1	12.6:1	8.4:1
Degraded chernozem	56.34	3.54	36.65	3.58	15.1:1	16.0:1	10.3:1
Deep chernozem	57.47	3.38	35.37	3.78	15.0:1	17.0:1	10.4:1
Ordinary chernozem	58.37	3.26	34.67	3.70	15.7:1	17.9:1	10.6:1
Chestnut brown	58.56	3.40	33.95	4.09	14.1:1	17.0:1	10.0:1

melanic acid. Its nature has thus far not been studied sufficiently. In his monograph on humic acids, Sven Oden pointed out that the alcohol soluble portion of natural organic matter was small. He considered it probable that haematomelanic acid might form from humic acid as a result of hydrolysis in an alkaline medium. . . . He was inclined to consider this acid an analogue of the ulminic acid of Mulder whose analyses show it to be a less oxidized compound than humic acid. . . . According to Sven Oden and Sostegni, haematomelanic acid differs from humic acid by a higher H content and slightly higher C content. Sven Oden quotes the figures of 58.2 per cent C and 4.3 per cent H for humic acid, and 62.2 per cent C and 5.28 per cent H for haematomelanic acid. Sostegni quotes the figures of 62-63 per cent C and 4.9-5.3 per cent H for haematomelanic acid.

Humic Substances Insoluble in Alkali.—The nature of humic substances insoluble in alkali is as unclear as that of the haematomelanic acid. Sprengel, who was the first to establish the identity of these substances in peat and soil organic matter, suggested the name humus coal. . . . To determine it, Sprengel suggested prolonged boiling with KOH after having extracted the humic acid in a solution of Na_2CO_3 at a temperature of 60-70°C. Upon boiling with KOH, the humus coal goes into solution from which it may be separated in the form of humic acid upon acidifying. Berzelius changed the term *humus coal* to *humin*, and Mulder differentiated ulmin and humin, corresponding to ulmic and humic acids, which are of a similar composition but differ in degree of oxidation; ulmin contains more hydrogen than humin. Berthelot and Andre have investigated humin substances produced from sugar and concluded that humin is an anhydride of humic acid, whose composition corresponds to the formula $C_{18}H_{14}O_6$ whereas the formula for humic acid is $C_{18}H_{16}O_7$. The view that humin is an anhydride of humic acid has been accepted by Oden.

According to Fuchs, the group of humic substances insoluble in alkali may be differentiated into: (a) humic acids insoluble in alkali and (b) humins. These acids are endowed with the same characteristic properties as the humic acids that are soluble in alkali. Upon exhaustive methylation they behave as hydroxycarboxylic acids. They liberate acetic acid from acetates, and their insoluble salts show some base exchange capacity. The presence of such insoluble humic acids was established in old brown coal. Their insolubility in alkali may be explained by a higher degree of polymerization and condensation accompanied by dehydration. On the basis of this extensive data, Fuchs considers the humins as reduced anhydrides of humic (hydroxycarboxylic) acids. He notes that humins are absent in peats. This conclusion may be arrived at also from the data on the analyses of peat by Stadnikov.

Thus, the composition of humic substances insoluble in alkali, i.e., humins or humus coal (old terminology) of soil organic matter, apparently differs substantially from an analgous group in more ancient formations—brown and anthracite coal. Together with the humic substances forming from humic acid by aging, there are probably substances in the stage of transition towards humic acid. The presence of substances of the first category (close to humins) may be expected in soils with a high content of humic acid, such as the chernozems. In the upper horizons of the podzolic soil type and peats, one may contemplate the presence of the second category (humolignins). This is incompletely humified lignin and other substances that are not soluble any more in acetyl-bromide but are not soluble as yet in alkali.

Other Compounds in the Makeup of Organic Matter

Besides the *groups* of complex substances of organic matter, Tyurin reviews the chemical *entities* of plant origin associated with these complex groups.

Lignins.—Speaking of the lignins, he points out that an appreciable portion of soil organic matter behaves like the lignin of plant residues. He cites the data of Grosskopf showing that in the strongly decomposed layer of forest litter the lignin content is small, 14.2 per cent against 41.6

per cent humic substances. He also quotes the data of Pichard on the lignin content of the organic matter in the following soils: peat—16.42 per cent; unmanured field soil—9.50 per cent; manured field—8.90 per cent; unmanured orchard soil—8.11 per cent; and manured orchard soil— 6.06 per cent. It is clear that the lignin content of soil organic matter is within the range of 5 to 10 per cent.

Hemicellulose.—On the origin of hemicellulose in soil organic matter, it is suggested that in all likelihood a portion of it stems from the plant residues and a portion is of microbial synthesis. One should not exclude the possibility that the hemicellulose of soil organic matter is nothing more than a part of a specific group of nitrogenous substances that have originated by way of the condensation of the split-products of polysaccharides and proteins. The first indications on the presence of polysacchrides in soil organic matter may be traced by the appearance of pentosans. They are determined by the separation of furfural by boiling with 12 per cent KCl. . . . Fraps has shown that there is a constant relationship between the pentosans and the proteins, 0.75:1.

With the discovery of uronic acid in soil organic matter by Shorey and Martin, the data on the pentosan content, based on the determination of furfural, have to be revised. The point is that uronic acids are subject to decarboxylizing reactions with the separation of CO_2 and the formation of pentoses which later separate out furfural.

Side by side with the derivatives of uronic acids and perhaps pentosans, a more or less considerable portion of the hemicelluloses of soil organic matter is represented by hexosans. The origin of these may be attributed to the more stable hexosans of plant origin and, primarily, apparently to the synthetic activities of microorganisms.

Besides its property to hydrolyze in hot dilute mineral acids, the hemicellulose of soil organic matter is partly soluble in boiling water and in dilute cold acid and more so in weak alkali.

Cold dilute acid treatment of soils dissolves small amounts of organic matter. However, in some podzolized soils dilute mineral acid extracts a considerable quantity of organic matter from A_1 as well as from the humus-illuvial horizon. With the organic matter, appreciable and sometimes large quantities of aluminum and iron go into solution. The extract shows the presence of some reducing sugars and an increased degree of oxidation which indicates the presence of uronic acids. A direct determination of these in a podzol of Karelia and a weakly podzolic tundra soil has shown that uronic acid accounts for only 16 to 25 per cent of the total organic matter soluble in $1.0N$ H_2SO_4. When the acid extract is neutralized slowly, practically all of the Al and uronic acids as well as the rest of the organic matter precipitate. Making the mixture slightly alkaline, all the precipitate goes in solution again. This phenomenon, which has been noted aso for the acid filtrate of humic precipitated from several podzolized soils, reminds one of the properties of apocrenic acid described by Berzelius.

Discussing the views on the origin of N-containing humic acids, the suggested reaction is probably the combination of amino-acids with the carbonyl, hydroxyl, and carboxyl groups of the humic acid. A similar reaction is theoretically possible with hemicellulose. It is more likely that in this reaction, the amino-acids combine, not with the hemicellulose but with the partially or fully hydrolyzed (under the influence of enzymes) products of their decomposition. In other words, they combine with the sugars and uronic acids that have free aldehyde and carboxyl groups. The possibiilty of such condensation reactions of sugars and oxy-compounds with amino-acids follows from the work of Maillard (34) and Stadnikov (65). From this point of view, the group of hemicelluloses of soil organic matter may be looked upon, at least in part, as initial products of condensation of carbohydrates and amino-acids. These products may lead to humic acids containing nitrogen.

Cellulose.—The cellulose content of soil organic matter is less than that of hemicellulose. Cellulose is decomposed under aerobic and anaerobic conditions and is not synthesized by microbes. The quantity of cellulose in soil organic matter does not exceed the 10 per cent mark in the undecomposed and semidecomposed forest litter. In the mineral horizon, the cellulose content varies from 1 to 6 per cent. Some investigators claims the absence of cellulose in mineral soils.

Nitrogen.—The total content of N in soil organic matter is on the average about 5 per cent, mostly in organic form. Very little of this form of N is water soluble. Solonetz, being highly dispersed, has the highest amount of water soluble N; chernozem has the least; and podzols are in the intermediate class. The nitrogenous substances seem to be tied up with the entire mass of soil organic matter, in the form of insoluble compounds. Heating the soil with 2 per cent HCl or 5 per cent H_2SO_4 (for the hydrolysis of hemicelluloses), a large share of the organic N, 30 to 50 per cent, goes into solution. According to the data of Jodidi (23) and Shmuk (58, 59), the following forms of N are found in the soil: amide, 20 to 25 per cent; mono-amino-acid, 60 to 65 per cent; and diamino-acid, 12 to 15 per cent.

The data cited, as well as those of other investigators who found greater fluctuations in the relative content of the different forms of N, lead to the conclusion that, in the hydrolysis of soil organic matter, the same type of products are obtained as in the hydrolysis of proteins. The only difference is that in the case of soil organic matter, there is a higher percentage of amide N, and besides, the percentage of the unhydrolyzed portion is much higher than in the case of proteins. On the basis of these data, most investigators are of the opinion that the main portion of N in soil organic matter is in the form of proteins. At the same time, it is well known that in a great many properties, the proteins of soil organic matter differ from those of plant origin.

Summary.—Tyurin sums up his extensive discussion on soil organic matter by classifying it into three groups. They are presented in table 23.

Table 23

Chemical composition of soil organic matter

(After Tyurin)

I. *Humic substances*	II. *Non-humic substances*
A. Insoluble in alkali (*humins*) 　1. Insoluble in alkali humic 　　acid (and humins?) 　2. Humolignins (*ulmin* of Mulder) 　3. Coal (accidental origin) B. Soluble in alkali 　1. Humic acids 　2. Haematomelanic acid and 　　dehydrohumic acids of 　　Fuchs.	A. Lignin B. Cellulose C. "Hemicellulose" D. "Proteins" 　(C and D represent a complex of specific products of the condensation of carbohydrates and uronic acids with amino-acids and polypeptides) E. Low-molecular products of 　decomposition (organic 　acids, amino-acids, etc.)

III. *Bitumens* (fats. waxes, fatty acids, resins, gums, etc.)

Tyurin points out (p. 147) that "these groups do not exist as independent entities; still they are genetically related and are not separated from each other. In the generally homogenous mass of soil organic matter, the groups enumerated present more complicated complexes as a result of the phenomenae of adsorption and association. These complexes may combine closely with the mineral portion of the soil, its bases and the clay fraction."

In his latest publication, Tyurin (73)* formulated the geographic regularity in the formation of soil organic matter as follows:

1. In the soils of the eluvial series, the organic matter content and nitrogen reach their maximum in the deep chernozem. In the soils north and south of this soil subzone, the quantities of organic matter decrease.

2. The distribution of organic matter in the soil profile is characterized by the following attributes: in the soils of the forest regions, the organic matter content of the 0-20 cm. layer makes up 50 per cent of the total organic matter present in a 100 cm. layer. In the steppe, chernozem soils, the organic matter content drops gradually with depth and the 0-20 cm. layer contains only 24-30 per cent of that present in a 100 cm. layer. In the chestnut brown and gray-semidesert soil zones, the 0-20 cm. layer contains 43-50 per cent of the organic matter present in a 100 cm. layer.

3. The relation of the C:N in soils presents the following regularity:

In chernozem the ratio is less than 10. As the organic matter content decreases, as in the gray podzolic soils of the forest steppe, the C:N ratio drops to 10-8. A similar ratio is encountered in the chestnut brown soils. The narrowest ratio is found in the gray semidesert soils, 6-5.5, an indication of a high N content. The widest C:N ratio is found in the red loams (krasnozem), 18.9 which indicates a low N content.

Composition Groups of Soil Organic Matter.—According to Tyurin, the following groups of complexes of soil organic matter are recognized: 1. Waxes and resins. 2. Humic acids. 3. Fulvic acids, in the terminology of Sven-Oden, or the crenic and apocrenic acids in the terminology of Berzelius and Mulder. 4. The residual organic matter, the *humins* which represent humic acids that are more oxidized and appear in the form of stable combinations with the mineral portion of the soil. Tyurin noted the fundamental regularities in the composition of soil organic matter of the principal soil types of Soviet Russia. These regularities have been formulated as follows:

First, humic acids are the most characteristic group of soil organic matter. *Second,* the relative content of humic acids increases as we move from the podzolized towards the chernozem soils and decreases again as we move towards the gray semidesert. *Third,* the change in humic acid content runs parallel with the changes in in total content of organic matter. *Fourth,* the change in fulvic acid content is less regular, but in general, it is in inverse ratio with the humic acids. *Fifth,* the ratio of humic acid to fulvic acid in chernozem and dark chestnut brown soils is close to unity. In other soils, especially the red loams (krasnozem) and podzolized soils, the fulvic acid content is 2 to 3 times higher than that of the humic acids.

ADVANCES IN SOIL ORGANIC MATTER RESEARCH

After following a long meandering road, the search for new avenues of approach in the study of soil organic matter has brought us back to where we started from. We have returned to the original researches of Berzelius and his followers, as outlined briefly in the first part of this

---

*The original was not available, and the excerpts given here have been taken from a paper by Kononova (31), one of Tyurin's collaborators on the problem of soil organic matter.

chapter. In capsule form, soil organic matter research has brought out the following fairly well defined three groups of organic entities.

1. *Humic acid,* the group of organic substances which may be obtained by extracting the soil with 0-1 or 0.2 N solutions of alkali at room temperature and precipitating the supernatant liquids with acid, 0.1 to 0.2 N.

2. *Fulvic acid,* the group of organic matter substances that remains in solution after the humic acid has been precipitated. This group is substantially what Berzelius distinguished as *crenic* and *apocrenic* acid.

3. *Humin,* the group of organic substances remaining behind after extracting the humic acid. This group may be extracted with hot alkali.

As the problem presents itself now, information is being sought on the groups of soil organic matter mentioned, their constituent parts, the interrelation of these groups, and the nature of the complexes produced in the transformations that take place in the residues of plant and animal origin as a result of microbiological, chemical, and physico-chemical reactions.

Natkina (43) studied the nature of the humic acids of chernozem and podzolized soils. For comparative purposes, the humic acids were determined before and after the soils had been hydrolyzed with 1.0 N H_2SO_4 for the removal of hemicellulose. Besides the elemental composition of the humic acids, the carboxyl and hydroxyl groups were determined by methylation and the exchange capacity by the adsorption of Ca.

Without hydrolysis, the yield of humic acid in chernozem was 27.5 grams and after hydrolysis 31 grams. The humic acid group of this chernozem comprised about 40 per cent of the total organic matter content. In the case of podzols, the yield of humic acid was 62.1 grams and 46 grams before and after hydrolysis respectively. The humic acid content in podzols was 15 per cent of the total organic matter content.

An alcohol-benzol extract of the humic acid of the two soil types shows that podzols have a higher content of the substances soluble in this reagent, 3.19 and 2.47 per cent of the total quantity of humic acid in the unhydrolyzed and in the hydrolyzed chernozem respectively, and 11.16 and 13.56 per cent in the similarly treated humic acid of podzols. The alcohol extract of these humic acids shows that the content of the so-called hematomelanic acids is low, 1.82 and 1.95 per cent for the unhydrolyzed and hydrolyzed chernozem respectively, and 1.72 and 2.40 per cent in the similarly treated podzols. On the basis of the results reported, it is considered superfluous to resort to a preliminary hydrolysis of the soil in order to obtain the so-called pure humic acid.

The elemental composition of the humic acids investigated by Natkina shows that chernozem has about 63.0 per cent C and podzols about 56 per cent. Because of this, the O:H and C:H ratios of the humic acids of chernozem origin are wider than those of podzols. This means that the chernozem is more oxidized and less dehydrated than the podzols. In this connection, the work of Tishchenko and Rydalevskaya (66) may be cited. In table 22 the different ratios for 7 soil types are presented. The data are in agreement with the work of Natkina.

For a comparative characterization of the humic acids of the two soils, determinations were made on the carboxyl and phenol-hydroxyl groups by methylation and subsequent determination of the ester- and ether-methoxyls and products of methylation. The content of methoxyls was determined by the method of Vieböck and Brecher. The carboxyl groups were determined by the Fuchs method. The methylation of the phenol-hydroxyl groups was carried out with di-methyl-sulfate by the Heuser, Schmidt and Gunkel method. The only difference between the two humic acids was in the phenol-hydroxyl groups. The chernozem had 4 and the podzols had 6 and 7 of these groups.

A determination of the exchange capacity of the humic acids, by the method of Ca-acetate (1.0 N), showed that the exchange capacity of the humic acid of the podzols corresponded to the H of the carboxyl and one hydroxyl groups. The exchange capacity of the humic acid of chernozem corresponded to the replaceable H of the carboxyl and phenol-hydroxyl groups. In terms of milliequivalents per 100 gms., the humic acid of podzols was 341.7 before hydrolysis and 364.7 after hydrolysis; for the humic acid of the chernozem, the corresponding values were: 509 and 511. The findings of Natkina for the podzols are in accord with those of Lein (33).

The replaceable Ca of the humic acid offers the opportunity of determining the equivalent weight of the humic acid, as shown by Oden (46). Natkina reports the value of 200 for the humic acid of chernozem and 280 for that of the podzols. McGeorge (40), who used the term lignin-humus for what amounts to humic acid, gave the equivalent weight values for 10 soils and they varied from 326 to 420.

Tyurin (71) reviewed the earlier investigations on crenic and apocrenic acids, from the days of Berzelius to date. It was Oden who grouped these acids under the name fulvic acid because of their yellow coloration—from pale to golden yellow (*fulvus* meaning yellow).

Tyurin reopened the investigations on fulvic acid. He used the A_1 horizon of a podzol and the A horizon of a leached (degraded) chernozem. The soils were decalcified with 0.1 N H_2SO_4, dialyzed, dried, extracted with a 1:1 mixture of alcohol and benzol in a Soxhlet apparatus, and then subjected to the regular procedure of extracting the humic acid with alkali (Tyurin used NH_4OH) and precipitating with acid.

The ammoniacal salts of fulvic acid in solution (for the details of obtaining these and their purification, the paper of Tyurin should be consulted) were treated with $BaCl_2$ to remove the sulfates, and the filtrates treated with $(NH_4)_2CO_3$ to remove the excess Ba and to decompose the Ba-salts of fulvic acid. The purified NH_4-salts of fulvic acid were then subjected to analyses.

As stated by Tyurin, "the results show that the elemental composition and equivalent weights of the fulvic acid are alike in podzols and chernozems. Hydrolyzing the fulvic acid preparation with 5 per cent H_2SO_4 gave 20-25 per cent reducing sugars, and by boiling with 12 per cent HCl, furfural was obtained, and CO_2 was released in quantities equivalent to 5-10 per cent pentosans and 15-20 per cent uronic anhydride."

Summarizing the results of the analyses, Tyurin comes to the following conclusions on the general character of the chemical nature of fulvic acid:

Fulvic acid of soil organic matter represents high molecular hydroxyl-carboxylic acids (also containing N) with an equivalent weight (in relation to NH_3) of about 300. Fulvic acid differs from humic acid by its light color, considerably lower content of C, solubility in H_2O and mineral acids, and considerably greater capacity to hydrolize in acids.

The variability in N content of fulvic acids of different origin (in the B horizon of podzol, the N content of the fulvic acid is 2 to 1 per cent) is explained by Tyurin by the following supposition:

The fulvic acid group of soil organic matter may be looked upon as products of condensation of carbohydrates and uronic acids with the intermediate products of the decomposition of proteins. The N content of such products apparently depends upon the relation of N free and N containing substances available for the reaction. The possible causes and mechanism of such a reaction is still an open question and requires more detailed study.

Tyurin also discusses the stability of the fulvic acid in soil organic matter. The point is, that when separated, fulvic acid is soluble in water and in acid, but when the soil is extracted with acid, no fulvic acid goes in solution. The stability of fulvic acid in soil organic matter or in peat is explained by Tyurin by its attachment to the humic acid in the form of ester-like complexes. Upon treatment with alkali, these complexes become saponified, and in this process the humic acid separates from the fulvic acid. Upon subsequent acidulation, these two acids do not recombine; the humic acid precipitates and the fulvic acid remains in solution. A study of the chemical nature of fulvic acid and methods of its preparation is presented by Ponomareva (46a).

In a study on the nature of humin, Tyurin and Gutkina (75) conducted experiments subjecting a chernozem soil, after extracting the humic acid, to a series of treatments: 5.0 N HNO_3 treatment (hydrolysis) by the method of Fuchs (12); HF treatment (to separate organic complexes from silicates) by the Rather (47) method; and acetyl-bromide plus HF and HNO_3 treatment of Springer (63, 64). When the soil containing the humin group was then extracted with alkali and the extract acidified, the products obtained were humic acid and fulvic acid.

It is suggested by Tyurin that the humin group consists of complexes of humic acid and fulvic acid (on the order of complex esters and anhydrides) which have lost a considerable portion of acid functions through polymerization and condensation. The treatments given to humin prior to the alkali extraction have a loosening effect on the condensated complex and cause depolymerization. Only then does the humin group behave like a complex of humic and fulvic acids which can be separated by the Tyurin method. It is of interest to note that the explanation offered on the nature of humin has been given by Tyurin in his earlier work.

Gillam (14) made a study of the humic acid (extracted with 4 per cent ammonia, precipitated with HCl, and purified by dialysis) of a gray-brown forest soil, muck (from Minnesota), and grassland. The last named soil represented a composite NH_3 extract of 300 samples from the Great Plains area embracing prairie, chestnut, and chernozem soils. Gillam found the humic acid to be negatively charged hydrophilic colloids, having a conductivity ranging from 400 to 2000 mhos. The humic acid from the three different sources were found to be of a similar elementary composition. However, the ash content of the podzolized soil (the forest soil from Michigan) had a much lower ash content, 3.6 per cent, than the other two soils, 7.7 and 6.8 for the muck and grassland soils respectively. The humic acids from muck and forest soils were more readily and more completely acetylated than the humic acid from grasslands. It is claimed that "the non-nitrogenous fraction of humic acid consists of a slightly modified lignin complex. This modification is probably brought about primarily by demethylation, hydrolysis, and other chemical reactions which could cause the formation of phenolic and carboxyl groups."

Sources of Soil Organic Matter

In a recent paper, Tyurin (74) discusses the manner in which roots and living microbes contribute to the store of organic matter in the soil.

Roots.—The dead roots, after the growing season is over, or after the life-cycle of the plant has been completed, are, by and large, the most important contributors to the store of organic matter in the soil. Next in importance are the continuously dying root hairs and cells of the outer layers of the main roots all through the growing season. And lastly, the exudations of organic substances from the root system.

In table 24, Tyurin presents data on the dry matter content of roots of a number of plants in different soil types. It is obvious that "annuals contribute 3 to 5 tons of organic (dry) matter per hectare. The perennials add similar quantities of organic matter in the form of roots. Under forests, the quantity of dying roots contributed by the trees is less than that under grass. However, the herbaceous and grass vegetation, as well as the forest floor debris, augment the contribution of organic matter to the soil under conditions of forests. The total quantity of organic matter contributed by forests approaches that of grasses. In the brown and chestnut brown soils, the roots supply less organic matter than in other soil zones."

Living Microbes.—The item of living microbes in the balance sheet of soil organic matter has not been explored sufficiently. In this connection, Tyurin's data and discussion are of interest:

"The quantity of organic matter in the form of living microbes has not been determined. Their presence and activities influence the chemistry of soil organic matter and some properties of the soil itself. It is, however, almost impossible to separate the living microbes from the rest of the soil organic matter."

Tyurin analyzes the problem of living microbes in the soil from many angles and comes to the conclusion that the average weight of a billion living microbes ranges from 0.1 to 0.3 milligrams. In table 25, Tyurin presents figures on this item. It varies from 0.7 to 2.4 metric tons per hectare. The grayearths, with a low organic matter content, contain the highest percentage of living microbes.

Miscellaneous Contributions on Soil Organic Matter

Kukharenko (32) determined the carboxyl and phenol groups of humic acid by treating it with Ca-acetate and titrating the acetic acid formed. Methylation of the humic acid with methanol gave the same results. He claims to have obtained stable Ca-humates. These findings are in contradiction with the work of Oden who reported these humates as easily hydrolyzable and unstable.

Norman and Bartholomew (45) show that 15 per cent of the organic carbon of surface soil seems to be present in uronide groupings. The proportion increases with depth, particularly in podzol soils, in which a marked accumulation may be found in the B horizon.

Tishchenko and Rydalevskaya (66), in their work with humic acid of a number of typical zonal soils, corroborated the findings of Fuchs (12)

Soils	Plant cover	Horizon in cm.	Humus	Roots Living Total	Roots Living Fine roots	Roots Dead
Podzolized loam	13 year old fallow	0-20	53.2	12.88	10.00	No data
	Rye	0-20	53.2	4.41	2.33	” ”
	Oats	0-20	53.2	3.68	3.25	” ”
	Mixed forest	0-12	32.1	18.58	7.00	” ”
	” ”	0-27	45.7	27.12	7.32	” ”
Strongly pod- zolized heavy loam	Old fallow	0-24	85.0	11.0	not determined	
	Conifer forest	5-10	16.1	8.8	” ”	
	” ”	5-25	43.5	12.4	” ”	
Dark gray, weak- ly, podzolized loam	Deciduous forest	0-15	130.7	15.95	8.14	6.3
	”	0-25	217.4	17.34	9.3	6.76
Degraded cher- nozem clay	Rye	0-10	88.1	3.44	No data	6.96*
	Virgin sod	0-10	101.2	8.54	6.59	2.12
	” ”	0-20	202.2	12.73	9.85	3.04
Deep cherno- zem clay	14 year old fallow	0-10	133.2	5.19	5.19	4.03
	” ”	0-25	291.0	8.68	8.68	4.19
	Virgin sod	0-15	75.2	3.25	3.25	2.68
Chestnut brown heavy loam	” ”	0-25	113.0	4.55	4.55	3.23
	3 year alfal- fa field	0-25	40.4	12.1	No data	No data
Gray semidesert		0-20	30.8	5.2	4.2	1.0

*Includes

who worked with humic acid of brown coal. Fuchs established in humic acid the presence of 4 carboxyl and 4 phenol groups capable of reacting with bases. The carboxyl groups are more active than the hydroxyls of the phenol groups. Khainskii (27), in his investigations of humic acid obtained from peat, has shown that the hydrogen of all carboxyl groups is replaced at a neutral reaction, and after that, a sharp jump in pH is observed on the potentiometric curve.

Rydalevskaya and Tishchenko (49) studied the cation exchange of humic acid obtained from different soil types "in relation to the character of the periphereal groups and the ability of the hydrogen of these groups for exchange reactions." They used the humic acid of a typical chernozem, a podzolized loam, and a peat-marsh soil. Buffered solutions of 0.1 N $BaCl_2$ at pH 4.5, 6.4, and 8.1, were passed through weighed portions of humic acid until the leachates showed the pH of the respective buffer solution. Upon washing out the excess of $BaCl_2$, the exchange capacity was determined by replacing the Ba with $0.05N$ HCl. "Recalculating the Ba in terms of H-equivalents, it was possible to figure out the number of per-

24

humus in soils, metric tons per hectare
Tyurin)

Per cent of total organic matter				Ratios		
Humus	Living roots		Dead roots	C-humus	N-humus	Source
	Total	Fine		C-roots	N-roots	
80.5	19.5	15.1	No data	4.8	17.1	Kachinskii (24)
92.3	7.7	4.0	" "	13.9	50.2	
93.5	6.5	5.7	" "	16.7	60.5	
63.3	36.7	13.8	" "	2.0	8.6	
62.8	37.2	10.6	" "	2.0	8.4	
88.9	11.6	No data	" "	9.0	44.4	Tyurin (74)
64.7	35.3	" "	" "	2.1	11.2	
77.8	22.2	" "	" "	4.1	21.6	
87.1	9.3	4.7	3.6	9.5	33.0	Malyanov (37)
90.1	7.1	3.8	2.8	14.5	50.3	
89.4	3.5	No data	7.1	29.7	86.0	
90.4	7.6	5.9	2.0	13.7	39.7	
92.8	5.8	4.5	1.4	18.4	52.9	
93.5	3.6	3.6	2.9	14.9	86.0	
95.8	2.9	2.9	1.3	39.0	112.0	
92.7	4.0	4.0	3.3	27.0	87.2	Savinov and Pankova (53)
93.5	3.8	3.8	2.7	28.3	91.5	
77.0	23.0	No data	No data	3.9	12.8	Kononova (30)
85.6	14.4	2.7	" "	6.8	22.5	Golodkovskii (15)

the stubble

iphery groups of molecules of humic acid participating in the reaction."
In table 26, the elementary composition of the humic acids and the exchange
capacity of these are given.

It is to be noted that the C content of the chernozem is highest, and
of the peat-marsh lowest. This fact

indicates a younger chemical age of the peat-marsh, a conclusion substantiated by
treating the humic acids with acetyl bromide. Practically nothing of the humic acid
of the chernozem was dissolved; however, 6.9 per cent of the humic acid of the podzolized soil and 51.2 per cent of the peat-marsh did dissolve by the acetyl bromide
reagent. Such a behavior corroborates the high hydration and the young age of the
peat-marsh humic acid. . . . The exchange capacity of the humic acids of the chernozem is higher than of peat-marsh. This increase is in all probability due to the replacement of the hydrogen in the phenol-hydroxyl groups. To study this replacement
by a cation, it was necessary to isolate the hydrogen of the carboxyl group. This is
possible by the methylation of the humic acid with methanol in the presence of dry
HCl, as shown in the equation:

$$R \text{ (humic)} \diagup^{COOH}_{\diagdown OH} + CH_3OH \longrightarrow R \text{ (humic)} \diagup^{COOCH_3}_{\diagdown OH} + H_2O$$

Table 25

The mass of living microbes per hectare in a 0-25 cm. layer

(After Tyurin)

Soil Type	Bacteria per ha., billions	Living bacteria, weight of one billion, mgs.	Weight of bacteria in one gram of soil, mgs.	Weight of soil layer, 0-25 cm., tons per ha.	Weight of bacteria in the 0-25 cm. layer, tons per ha.		Mass of bacteria, per cent of organic matter
					Living state	Dry matter	
Grayearth	2.7	0.13	0.35	3500	1.22	0.24	0.60
Chernozem	3.0	0.20	0.60	3000	1.80	0.36	0.18
"	4.0	0.20	0.80	3000	2.40	0.48	0.24 — 0.16
Podzol	1.3	0.16	0.21	3500	0.74	0.15	0.30
"	2.0	0.20	0.40	3500	1.40	0.28	0.50

Table 26

Elementary composition of humic acids from several sources and their exchange reactions
(After Rydalevskaya and Tishchenko)

Soil type	Elementary composition					Exchange reactions					
	Ash	C	H	O	N	At pH 4.5	Acid goups	At pH 6.4	Acid groups	At pH 8.1	Acid groups
	per cent	per cent	per cent	per cent	per cent	m.e.*	number	m.e.	per cent	m.e	number
Chernozem	0.70	58.29	3.23	33.76	3.72	292.2	4	432.9	6	590.5	8
Podzolized	3.40	56.19	4.23	35.84	3.74	243.0	3-4	410.0	5-6	548.7	7-8
Peat-Marsh	0.42	54.29	4.53	37.34	3.84	170	2-3	286.3	4	400.0	5
Peat						182.8	2-3	305.6	4		

*m.e.=milliequivalents per 100 gm. of dry substance.

The complex esters thus obtained were analyzed for methoxyls. The esters of the humic acids of different soils show minor differences in the quantity of methoxyls, by which the molecular weight of 1400 has been calculated for the humic acids. Apparently, the exchange capacity of the complex esters, where the hydrogen of the carboxyl groups is replaced by methoxyl, depends on the reactivity of the remaining free phenol groups. The hydrogen of these groups participates in the cation exchange reactions.

Rydalevskaya and Tishchenko present more evidence on the cation exchange capacity of the phenol hydroxyls and come to the following conclusions:

1. The humic acids of soils have the characteristics of phenol-carbonic acid.
2. The acid nature of humic acids is due to the presence of phenol hydroxyl and carboxyl groups in their molecule.
3. The exchange capacity of the humic acids of chernozem and podzolized soils is higher than that of the humic acid of peat-marsh soil at all pH values.
4. At neutrality, the hydrogen of the acid radicals as well as the hydrogen of the phenol hydroxyls participate in the cation exchange reactions of the humic acids of chernozem and podzolized soils.
5. At neutrality, the exchange capacity of the humic acid of the peat-marsh soil corresponds to 4 carboxyls.
6. In an alkaline medium (pH 8.1), the carboxyl as well as the phenol groups are completely replaced in the humic acids of the chernozem and the podzolized soils.

Forsyth (11) prepared humic acid from heather humus, garden soil (actually from a stack of sod 6 years old), sphagum peat, pine raw humus (from the lower part of the A_0), cabbage compost, and fresh grass. For the alkali extraction, he stirred 100 gms. of organic matter or soil with 0.5 N NaOH for 48 hours. The supernatant liquid was siphoned off, filtered through cotton and then by suction through a sinter-glass funnel. The filtrate was treated with dilute HCl and left for 2 days to settle. To expel the excess water from the humic acid after filtering, it was frozen at —10°C. (syneresis), allowed to thaw, and filtered again with suction.

Summarizing his results on the fractionation of the humic acid, Forsyth concludes:

The humic precipitate is always a mixture of true humic acid with varying amounts of coprecipitated material . . . While the various humic acids have similar molecular structures, the number and kind of reactive groups depend on the conditions and length of time under which the humus was formed. Humification would appear to be a combination of a hydrolysis and oxidation of the original lignin.

Kojima (28) shows that a considerable part of the organic N of the hydrolytic products of organic matter is of amino acid character. Of the total N in muck, 37 per cent is in the form of a-amino acid; aspartic acid amounts to 6-7 per cent of the total amino acids; glutamic and hydroxy-glutamic acid make up about 5 per cent; hydroxyamino acid accounts for 18 per cent. Other data on the nature of organic N are given.

Sallans, Snell, Mackinney, and Mckibbin (51) analyzed an aqueous extract of raw humus from a Quebec podzol soil. From 1000 grams of raw humus extracted successively with a total of 4.3 liters of water, 3.5 grams of dry matter were collected. The pH of the extract was 3.3, and the total acidity was equal to 5.2 ml. of normal acid. Following a procedure of extractions, distillations, and fractionations with different reagents, they separated the volatile acids, formic acid (0.012 gm. per kgm. of raw humus) and acetic acid, 21 and 79 per cent respectively. Mannitol made up 3-4 per cent of the total soluble organic matter. A series of other substances have been isolated, but their identity was not determined.

Tyurin (71) extracted the water soluble organic matter from 750 gms. of A_0 and from 3.5 kgms. of A_1 of a podzol soil, using 12.5 and 17.5 liters of water respectively, with the aid of Buchner funnels. The extracts were filtered through membrane ultrafilters and concentrated to 250 ml. by evaporation under reduced pressure at 40°C. Aliquots of the concentrate were used for the different analyses.

The yield of water soluble organic matter from the A_0 was 0.39 per cent of the total (this figure is in good agreement with the one quoted above by Sallans and associates for the raw humus). The yield from the A_1 horizon was 0.113 per cent of the total soil. The pH of the respective extracts was 5.8 and 4.15; the titrable acidity, milliequivalents per 100 gms. of dry matter, 123 and 250; the ammonia content was 5.24 and 3.63 per cent of the dry matter of the extracts; the organic matter content—77.04 and 74.52 per cent; the P_2O_5 content 4.38 and 0.29 per cent (the utilization of the P by the root system of the pine forest from the A_1 may explain the low P_2O_5 in the water extract); the quantity of bases (Ca, Mg, K, Na) was about the same, 215 and 227 milliequivalents; the C content of the organic matter 49.02 and 50.77 per cent; the N content—2.28 and 1.73 per cent.

There was no humic acid in the soluble organic matter. This fact led Tyurin to the conclusion that humic acid does not participate directly in the migration of mineral constituents in the process of podzolization. A similar deduction was made with reference to the bitumens, the content of which decreased to a very small quantity in the A_1 horizon. The presence of fulvic acids in the soluble organic matter was considered by Tyurin as evidence that these acids are among the active agents of podzolization.

Springer (64) fractionated soil organic matter and some of its groups by means of alkali and acetyl bromide treatment. He reported two types of humic acids: 1, brown humic acid from peat and acid soils; 2, gray humic acid from chernozem and rendzina. About 30 per cent of the organic matter of these soils was the gray humic acid. Springer considered the probability of the chemical union of certain organic substances of chernozem and rendzina with the clay minerals, forming the so-called humus-clay complexes.

Meyer (41) concluded that the organic component is an integral part of the crystal lattice of the humus-clay complex. He precipitated the complex from a mixture of Na-silicate and Na-humate in the presence of $AlCl_3$, forming an $Al_2O_3:3SiO_2$ in the complex. His precipitates approached the properties of the organo-mineral gels described by Tyulin (68, 69).

Discussions and analytical data on the interaction of humates with the mineral portion of the soil are presented by Sakun (50) and Vino-kurov (77). Their work is also related to that of Tyulin on the organo-mineral gels.

Aleksandrova (1) analyzed quantitatively and qualitatively the composition of humic acid, fulvic acid, and humin from solonchak, solonetz, and solodi. In solonchak, the humin group makes up one half of the total organic matter in the profile. In the surface horizon, 15-16 per cent of the total organic matter consists of humic acid; the fulvic acid makes up 16-21 per cent. In the carbonate horizon, the bulk of the organic matter contains no humic acid; most of the organic matter is in the form of fulvic acid. In the columnar horizon of solonetz, the quantity of humic acid is 13.2 per cent. In the carbnate horizon, the bulk of organic matter consists of fulvic acid. In solodi, large quantities of humin are found in the surface horizon. With depth the humic acid content increases up to 50 per cent of the total organic matter. The fulvic acid content is low. In all cases, the N content of the fulvic acid was high. The N content of the humic acid in the saline soils varied from 3.3 to 4.7 per cent. Data are also given on the ash content of organic matter in saline soils and its composition.

Vinokurov (76) shows that, in general, the higher the organic matter content of the soil, the higher its exchange capacity. He presents data on the exchange capacity of a series of soils, from a weakly podzolized soil to a solodi. He shows that the exchange capacity per gram of organic matter increases with depth in the profile, but in the southern steppe and semidesert soils, this does not hold true. Malquori (36) also discusses the base exchange capacity of organic substances and their influence on the swelling of clays.

Gemmerling and Zyrin (13) present data on X-ray analyses of humic acid showing that it gives Debye rings similar to high polymers. Sedletskii (57) points out that the interference Debye rings show the crystalline nature of humic acid. This has been shown earlier by Elbe (8) in a study of humic substances prepared from sucrose caramel. Sedletskii also shows that the humates of Al, Ca. and Na give different X-ray patterns than humic acid itself.

Schmuziger (54) presented a dissertation on the distribution and chemistry of soil organic matter in the profile of several soil types of Switzerland.

Kononova published a series of papers on the process of humification. Her experimental approach is to follow microscopically, and by other means, the transformation of plant material step by step, from the day it is placed in the soil until its component parts, histological and chemical, can be traced no longer.

In a monograph on *The Life of Desert Soils,* Feher (9) records ecologic studies on the microbial flora of the Sahara desert, between the parallels 38° and 16° northern latitude. Besides the strictly microbiological studies, the work covers investigations on organic matter content of the soils. In general, it is low, 0.01 to 0.08 per cent with 0.02 to 0.05 per cent N of the total soil. Of specific interest is the development of microbial life in desert sands which do not contain liquid moisture. Apparently, the moisture in vapor form, upon condensation or as such, may be utilized by the microbes. In her latest paper, Kononova (30) takes up the significant role of the fauna in the process of humification and the changes taking place in the oxidation-reduction system in the course of the process. The experiments have been conducted in the laboratory and in the field, and the experimental plant was alfalfa.

Franz (10) discusses the role of the soil fauna in the transformation of organic matter.

The most numerous of the lesser fauna are the nematodes of which 200 and more are often found in 1 cc. of soil. Most of these are harmless to living plants, but play an important role in the decomposition of cellulosic plant residues. Different kinds of earthworms behave differently. *Octolasium* spp. feed off humified material which is thereby destroyed; *Lumbricus* spp. feed off fresh plant residues which are excreted as humus intimately mixed with mineral matter. There is evidence that diplopods, slugs, land lice, midges, *Collembola,* larvae and caterpillars take an active part in the humification of different organic materials. Attempts were made to determine the amounts of humic matter (insoluble in acetyl bromide) formed per day by different animals from different raw materials. In 100 days an earthworm produced 0.53 gm. of humus from black alder leaf residues, and a louse 0.09 gm. The corresponding figures for beech leaves were 0.24 and 0.02 gm. Earthworms appeared to be the most active humus formers. Though the amount of humification per insect or animal is small, the total numbers of the soil fauna are often very high and may account for a considerable proportion of the humus produced.

The early researches of Mattson on the electrokinetic behavior and the amphoteric nature of the protein-humic acid complexes, referred to earlier in this chapter, have been extended into "the acid-base condition in vegetation, litter, and humus." Data on this topic are presented by Mattson and Koutler-Anderson (39) in a series of 8 papers. In their own words, "the aim of this work was to study the acid-base balance in plant materials during various stages of transformation and under various conditions in the laboratory and in nature". To get merely a glimpse into the contents of the scholarly contributions packed into these papers, the subtitles are enumerated. The first 4 papers discuss "the acids, acidoids, and bases in relation to decomposition, to soil types, acidoid formation in relation to base status, and the strength of the acidoids and the relation to nitrogen." Paper No. 5 discusses "products of partial oxidation and ammonia fixation." Paper No. 6 discusses "ammonia fixation and humans nitrogen." Paper No. 7 discusses "the acid-base condition during growth of wheat, barley, and red clover." Paper No. 8 discusses "forms of acidity."

References

1. Aleksandrova, L. N. 1944 The composition of the organic matter of saline soils. *Pedology* (U.S.S.R.) No. 10: 471-481.

2. Berthelot, M., and André, G. 1886 Sur les principes azote de la terre végétale. *Comp. Rend. Acad. Sci.* (Paris) 193: 1101-1104.

3. Berthelot, M., and André, G. 1891-2 Recherches sur les substances humique. *Comp. Rend. Acad. Sci.* 112: 916-922; *Ann. Chim. et Phys.* (6), 25: 364-403.

4. Berzelius, J. J. 1839 Lehrbuch der Chemie. Ubersetzt von Wöhler . VIII B.

5. Dehérain, P. P. 1902 Traite de chimie agricole, Ed. 2, Paris.

6. Detmer, W. 1871 Die natürlichen Humuskörper des Bodens und ihre landwirtschaftliche Bedeutung. *Land. Ver. Sta.* 14.: 248-300.

7. Doyarenko, A. G. 1901 Humic substances as the component nitrogen part of the soil. *Izvest. Moskov. Sel.-Khoz. Inst.*, pt. 6, no. 4.

8. Elbe, G. von 1936 The nature of sucrose caramel. *Jour. Amer. Chem. Soc.* 58: 600-601.

9. Feher, D. 1946 Der Wüstenboden als Lebensraum. *Publicat. de l'Inst. Botan. de l'Univer. Hongroise pour les Sci. Tech. et Econom., Sopron (Hongrie)* No. 10: 1-128.

10. Franz, H. 1943 Bildung von Humus aus Pflanzlichen Bestandsabfall und Wirtschaftsdünger durch Kleintiere. *Bodenk u. Pflanzenernähr.* 32 (77). H. 6: 336-351 (Quoted from Imp. Bureau of Soil Sci. 7(1944), p. 149).

11. Forsyth, W. G. C. 1947 The characterization of the humic complexes. *Jour. Agr. Sci.* 37, pt. 2: 132-138.

12. Fuchs, W. 1927 Brenn Chem. No. 8: 337 (After Tishchenko and Rydalevskaya); see also No. 9 (1928).

13. Gemmerling, G. V. and Zyrin, N. G. 1942 X-ray analyses of humic acid. Sbornik pamyati Williams. Acad. Sci. (U.S.S.R.). *Doukuchaev Soil Inst.* 24: 149-153.

14. Gillam, W. S. 1940 A study of the chemical nature of humic acid. *Soil Sci.* 49: 433-453.

15. Golodkovskii, L. I. and Golodkovskii, L. L. The root system of alfalfa and soil fertility (From Tyurin's paper in *Pedology* (1946) No. 1.

16. Gortner, R. A. 1916 The organic matter of the soil. I. *Soil Sci.* 2: 395-444; II. *Soil Sci.* 2: 539-548; III. *Soil Sci.* 3:1-8. See also Cortner and Bliss, *Jour. Amer. Chem. Soc.* 37: 1630-6; *Jour. Biol. Chem.* 26: 177-204; Gortner and Holm, *Jour. Amer. Chem. Soc.* 39: 2477-2501.

17. Gottlieb, S., and Hendricks, S. B. 1945 Soil org. matter as related to newer concepts of lignin chemistry. *Proc. Soil Sci. Soc. America,* 10: 117-125.

18. Grachev, M. M. 1902 The application of the Tacke method of determining the acidity of peat soils to soils in general. *Zhur. Opyt. Agron.* 3: 355-364.

19. Grandeau, L. 1872 Recherches sur la rôle de matieres organiques dans les phenomenes de la nutriton des plantes. Nancy. See also his Traite d'analyse des matieres agricoles, Ed. 3, 1897.

20. Gustavson, G. G. 1886 Twenty lectures in agricultural chemistry. (Russian).

21. Hobson, R. P. and Page, H. I. 1932 Studies on the carbon and nitrogen cycles in the soil. VI. The extracting of org. nitrogen of the soil with alkali. *Jour. Agr. Sci.* 22: 297-299. VII. 497-515; VIII. 516-526.

22. Hoppe-Seyler, F. 1889 Uber Huminsubstanzen, ihre Entstehung und ihre Eigenschaften. *Ztschr. Physiol. Chemie.* 13: 66-121.

23. Jodidi, S. L. 1909-1913 Mich. Agr. Expt. Tech. Bul. 4: Iowa Agr. Expt. Sta. Bul. 1, 3; *Jour. Franklin Inst.* 175: 483-495; 176: 565-573.

24. Kachinskii, N. A. 1931 A study of the physical properties of the soil in relation to the root system of plants (Russian). Moscow.

(See also Kachinskii and Ossin (1935) *Trans. Inter. Soc. Soil Sci. Soviet section,* V. A.: 5-19).

25. Karrer, P. 1925 Zur Kenntnis des Lignin, Diss. Univ. Zurich (Quoted from Mattson and Koutler-Andersson, paper No. VI).

26. Khainskii, A. I. 1916 The organic substances of soil humus. *Pochvovedenie* (Pedology) 18, No. 3-4: 49-97.

27. Khainskii, I. A. 1936 Investigation on the process of humate formation by electrometric methods. *Kolloid. Zhur.* (U.S.S.R.) v. 2, No. 1.

28. Kojima, R. 1947 Soil organic matter. *Soil Sci.* 64: 157-165; 245-252.

29. Kononova, M. M. 1942 Organic matter of the soils of the arid steppe of Zavolozh'e and the process of its transformations under conditions of irrigation (Russian—from Tyurin's paper in *Pedology* (1946) No. 1).

30. Kononova, M. M. 1944 The process of formation of humus substances. *Pedology* (U.S.S.R.) No. 10: 456-470 (English summary).

31. Kononova, M. M. 1947 Basic summaries of investigations on soil organic matter in the U.S.S.R. for the last 30 years. *Pedology* (U.S.S.R.) No. 10: 590-599.

32. Kukharenko, T. A. 1946 Reaction of humic acid with heavy metals. *J. Appl. Chem.* (U.S.S.R.) 19: 187-195.

33. Lein, Z. Ya. 1940 The exchange capacity of various humus substances and their complexes (Russian) Materialy po izuchen. organ. veshchestva pochv. *Trans. Dokuchaev Soil Inst.* 23: 59-85.

34. Maillard, L. C. 1912-1917 *Comp. Rend. Acad. Sci.* 154: 66-68; 155: 1554-1556 (1913); 156: 1159-1160; 157:850. *Ann. Chim.* (1916) (9) 5: 258-317; (1917) 7: 113-152. (Quoted from Tyurin), see also his work: Genese des matieres proteiques et des matiere humiques. Paris (1913).

35. Maiwald, K. 1931 Organische Bestandteile des Bodens. Blanck's Handbuch der Bodenlehre 7: 113-204.

36. Malquori, A. 1944 Behavior of organic matter in clay-bearing soils: I. Influence of org. matter on swelling of clays. II. Base exchange capacity of org. substances and of humic acid and its relation to the base-exchange capacity of clay. *Ann. Chim. Appl.* 34: 99-110, 111-126.

37. Malyanov, A. P. 1937 The physical properties of soils and the

root systems of plants in Baskiriya. (Russian) *Uchen. Zapis. M.G.U.,* v. 12.

38. Mattson, S. 1932 The laws of soil colloidal behavior. VII. Proteins and proteinated complexes. *Soil Sci.* 33: 41-72. (See also 31: 57-71).

39. Mattson, Sante and Koutler-Anderson, Elisaveta. 1941-1944 The acid base condition in vegetation, litter, and humus: I. *Annals Agr. College,* Sweden, 9 (1941): 1-26; II, 9 (1941): 27-37; III, 9 (1941): 38-56; IV, 9 (1941): 57-73; V, 10 (1942): 284-332; VI, 11 (1943): 107-134; VII, 11 (1943): 207-217; VIII, 12 (1944): 70-100.

40. McGeorge, W. T. 1931 Organic compounds associated with base exchange reactions in soils. Univ. of Ariz. College of Agr. Expt. Sta. Tech. Bul. 13 (See also Bul. 30).

41. Meyer, L. 1941 Ton-Humus Komplexe als Träger der Boden-fruchtbarkeit und also Bodenverbesserungsmittel. *Forschungs-dienst* II: 344-355.

42. Mulder, G. J. 1839 Untersuchungen über Humussubstanzen. *Jour. für prak. Chem.* Bd. XVI, p. 495; Bd. 21: 203-240; 321-370 (1840); also *Chemie der Ackerkrume.* Bd. I-II (1863).

43. Natkina, A. I. 1940 An investigation of the composition and properties of humic acids of chernozem and podzolized soils. *Trans. Dokuchaev Soil Inst.* 23: 23-40.

44. Norman, A. G. 1942 Problems in the chemistry of soil organic matter. *Proc. Soil Sci. Soc. America* 7: 7-15.

45. Norman, A. G. and Bartholomew, W. V. 1943 The distribution of uronic carbon in some soil profiles. *Soil Sci.* 56: 143-150.

46. Oden, S. 1919 Die Huminsauren. *Kolloidchem. Beihefte.* II: 75-260; see also *Trans. Faraday Soc.* 17: 288-294 (1922)

46a. Ponomareva, V. V. 1947 On the methods of separating fulvic acids and their chemical nature. *Pedology* (U.S.S.R.) No. 12: 714-723.

47. Rather, I. 1918 An accurate loss on ignition method for the determination of organic matter in soils. *J. Ind. Eng. Chem.* No. 10: 439-442; see also Ark. Agr. Expt. Sta. Bul. 140 (1917).

48. Rode, A. A. 1944 Life and activity of Prof. Ivan Vladimirovich Tyurin. *Pedology* (U.S.S.R.) No. 10: 501-503.

49. Rydalevskaya, M. D. and Tishchenko, V. V. 1944 On the cation exchange of humic acid of different soil types. *Pedology* (U.S.S.R.) No. 10: 491-499.

50. Sakun, N. E. 1942 On the interaction of humates with the mineral portion of the soil. *Pedology* (U.S.S.R.) No. 8: 3-20.

51. Sallans, H. R., Snell, J. M., Mackinney, H. W., and McKibbin, R. R. 1937 Water soluble acid substances in the raw humus of podzol soils. *Can. J. Res.* 15, B: 315-320.

52. Saussure, Th. de. 1804 Researches chimique sur la vegetation. Paris.

53. Savinov, N. I. and Pankova, N. A. 1942 The root system of plants in sod in the steppe of Zavolozh'e and a new method of studying it (Russian). In Memory of Acad. V. R. Williams. Moscow-Leningrad (An extensive bibliography on the problem of root system).

54. Schmuziger, A. 1935 The distribution and chemistry of humus substances in the profile of several soil types of Switzerland. Promotions-Arbeit, Turbenthal, pp. 125.

55. Schreiner, O. and Shorey, E. C. 1910 Chemical nature of soil organic matter. U. S. Dept. Agr. Bur. Soils, Bul. 74.

56. Sedletskii, I. D. 1936 Humus as a natural body and humic acid as its natural expression. *Khimiz. Sotsialist. Zemled.* (U.S.S.R.) No. 11: 77-87.

57. Sedletskii, I. D. 1942 New data on the crystalline structure of humic acid. Sbornik pamyati Williams. Acad. Sci. (U.S.S.R., *Dokuchaev Soil Inst.*, 141-148.

58. Shmuk, A. A. 1924 On the chemistry of soil organic matter. *Trudy Kubans. Sel'skokhoz. Inst.* 1, No. 2: 1-92.

59. Shmuk, A. A. 1930 Byullet. Pochvoveda No. 5-7: 35-80 (Quoted from Tyurin).

60. Slezkin, P. 1900 Etudy o gumuse (Essays on Soil Organic Matter) Kiev.

61. Sprengel, C. 1826 Uber Pflanzenhumus, Humussäure, und humus-säure Salze. *Kastner's Archiv. für die gesammte Naturlehre* 8, No. 2: 145-220.

62. Springer, U. 1931 A new method for the investigation of the organic substances in the soil and their application to soil types and humus forms. *Ztsch. Pflanzenernäkr., Düng. u. Bodenkunde* 22A: 135-152; 23A: 1-40 (1932).

63. Springer, U. 1938 Die heutige Stand der humusuntersuchungs methodik mit besonderen Berücksichtigung der Trennung, Bestimmung und Charakterisierung der Humussaüeretypen. *Bodenkunde u. Pflanzenernähr.* Bd. 6 (51) H 5/6: 312-373.

64. Springer, U. 1943 The fractionation of true humus substances. *Bodenk. u. Pflanzenernähr.* 32: 129-146.

65. Stadnikov, G. L. 1910 Investigations in the realm of amino-, imino-, and nitrilo-acids (Russian) (Quoted from Tyurin).

66. Tishchenko, V. V. and Rydalevskaya, M. D. 1936 Chemical investigations of the humic acid of different soil types. *Compt. Rend. de l'Acad. du Sci.* (U.S.S.R.) v. 4 (XIII) No. 3 (107): 141-143 (in English).

67. Trusov, A. G. 1917 Contributions to the study of soil humus. I. Processes of formation of humic acid. *Materialui po izuchenii russkikh pochv.* 26-27: 1-210. Petrograd.

68. Tyulin, A. Th. 1938 The composition and structure of the soil organo-mineral gels and soil fertility. *Soil Sci.* 45: 343-357.

69. Tyurin, I. V. 1935 The characteristics of the sod process of soil formation (Russian). In honor of the 50th anniversary of the pedogogic and public service of the Academician V. R. Williams. Moscow-Leningrad.

70. Tyurin, I. V. 1937 Organicheskoe veshchestvo pochv (Soil Organic Matter) Leningrad-Moscow, pp. 1-286.

71. Tyurin, I. V. 1940 On the nature of fulvic acid in soil organic matter. *Trans. Dokuchaev Soil Inst.* 23: 23-40.

72. Tyurin, I. V. 1944 The process of podzolization. *Pedology* (U.S.S.R.) No. 10: 441-455 (English summary).

73. Tyurin, I. V. 1946 The geographic regularity of soil organic matter formation. Doklad na yubil. Dokuchaev. sessii (A paper presented at the Jubilee session on Dokuchaev) (Quoted from Kononova).

74. Tyurin, I. V. 1946 The quantitative participation of living matter in the makeup of soil organic matter. *Pedology* (U.S.S.R.) No. 1: 11-30.

75. Tyurin, I. V. and Gutkina, E. L. 1940 Contributions to the study of the nature of humins in chernozem. *Trans. Dokuchaev Soil Inst.* 23: 41-57.

76. Vinokurov, M. A. 1941 Exchange capacity of the mineral and organic complexes. *Pedology* (U.S.S.R.) No. 5: 33-43.

77. Vinokurov, M. A. 1942 The content and composition of organo-mineral gels in soils. *Pedology* (U.S.S.R.) No. 3-4: 73-88.

78. Waksman, S. A. 1936 Humus. Williams and Wilkins, Baltimore, Md.

79. Waksman, S. A. and Iyer, K. R. N. 1932 Contribution to our knowledge of the chemical nature and origin of humus. I. On the synthesis of the humus nucleus, *Soil Sci.* 34: 43-69; II. The influence of synthesized humus compounds and of natural humus upon soil microbiological processes, 71-77. (1933) III. The base exchange capacity of "synthesized humus" and of "natural humus complexes." *Soil Sci.* 36: 57-67; IV. Fixation of proteins by lignins and formation of complexes resistant to microbial decomposition, 69-82.

80. Zolcinski, J. 1928 A new genetic physico-chemical theory of humus, peat, and coal. *First Inter. Cong. Soil Sci.* 3: 335-338; see also Wissensch. Arch. f. Landw. A. 4: 196 (Quoted from Tyurin).

Part II

Soil Systematics
Climatogenic Soil Types

CHAPTER VIII

DESERT, SEMIDESERT, AND ARID TYPES OF SOIL FORMATION: GRAY, BROWN, AND CHESTNUT BROWN SOIL ZONES

Introduction.—Soil systematics deals with the arrangement of soil types according to their natural features and properties. Following the scheme outlined in the preceding chapter, the soils of the world are grouped on the basis of climatic factors which are, in the main, responsible for their formation. We thus have climatogenic soil types. However, the continuity of the climatic soil zones is in places disturbed by specific factors, such as relief, local climate, level of water table, parent material, and others. These factors impart some specific characteristics to the soils and give the profile constitution properties which are largely independent of the climatic or biotic factors. These soils are classified as climatogenically subdued and are dealt with in Part III of this treatise.

DESERT-SEMIDESERT TYPE OF SOIL FORMATION

Geographic Distribution.—The desert-semidesert regions are situated within the climatic belts of the lower latitudes (warm desert climate) and the middle latitudes, with an average annual rainfall of 6 to 10 inches, not sufficient to maintain a continuous plant cover. It has been estimated that 12 to 15 per cent of the land area of the earth is taken up by desert.

The warm desert climate prevails over the vast stretches of the Sahara and Tripoli-Libyan deserts in North Africa; the Arabian and neighboring deserts of Eastern Asia and of Southern Persia and adjoining countries; the deserts of Peru and Chile in South America; and the deserts of about half of Australia.

The largest region of the middle latitude desert-semidesert is located in Central Asia, the famous Gobi desert of Turkestan, the deserts of Mongolia, western Hindustan, and adjoining lands. In North America, these climatic regions encompass some sections of California, Arizona, Nevada, and adjoining areas; in South America, portions of Patagonia and adjoining countries.

Soil Forming Process.—Rainfall deficiency and hence low percolation are the most characteristic features of the desert-semidesert process of soil formation. The warm desert climate supports a sparse vegetation consisting of cacti reaching the size of trees, thorny bush, creosote bush, "cat's claw" vines, and a few bunch grass plants. The middle latitude desert climate is known for the sagebrush (*Artemisia tridentata*). The plants are usually 3 or more feet apart and from 2 to 7 feet high. Shantz (25) describes the flora of these regions in detail. Very little biological activity occurs there, and the little chemical weathering that takes place, independently of and simultaneously with the process of soil formation, is almost devoid of organic reactions. In general, it is primarily physical weathering that predominates in the desert-semidesert regions.

An excellent discussion on the desert type of soil formation has been presented by Nikiforoff (16) in connection with his studies of the desert of Southern California. He states that

the outstanding feature of the by far the greater majority of the individual soil types in the desert alluvial fans is that the upper section of their profiles is hardly even touched by a strictly soil-forming process. Generally it is just a mechanical layer of an unassorted and more or less recently deposited drift. . . The only modification of this is an occasional development of the desert pavement. Another striking characteristic of the soil of alluvial fans, as well as of many other desert regions, is a frequent and strong development of hardpans at some depth from the surface.

One of the principal characteristics of the desert is that it is a natural region of exceedingly low biological pressure, which in turn is a natural consequence of climatic conditions decidedly unfavorable for biochemical activity: a deficiency of moisture is the principal limiting factor. . . . An outstanding feature of the desert type of soil formation in which it differs from the other zonal types rather sharply, is that the direct influence of the climate on soil formation seems to be much stronger than that of living nature: it is predominantly an abiotic type. . . . In the desert soil zone the amount of rainfall is reduced to a very low limit. Consequently temperature begins to dominate the other climatic forces in a desert soil-forming process.

In discussing the desert type of soil formation, Nikiforoff brings out the point that "we may assume the existence of not less than three broad types of soil formation. These three correspond to the three principal types of vegetation which are mainly responsible for the turnover and pulsation of the biopedogenic cycles. Accordingly, the principal types of soil formation may be designated as a woodland type, a grassland type, and a shrubland type." The last one is the desert type.

Desert Crust.—In many sections of the desert—semidesert, salts move from the lower levels to the surface. In some cases, cementing agents, $CaCO_3$ and $CaSO_4$, form crusts. Not infrequently, a flaky crystalline mass of $NaCl$ and Na_2SO_4 accumulates on the surface to be carried away sometimes by the winds. In this unique way, the soil may lose appreciable quantities of easily soluble mineral salts. A detailed description of such crusts given by Blanckenhorn is summarized by Glinka (p. 407-409) as follows:

PLATE 18
Lime crust formation in Palestine
(After Reifenberg)

In the valley of Tunis, a crust of $CaCO_3$ one meter thick is found on the elevated areas where evaporation is highest. In the Algiers plateaus and in the inner parts of Morocco, a large stretch of the country irrespective of topography is covered with a crust 50 cm. thick. In the region between Bogar and Djelfha, where the crust is underlaid by sand the natives dig their underground dwellings beneath these crusts.

Blanckenhorn found similar soil formations reaching a depth of 50 cm. at the edges of the Syrian desert in the vicinity of Homs, Selemije, and Aleppe in Northern Syria. Fraas (6) described similar crust formations in Palestine long before Blanckenhorn. These formations are known as "nari." According to Blanckenhorn these nari are often 2 meters thick.

Similar lime crusts were found in the desert regions of New Mexico and Texas. Walther (34) described these formations and pointed out that the crystalline and Paleozoic formations in those regions are covered with a white lime crust.

Glinka (p. 409) cites the composition of such crust material from Syria: SiO_2—3.2 to 7.2 per cent, Al_2O_3—1.0 to 2.1 per cent; Fe_2O_3—0.08 to 1.2 per cent; $CaCO_3$—85.2 to 88.4 per cent; $NaCl$—1.3 to 10.0 per cent; H_2O—2.4 to 4.2 per cent.

Besides lime carbonate crusts, gypsum crusts with or without lime carbonate have been reported. In some parts of Egypt, the fellahs (Egyptian peasants) mine this gypsum as it forms, for building purposes. Glinka cites Picard's analysis on samples of gypsum crusts from the North African desert: sand and clay—62.9 per cent, $CaCO_3$—0.8 per cent, $CaSO_4$—27.5 per cent, $KCl + NaCl$—0.16 per cent, H_2O and organic substance—8.64 per cent.

The accumulation of lime or gypsum on the surface indicates a phenomenon similar to solonchak formation. There is, however, another view, namely, that these crusts are nothing more than the carbonate horizon of illuviation, typical for the desert region. In the true desert regions, this layer comes to the surface. Glinka cites the observations of Passarge (20) who encountered such crust formations in the desert steppes of Algeria covered with a layer of soil material from 0.25 to 1 foot thick. Similar observations in Algeria have been recorded by Dranitsyn (Ch. 2, 18), who encountered no crusts but true carbonate illuvial horizons. Fraas (6) considered the crusts in Palestine as relics formed under conditions of a more humid climate. Passarge and Rolland shared this view also for the crusts in North Africa. Another example of this type of formation is the *caliche,* a calcareous hardpan layer found in the desert regions of Nevada, Arizona, and other states.

Glinka believed that many of the described crusts "are true illuviation horizons, that others are eluviation formations, and that the entire question needs further study." The *desert pavement* in Southern California, Nevada, and other desert areas in the United States are apparently examples of true illuvial horizons. The varnished and cemented gravel and stone of the desert pavement may be nothing more than an exposed layer, once covered with fine material and since carried away by erosion. A description of desert pavement is given in Marbut's Atlas (13). Nikiforoff (16) gives a comprehensive review of desert crusts. He considers the desert crust a kind of hardpan formation. He does not agree with Glinka's suggestion that the crust might be the remnant of an illuvial horizon exposed by erosion. The hardpan, according to Nikiforoff, is the result of the upward movement of salts. Thus, the desert crust is to be associated with solonchak formation.

In a later publication (18), discussing the problem of hardpan formation in some soil complexes of California, Nikiforoff reiterates his contention that this formation is not associated with illuviation. He cites no data to prove that the cementing materials have formed "by a decomposition of alumino-silicates in place," or that "the cementing materials of the hardpan were carried into it by ascending or descending solutions." If the formation of hardpan were not associated with illuviation or any movement of soil constituents, a chemical and physico-chemical analysis of the respective layers should tell the story. Nikiforoff arrives at his conclusion by inferences based on interesting scholastic discussions.

Gray Soils

As we emerge from the true desert to areas where the rainfall permits sufficient vegetation to participate actively in the process of soil formation, we find typical soil development. We still encounter the desert pavement, but, in the midst of the desert formations, a characteristic soil type appears. In the desert-semidesert regions of Turkestan, the Russian pedologists have recognized the gray type of soil formation. In other localities of these regions, the soil is not gray in color, but grayish brown to red.

Profile Characteristics.—The gray soils of the semidesert have been studied very extensively by Neustruev (15) and Dimo (Ch. 2, 10). According to the former, a characteristic feature of this zone is the presence of calcium carbonate close to the surface, irrespective of the parent material, be it loess, alluvial clay, or conglomerate. Glinka (p. 550) points out that

> . . . The entire belt of the foothill country (in Turkestan) with its gray soils is distinguished climatically by its aridity. Less than 300 mm. (as low as 150 mm.) of rainfall is the yearly precipitation of the region, with a mean annual temperature of 10°C. Vast stretches of this type of soil formation, primarily on loess, cover the Turkestan country, Bukhara, and adjacent territories. It is also encountered in Transcaucasia on volcanic formations.

> Along the Suir Dar'ya river valley (Turkestan) to the north of Karatai, the country is very flat and the surface drainage is, therefore, poor. The result is that notwithstanding the low rainfall, 150 mm., the water table is only 2-3 meters below the surface and in the depressions it comes to the surface causing a salinizing of the soils. We thus have the gray form of solonchak, just as we have the black form of solonchak under somewhat similar conditions in the chernozem zone.

The prevalence of typical gray soils in the foothill country of the Turkestan tempted Neustruev to place them in the large group of the vertical zonation scheme, but their wide distribution in the plains makes them eligible as a climatogenic soil of horizontal zonation. According to Glinka (p. 555): "All the data available prompt us to distinguish a zone of grayearths (serozem) to which belong not only the soils of the foothill country, but also those of the plains, even though the latter are frequently of a solonchak character."

The lack of a continuous plant cover excludes the formation of a typical A_0 layer. Organic matter is limited primarily to the A_1 horizon, in the upper 10 cm., and does not go above 2 per cent. The following, taken from Zakharov (p. 318), describes a typical gray soil profile:

A_1: 0-10 cm. Characteristic straw-colored-gray with various shades: yellow, brown, red, pink; scaly, laminated structure, fairly open constitution.

A_2: 10-30 cm. A transition horizon, lighter in color than A_1, at times having a brown shade; of a spongy constitution, honeycombed with tracks of burrowing animals.

B: 30-80 cm. Illuviated, lighter in color, usually straw-colored, at times gray because of the numerous minute lime veins, more compact, with a fine porosity. White spots known as "beloglazki"—white eye spots—are frequently encountered.

C: 80 cm. The parent material, at the surface of which sulfates and chlorides are frequently found alongside the lime carbonate.

Drainitsyn (Ch. 2, 27, p. 383) describes a light gray soil with solon-chak tendencies as follows:

0-0.25 cm.: A smooth whitish gray crust, porous underneath; thin cracks may be observed.

0.25-10 cm.: Porous, laminated, light gray mellow mass.

10-85 cm.: Compact porous mass which breaks into clumps with sharp angles; salt spots are scattered at a depth of 35-50 cm.

85-130 cm.: Very porous, compact, slightly moist; salt separations are apparent.

A comprehensive review of the gray soils in Turkestan may be found in the early work of Neustruev (15) and Glinka (7). A recent discourse on these soils has been presented by Korovin and Kashkarov (8). In line with the ideas of Williams on the oneness of the soil forming processes, Sinyagin (28) has proposed a hydromorphic origin of the gray soils in the alluvival valleys of southern Kazakhstan. These soils have supposedly developed from the meadow soils which have prevailed as a result of the glaciation in Quaternary time. The change came about when the level of the ground waters dropped. This type of change need not necessarily be singled out as hydromorphic. Transformations of this kind may be explained on the basis of endodynamomorphism.

In the United States, this type of soil formation is described by Wol-fanger (35, p. 31) as one having a surface horizon consisting of "a thin 'desert crust' of a thin pebbly layer which forms the so-called 'desert pave-ment.' Its substructure, the desert mulch, is a light, porous material of little compaction. The upper subsoil is also porous, but it is compact and brown in color. It is underlain by the zone of lime accumulation which under the low rainfall conditions of the desert is shallow and which in the older soils frequently forms a firmly developed hardpan." Hardpan form-ation in gray soils is probably associated with salinization.

That chemical weathering is subdued in the semidesert region was recognized by Hilgard (Ch. 2, 30), who stated: "Since kaolinization is also a process of hydration, the presence of water must greatly influence its intensity, and especially the subsequent formation of colloidal clay, so that rocks forming clay soils in regions of summer rains may in the arid regions form merely pulverulent soil materials (p. 47). . . There is little or no clay to be washed down into the subsoil (p. 163)."

A closer examination of the chemical composition of the gray soils also reveals a meager differentiation of soil constituents in the profile. The water extract (table 27) shows that even chlorides and sulfates which are usually associated with the soils of the desert-semidesert regions, are low, and yet there is a definite increase of sulfates in the B horizon. This latter fact will explain why gypsum is frequently encountered in appreci-

Table 27

Water extract of a gray soil

(After Vityn)

Horizon	Depth	Reaction	Dry residue	After ignition	Loss on ignition	Mineral substances in dry residue	HCO_3	Cl	SO_4
	cm.		per cent	per cent	per cent	per cent	per cent	per cent	per cent
A₁	0-7	Alkaline	0.0552	0.0281	0.0271	50.91	0.0355	0.0014	0.0016
A₂	13-26	"	0.0345	0.0254	0.0091	73.62	0.0344	0.0014	0.0010
B	50-60	"	0.0351	0.0290	0.0061	82.62	0.0368	0.0014	0.0046
C	103-110	"	0.0273	0.0188	0.0085	68.86	0.0307	0.0014	0.0011
C	172-180	"	0.0386	0.0267	0.0119	69.17	0.0376	0.0028	0.0020

able quantities in the B horizon of the gray soil, a feature seldom found in any other soil zone. The meager percolation through the soil of this climatic zone is not enough to carry away all of the gypsum. However, the more significant attribute is the high accumulation of $CaCO_3$ in the B horizon, as shown in table 28. Because of the prevailing alkaline reaction, none of the R_2O_3 is released from the horizon of eluviation. On the contrary, there seems to be a relative increase of iron and aluminum. In this respect, the gray soils, formed under conditions of a relatively high temperature, show a remote similarity to the soils of the humid subtropics and tropics where accumulation of R_2O_3 is the distinctive feature of the lateritic process of soil formation. However, laterites lose SiO_2 and the gray soils do not. It is also significant that there is no appreciable translocation of organic matter in the normal gray soil profile.

Because of the alkaline reaction of this soil, the complex capable of base exchange is saturated. Using the saturation state as a basis for the genetic classification of soils, Gedroiz (Ch. 6, 10) placed the process of gray soil formation in the class of soils saturated with bases. Because of the low organic matter content and the slow decomposition of the mineral complexes, the total cation exchange capacity is relatively low. In other words, the colloidal fraction in the normal gray soils is low.

In connection with the distribution of iron in the profile of gray soils, it is well to recall the desert red soils described by Dranitsyn and others, as quoted by Glinka (Ch. 2, 27, p. 838). These soils have the profile characteristics of the gray soils, but they are red instead of gray. In view of the similarity of the desert red and gray soils, Afanasiev (Ch. 2, 2) suggested that the soils of the desert-semidesert be designated not by the color but by the climatic type of soil formation, namely, the *desert type*. This would include the red soils of the North African desert, of Asia Minor, Palestine, Syria, Arabia, and other countries. Thorp (30, p. 142) describes a "reddish phase" of the yellow-gray desert soils of China.

In a review of the genesis and morphology of desert soils in the United States, Lapham, (12) adheres to the classification of Afanasiev and divides the desert soils into two major subregions; namely, the Northern Desert and the Southern Desert. On the Northern Desert he says:

The Northern Desert.—The northern part of the desert region, designated as the Northern or Cooler Desert, occupies the greater part of the region north of extreme southern Nevada and the Grand Canyon and the little Colorado River in northern Arizona. It is estimated by Shantz to cover about 10 per cent of the area of the United States. The soils are predominantly gray or light grayish brown in color and are designated as the Gray Desert Soils. They are dominated by sage brush or scattering sage brush (*Artemesia tridentata*) and bunchgrass vegetation.

Normal soils of the Northern Gray Desert region are represented by the Portneuf silt loam. This is one of the most extensive and uniform soil types of the Western United States. It is most uniformly and typically developed in the Snake

Table 28

Total analyses of a typical gray soil from Turkestan

(After Zakharov)

Horizon	Depth of sampling	Hygro-scopic	Humus	CO_2	SiO_2	Al_2O_3	Fe_2O_3	CaO	MgO	P_2O_5	SO_3	Alkalies by differ- ence	Chemi- cally com- bined water
	cm.	per cent	per cent	per cent	per cent	per cent	per cent	per cent	per cent	per cent	per cent	per cent	per cent
A_1	0-7	1.34	1.61	5.10	59.84	11.18	5.19	7.24	3.08	0.201	0.533	4.98	1.02
A_2	8-15	1.31	1.08	5.52	59.66	11.33	5.35	7.66	2.82	0.230	0.160	4.84	1.41
B	90-100	1.44	0.23	10.31	52.86	10.25	4.89	13.06	3.01	0.104	0.223	4.11	0.95
C	137-145	1.47	0.21	9.34	53.76	10.18	5.30	12.11	2.32	0.130	0.059	4.68	1.41

River Plains in southern Idaho. The Portneuf soils are developed under mean annual rainfall of about 11 inches. Yearly precipitation, however, is variable, ranging from a minimum of 3.05 inches at Buhl in the western part of the Twin Falls area for the driest year, to a maximum of 19.39 inches at Murtaugh in the eastern part of the area for the wettest year. The mean precipitation at Twin Falls for seasonal periods is as follows: winter, 3.40; spring, 3.40; fall, 2.85; summer 1.68 inches. The rainfall is quite uniformly distributed save during the summer which is only 49 per cent of that of the winter or spring months. There is an average annual snowfall of from 21.8 inches in the western and drier to 32.5 inches in the eastern or more humid part of the area. There is an average growing season of 129 to 148 days at official stations in Twin Falls County. Killing frosts have occurred at Twin Falls as late as July 14 and as early in fall as September 5.

Lapham's description of a typical Portneuf silt loam follows:

A_1: 0-2″. Light grayish brown silt loam or very fine sandy loam, forming combined desert crust and mulch layer in dry areas. This is developed only in open spaces intervening between clumps of desert shrubs or grasses, and appears to be well developed only in soils of silt loam or of similar texture. The surface is checked by a system of fine cracks into plates 3 to 5 or 6 inches in diameter and of irregular shape. These are thin, very soft and fragile, smooth and frequently slick on the upper surface, but below the thickness of 1/16 to 1/4 inch are of vesicular structure, made up of a matrix of soft fine floury material including small spherical cavities of the size of fine bird shot. These plates may, with care, be lifted out upon a knife blade, but fall into an incoherent powder upon slight pressure. The vesicles appear to have been formed by imprisoned air at time of showers during dusty periods. In places this layer is only about 1/2 inch thick, varying to 3 inches. When moist this surface horizon absorbs water almost instantly. It is leached of lime.

A_2: 2″-15″. Light brown to brown silt loam, somewhat richer or more pronounced brown than the surface layer. Of somewhat feeble to well developed columnar structure, columns 2 to 4 or more inches in diameter, breaking down to friable structureless or soft cloddy material. This horizon is penetrated by numerous roots and by tunnels and burrows of insects. There is little evidence of leaching or podzolization. The cavities are lined with lime carbonate in the lower part of the horizon which is mildly to moderately calcareous.

B_1: 15″-36″. Compact pale yellowish or light yellowish gray to cream colored silt loam of smooth floury texture, slightly heavier than the surface layer, high in accumulated lime with frequent small irregular lime carbonate nodules. This horizon is very hard and compact when dry but becomes soft and easily penetrated with the auger where irrigated and moist. In areas of excessive lime accumulation it is putty-like when wet. It is easily penetrated by roots and water. The columnar structure is feebly developed.

C: 36″ plus. Light brown mellow silt loam or very fine sandy loam without definite structure. Moderately calcareous with occasional pea-like carbonate nodules. This continues to basaltic bedrock substratum occurring at variable depths, usually 4 to 10 feet, the upper part of which is scattered and fragmentary, the fragments usually cemented firmly by lime carbonate and forming an irregular or somewhat fissured hardpan from 2 or 3 to 10 or more inches thick.

From the description given, some doubt arises whether or not the profile under consideration is typical of the gray soils. The columnar structure noted in A_2 is characteristic of the solonetz type of soil formation. It is very probable that the area investigated is a degraded solonchak. Apprarently, Baldwin and Youngs (2), who made the survey, did not at the time appreciate fully the divisions of non-climatogenic soils, soil complexes, and normal gray soils in the desert region. In table 29, adapted by Lapham (11) from Marbut, the chemical composition of a gray soil from the Northern Desert region is given. Even though the data are not on the horizon basis, one can easily see a definite shift of constituents in the profile. Especially is this noticeable with respect to the alkaline earth bases. There is also an increase of SO_3. Apparently, we have here an

Table 29

Chemical and mechanical analysis of a gray soil in Idaho

(After Lapham)

Component	Depth		
	0-3"	4-14"	15-35"
	per cent	*per cent*	*per cent*
SiO_2	72.44	68.69	58.06
TiO_2	0.64	0.65	0.49
Fe_2O_3	3.92	4.30	3.10
Al_2O_3	12.16	12.91	9.67
MnO	0.06	0.05	0.05
CaO	2.04	2.73	10.80
MgO	1.47	1.75	3.41
K_2O	2.57	2.42	1.98
Na_2O	1.77	2.01	1.80
P_2O_5	0.17	0.20	0.18
SO_3	0.13	0.08	0.20
Loss in ignition	3.63	4.85	11.30
Nitrogen	0.07	0.08	0.03
Silt	54.6	50.5	55.0
Clay	9.8	10.5	8.4

accumulation of Ca and Mg carbonates and some $CaSO_4.2H_2O$, a phenomenon frequently noted by Dimo (Ch. 2, 10). The decrease in SiO_2 is probably only relative, since there is a distinct increase in Ca and Mg.

The Southern Desert.—The soils of the Southern Desert cover the extreme southern part of Nevada, the desert region in southern California, southern and western Arizona south of the Grand Canyon, and parts of southern New Mexico and western Texas. This type of soil is described by Lapham (11) as follows:

The soils of this region are typically of pale reddish gray or pinkish cast to pronounced deep red color, the red color being most pronounced where moist and in the areas of the more mature soil development.

The Southern Desert is a region of prolonged high summer temperatures, excessive evaporation, uncertain and transient rainfall with protracted drought periods which may be broken by precipitation of cloudburst proportions. In certain localities not more than a trace of rainfall may occur in the period of a year or more, yet at Yuma at which the mean annual rainfall is but a fraction more thn 3 inches, more than this amount has been recorded in a single storm period of 24 hours. In general the region is, however, characterized by summer and winter rainy periods. It falls mainly under the classification of Shantz in the Southern Desert shrub or creosote bush (*Covillea glutinosa*) type of vegetation, but in contrast to the monotony of the flora of the Northern Desert Region, it supports a much greater variety of desert shrubs, cacti, and flowering annuals.

As a representative of the soils in the Southern Desert, Lapham (11) describes Mohave series, a sandy loam profile, as follows:

A: 0-7". Rich reddish brown or red sandy loam, slightly compact but friable and with coarse granular or small soft cloddy structure. Gritty texture owing to abundance of small sharp angular fragments of parent rock, mainly quartz. A small amount of mica flakes are scattered through the material. The coarse sharp sandy and fine gravelly material is frequently accumulated on the surface through removal of the fine material by wind. Although of light and coarse texture, the material is loamy when moist, is retentive of moisture, and is unleached of mineral plant-food materials and is productive under irrigation. There is very little visible humus layer or organic matter except for roots of grasses and shrubs which are abundant adjacent to individual plants but infrequent in the intervening spaces. This horizon is permeable and easily penetrated by moisture and plant roots. Tunnels and cavities formed by ants, beetles, and small rodents frequently occur. This horizon is typically leached of lime, the depth of the leached layer, however, being variable with texture and local conditions of rainfall and of slope, run-off, and internal drainage.

B₁: 7"-15". Somewhat heavier textured sandy loam or light loam of more pronounced red color, slightly to moderately compact, being noticeably more compact than the surface horizon and more sticky when wet. This has a rather imperfectly or feebly developed columnar structure, hard when dry, but friable and breaking down into soft small cloddy structure when moist. In related types of heavier texttrue, the columnar structure is more pronounced. This horizon is mildly calcareous, the lime content increasing in the lower part in which some light colored mottling or small nodules of lime carbonate may occur.

B₂: 15"-30". A gritty loam or clay loam of compact and usually of more or less well developed columnar structure and of high lime accumulation. This material is pale reddish-brown or pinkish in color, usually much mottled with light gray accumulated lime and frequently contains irregular lime carbonate nodules of the size of a pea to that of a hickory nut. Structural columns are irregular and break up into angular clods. There is little difference in color of these in the rough and when crushed, but root and other cavities may be lined with lime carbonate. During prolonged dry seasons this horizon is very hard, necessitating heavy digging with pick or crowbar; when moist it can be penetrated readily with the soil auger.

B₃: 30"-60". A gritty loam of pinkish or pale reddish gray to brownish gray color, much mottled with lime and containing lime carbonate nodules. The columnar structure and red color is less pronounced than in the horizon above. This is the horizon of maximum lime accumulation. It becomes very hard when dry but softens when moist and is penetrated by plant roots. It is of variable thickness and depth. It is succeeded by the C horizon of pale reddish sandy loam of gritty texture, usually calcareous but of lower lime content and of more friable character, apparently unweathered.

In the desert region bordering Nevada, western Arizona and eastern California, typical gray soils are encountered. From the description of a number of California soils, as given by Shaw (27), they have desert pavement and a vesicular layer below it, are gray in color, and possess the typical features of the gray soil profile.

A closer examination of Laphan's description for the Mohave soil series of the Southern Desert seems to point again, as in the case of the Portneuf series for the Northern Desert, to the solonetz features of the soil, which probably developed from the degradation of a calcium and, perhaps, a magnesium solonchak. This may be the reason why the profile is so deep, a feature not common in the normal desert type of soil formation.

A critical analysis of the data on the mechanical (table 30) and chem-

Table 30

Mechanical composition of a gray soil

(After Vityn)

Horizon	Depth of sampling	Diameter of particles in mm.				
		1-0.5	0.5-0.25	0.25-0.05	0.05-0.01	<0.01
	cm.	per cent	per cent	per cent	per cent	per cent
A	0-7	0.06	0.04	19.15	33.04	47.71
B,*	13-26	0.01	0.02	19.66	33.01	47.30
B₂	50-60	0.06	0.02	14.77	35.47	49.68
C	103-110	0.02	0.02	27.57	31.89	40.50
D	172-180	—	0.01	17.32	40.85	41.82

*This is probably the A₂ horizon. When these results were compiled the letter designations for the various horizons were not as yet uniformly accepted.

ical composition (table 28) of typical gray soils brings out their distinctive features and characteristics. First to be noticed is very slight horizon differentiation. The mechanical fractions are about the same throughout the profile, with little of either the large or very small particles. This profile is high in silt and low in clay, which indicates the desert type of weathering; i.e., more distintegration and less decomposition. Similar trends may be inferred from the voluminous data and discussion presented by Marbut (13, 93-94).

Brown and Drosdoff (4) have studied the profile composition—total analyses of the soil and their exchangeable cations and similar analyses on their colloids—of soils from the Mohave (Mojave) desert. One soil profile formed on granite and the other on alluvial fans. An interesting feature of the analyses is the ratio of Ca:Mg in the colloids; it varies from 2 to 4. The authors conclude that there is appreciable alteration in the profile of the desert soils. Their data, however, hardly warrant the conclusion.

Kudrin and Rozanov (10) present analyses of gray soils on the middle terrace of the Syr-Dar River in Turkestan formed on dolomitic parent material and on deluvium of dolomite. The Mg content in exchangeable form is attributed in part to the high Mg content of the ground waters.

Sabanin (24) describes a serozem (grayearth) of the vertical zonation in Bogar, a mountain region in Central Asia. The conditions of the serozem are characterized by an annual precipitation of 200 to 500 mm, the bulk of which comes during the fall, winter, and early spring. The summers are usually rainless. The average annual temperature is 12 to 14°C, with maximums up to 42 and minimums to 28°.

Kudrin (9) reports that the fine fractions of gray soils of limestone origin contain more P than the coarse fractions. No difference in P content has been found in the respective fractions of soils formed from granite. The difference noted in the two soils is explained by the fact that there is little chemical weathering in the desert regions and, therefore, no apatite is set free from the granite. The weathering of limestone rock under desert condition is more conducive to decomposition.

Olovyanishnikov (19) notes that, in general, the morphology and chemistry of gray soils do not indicate sharp differences in the profile and constitutional makeup. An examination of the 1.0 to <0.001 mm fractions shows very little movement of constituents in the profile. However, an analysis of the individual fractions reveals that whereas $CaCO_3$ accumulates at some point in the profile, the $MgCO_3$ content remains relatively constant. An interesting observation made by Olovyanishnikov is that the fraction of <0.001 mm. does not contain carbonates.

Biology of the Desert-Semidesert Soils.—Most of the representatives of animal life in the desert region must, by force of natural circumstances, take to the soil as a place of habitation. Thus, rodents, worms, insects, and many other forms harbor in the soils of this region. The rodents infrequently make difficult the differentiation of the horizons by disturbing the soil profile.

There seems to be no agreement as to the prevelance and activity of earthworms in the soils of the desert and semidesert regions. Glinka (Ch. 2, 27, p. 379) ascribes the structure of the soils in these regions to the activity of earthworms. Similar views are maintained by Neustruev (Ch. 2, 50, p. 138) and other Russian pedologists. On the other hand, Seton (see Chapter V) is of the opinion that no earthworms are to be found in western arid regions. Lapham (11) challenges the statement of Glinka, stating: "Any fisherman who has resorted to digging for the humble earthworm in the desert region knows how futile is the task."

A comprehensive discussion of the role and significance of insect life in the gray soils of Turkestan has been presented by Dimo (5).

Very little work has been done on the microbiological flora of the gray soils. The few investigations available have been cited (see p. 145). Of special interest are the contributions of Kononova (Ch. 5, 54) on the distribution of Azotobacter and nitrifying organisms in the gray soils of Turkestan and of Rokitzkaya (23) on the microbiological flora of the soils in Turkestan in general. A comprehensive ecologic study of microbes in desert soils is presented in a monograph by Feher (Ch. 7, 9).

Summary Statement on the Soils of Desert-Semidesert.—The following may be stated in summarizing the process of soil formation and in presenting the zonal soils of these regions:

1. *The biosphere as a factor of soil formation is reduced to a minimum because of the poor return of bases by way of the vegetation cover.* The scant bunch vegetation does not recover the bases leached by the precipitation. Besides, the surface vegetation "burns up" before the meager microbial flora has a chance to humify and mineralize it. These circumstances may explain the ambiguity noted by Lapham that the surface 2.5 inches of a Mohave soil has a pH of 6.8. He quotes Marbut's opinion, based on data of Storie and Carpenter, (39), on the probability of an acid condition in the upper part of these soils. The misconception about the universal prevalence of an alkaline condition of the soils in the gray zone is due to the widespread distribution of saline soils in this zone.

2. The temperature, rather than precipitation, is the important element of climate in the process of soil formation of this zone.

3. A characteristic feature of the A horizon is the vesicular structure. In this connection, it is of interest to note an experience reported by Nikiforoff (18, p. 39) while investigating profiles on the gray soils of California:

> According to an agreement with the owner, the trenches in field A were to be excavated with the least possible damage to the young grass and to be refilled carefully so that there would be no danger to the young steers in the pasture. Accordingly, all earth from one trench was collected on both sides of the excavation. On completion of the work, all this material was put back into the hole. Surprisingly, there was not enough to fill the trench. After all the earth remaining on the surface was carefully replaced, between 40 and 45 cubic feet remained unfilled. The total volume of the excavation, as calculated from the profiles, was about 420 cubic feet. This incidental observation indicates that the natural porosity of the mound material is considerably greater than its porosity after digging.

4. The desert crust or desert pavement, the origin of which is not clear.

5. The retention of gypsum and calcium carbonate at some point in the soil profile.

6. The comparatively high content of exchangeable Mg and the consequent narrow Ca:Mg ratio.

7. The comparatively low water-soluble salts in the normal soils of this zone.

8. The slight variation in the mechanical composition of the different horizons.

9. The red soils of the desert-semidesert (primarily in the regions of the warm climate) seem to be the result of an identical process as for the gray soils. The difference in color is probably due to the origin of the parent material. Further studies of the soils in these regions may justify the name *gray-red soil formation.* The red color may be due to lateritic parent material formed in an earlier humid tropical climate.

10. The soil cover of these regions is frequently spotted and is, therefore, to be associated with the concept of *soil complex or catena,* the latter concept being used in a more inclusive sense than originally defined by Milne (14). Any soil complex in the gray-red soils may include soils associated with the process of salinization (see Index). In interpreting data on the desert-semidesert soils, the factors mentioned have to be evaluated.

ARID STEPPE TYPE OF SOIL FORMATION

The steppe country starts in the chernozem zone, passes through the chestnut brown and brown zones, projects into the gray soil zone of the desert-semidesert, and terminates there. The succession of soil types in the steppe is accompanied by a succession of vegetation, as pointed out by Dimo and Keller (Ch. 2, 11). Thus, in the chernozem zone we have herbaceous and tall grass vegetation which, with the increase in aridity, is succeeded by a pure graminae steppe vegetation, such as *Stipa lessingiana, Pao bulbosa, vivipara, Festuca sulcata, Amygdalus nana, Spires, Koeleria cristata,* and others. These are followed by the arid steppe vegetation *Pyrathrum achillaefollum, Artemisia,* and *Salsolaceae* in the extermely arid regions and semidesert.

The arid steppe of the United States (the Great Plains region west of the chernozem belt) includes the brown and dark-brown soils which are charted by Marbut as separate belts on his map (13, plate 4) of the soils of the United States. Some of Marbut's classification units, as given in his monumental monograph "The Soils of the United States," have been modified by his successors. The brown soils were divided into *brown* and *reddish brown;* the dark-brown were divided into *chestnut* and *reddish chestnut.* These groupings correspond to Marbut't northern and southern varieties of these soils. As described by the Soil Survey (25, p. 1080-1095), the profile features of these soils, except for color, do not identify them as genetically specific. The color nomenclature is, however, used for rating the soils in terms of productivity and land utilization.

The predominating vegetation of the brown soils consists of short grass, bunch grass, and mesquite; of the dark-brown soils—mixed grasses, mostly short grass (largely buffalo and grama) and some coarse grasses, such as bluestem.

A characteristic feature of the arid steppe region is paucity of precipitation which is sufficient, however, to support an entire grass cover. Data presented by Glinka (Ch. 2, 27, p. 353) show that the mean annual rainfall in the zones of the brown and chestnut brown soils of Russia reaches 300-310 mm., with 260 mm. as a minimum and 370 mm. as a maximum. The mean annual temperature is 7-8°C. Kravkov (Ch. 6, 20) points out that in the region of brown soils the winters are cold (-10 to -17°C), the summers are hot (20 to 25°C), and the humidity is low (50 to 60 per cent). For the chestnut brown soils, the precipitation is higher and the temperature lower.

There seems to be no concordant agreement among the Russian pedologists as to whether the brown and chestnut soils should be treated as one or as two separate zones. Although there are certain differences, particularly in color and percentage of organic matter, these are not sufficiently marked to justify the separation of two zones. Besides, the process of soil formation is very similar; both are formed under conditions of low moisture, high summer temperatures, cold winters, a fairly heavy snowfall, high evaporation, and grass cover. Glinka (p. 376) is inclined to separate the soils into two distinct zones, whereas Zakharov (Ch. 2, 91, p. 322) favors placing them into one brown zone. However, in describing the brown and chestnut brown zone, Zakharov divides it into two subtypes and resorts to the same source of information for his subtypes as does Glinka for his special zones.

Kravkov (Ch. 6, 20, p. 207), in discussing the arid steppe type of soil formation, notes: "At present, the brown soils are identified with the light chestnut brown soils and because of that the term 'brown soils' seldom appears in the literature." A similar view is expressed by Prasolov and Antipov-Karataev (22).

Marbut, in discussing these soils does not separate independent brown and dark-brown soil zones or belts. He does, however, show on the Soil Map of the United States (plate 4) a large area of brown soils. In describing the dark-brown and brown soils (p. 76), Marbut states: "In a large area of the Great Plains of Montana, with the town of Shelby occupying approximately the center, the soils are brown. This is an area in which the rainfall is low, amounting to only about 14 inches, and the grass cover has not been sufficiently dense to give the soil a dark-brown color. The zone of carbonate accumulation lies at less depth, usually very little more than a foot, than in the dark-brown belt. . . The brown soils, on the basis of information obtained to the preesnt time, occur in a discontinuous belt."

Brown Soils

According to Glinka (p 376) :

> Dokuchaev, who observed the development of the brown soils in the region adjacent to the Caspian Sea, placed them into a distinct group. He differentiated the soils of European Russia primarily on the basis of color and humus content, and in the case of the brown soils, he resorted to this method without a detailed study of their morphology. It is questionable whether one is justified in drawing a line between the brown and chestnut brown soils simply because of color differences, especially since the constitution of the two differs but little.
> While separating the two groups of soils, the investigators were confronted with another fact. It turned out that the soils south of the chestnut brown zone in Asiatic, as well as in certain parts of European Russia, interlink with soils not only of a lighter color, but also with soils having a distinct compactness at certain depths. In other words, this soil zone adjoins soils containing a clearly defined compacted illuvial horizon B, almost on a level with the A horizon. Such soils were separated by a number of investigators into a special group of solonetzic soils, and Tumin was inclined to substitute the term "solonetzic" for brown soils." However, it became apparent that the term did not cover what was known to be true brown soils, and moreover, one might encounter among the brown and chestnut brown soils both the solonetzic varieties.
> Since the color shade of the soil is not an accidental occurrence, except if it be determined by the color of the parent material, but is one of the attributes which remains constant for thousands of kilometers of soils in the various zones, it should be of no less significance than, for instance, the structure of the soil, or the appearance of a compact B horizon, etc. For this reason, the author finds it appropriate to separate the brown from the chestnut brown soils. It is to be understood that we designate as brown soils only those varieties which have no compact B_1 horizon.

Glinka emphasizes further the fact that whenever a compact layer appears, the typical solonetzic soil can be demonstrated, but it is not always typical for brown or chestnut brown soils.

The brown soils differ from the chestnut brown soils by their lighter brown-gray color. Because of this gray shade which, incidentally, is characteristic for all the soils of the steppe, the humus horizon of the brown soils cannot be differentiated at times from the underlying horizon. The grayish brown predominates over the dark colored humus which is not too abundant in the brown soils. On the average, brown soils contain 2 to 3 per cent organic matter.

Large areas of the brown zone are covered with solonetzic, solonetz, and solonchak complexes. It is within this zone that the structural solo-

netz is encountered for the first time as a distinct type. Dimo and Keller
(Ch. 2, 11) observed that "on the level, high watersheds there are soil
complexes consisting of as much as two-thirds of the solonetzic varieties.
Where the topography is undulating, the prevailing soils are the normal
brown soils." In the United States, typical brown soils are found in the
eastern and western portion of Colorado, in Wyoming, Montana, and New
Mexico. While on the trip with the First International Congress of Soil
Science, in 1927, Glinka pointed out typical brown soils at Ordway, Colorado. Vilenskii (32) observed slightly solonetzic features in the brown soils
of the same area. Zakharov (Ch. 2, 91, p. 322) gives the following morphological description of a brown soil profile:

A₁: 0-15 cm. Humus horizon, straw-colored gray with a brown or chestnut
brown shade, laminated structure, friable with a finely porous constitution.

A₂: 15-26 cm. Slightly compacted, a brighter chestnut brown shade, columnar-like, partly crumbly structure.

A₃: 26-45 cm. Lighter straw-colored, with brown streaks and tongue-like
projections, crumbly, nutty structure, more friable constitution, with
many worm tracks.

B: 45-75 cm. Illuvial horizon, straw-colored with white spots and veins
of lime carbonate, slightly prismatic, porous and feebly cracked.

C: 75 cm. Loess-like or some other parent material which sometimes contains soluble salts.

The soil is alkaline in reaction, effervesces at A_3, and at times even
slightly at the surface.

Unfortunately, there are not many complete analyses of brown soils
which may help to interpret the process of their formation. In tables 31-32,
data are presented on water extracts and partial analyses. The water
extract shows a low content of soluble salts which indicates the non-
saline features of the normal soils of this would-be zonal type. The
soluble salt content is, however, slightly higher than in the normal gray
soils. The brown soils also show a higher loss on ignition, which means
a higher content of soluble organic matter, 1 to 2 per cent. As to the
total analyses, the data in table 32 offer very little. Not much may be
inferred about the movement and translocation of the constituents in the
profile of these soils. The fact that there is an increase in CO_2 content
with depth in the profile indicates accumulation of carbonates, hence some
translocation. Table 33 presents data on the exchangeable bases. The
narrow Ca: Mg ratio is very pronounced, indicating very little movement
of Mg. The solonetzic character of one of these soils may be noted from
the high Na content in the profile, especially in the A_1 horizon. For comparison, data are presented on the exchangeable bases of chestnut brown
and a transition to chernozem soils.

Table 31

Composition of a water extract on a brown soil, per cent of total

(After Prasolov)

Depth	Color of extract	Residue on drying	Residue on ignition	Alkalinity as HCO₃	Cl	SO₃	CaO	MgO
cm.		*per cent*	*per cent*	*per cent*	*per cent*	*per cent*	*per cent*	*per cent*
0-8	Faint yellow	0.0565	0.0033	0.0343	0.0014	Trace	Perceptible traces	Trace
13-50	Colorless	0.0410	0.0276	0.0274	0.0007	—	Perceptible traces	Trace
65-75	Colorless	0.0323	0.0241	0.0205	0.0017	—	Trace	Faint trace

Table 32
Analyses of a brown loam soil from Semirechie, per cent of total soil
(After Prasolov)

Locality	Depth cm.	Organic Matter	Water at $100°C$	Combined water	Loss on ignition	CO_2
At Tarbo-gatai, north of Bakhty	0-7	1.878	1.625	2.987	6.649	0.859
	10-26	1.210	1.528	2.536	7.335	2.061
	40-45	0.844	1.662	2.001	9.233	4.726
Behind Lake Ala-Kul near Karaagach	0-8	1.750	1.275	2.729	6.156	0.401
	10-22	0.936	1.875	3.377	7.776	1.412
	45-50	0.690	2.991	3.065	8.710	1.964
	70-80	0.349	1.650	3.016	——	1.949
In the vicinity of Lake Tau kekyl	0-6	2.04	1.06	0.41	4.89	1.41
	8-24	1.41	1.61	0.88	7.50	3.60
	26-40	0.495	2.29	1.52	12.85	8.04
	60-80	0.240	1.06	1.08	19.67	17.31
	90-95	0.207	0.87	0.80	9.30	7.42

Table 33
Base exchange capacity and composition of absorbed cations in brown and chestnut brown soils
(After Prasolov and Antipov-Karataev)

Horizon	Depth	Exchange capacity	Percentage composition of absorbed cations			
	cm.	m.e.	Ca	Mg	K	Na
Brown solonetzic soil						
A_1	0-10	22.73	59.2	21.6	10.0	9.2
A_2	15-25	25.40	52.6	37.5	2.3	7.6
B_1	30-40	25.34	48.1	42.5	3.8	5.6
Brown soil						
A_1	0-10	17.96	73.2	22.8	4.0	—
B_1	16-28	27.76	67.0	24.5	3.1	5.4
Normal chestnut soil					$K+Na$	
A_1	1-6	39-89	76.5	16.2	7.3	
A_2	15-20	26.64	58.5	17.1	24.4	
B_1	25-30	20.11	48.4	15.9	35.7	
Transition soil: from chestnut to chernozem						
A_1	1-6	48.54	76.1	17.2	6.7	
A_2	20-25	39.72	71.9	17.1	11.0	
B_1	35-40	17.92	58.3	24.0	17.7	

Chestnut Brown Soils

Geographic Distribution.—Prasolov and Antipov-Karataev (22), discussing the chestnut brown soils of the arid steppe (in collaboration with Sedletskii who presents X-ray data on the colloid fraction of one profile), point out that, according to Glinka's soil map of the world, the total area of this soil zone is equal to 6,279,000 square kilometers. They quote Marbut's figure of 548,300 square kilometers for the chestnut brown soils of the United States. The figure for the USSR is 1,850,000 square kilometers. These soils are also widespread in South America, in Africa, and Australia. Prasolov and Antipov-Karataev estimate that about one third of these soils is affected by the solonetzic type of soil formation. In Europe, they have been recognized in Rumania, Hungary, and Spain. In the latter, they are found, according to Glinka, as a result of vertical zonation. In the United States, they are found in a belt extending through eastern and central Montana, eastern Wyoming and Colorado, the southwestern corner of North Dakota, the western half of South Dakota, western Nebraska, west of the Nebraska sand hills, western Kansas, a strip in western Texas, and eastern New Mexico. Vilenskii (32) describes the soils at Tribune, Kansas, as typical light chestnut soils.

Glinka cites the climatic conditions of the chestnut brown soils in the Kazakhstan Republic as being hot in the summer and cold in the winter. The average annual temperature in this region is about 2° C. and the average rainfall, about 300 mm. In some sections, the temperature is occasionally as high as 5 to 6° C. with 350 mm. of rainfall. In the region of the chestnut brown soils in the United States, the rainfall increases, from 230 to 500 mm., from north to south, with a corresponding increase in temperature.

Profile Characteristics.—The constitution of a chestnut brown soil has been described by Tumin (31) as follows:

A_1: In the upper part (5 to 7 cm.), it is characterized by a foliated structure, relatively friable, and a light coloration. The lower part of this horizon is structureless and somewhat compact. Dry lumps, upon being crushed, become powdery. In all, this horizon extends to a depth of 20 cm.

A_2: Slightly lighter in color than A_1, somewhat compact, as in the lower part of A_1, with tongue-like projections and spots of organic matter. The granular and nutty structure of the soil is not apparent.
   The total maximum depth of the humus horizon is 60 cm. The point of effervescence is usually found in A_2, but infrequently it starts at the surface. In the latter case, it is usually associated with a parent material rich in carbonate.

The humus horizon of these soils may be divided into several subhorizons.

Below the humus horizon, there is a considerable accumulation of lime and sometimes also of gypsum. Prasolov (21) emphasizes the point that chestnut soils have no distinct granular structure.   This phenomenon has also been noted by Kravkov (Ch. 7, 20, p. 212).

A₁: Usually somewhat grayish; the clods easily break into horizontal plates; at the surface it is frequently loose and finely powdered, about 10 cm. deep.

A₂: It is of a looser constitution than A₁, with a more conspicuous brown tint and small cloddy structure, about 10 cm. deep.

B₁: Markedly compact, of a reddish brown tint, breaks into prisms or clods with sharp edges, about 13 cm. deep.

B₂: The humus rapidly disappears, the structure becomes coarser, prismatic clods are apparent, and it effervesces strongly.

The chestnut brown soils are distinguished for their dark colored humus-impregnated horizon which resembles the color of ripe chestnut. Its organic matter content runs from 2 to a maximum of 5 per cent.   The lime content runs from 2 to a maximum of 5 per cent.   The lime content increases with depth, but the other constituents remain almost constant throughout the profile.   The water-soluble constituents are low: 0.05 per cent in the surface horizon, and 0.07 to 0.08 per cent in the lower horizons, with appreciable quantities of bicarbonates.   Glinka points out that the humus content of this soil type decreases gradually with depth.   There is no appreciable translocation of soil constituents.   Even the calcium and magnesium show no appreciable accumulation in the B horizon.   This indicates a parent material poor in alkaline earth bases.

Prasolov (21), in a contribution on the soils of Turkestan, points out that "the solonetzic complexes comprise one of the elements of the chestnut soil zone."   On the basis of the solonetzic character of the brown soils, Bezsonov (3) favors the abolition of the special brown zone.   In this interpretation, the brown and the chestnut brown are one and the same type with the solonetzic character as one of the elements in this zone. Prasolov and Antipov-Karataev (22), in their comprehensive study of the chestnut soils, come to the conclusion that "all the chestnut soils, with their double horizon, friable and silty at the surface, and compact and cloddy at the bottom, are to be considered, in the light of the theories of Gedroiz, as more or less 'solodized.'   The variations in form and transitions observed in these soils are the result of an irregular salt content in their early stages of development, irregularity in the salinity of the parent rocks, or in the irregular subsequent distribution of the salts in the profile."

Kravkov (Ch. 6, 20, p. 209) treats the brown and chestnut brown soils as a group of the arid (desert-like in Kravkov's terminology) steppe type of soil formation having some solonetzic properties.   Among the characteristic physical features of this type, Kravkov singles out the accumulation of fine silt and clay in the B horizon. Chemically, this horizon is distinguished by a higher R_2O_3 content. Because of some mechanical and chemical translocation of constituents, "the B horizon (and sometime also the lower A horizon) is more or less compact and attains at times a somewhat darker coloration." Kravkov cites data of a profile "having 3.96 per cent fine silt and 8.43 per cent clay in the A horizon and 6.36 and 20.2 per cent of these separates in the B horizon. These horizons contain 3.04 per cent Fe_2O_3 and 2.21 per cent Al_2O_3 in A and 5.41 and 6.17 per cent of these in B." Kossovich (Ch. 2, 40, p. 115) recorded this phenomenon. He stated: "In these soils, the process of leaching carries from the A horizon not only the easily soluble salts and alkaline earth bases, but also some R_2O_3. The latter are responsible for the compactness of the lower portion of the A horizon. The exact nature of the translocation of the R_2O_3 still remains unexplained." It is very probable that the movement of these constituents is associated with the splitting of silicates in the process of solonetz reactions.

There is no granular or crumb structure even in the A horizon of these soils. A platy, scaly, or laminar structure is very common. In this respect, these soils resemble the gray-red desert-semidesert soils. The gradual decrease in organic matter content within the depth of the A horizon ties them to the chernozem type of soils.

Prasolov and Antipov-Karataev (22) differentiate two subdivisions in the chestnut brown soils: a light and a dark chestnut brown. The light chestnut brown soils are described as having a shallower A horizon and a lower exchange capacity than their darker brown counterpart. In plate 19, the soluble salts and exchangeable base content of these soils are presented graphically. It is to be noted that very little soluble salt is present in the profile down to a depth of about 160 cm. This depth indicates the penetration of the fall and winter rains. The region from 160 to 300 cm. shows an accumulation of salts which, as a rule, represents the limit of the capillary rise of ground waters.

The dark chestnut brown soils are characterized by Prasolov and Antipov-Karataev as getting more rainfall, the depth of percolation reaching the 200 cm. level, the average annual precipitation being 304 mm.; the average temperature, 4.8° C.; the relative humidity, 72 per cent; the number of days having some precipitation, 105, chiefly during November-February; the average moisture deficit (difference between precipitation and evaporation), 570 mm.; depth of freezing of soil, from middle of January to middle of April, 150 cm.

The depth of the A horizon varies from 15 to 30 cm., of the B horizon

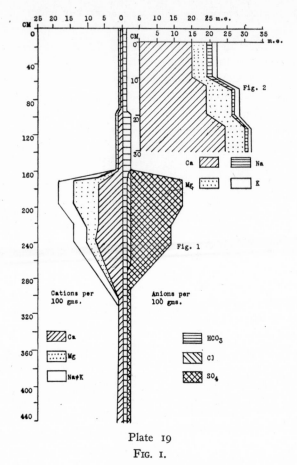

Plate 19

FIG. 1.

Distribution of water soluble salts in a light chestnut brown soil, m.e. per 100 *grams of soil*

FIG. 2.

Distribution of exchangeable cations in soil of figure 1, *m.e. per* 100 *grams of soil.*

(After Prasolov and Antipov-Karataev)

30 to 50 cm.; effervescence begins at 10 to 40 cm. from the surface; carbonate deposition extends through the layer 35-140 cm.; at times sulfates are encountered at 115-180 cm. layer.

The organic matter of the dark chestnut brown soils, like that of the chernozem, consists of the more stable types: humic acid, 28-29 per cent, and lignin-humin, 24-26 per cent. In the carbonate layer, the humic acid content drops, 7 per cent at the 50 cm depth, with a rise in the lignin-humin content, 43-45 per cent. Such fluctuations in the two types of organic matter are attributed to the increase in alkalinity. . . . Hemicellulose and cellulose make up 3 to 8 per cent of the total organic matter.

The rest of the organic matter, 17 to 25 per cent, consist of other hydrolyzable substances.

The C:N ratio of the organic matter is 12:1. Only 10 to 18 per cent of the total nitrogen is hydrolyzed with 1 N H_2SO_4, which indicates a low N coefficient for the organic matter of this soil

Contrary to the data of Kravkov, cited above, Prasolov and Antipov-Karataev conclude that "the process of soil formation of the chestnut brown (non-solonetzic) soils does not cause a translocation of finely dispersed particles of parent material through the profile." The apparent contradiction may lie in the divergence of opinion, Kravkov considering the brown and chestnut brown soils as a group affected by solonetzic properties. A mineralogic analysis of the profile, the > 2 μ fraction, of a dark chestnut brown soil, cited by Prasolov and Antipov-Karataev, shows no difference in the type of minerals. This conclusion is substantiated by the X-ray analyses of this profile.

Tables 34-36 give the total analyses of a light and dark chestnut soil and of the colloids of a chestnut brown soils. Of interest is the accumulation of Ca and Mg carbonates. The soluble salts of Na, K, and Mg are removed from the surface horizon, the cations being partly adsorbed by the exchange complex. The percentages of adsorbed cations in typical soils are: Ca—65 to 75 per cent, Mg—20 to 30 per cent, and K and Na making up the rest. Some data on the exchangeable bases in the profile of a chestnut brown soil may be found in table 37. For more extensive data on the exchangeable bases of these soils, the reader is referred to the paper of Antipov-Karataev and Sedletskii (1). The data on the composition of the colloids show a slight removal of SiO_2 and a retention of some Al_2O_3 in the uppermost layer.

Shavrygin (26) made a study of the effect of different cations—Li, Na, K, NH_4, Mg, Mn, Ca, Ba, Al, and Fe—on the following properties of a chestnut brown soil: hygroscopicity, maximum hygroscopicity, maximum molecular moisture capacity, total moisture holding capacity, capillary rise of water, dispersion, stickiness, placticity, and heat of wetting. On the last named property, comparisons have been made with podzols, chernozem, gray forest soils, and solonetz. It is brought out that a chestnut brown soil saturated with Mg behaves in many respects like one saturated with Na. In table 37, the effect of the cation on the physical properties of the soil are clearly brought out. The work of Eaton and Horton (5a) and of Joffe and Zimmerman (7a) on the effects of Na and Mg on some physical properties of soils corroborate the findings of Shavrygin.

Minerals in Gray and Chestnut Brown Soils.—From table 14 (Ch. 4), it is evident that the type of minerals varies with the soil type and

Table 34

Composition of a light chestnut brown soil, per cent of dry soil

(After Prasolov and Antipov-Karataev)

Horizon	Depth	Organic matter	CO_2	SiO_2	Fe_2O_3	Al_2O_3	CaO	MgO	K_2O	Na_2O	P_2O_5	SO_3
	cm.											
A_1	0-4	1.60	—	73.17	4.08	10.00	1.43	1.05	2.68	1.75	0.09	0.26
A_2	13-21	4.31	—	69.73	5.74	13.14	1.44	0.77	2.91	1.96	0.08	0.22
A_3	23-36	1.43	0.19	66.30	6.47	13.50	2.17	1.93	2.68	1.94	0.11	0.51
B	60-68	0.24	5.55	60.80	5.24	11.24	8.30	1.98	2.35	1.90	0.08	0.50
C	100-108	0.54	5.60	60.64	5.09	11.53	8.07	1.94	2.32	1.65	0.05	0.48

Table 35

Total analyses of a dark chestnut brown soil, per cent of dry soil

(After Prasolov and Antipov-Karataev)

Depth cm.	Organic Matter	CO_2	SO_4	SiO_2	TiO_2	P_2O_5	Al_2O_3	Fe_2O_3	MnO	CaO	MgO	Na_2O	K_2O
0-15	4.25	0.00	0.17	64.91	0.06	0.10	11.85	4.80	0.40	1.61	4.08	1.32	1.41
15-25	4.35	„	0.13	64.79	0.06	0.08	11.92	4.90	0.40	1.55	3.87	1.23	1.33
25-40	2.62	0.52	0.20	64.44	0.06	0.12	11.95	4.87	0.40	1.55	4.67	0.95	0.75
40-55	2.35	3.32	0.18	60.25	0.06	0.06	11.44	5.02	0.40	4.73	5.41	0.88	1.66
55-75	1.73	4.85	0.17	58.90	0.06	0.09	11.28	5.10	0.40	5.91	5.98	1.15	1.65
75-85	1.04	6.31	0.16	55.62	0.06	0.08	10.86	5.00	0.40	7.40	6.01	1.09	1.54
85-105	0.58	6.88	0.09	55.52	0.06	0.07	11.45	5.20	0.40	8.41	6.00	1.27	1.75
105-130	0.36	5.88	0.31	58.65	0.07	0.12	12.51	5.29	0.38	8.48	2.52	1.26	1.73
130-150	0.34	5.65	0.22	59.50	0.07	0.19	13.20	4.66	0.38	7.79	2.63	1.37	1.94
150-170		5.23	0.24	59.22	0.07	0.12	13.43	4.64	0.45	4.72	2.60	1.36	1.99

Organic matter, carbonate, and sulfate-free basis

Depth cm.	SiO_2	TiO_2	P_2O_5	Al_2O_3	Fe_2O_3	MnO	CaO	MgO	Na_2O	K_2O
0-15	67.83	0.06	0.10	12.38	5.02	0.42	1.68	4.26	1.38	1.47
15-25	68.22	0.06	0.08	12.55	5.16	0.42	1.63	5.13	1.29	1.40
25-40	67.08	0.06	0.12	12.44	5.07	0.42	0.78	4.86	0.99	1.82
40-55	67.18	0.07	0.07	12.75	5.60	0.45	1.80	4.40	0.98	1.85
55-75	67.56	0.07	0.10	12.94	5.85	0.46	1.80	4.42	1.32	1.89
75-85	67.52	0.07	0.10	13.18	6.07	0.48	1.81	4.19	1.32	1.87
85-105	66.12	0.07	0.08	13.64	6.19	0.48	1.85	4.38	1.51	2.08
105-130	67.68	0.08	0.14	14.44	6.10	0.44	0.81	2.91	1.45	2.00
130-150	68.07	0.08	0.22	15.10	5.33	0.43	0.46	3.01	1.57	2.22
150-170	66.86	0.08	0.13	15.16	5.24	0.51	0.92	2.93	1.53	2.25

TABLE 36

Total analyses of colloids of several layers of a chestnut brown soil, per cent of dry colloids

(After Prasolov and Antipov-Karataev)

Depth Cm.	Hygroscopic water	Organic matter	SO_3	SiO_2	TiO_2	Al_2O_3	Fe_2O_3	P_2O_5	MnO	CaO	MgO	Na_2O	K_2O	$\dfrac{SiO_2}{Al_2O_3}$	$\dfrac{SiO_2}{H_2O_3}$
0-15	15.13	9.99	0.29	43.19	0.29	19.08	9.92	0.18	0.05	0.31	2.60	0.14	2.20		
15-25	14.68	6.17	0.29	45.25	0.25	19.13	10.55	0.24	0.06	0.26	2.80	0.32	2.30		
85-105	10.97	1.44	0.33	50.10	0.35	21.10	11.72	0.19	0.04	0.23	2.91	0.58	1.81		
190-210	11.46	1.19	0.30	50.76	0.27	19.76	12.17	0.19	0.03	0.27	3.02	0.63	2.01		
230-250	13.61	1.17	0.26	50.62	0.29	18.24	12.27	0.13	0.04	0.30	3.16	0.24	1.89		
390-410	9.16	1.57	0.23	50.59	0.28	20.28	11.51	0.08	0.06	0.54	2.88	0.65	2.36		
Organic matter free basis															
0-15				48.20	0.32	21.29	11.07	0.20	0.05	0.34	2.90	0.16	2.45	4.00	3.00
15-25				48.51	0.27	20.51	11.31	0.26	0.06	0.28	3.00	0.34	2.53	4.04	2.98
85-105				50.70	0.35	21.35	11.86	0.19	0.04	0.23	2.94	0.59	1.83	4.04	2.98
190-210				51.57	0.27	20.08	12.36	0.19	0.03	0.27	3.07	0.64	2.04	4.36	3.13
230-250				51.43	0.29	18.53	12.47	0.13	0.04	0.55	3.21	0.24	1.92	4.72	3.30
390-410				51.60	0.28	20.68	11.74	0.08	0.06	0.31	2.94	0.66	2.41	4.24	3.11

is influenced by the composition of the rock. Beidellite and illite persist in the gray semidesert region. Montmorillonite and illite seem to dominate the chestnut brown soils. More data are wanted on the mineralogic composition of these soils, their subdivisions and varieties.

Table 37

Effect of Ca, Mg, and Na on the physical properties of a chestnut brown soil
(After Shavrygin)

Property studied	Cations saturating soil		
	Ca	Mg	Na
Hygroscopicity: per cent	5.05	5.69	4.48
Maximum hygroscopicity: per cent	9.83	10.09	12.27
Maximum molecular moisture capacity: per cent	15.28	15.74	18.00
Moisture holding capacity: per cent	62.00	69.00	103.00
Capillary rise to a height of 9.5 cm: hours and minutes	3.30	6.45	3 months*
Dispersion: per cent	0.28	0.56	7.16
Stickiness: gms. to sq. cm	17.40	20.00	30.70
Attenberg constants:			
a) Lower limit of flow	31.90	35.40	38.40
b) Rolling limit	15.60	15.70	14.00
c) Plasticity	16.30	19.70	24.40
Heat of wetting: small calories per gm of soil	7.82	6.79	5.07

*In these 3 months the moisture has risen 3 cm. only

References

1. Antipov-Karataev, I. N. and Sedletskii, I. D. 1937 Physico-chemical processes of solonetz formation. *Pedology* (U.S.S.R.) No. 6: 883-907.

2. Baldwin, M. and Youngs, F. O. 1921 Soil survey of the Twin Falls area, Idaho. U. S. Dept. of Agr. Bur. of Soils. Advance Sheets, Field Operations, pp. 1377-1381.

3. Bezsonov, A. I. 1926 About the brown zone and the brown soils. *Pedology* (U.S.S.R.) No. 2: 25-45.

4. Brown, I. C. and Drosdoff, M. 1940 Chemical and physical properties of soils and of their colloids developed from granitic materials in the Mojave Desert. *Jour. Agr. Res.* (U. S.) 61: 335-352.

5. Dimo, N. A. 1916 The role and significance of termites in the life of the Turkestan soils. (Russian). Rus. Pochvoved.

5a. Eaton, M. F. and Horton, Ch. R. 1940 Effect of exchange sodium on the moisture equivalent and the wilting coefficient of the soils. *Jour. Agr. Res.* 61 : 401-425.

6. Frass, O. 1868 Geologisches aus dem Orient.

7. Glinka, K. D. 1909 On the classification of Turkestan soils. *Pochvovedenie* (Pedology) 11 : 255-318.

7a. Joffe, J. S. and Zimmerman, Miryam. 1944 Sodium, calcium, and magnesium ratios in the exchange complex. *Proc. Soil Sci. Soc. Amer.* 9: 51-5.

8. Korovin, E. P. and Kashkarov 1934 Types of deserts in Turkestan. *Geobotanika* (U.S.S.R.) No. 1: 301-330.

9. Kudrin, S. A. 1942 The content and mobility of phosphates originating from various parent materials. *Pedology* (U.S.S.R.) No. 5-6: 19-25.

10. Kudrin, S. A. and Rozanov, A. N. 1938 Contribution on the characteristics of serozem with a high content of adsorbed magnesium. *Pedology* (U.S.S.R.) No. 6: 836-855.

11. Lapham, M. H. 1926 Some profiles of represent. western soils. *Amer. Soil Survey Asso. Bul. VII.* 1: 25-42.

12. Lapham, M. H. 1932 Genesis and morphology of desert soils. Report of the 12th Annual Meeting of the *Amer. Soil Survey Assn. Bul.* XIII. pp. 34-52.

13. Marbut, C. F. 1935 Soils of the United States. Atlas of American Agriculture, pt. III. U. S. Dept. of Agriculture, Advance Sheets No. 8.

14. Milne, G. 1936 A provisional soil map of East Africa. East Africa Agr. Res. Sta. (see also Bushnell, T. M. Some aspects of soil catena concept. *Proc. Soil Sci. Amer.* 7: 466-476) (1942).

15. Neustruev, S. S. 1909 Results of investigations in the Suir-Dar region. *Pochvovedenie* (Pedology) 11: 92-95. See also Ch. 2, 50.

16. Nikiforoff, C. C. 1937 General trends of the desert type of soil formation. *Soil Sci.* 43: 105-131.

17. Nikiforoff, C. C. 1937 The inversion of great soil zones in Western Washington. *Georg. Rev.* 27: 200-213.

18. Nikiforoff, C. C. 1944 Hardpan and microrelief in certain soil complexes of California. Tech. Bul. No. 745, U. S. Dept. of Agriculture, pp. 45.

19. Olovyanishnikov, G. I. 1937 The distribution of $CaCO_3$, $MgCO_3$, SiO_2, and R_2O_3 in the mechanical fraction of serozem of Middle Asia. *Pedology* (U.S.S.R.) No. 7: 710-720.

20. Passarge, S. 1909 Verwitterung und Abtragung in den Steppen und Wüsten Algeriens. *Geograph. Ztsch.* 15, Heft 9: 493-510.

21. Prasolov, L. I. 1926 The soils of Turkestan. (Russian). Leningrad.

22. Prasolov, L. I. and Antipov-Karataev, I. N. 1929-1930 On the solonetzic character of the chestnut soils in Ergeni and the method of determining it. *Trudy Pochv. Inst. Dokuchaeva,* Akd. Nauk, Contr. 3-4: 161-206.

23. Rokitzkaya, A. I. 1932 Soil microflora of Zolotaya Orda in Turkestan. *Proc. and Papers, Second Inter. Cong. Soil Sci.* 3: 266-267.

24. Sabanin, I. G. 1943 Some agrohydrologic peculiarities of the soils of the Bogar zone in Central Asia. *Pedology* (U.S.S.R.) No. 7: 34-47.

25. Shantz, H. L. 1938 Plants as soil indicators. *Soil and Men.* Yearbook of Agriculture. U. S. Dept. of Agr. pp. 835-860.

26. Shavrygin, P. I. 1935 On the physical properties of chestnut brown soils and their relation to the exchangeable bases (in English). *Studies in Genesis and Geography of Soils.* Acad. of Sci. (U.S.S.R.) *Dokuchaev Soil Inst.* 213-223.

27. Shaw, Ch. F. 1927 The transcontinental excursion of the First International Congress of Soil Science. Appendix X.

28. Sinnyagin, I. I. 1939 On the genesis of gray soils. *Pedology* (U.S.S.R.) No. 5: 17-32.

29. Storie, R. E. and Carpenter, E. J. 1929-1930 Soil survey of the El Cajon and Oceanside Areas, Cal. U. S. Dept. of Agr. Bur. of Chem. and Soils. Unpublished.

30. Thorp, J. 1936 Geography of the Soils of China. National Geogr. Survey, etc. Nanking, China.

31. Tumin, G. 1909 The soils of Vermensk County, Semirechie Region, Trudy Pochv. Botan. Expedit. po Issledov. Koloniz. Raionov Aziat. Rossii, Pochv. Issled. za 1908, Bul. 4, (Quoted from Glinka).

32. Vilenskii, D. G.   1928   Principal features of distribution of soils and vegetation in the U. S. and Canada.   *Soil Res.* (Inter. Soil Sci. Soc.) No. 2: 108-137; also *Pedology* (U.S.S.R.) No. 1-2: 99-138 (1928).

33. Vysotskii, G. N.   1906   The oroclimatogenic basis of classifying soils.   *Pochvovedenie* (Pedology) No. 2: 1-17.

34. Walther, J.   1901   Das Gesetz der Wüstenbildung.

35. Wolfganger, L. A.   1930   The Major Soil Divisions of the United States.   Wiley & Sons, New York.

CHAPTER IX

CHERNOZEM TYPE OF SOIL FORMATION

*In the history of pedology, chernozem
has played as important a role as frogs
have in the history of physiology,
calcium—in crystalography, and
benzol—in organic chemistry*

VERNADSKII

Introduction.—Literally translated, the Russian word *chernozem* means
black earth, in German *Schwarzerde,* and in French *terre noire.* Pedologically, chernozem represents a process of soil formation in the steppe regions
where the climate may be referred to as semiarid-subhumid. No type of
soil has been studied and written about as much as the chernozem. The
fundamentals of pedology have been worked out by Dokuchaev in nature's
laboratory, the chernozem type of soils. In his monumental work *Russkii
Chernozem* (Russian Chernozem), published in 1883 (Ch. 2, 15), we find
a clear exposition of the principles of pedology. To this book, the pedologist may turn even now for stimulating ideas on soil development. Over
250 analyses on the organic matter content of chernozems are recorded
in this book. It also gives a comprehensive historical review of the studies
on chernozem. Among these, the investigations and theories of Ruprecht
(Ch. 2, 63) are not just of historical interest. He was among the first to
appreciate the interrelations between the grass vegetation and chernozem
formation, but he did not recognize the climate as a factor in the formation
of chernozem. Kostychev (Ch. 2, 41), one of the critics of Dokuchaev's
climatogenic theories on the formation of chernozem, made a thorough
study of chernozem, and one of his fundamental contributions was the
theory that *plant roots are responsible for the accumulation of organic
matter in soils.*

Geographic Distribution.—In Europe, the chernozem extends, according to the map of Glinka, as published by Prasolov (Ch. 2, 59), in a belt
running southwest to northeast through northern Bulgaria, Hungary,
Galicia, Rumania, and Russia. In the western part, it is found approximately at the parallel 45° north latitude, and in the eastern part, at the parallel 57° north latitude.

In Asia, the chernozem belt is an extension of the European belt and terminates approximately at the meridian 93° longitude east of Greenwich. A few scattered areas of chernozem and chernozem-like soils are found in northern China.

In North America, the chernozem belt runs from north to south between the parallels 50° and 27° north latitude. In the United States, it occupies approximately three-fourths of North Dakota, one-half of South Dakota and Nebraska, three-fourths of Kansas, one-half of Oklahoma and Texas. To these, we have to add the prairie soils of Minnesota, Iowa, Illinois, Missouri, Kansas, Oklahoma, and Texas. Some chernozem and prairie soils are to be found in Idaho, Oregon, and Washington. The chernozem soils occupy an area of 280,200 square miles and the prairie soils 283,500 square miles.

In South America, a meridianal belt (between the meridians 55° and 65° longitude west of Greenwich) of chernozem and chernozem-like soils is located between the parallels 26° and 38° south latitude. The nature of these soils has not been clarified. It appears, that they are of the southern variety of chernozem.

Climate.—The general features of the climate in the chernozem zone have been elucidated by Dokuchaev (Ch. 2, 15). They are: continentality, deficiency of rainfall, low humidity, hot summers, cold winters, and sharp fluctuations in temperature, (the annual average for Russia being about 5° C.). The rainfall deficiency is caused not so much by the low rainfall (in the Russian belt of chernozem the average annual precipitation is between 400 and 550 mm.) as by the character of fall and seasonal distribution. In the steppe regions, the rain comes frequently in downpours, resulting in considerable runoff. The highest fall comes during the summer. Because of the high temperatures, low humidity, and high evaporation, less moisture is available for percolation and leaching. In Siberia, precipitation is in places as low as 300 mm.

In the chernozem belt in the United States, a somewhat different climatic situation exists. The rainfall and temperature increase from north to south, as may be seen from table 38. It is clear that the increase in precipitation is offset by the increase in temperature, and the net effect is a chernozem type of soil formation. Of course, the unique combination of the climatic elements introduces variations creating chernozem subtypes which will be discussed presently. In this table are interdispersed climatological data for a few points in Europe and one in Siberia. The pampas in Argentina, famous in song and story, are boundless plains of treeless grasslands, with a chernozem soil cover. The high rainfall in the pampas, 30

Table 38

Rainfall and temperature conditions in the chernozem belt in the United States, European Russia, Siberia, Hungary, and Rumania

State*	Average annual precipitation		Average annual temperature	
	mm.	inches	°C	F°
North Dakota	447.5	17.9	3.8	38.8
Omsk (Siberia)	316.6	12.0	0.3	32.4
South Dakota	525.0	21.0	7.5	45.5
Kharkov (Russia)	490.1	19.6	7.3	45.1
Nebraska	588.5	23.5	9.2	48.7
Budapest (Hungary)	544.0	21.8	10.7	51.2
Kansas	669.5	26.8	12.5	54.5
Dnieprpetrovsk (Russia)	542.2	21.7	8.2	46.7
Oklahoma	836.2	33.6	15.7	60.3
Bukharest (Rumania)	591.0	23.6	10.6	51.1
Texas	722.5	29.0	18.8	66.0
Saratov (Russia)	371.3	14.8	5.6	42.1

*The States (U.S.) are arranged in the order from north to south and are paired with corresponding latitudinal positions in other parts of the world.

to 35 inches, is offset by the high average temperature, 16 to 17° C. The winters in the chernozem belt are, as a rule, severe, with little snow. The average annual relative humidity in the chernozem belt of Russia is 70 to 80 per cent, August being the driest month with a humidity of 45 per cent.

Parent Material.—Chernozem is found on a great variety of soil textures, mostly of the heavy types—the loams. The principal parent material of the vast region of chernozem in Russia is loess. Large areas of chernozem are located on lime marls, limestone, basalt, granites sandstones, and others. In the United States, the typical chernozem soils, the Barnes series (North Dakota, South Dakota, and western Minnesota), have originated on glacial drift; of the Boyd series—on Cretaceous shales; the Holt series—on Tertiary sandstone. Some of the prairie soils have developed on cherty limestone, calcareous glacial drift, fine grained sandstone, limestone, and many other types of rocks of various geologic ages. Vast areas of the chernozem soils lie on loess.

LOESS

Extensive deposits of loess in China were investigated by Richthofen (Ch. 2, 61). He described it as a fine calcareous silt or clay, the bulk consisting of particles 0.05 to 0.01 mm. in diameter, yellowish or buff in color, mellow and yet coherent. When cut by stream action, it is found to stand with vertical walls, sometimes hundreds of feet high. It is not rich in organic matter but is high in mineral colloidal complexes. One of the characteristic features of loess is the abundance of minute tubes, lined with lime, which traverse it vertically, and which are assumed by some to be due to root fibers. According to Merrill (Ch. 4, 49) :

. . . It is the presence of these, presumably, that causes the vertical cleavage and at the same time the remarkable absorptive qualities for which the loess is noted.

Its distribution in Europe is given as extending from the French coast at Sangatte, eastward across the north of France and Belgium, filling up the depressions of the Ardennes, passing far up the valleys of the Rhine and its tributaries, the Neckar, Main, and Lahr ; likewise those of the Elbe above Meissen, the Weser, Mulde, and Saale, the upper Oder, and Vistula. Spreading across the upper Silesia it sweeps eastward over the plains of Poland and southern Russia, where it forms the substratum of the chernozem or black earth. It extends into Bohemia, Moravia, Hungary, Galicia, Transylvania, and Rumania far up into the Carpathians, where it reaches heights of from 2000 to 5000 feet above sea-level.

In northern China, the loess covers an area of about 300,000 square miles, primarily in the region drained by Hoang-Ho, in the provinces of Shansi, Shensi, and Kansu, reaching almost to the edge of the Mongolian Plateau. It is also found in Turkestan, Persia, and other parts of Asia.

In the United States, the loess is found primarily in the drainage basin of the Mississippi River. The adobe of the southwestern part of the United States shows many similarities to loess, and the pampas of South America are probably in part of similar material. An extensive discussion with an exhaustive bibliography on the subject is to be found in the work of Free (25).

Origin of Loess.—The origin of loess has long been a moot question. In the early days, loess was considered a result of the action of great floods with a sudden change of drainage. If that were the case, one should find in loess deposits traces of the rapidly moving streams. This view was held by Walther (Ch. 2, 85), Johnson (43), Durand (18), and others. Bennigsen-Förder (11) and Fallou (21) advocated a marine origin for the European deposits, and Kingsmill (45) adopted this theory for the Chinese loess. In this connection, Free pointed out:

. . . it is difficult to explain by this means the fact that over many areas, especially in North America and China, an apparently continuous and uniform sheet of loess is found at altitudes varying amongst themselves by several (or in China, many) hundreds of feet. Nor are there any signs of ancient shore lines or beaches or of marine fossils. These and other less weighty considerations have led to the entire abandonment of the marine hypothesis, at least in application to all loessial deposits of wide extent. There are, however, many localities in which the minor features of the loess speak for some manner of aqueous deposition, and the various forms of the lacustrine and fluvial theories have continued to be held until the present day. The controversies have been waged between, on the one hand, the adherents of these theories, and on the other the followers of Richtofen in his brilliant hypothesis, elaborated with regard to the Chinese loess.

According to Richthofen, the desert mineral dust was carried by winds to the more humid regions where it settled and became fixed in place by the beating of rains and entanglement with vegetation. A cover of such dust forced the grasses to extend their aerial parts, with the buried parts undergoing the processes of oxidation. This gave rise to the formation of the tubules which are so characteristic of the loess. These served as moisture channels, on the walls of which lime precipitated. To explain the frequent occurrence of fresh water shells in loess and the evidence of stratification, the theory was advanced that the mineral dust from the deserts also settled in the water basins which in the geologic history have since disappeared.

Free, divided the loess problem into two phases, the source of the material and mode of deposition. According to him:

The chronology of the formation is fairly well fixed. Innumerable indications connect it with the glacial period and probably with the stages of retreat or decay of the ice sheet. These indications are clearer and more certain in North America than elsewhere, but are also unmistakable in Europe and probably not less apparent in China, though in the latter country the detailed investigations of Pleistocene geology is still in its infancy. The evidence includes not only the position of the loess in the stratigraphic series, but the parallelism (in N. America) of the belt in which it is developed with the margin of the ice sheet and not infrequent interstratification of loess with marginal drift and till of undoubted glacial origin. It seems very probable that there were several subperiods of loess formation all lying within the glacial epoch and each related to one of the successive periods of retreat of the ice sheet. That the American loess was deposited at the time of glacial retreat is believed by the authors of the three most thorough and comprehensive works dealing with the region in question,* and this opinion has been generally accepted by geologists.

Turning now to a consideration of the evidence behind the Eolian and the aqueous hyoptheses, respectively, it will be advisable to discuss first the manner of deposition, as it is this which is largely responsible for the pecularities of the deposit and because it is over this problem rather than over the problem of source that the controversies have been waged.

It is known that the most important single item of evidence in favor of the Eolian hypothesis is the terrestrial character of the loessal fauna. The occurrence of other than land fossils is sporadic and perhaps adventitious, and there can be no question that the vast majority of the organic remains in loess are those of animals which lived altogether on land. The mere presence of land shells in fluvial, lacustrine, or marine deposits is of course nothing extraordinary, but the absence of aqueous forms from fossiliferous strata of such origin would be very remarkable indeed. It is not the occurrence of terrestrial forms but the non-occurrence of any others that seems to favor so strongly the deposition of the loess over a dry land surface.

The absence of stratification, the great uniformity of the deposit, and in general the lack of traces of water action so characteristic of ordinary sedimentary deposits is in itself another strong argument for the Eolian hypothesis. It is possible that material deposited in permanent and nearly currentless lakes or in very sluggish rivers might show no traces of water action, but such material, if fossiliferous at all, should show a fresh water fauna with only occasional terrestrial examples. Continuous aqueous deposition cannot explain the terrestrial fauna, and intermittent floodplain deposition is probably inconsistent with the absence of stratification and other traces of water action.

---

*Free is referring to the work of Chamberlin and Salisbury (16), McGee (58), and Leverett (52).

On the other hand, the aqueous hypothesis is favored by the unmistakable relation of much loess, especially in N. America, to the stream valleys. This is true not alone in horizontal but also in vertical projection. The belt of loess is not only more or less parallel to the stream, but is often thicker near its banks, forming a natural levee and indicating deposition from flood waters flowing outward from the channel and rapidly losing their load because of loss of velocity and by entanglement in vegetation. Shimek has urged, however, that even Eolian loess would be thicker along stream courses because there the vegetation would be more extensive, more vigorous, more permanent, and consequently more dust would be entangled and retained.

A more certain indication of aqueous deposition is the undoubted presence in some occurrences of loess of well developed strata and intergradations of finer and coarser material, which appearances can be ascribed to nothing else than deposition from water. These strata can by no stretch of the imagination be considered similar to the false bedding of Eolian sands and the evidence is perfectly conclusive for those deposits from which it has been obtained.

These apparently contradictory conclusions can be reconciled only by the obvious deduction that the manner of deposition of the loess was not everywhere the same. There is both Eolian and aqueous loess, and it is quite conceivable that there is loess which is both aqueous and Eolian. Loess is no more a specific thing than is sandstone, or shale, or conglomerate; and as there are sandstones which have been formed from dunes, or by rivers, or in the sea, so there are "loesses" which are Eolian, or fluvial, or (perhaps) marine.

All this concerns mainly the agent or agents by which the loessial material was deposited. A word now as to the source of the material itself. It would seem that only in two ways could such a large amount of finely comminuted debris have been produced, either by long-continued secular decay of the rock with accompanying removal of the debris, or by the grinding of moving ice. In either case the material has undoubtedly undergone a remarkable efficient sorting process either by wind or water or by both. With regard to the American deposits, the weight of evidence and opinion seems to favor the conclusion that the loessial material is probably rock flour from under the ice sheet. The physical properties of the loessial grains are quite consistent with such an origin, and it is known that much material was prepared and supplied in this way. It is by no means necessary, however, to assume that glacial debris is the exclusive material of the formation.

In a very general way the primary American deposits of loess may be considered as made up mostly of glacial silt, but partly of windborne rock debris from the arid regions to the west these two materials separate or mixed, having been collected or deposited either by Eolian action, or on the flood-plains of great but sluggish rivers, or perhaps in more or less permanent shallow lakes.

The features of the formation in Europe are probably not essentially different from those in North America, but in China it seems that the share of the wind in loess formation has brobably been much greater, especially in the transportation of the material from the region of production in Central Asia to the localities where it is now found.

Mills (59), in the report of a study made in the 80's on the loess deposits in Brazil, argued against the Richthofen eolian hypothesis. He proved that the deposition of loess was a result of stream action and, referring to the origin of loess in the Mississippi Valley, stated:

In the Mississippi Valley, loess is a deposit made upon a low-lying region by the overflow of overloaded streams, that is, by the overflow of streams bearing to the region more sediment than they could carry through it with the descent consequent velocity of their current due to its elevation.

Agafonov (4) and later Agafanov and Malychev (5) attempted to explain the tubular formation in loess and, touching again on the theory of the origin of loess, expressed their adherence to the eolian theory.

An excellent review (in English) of the theories and hypotheses on the origin and deposition of loess and a critical analysis of the contributions on this subject up to 1927 are given by Berg in his summary paper (12). He points out that the loess-like deposits, such as loess-like loam, clay moraine material, and lake loess, are indisputably of alluvial origin. As to typical loess, which some investigators still ascribe to eolian origin, Berg presents evidence showing that in general it does not differ from that of the loess-like deposits. In his conclusions Berg states:

> Loess and loess-like deposits have one common origin. They are found in situ from various rocks, always highly calcareous, as a result of weathering and soil forming processes under conditions of a dry climate. The mode and time of deposition of the parent rock of loess must be distinguished from that of the transformation of these rocks into loess. The parent rock of European loess had accumulated chiefly during the glacial period when the rivers discharged great quantities of silt. The formation of loess from these rocks occurred during the dry interglacial periods and during the post-glacial epoch. The dust, in the case of Turkestan and Central Asia, is an artificial product, generally the result of the dispersion of the loess itself. There is nothing to prove the formation of loess by dust-drifts in the recent epoch. The eilian hypothesis is not based on facts observed in the present epoch.

Berg (13) returns to the subject once more and discusses loess in relation to the fauna, reviewing and analyzing the different theories on loess formation. Gerasinov and Markov (29) and Gerasinov (28) have added evidence in support of Berg's theories. Krokos studied the loess formation in Ukraine, correlating his findings with geological and in a large measure pedological (buried soils) evidence. He associated the formation of loess with the glaciation period and considered the "glacial winds" as the primary factor in the distribution of loess. Sokolovskii (84), from his studies on the properties of the absorption complex of Ukranian loess, concluded that the theory of Tutkovskii (89) on the eolian origin of loess and the aridity of the climate during that period was correct. In a later publication (85), Sokolovskii reiterated his idea on the eolian origin of loess. He claims that the mass of material for the loess comes from the A horizon of the gray, brown, and chestnut brown soils as a result of the dispersed condition due to the salimization and desalimization of these soils. Loess is, therefore, "a product of pedogenesis, but of an allochtonic nature. The material moved with the air masses from the glacial anticyclone." Local sources of alluvial origin accompanied by wind action may be encountered. He shows that loess is unsaturated, with very little Ca in the exchange complex, in spite of the presence of $CaCO_3$, the origin of which he does not explain satisfactorily. Polynov (Ch. 4, 62, p. 175) attempts to explain the origin of carbonates of Ca and Mg by the upward movement of salts. Sokolovskii does not meet the objections raised by Sobolev (83) on the source of the huge loess deposits known. According to Sobolev's calculation, the would be areas of eolian supply can not account for the existing deposits of loess.

Sobolev (83) reports a discussion of the loess problem at a meeting of the Soviet section of the International Association on the Study of Quaternary Deposits (INQUA). Mirchik, one of the prominent geologists of Russia and proponent of the eolian origin of loess, pointed out "that the lowland between the glacier and the Alp-Carpathian mountains system represented a kind of a corridor which broadened out in the east and west. . . . It seems as if the fens originating in the glacier and mountains farther south caused a constant blowing of winds in the corridor. These winds (glacial winds:J.S.J.) blew to the west into France and to the east into Ukraine." In this manner, Mirchink explains the mantle type of deposition of Wurms loess in Ukraine.

Sobolev presented data showing that the loess area of Ukraine which has supposedly received its material from the corridor mentioned by Mirchink is 574,000 square kilometers. Taking the average depth of loess as 3.01 meters, it would require an area of 2,296,000 square kilometers of land to supply the loess accumulation. Even the entire surface of European Russia, let alone the corridor, could not supply that quantity of wind blown material. Sobolev goes on to support and develop the theory of the alluvial origin of loess. On epeirogenetically rising regions, there is less depth and fewer deposits of loess, whereas in epeirogenetically sinking regions, an array of deposits and great depths of loess may be found. He considers epeirogenetic movements as an important factor in loess accumulation.

Petrov (69) presents extensive data on the composition—chemical and mineralogical—of loess in the Biisk forest-steppe (Altai region of Siberia). He favors the theory of alluvial origin of loess and argues against the Il'in (35) concept of loess being a product of soil forming processes. Analyses show the presence of heavy minerals and an abundance of a great variety of minerals in general. In soils, this kind of mineralogical makeup is out of the question.

A serious objection to the alluvial origin of loess is the lack of stratification in loess deposits. Longwell, Knopf, and Flint (53) explain this condition by the activities of earthworms and plants in the process of deposition.

Russell (78) reviews the problem of loess formation and its origin. He differentiates loess and loess-like deposits. "Loess is unstratified, homogeneous, porous, calcarous silt; it is yellowish or buff; tends to split along vertical points; maintains steep faces; and ordinarily contains concretions and snail shells. From the quantitative standpoint, at least 50 per cent, by weight, must fall within the grain size fraction 0.01-0.05 mm. and it must effervesce freely with dilute hydrochloric acid." Russell points out that "over half of the American literature on loess actually refers to loess-like terrace silts."

Russell investigated the Lower Mississippi loess and evaluated his findings with practically all the theories advanced on the origin of loess. He compared the loess of the Mississippi Valley with that of the Rhine Valley and other parts of Europe. He concludes that:

field relationships preclude the possibility of eolian, lacustrine, fluvial or other direct sedimentary origin of loess . . . and demonstrate derivation of Lower Mississippi Valley loess from backswamp deposits of Pleistocene formation, expecting that none is known to have been derived from the youngest, or Prairie, formation. It occurs on slopes leading up to fine-grained, calcareous, and organic parts of terrace deposits and is absent from slopes leading to coarser materials, such as characterize meander belts. It thickens downslope into valleys, forming a mantle generally conforming to the topography. It crosses truncated Teritary and Quaternary beds and at many places incorporates materials from them, notably gravels from the lower parts of terrace formations, and, in some cases, lignite.

In the lower Mississippi Valley loess development correlates mainly with two main factors: (1) the presence of backswamp deposits in terrace formations, and (2) deep dissection. To be acceptable a theory of origin must harmonize with these facts.

The process of loessification starts in parent material that originally was deposited as alluvium on flood plains during the Pleistocene. It affects the finer parts of such deposits, especially those that have accumulated in backswamps and are present only in minor amount along Pleistocene meander belts. It is restricted to parts of terrace formations that now stand considerably above flood plains. The deposits must consist mainly of silt and clay. They are somewhat calcareous and contain carbonaceous matter derived from plant remains.

The initial stage of the process is weathering and differentiation of soil profiles. While pedogenic processes are active, much of the original calcareous content, including any fossil shells that may be present, is lost to ground waters. The resulting product is a brown loam that thickens residually on flats but is relatively mobile on slopes. In deeply dissected territory it creeps into valleys, where it accumulates to considerable thickness.

That there is a loess problem seems to result from two main causes: (1) the identification of many loesslike materials as loess, and (2) the insistence that the origin be eolian.

To eliminate confusion resulting from the first cause many deposits should be reexamined. The abode of the Southwest should be dropped from consideration. Terrace deposits should be excluded. Only material such as occurs at Council Bluffs or Muscatine, Iowa, should be accepted as loess. Widespread horizontal deposits of any kind and beds containing numerous vertebrates, such as occurs in the vicinity of Lincoln, Nebraska, may be suspected as not being loess. In general way all materials not containing terrestrial snail shells should be regarded with suspicion. Acceptance of a rigorous physical definition will exclude so many loesslike deposits that the problem is reduced to relatively simple and soluble terms.

Russell's scholarly interpretation of geologic events associated with loess formation gives weight to his deductions and conclusions. Were he acquainted more intimately with the Russian contributions (the ones he quotes and more so those that he does not quote), his own brilliant analysis of the loess problem would have been still more illuminating and convincing. His bibliography, outside of the Russian, is excellent.

The German monograph on loess by Scheidig (79) adds little in clarifying the controversy on the problem. Denisov (17) disagrees with Ganssen on the coagulating effects of Ca and Mg in the aggregation of loess. Rode (75) believes $CaCO_3$ to be essential in the formation of loess and discusses the manner in which Ca might have contributed to the aggregation of loess. A symposium on loess held under the auspices of the Nebraska Academy of Science, reported in a series of 12 papers (7), discusses the different phases of the problem. Smith (81) discusses variations in loess of Illinois.

Pyaskovskii (74) presents evidence on the plausibility of loess being the product of soil formation in the steppe region. He considers loessification as the result of reactions taking place in the subsoil in association with the biosphere. He cites Vysotskii's report on wheat roots penetrating to a depth of 2.5 meters and some steppe grasses to a depth of 13 meters. It stands to reason that the salts not retained by the B horizon might in their downward movement under steppe conditions distribute themselves very gradually and uniformly to great depths, following the root channels and domain of microbial activity and entering into some reactions which would produce loess.

ORIGIN OF CHERNOZEM

Several hypotheses have been advanced to explain the formation of chernozem. A comprehensive review of these has been presented by Dokuchaev in his monograph *Russkii chernozem* (Russian chernozem). The digest of these, as interpreted by Kossovich (Ch. 2, 40) and Glinka (Ch. 2, 27) follows.

Lomonossov (1711-1765), the famous Russian physicist and chemist, discussed the origin of chernozem. His conclusion was that chernozem originated from the decomposition of animal and plant bodies. Fine particles separate from these bodies and accumulate in the lakes by sedimentation to form a stratified rock. In classifying surface formations, he recognized a series of soil types. To him, any black soil was chernozem, and yet, as pointed out by Pavlov (68), he differentiated a number of chernozem subtypes.

Murchison (61) advanced the idea that the Arctic Ocean once extended as an inland sea, depositing the coarser sediments, sands and pebbles, in the northern areas and carrying the fine muds to the region now occupied by the chernozem. These muds were considered as wash material from the black Jurassic clays. A similar view was expressed by Petzhold (71), but in his opinion, it was the Black and Caspian Seas that submerged at one time the Russian plains, depositing muds derived from calcareous sandstone and limestone formations. The high organic matter content was ascribed to the residual marine animal life; this would explain the high nitrogen content of the chernozem. Kossovich (Ch. 2, 40) justly remarked: "These two hypotheses are only of historical interest and now have no foundation at all."

A sort of a combined source of origin—marine and bog—of chernozem was suggested by the explorer Pallas (67) at the close of the 18th century. On his visits into the Stavropol steppe region, Northern Caucasus, Pallas observed patches of saline soils in the chernozem. He concluded that the chernozem was a relic of a salt marsh, frequented by invasions from the ancient Caspian, Black, and Azov Seas which brought in the fine sediments. In the words of Pallas: "These sediments, together with the decomposed masses of sedges and grasses which remind one more of a salt marsh than of a mull which is found in the forests, form the deep layer of black earth, where no traces of forest are recognizable."

Eichwald (19), an exponent of the bog hypothesis, analyzed critically the marine hypothesis and advanced the idea that the chernozem was the remnant of ancient tundras and marshes. The present-day accumulations of organic matter in swamps and meadows were offered as evidence in support of the bog hypothesis. The existence of lakes, swamps, and even forests along the water courses in southern Russia was cited as more evidence for the hypothesis advanced. This raised the question of the existence of forest throughout the steppe region. Ruprecht (Ch. 2, 63) pointed out, however, that as far back as the time of Herodotus, the wandering tribes complained about the treeless nature of the steppe.

Orth (66) identified chernozem as a meadow formation which requires a high precipitation for organic matter accumulation. In other words, it is the bog type of soil formation with which Orth and the other Western European investigators were acquainted.

A very original but far-fetched theory was presented by Vangengein-von-Kvalen (92). According to him, the chernozem might have originated from the peats in the north which were later shifted southward by flood waters.

Ruprecht (Ch. 2, 63) was, in Dokuchaev's estimation, the father of the scientific approach to the problem of the origin of chernozem. He discarded the marine and bog hypotheses and took the position that the origin of chernozem is primarily a botanical question. He eliminated the forests as a factor in its formation, although his reasons for so doing were not very conclusive, as pointed out by Glinka (Ch. 27, p. 349). This does not minimize his chief contribution—even though not fully established by him—that the steppe grass vegetation is primarily responsible for the accumulation of organic matter. He did not, however, tie up the type of vegetation and the mode of accumulation of organic matter with the climatic conditions of the chernozem belt.

Ruprecht's exclusion of forest vegetation in the process of chernozem formation was contested by a number of investigators. Bogdanov (14) cited areas in the governments of Saratov and Simbirsk where chernozem-like soils could be found under forests. He failed, however, to disprove Ruprecht's view that such forests invaded the steppe region after the chernozem had been formed. Barbot-de-Mart and Karpinskii (10), Kontkevich (46), and Agapitov (6) maintained that the chernozem type of soil formation was associated with loess as parent material.

It remained for Dokuchaev (Ch. 2, 15) to settle the problem. According to him, the now-prevailing climate was the all-important factor in the formation of chernozem, which means that, geologically speaking, the chernozem was a recent formation. From this very striking fact, Glinka made the generalization that the *present-day soil cover is a product of the present-day prevailing climate.*

The salient features of Dokuchaev's researches on the chernozem are summed up by Kossovich as follows:

1. The chemical properties and physical makeup of the chernozem in its normal position are intimately related genetically to the parent material. 2. The humus of chernozem originates from steppe grass and not from forest vegetation. 3. Chernozem has a definite depth, not exceeding 5 feet. 4. Chernozem is endowed with a definite structure — granular — and has crotovinas. 5. Chernozem forms on various parent materials: loess, limestone. Jurassic clays, and the weathered products of granite. 6. Chernozem is very intimately related to the climate. 7. Forest vegetation forms no chernozem, but specific forest soils. 8. The organic matter of chernozem has its origin in the decaying roots as well as in the organic materials which penetrate from the surface vegetation.

Dokuchaev isolated in the chernozem zone isohumus belts (belts with a uniform quantity of humus) which follow rather closely definite isothermal lines, and formulated the dryland-surface hypothesis as follows:

There is a persistent parallelism between the chernozem belt and definite isotherms from southwest to northwest but not along the latitudinal parallels; it also follows definite atmospheric precipitation lines, definite grass associations, and certain forest vegetation lines. The same direction of distribution is maintained by the specific isohumus belts. The belt richest in organic matter is found in the center of the great belt. From this point on, in the direction of the northwestern and southeastern borders of the general belt, the organic matter gradually decreases to a minimum.

In places, there is a distinct conincidence between the change in the character of the steppe flora and the gradual disappearance of chernozem.

Kostychev's (Ch. 2, 41) conclusions were somewhat at variance with those of Dokuchaev. As mentioned earlier, he was not in full accord with the theory that the climate is the dominating factor in the formation of chernozem. Over the zone of the general chernozem belt, a range of climatic conditions could be separated, and similar climatic conditions also prevailed over areas where no chernozem was found. Kossovich (Ch. 2, 40) remarked that Kostychev "compared the climates with respect to atmospheric precipitation and temperature without considering the humidity and evaporation." Neither did Kostychev share Dokuchaev's view that the aerial parts of the plant contributed to the accumulation of organic matter in the soil.

Kostychev identified the formation of chernozem with the physical properties—primarily moisture conditions—of the parent material. He maintained that chernozem formed exclusively on fine-textured soil materials which, on the one hand, do not imbibe readily the precipitation waters and, on the other hand, evaporate these rapidly. Under such conditions, the organic matter decomposed slowly and hence there was an accumulation. He pointed out that on sandy parent materials in the chernozem zone coniferous forests sprang up and no accumulation of organic matter took place.

Afanaséva (3) revived the old concept of a meadow stage in the region of chernozem in European Russia preceding the steppe type of vegetation. She goes back to the ice age of 300,000 years ago, with the meadow stage lasting only the first 2000 to 3000 years. Nothing is being said on the geologic history of the period. According to Afanaséva, the age of the chernozem of European Russia is close to 300,000 years, minus the 2000 to 3000 years of the meadow stage. Among the prominent adherents of the meadow stage in the formation of chernozem was Williams. He looked upon chernozem as "a product in the historical development of one stage in the continuous soil forming process that followed the marsh stage."

In his monumental work, Marbut (Ch. 8, 20) speaks of chernozem in the United States having developed on recent (Wisconsin) glacial material, on lake-laid material accumulated in ancient glacial Lake Agassiz, lacustrine deposits, lime marls, and calcareous sandstone. In general, chernozem formation is traced to recent geologic deposits and age.

PROCESS OF SOIL FORMATION

Movement of Constituents by Percolation.—The increased precipitation in the chernozem zone causes more leaching. Deep percolation takes place during the wet periods of the fall and early winter; the salts that have accumulated during the summer are washed downward. In addition, the humification and mineralization of the roots of the plants that become active after the summer dry period send into circulation more salts. During the winter and early spring seasons, biological activity is dormant; the leachings are, therefore, relatively free of carbonic acid and very little bicarbonates of the alkaline earths may form. During the period of biological activity (most of spring, wet spells during the summer, and early fall seasons), the increased CO_2 content of the soil air brings about a movement of the alkaline earths, especially Ca. If not removed by percolation, the bicarbonates precipitate as carbonates in the B horizon at the depth penetrated by the percolating waters. This depth varies with the geographic position, being deeper at the edge of the steppe, along the forest zone, and not so deep at the border of the chestnut brown soils. In some areas, lime may begin to accumulate at the bottom of A. It is also likely that during the period of high CO_2 production, Ca and Mg, moving with other salts by capillary action, precipitate as carbonates at some point in the profile. Of course, leachings in the late fall also carry to the ground waters some of the alkaline earths as bicarbonates. It should be mentioned that, in years of low precipitation, even the soluble salts are not removed fully from the profile.

During the winter, when the soil is frozen, the vapor pressure of the soil air below the frost line increases because of the higher temperature. This condition causes an upward movement of water vapor which, upon striking the frost line, condenses and moves as liquid water downward.

Topography has a definite effect on the leaching of constituents. More leaching occurs on slopes. Seepage from higher to lower levels may bring in salts that would influence the profile characteristics.

Of the alkali bases, Na is leached from the profile, but some is returned by the flora. Potassium is undergoing a similar cycle. In addition, as a result of the prevailing high temperatures and desiccation effects during the summer, some potassium becomes fixed in the exchange complex (40) of the surface few inches of the soil. Appreciable quantities of phosphorus, in all probability in organic form, also accumulate in the surface few inches of soil. There is practically no movement of sesquioxides in the chernozem profile, and in rare cases, gypsum is encountered in the lower part of the B horizon. One such case has been reported by Nikiforoff (62) in the southern (Azov) chernozem of European Russia.

Small quantities of soluble organic compounds move from the upper portion of the A horizon to the lower portion of this horizon, and, in rare cases, into the upper B where they precipitate and become partially fixed during the desiccating summer temperatures.

Organic Matter Accumulation.—No other characteristic of chernozem is as well known as its deep A horizon containing from 4 to 15 and even more per cent organic matter. A striking feature of this horizon is the gradual decline of organic matter with depth. This is shown in table 39 and in any data recording analyses on chernozem soils.

Table 39

Distribution of organic matter in the chernozem profile

(After Glinka)

Depth	Leached chernozem	Deep chernozem	Ordinary chernozem	Southern chernozem
cm.	*per cent*	*per cent*	*per cent*	*per cent*
1-5	8.0	10.5	7.0	4.5
20-25	6.5	9.0	5.5	3.0
40-45	5.0	7.5	4.0	1.5
60-65	3.5	6.0	2.5	1.0
80-85	2.0	4.5	1.0	0.5
110-120	0.5	1.5	0.5	—

Organic matter accumulates in the grasslands as a result of circumstances inherent in the steppe flora and in the chemical and physico-chemical and biological reactions brought about by the specific climatic conditions. It is well known that in the spring and early summer, the moisture and temperature conditions in the steppe are optimum for grass growth. The prevailing neutral reaction and abundance of nutrients, mobilized in the soil during the spring, stimulate growth of the grasses. Their short growing cycle is complete just about when the hot weather comes on, and the tops and the largest share of the fine roots die. However, no decomposition of the plant residues takes place at that time because of the lack of moisture. During this period, the organic colloids age, stabilize, and become irreversible, i.e., they gel and become lyophobic instead of lyophilic. The intermittent wetting and drying effects, due to the erratic summer rainfall, accentuate these reactions, and the result is that, even after the rainy season, these substances remain highly resistant to decomposition.

In the version of Kossovich:

the vegetation of the chernnozem region is biologically represented by plant associations with a short growing season, capable of withstanding prolonged droughts and being tolerant to excesses of mineral salts in solution. Among the representatives of the steppe grasses, the biennials and perennials with shortened underground wintering stems and aerial parts (internodes) predominate. These plants are abundantly supplied with nutrients which the grasses utilize early in the spring to start their stolons and to complete their development with the production of seeds, in a rather short period. With the advent of the summer drought, life in the steppe fades, the grass dries out, and the steppe takes on a grayish-brown hue. A reawakening of the steppe grasses comes again in the fall. During the winter, the snow becomes entangled in the grass. In the spring, the thick mat of the dry stems and the dead grass cover hinders the development of new shoots.

Because of the moisture relationships in the region of the steppe, grasses develop an elaborate and deep root system, as shown in plate 20. These roots add large quantities of organic matter throughout the A horizon. It is probable that the fine network of roots permeating the mineral aggregates is in large measure responsible for the stable structure of chernozem.

Calcium and Accumulation of Organic Matter.—The factor of organic matter accumulation in relation to Ca was alluded to by Hilgard (Ch. 2, 30), who pointed out that lime preserved the organic matter. An experimental approach to the mechanism of the colloidal reactions involved in the coagulation and stabilization of organic matter in the presence of Ca was made by Ivanov (36, 37). He has shown that the Ca ion is more effective as a coagulating agent of organic colloids in the presence of mineral dispersoids. Such is the case in the chernozem region, where the Ca, even though leached from the surface layer, returns in circulation and is instrumental in helping to fix the organic matter. In a large measure, the stabilization of the organic matter is responsible for the typical granular structure of these soils, which in turn affects the moisture regime in the soil, allowing it to dry out to a considerable depth and thereby hindering the decomposition activities of the microorganisms.

Tanfiliev (87), the eminent Russian geographer, geobotanist, and pedologist, points out that, "even a cursory examination of the parent material on which chernozem is found always shows the presence of Ca. Loess, the prevailing parent material, is a calcium bearing silt and clay. Sandstones in the most elevated regions of the Don mountain chain also give rise to chernozem because they are rich in Ca. A similar situation is to be found on the volcanic rocks of the Armenian plateau. Even quartz sand will give rise to a chernozem, if it is somewhat calcareous. As a rule, however, this parent material lacks the Ca, and the result is the podzol type of soil formation. This holds true for the soils which develop on sandstones even deep in the heart of the steppe." Tanfiliev, therefore, comes to the conclusion that, "without Ca, which in part might be substi-

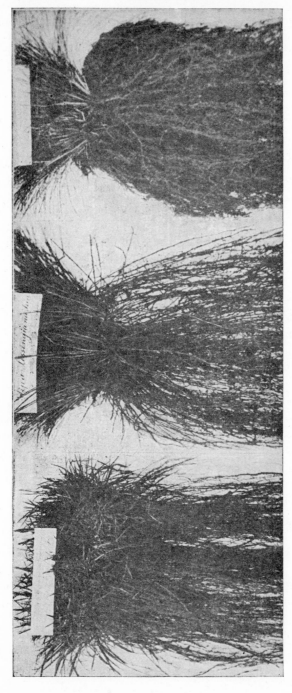

PLATE 20

Root development in chernozem

(After Kossovich)

tuted by Mg, no chernozem might form. This, however, does not imply that the presence of Ca will always give rise to a chernozem. Other conditions, climatic and biospheric, are imperative for the formation of chernozem."

Gedroiz (26,27) expounds the relation of Ca to chernozem formation as follows:

The decomposition of organic remains in a normal chernozem takes place in a medium sufficiently rich in Ca to saturate the absorption capacity of organic matter, thereby fixing it and lowering its solubility and degree of dispersion. Mineralization of the organic matter is interrupted at an early stage and, because of its saturation with Ca, it attains a large grained stable microstructure, becomes stable towards water, and colloidally dissolves but little. The soil microorganisms find little organic matter at their disposal, even though all other conditions might be favorable for their activities. The organic substances, non-nitrogenous and nitrogenous, are only slightly mobile notwithstanding the large quantities present in the soil.*

Besides, when moisture and temperature conditions are favorable for microbes, there is an abundance of fresh juicy plant residues at their disposal.

Humates and Sesquioxides.—Another point to consider in the chernozem process of soil formation is the influence of the alkaline earth bases on the colloidal behavior of the R_2O_3 and their relation to the organic complexes. It is shown by Mattson (Ch. 4, 48) that "where the pH is higher, the Al and Fe silicates become more highly hydrolyzed, i.e., the silicate ions are displaced by OH, resulting in a liberation, dispersion, and solution of silica. This is, however, true only when the rainfall is heavy enough to remove the bases, especially the divalent Mg and Ca which themselves form slightly soluble compounds with silicic acid and which are powerful coagulants of negative colloids." Because of the constant circulation of large amounts of Ca and Mg, the stability of the Al and Fe complexes is maintained and no SiO_1 or Al or Fe is lost. The high acidoid residue in chernozem—the humates of which are isoelectric at low pH values and above which they become increasingly electro-negative—gives it a high base exchange capacity. The presence of Ca and Mg suppresses the electro-negative charge and keeps the exchange complex saturated and therefore stable.

Soluble Organic matter and Structure.—Another property of chernozem is its low solubility, 0.02 to 0.05 per cent of the total, as shown in the

---

*From an agronomic point of view, this coagulating power of Ca introduces a rather unique situation. The organic complex in the coagulated state is not attacked by microorganisms. Gedroiz points out that in order to mobilize the N from such soils, it would be advisable to impart to them a certain degree of solonetzousness by means of sodium compounds.

voluminous data assembled by Kossovich. It is of interest that the organic matter comprises 50 per cent of the total solids extracted by water from chernozem, and yet the soluble organic matter, as a rule, does not reach the B horizon; it becomes fixed in its downward movement in the A horizon. This phenomenon, perhaps, is responsible for the gradual decline of organic matter through the depth of the A horizon.

Some of the soluble organic matter moves through the profile as salts of different cations, among which calcium, combining with the so-called humates, plays an important role in the granular structure of chernozem. The calcium humates penetrate into the clay-bound fine particles of clay, silt, and sand and coat them with thin glue-like membranes. Upon drying out, the humates of calcium, being by nature an irreversible colloid, become insoluble. The longer the period of desiccation, the more stable become the membranes. When moistened, they do not break and thus prevent the slaking of the clay bound particles. The cohesive and, in smaller measure, adhesive forces of these membranes keep a number of these particles aggregated into the well-known granular structural units. These granules are held together loosely by adhesive forces and give rise to large crumbs and other larger size units. Upon wetting, the adhesive forces are not sufficient to hold these large units together. However, the rigid and, at the same time, elastic aggregates of unit particles do not break down, and the soil thus maintains its granular structure.

It is very likely that the colloidal reactions of synerisis and coagulation, induced by the low winter temperatures and adsorption of calcum ions, add to the stability of the organic matter in general and to the structural aggregates in particular. The relation of the moisture content to structure is discussed by Vilenski and Germanova (93) and Koposov (47).

Morphological Characteristics

Descriptions of the unique features of chernozem, such as color, structure, constitution, and proverbial fertility may be found in the sagas, ballads, and folklore of the people who lived in this geographic region. Travelers, reporters, novelists, and poets have contributed a great deal to the popularity of this type of soil.

Color.—In referring to the color of chernozem, it is the surface layer that is usually singled out. The color is black, with a pronounced gray tinge in the more humid sections of the general belt and a brownish chestnut tinge in the more arid sections. When wet, it looks darker, and a freshly plowed field has the hue of plush with a dark-blue tone. With depth, the black is replaced by a dark brown and finally by a light brown color in the zone of lime accumulation.

Constitution.—The makeup of the profile constitution of chernozem is distinct, even though the different varieties of this type of soil may have specific features.

A_0: This layer is a mat of dead vegetation, consisting of an interwined mass of remnants of surface roots, subaerial stems, and some dead grass crushed by the pounding rains and mineral material, in the form of dust, carried by the winds. It is within the lower layer of this mat that some humification goes on. Very little of it is possible on the surface of the A_0 because of the exposure to the heat of the steppe sun and the desiccating hot winds. If anything, chemical oxidation, hydration, and solution are responsible for some of the changes that take place in the A_0.

A: The horizon of eluviation is one from which constituents are removed. It is at the same time the horizon of organic matter accumulation, distributed to considerable depth. This accumulation should not be confused with illuviation.

The thickness of the A horizon varies, 4 to 6 feet in the chernozem of Ukraine and more of the Azov region in Russia. According to Marbut, no such depths have been encountered in the chernozem belt of the United States. Generally, the A horizon does not attain a thickness of more than 20 inches (50 to 60 cm.). A similar thickness for the A horizon has been reported by Mirimanyan (60, p. 193) for the chernozem in Armenia. Reports on chernozem from Canada (20) show a deeper A horizon than in the chernozem of the United States. Within the United States, the thickness of the A horizon tends to decrease from north to south.

The structure of the A horizon is generally granular immediately below the A_0 layer, the granules increasing with depth, becoming small pea-like aggregates to small nuts and lumps at the bottom of this horizon.

The dark color of the upper part of the A horizon is gradually replaced by a lighter coloration of brown and yellowish brown to reddish-brown (in the southern belt of the United States), with streaks and tongue-like projections of dark colored humus over the structural units.

The dark brown to black color of the soluble organic matter permeates the individual granules of the structural units. The thoroughness of the penetration of the organic matter (this property is in a measure responsible for the stability of the aggregates, as pointed out earlier) may be judged from the fact that the black color persists in the fine particles even after the aggregates have been crushed to a powdery mass. This property of chernozem is in sharp contrast to that of crushed dark colored soil of types other than chernozem. The powdery mass of these soils shows the color tinge of the mineral component, indicating that the organic matter has not penetrated into the fabric of the structural unit. This fact explains in part their instability.

B: There is no sharp line of demarkation between the A and B horizons. The color gradually changes to light gray or brownish gray. The structure becomes coarser, lumpy, nutty, prismatic, blocky, or even columnar, the latter being an indication of solonetzic character.

White thread-like webs resembling fungus mycelium (it is called pseudomycelium), appear on the darker background of the lower A or upper B horizons. These webs are nothing more than carbonates of Ca and some Mg. In all probability, the crystallization of these has followed the course of the movement of water charged with lime along the network of fine roots.

With depth, the accumulation of lime increases in the form of concretions of various shapes and sizes, also as soft spots. The more compact, hard concretions form in worm holes and passageways of spiders and other forms of animal life that the chernozems harbor.

A typical feature of the B horizon in the chernozem soils of Russia is the presence of crotovinas. They appear as dark-colored spots on the light-colored background of the B horizon, and as light-colored spots on the black background of the A horizons. The bulk of crotovinas appear in the B horizon and deeper. No well defined crotovinas have been reported in the chernozem of the United States. Smith and Rhoades (82) do report rodent burrows. Mirimanyan (60) makes special notice of the absence of crotovinas in the chernozems of Armenia.

The depth of the B horizon extends to the point where the accumulation of limestone ceases. This point is easily determined on parent material poor in Ca, which might even be neutral or slightly acid.

In some chernozem, especially at the border with the chestnut brown soils, gypsum accumulations are at times encountered below the point of lime accumulation. It is very probable that this gypsum is the result of the upward movement of salts, a kind of incipient salinization which has been interrupted for one reason or another.

Vysotskii (Ch. 2, 84) reported two zones of lime accumulation in the more arid sections of the chernozem belt—one at a depth just below the A horizon and the other 4 to 4.5 meters below the surface. According to

Vysotskii's interpretation, there is not enough moisture in these sections of the chernozem belt to move the less soluble salts to the ground waters, except in extremely wet seasons. At the same time, the upward movement of the ground waters causes an accumulation of carbonates at the upper limits of the rise of these waters. The result is that a layer exists between these limits and the lower limits of the percolating waters. This layer, 2 to 4 meters deep, Vysotskii named the *dead horizon*. Except for the very soluble salts nothing passes this horizon.

In some soils of Ukraine, a dark-colored layer has been noted occasionally on loess and loess-like parent material in the C horizon, 3 to 4 meters below the surface. Makhov (55) suggested that these layers were nothing more than the A horizon of buried soils.

Kravkov (Ch. 7, 20) presented an opinion, which appears to be sound, that the accumulated organic matter in the C horizon might be the result of the movement of water soluble organic matter. It is possible that, for one reason or another, a solonetzic condition or degradation effects had set in temporarily causing a movement of organic matter. There should be no difficulty in finding substantiating pedologic evidence to prove each case encountered.

Chemical Properties

Only typical chemical analyses and properties of chernozem can be presented in a general treatise on pedology. Variations and departures from the normal, which give adventitious traits to some soils, are to be noted. They are the result of local climate, microrelief, and hydrologic and lithologic elements, which are not sufficiently expressed to impart to the soil the so-called intrazonal characteristics. They do, however, impart some specific chemical features to the profile and bring out varieties of this type of soil formation.

A vast amount of chemical data has accumulated on the composition of chernozem. A wealth of information can be found in the work of Marbut (Ch. 8, 13), who succeeded in taking analytical data on soils sampled at arbitrary depths (in the early days of the soil survey work in the United States) and giving a pedologic interpretation. In tables 40-63, analyses of representative chernozem soils from different parts of the world are given. They illustrate the points discussed earlier and those that follow.

Organic Matter.—As high as 15 to 20 per cent organic matter has been reported for chernozem in the eastern hinterland of the Volga region. It is of interest to note that thickness of the A horizon is no criterion of a high orranic matter content. The chernozem of the Volga region is designated by

Chemical composition of chernozem at various depths from North Dakota;* per cent of total

*From Expt. Sta. Tech. Bul. 246 (1931)

Soil type (textural) and location	SiO₂			Al₂O₃			Fe₂O₃			CaO			MgO		
	0-7"	7-20"	20-40"	0-7"	7-20"	20-40"	0-7"	7-20"	20-40"	0-7"	7-20"	20-40"	0-7"	7-20"	20-40"
Barnes Loam Cass County	72.7	73.3	62.7	10.0	9.4	7.8	3.0	3.3	3.3	1.78	3.04	9.10	.92	1.31	2.82
Barnes Loam McHenry County	72.0	73.0	63.5	10.4	11.8	9.6	3.5	4.3	3.5	1.29	1.69	7.26	.82	1.51	2.89
Bearden Loam Cass County	75.4	74.4	57.4	9.5	9.1	7.9	3.0	3.3	2.9	1.69	3.38	12.5	.84	1.33	2.68
Lamoure Loam Cass County	71.2	67.5	58.2	9.1	9.1	8.6	3.1	3.4	3.4	2.75	5.27	10.7	1.28	1.96	3.15
Lamoure Loam McHenry County	62.4	66.4	57.2	7.4	8.0	8.4	2.8	3.1	3.6	5.62	7.25	12.3	2.36	1.48	1.63
Maple Loam Cass County	68.4	76.8	75.4	7.7	8.6	7.4	2.3	2.0	2.3	.2.23	3.08	5.3	.89	.98	1.43
Maple Loam McHenry County	41.0	41.6	44.2	3.8	3.4	3.8	1.2	1.2	1.7	17.7	23.1	247	6.41	2.65	1.57
Sioux Loam Cass County	74.4	74.9	63.0	9.8	8.4	8.0	2.7	2.6	2.2	1.88	3.30	10.4	.83	1.31	2.66
Sioux Loam McHenry County	75.2	77.3	70.5	9.7	10.3	7.9	3.6	3.7	4.1	1.64	1.61	5.48	.83	1.05	2.26

Soil type (textural) and location	K₂O			P₂O₅			SO₃			N			Organic C		
	0-7"	7-20"	20-40"	0-7"	7-20"	20-40"	0-7"	7-20"	20-40"	0-7"	7-20"	20-40"	0-7"	7-20"	20-40"
Barnes Loam Cass County	1.81	1.67	1.46	.147	.109	.105	.193	.527	1.25	.356	.162	.060	4.32	1.81	.59
Barnes Loam McHenry County	1.92	2.08	1.63	.158	.107	.143	.201	.181	.180	.293	.134	.082	3.29	1.27	.76
Bearden Loam Cass County	1.73	1.71	1.38	.105	.078	.103	.186	.216	1.71	.266	.100	.054	2.99	1.06	.56
Lamoure Loam Cass County	1.59	1.38	1.35	.149	.132	.122	.218	.226	.255	.298	.176	.092	3.92	2.10	1.06
Lamoure Loam McHenry County	1.33	1.34	1.28	.209	.182	.176	.353	.111	.231	.585	.249	.197	6.22	2.55	1.95
Maple Loam Cass County	1.47	1.45	1.28	.169	.082	.110	.466	.137	.115	.733	.126	.027	7.79	1.38	.29
Maple Loam McHenry County	.73	.69	.71	.235	.127	.102	.408	.250	.207	.661	.118	.024	5.72	3.40	1.74
Sioux Loam Cass County	1.26	1.63	1.45	.149	.152	.090	.176	.184	.112	.336	.196	.030	3.98	2.01	.32
Sioux Loam McHenry County	1.66	1.81	1.69	.122	.109	.155	.172	.239	.199	.242	.125	.079	2.72	1.18	.65

Table 41

Chemical analyses of some chernozem soils in Canada

(From the Soil Survey Reports of the respective provinces)

Horizon	Depth	N	P	Ca	Mg	Carbonates in terms of $CaCO_3$	Reaction
	inches	per cent	per cent	per cent	per cent	per cent	pH

Soil Survey of St. Ann Sheet, Alberta, Canada
Incipient podzolic soil (degraded chernozem?)

A_1	0-6	.530	.100	1.17	.84	None	6.9
A_2	6-11	.140	.071	.66	.98	None	6.8
B_1	11-24	.099	.062	.91	1.22	None	7.4
B_2	24-36	.079	.054	3.32	1.29	7.45	7.4
C	36-	.057	.057	2.58	1.20	5.23	7.4

Black soil: loam

A_1	0-10	.544	.118	1.04	.47	None	6.8
A_2	10-20	.213	.059	.79	.71	None	6.9
B_1	20-36	.073	.043	.69	.59	None	6.9
B_2	36-48	.043	.056	2.56	.58	6.20	7.3
C	48-	.033	.060	1.56	.56	3.61	7.4

Oxbow loam, Saskatchewan

	0-7	.591	.081			1.365	
	7-15	.193	.048			1.484	
	15-24	.079	.054			20.20	
	24-40	.044	.045			21.23	

Black "park" (chernozem) soil, Lestock series, Alberta*

Depth	Organic matter	N	SiO_2	Al_2O_3	Fe_2O_3	CaO	MgO	P
inches	per cent	per cent	per cent	per cent	per cent	per cent	per cent	per cent
0-7	11.2	.551	70.03	10.25	3.44	3.12	1.76	
7-15	2.3	.128	76.40	14.84	4.05	4.28	2.11	
15-30			58.99	8.73	3.50	11.32	4.16	
30-48			59.75	8.69	3.37	9.89	4.04	
48-			62.13	8.84	2.70	11.60	4.48	

Oxbow series from black Park soils, Alberta*

0-4	10.9	.546	69.93	9.93	2.58	1.57	.80	.075
4-10	4.32	.216	70.78	12.52	3.26	1.64	1.25	.062
10-26	1.98	.099	64.60	10.54	3.23	7.97	2.32	.050
26-	.90	.045	63.14	11.08	3.43	6.82	2.92	.047

*From Joel, Proceed. & Papers First Int. Cong. Soil Sci. v. 4 (1928) pp. 200-222.

the Russian peasants as "fat" (rich in fertility). It is dark-black in color and has a thickness of only 20 inches. The chernozems of Ukraine, and more so of the Azov region, have an A horizon 4 to 6 feet thick, but the organic matter content is seldom higher than the 10 per cent figure. The chernozems of the United States are not rich in organic matter, being lower in the southern sections of the belt. The A horizon is generally not much deeper than 20 inches. A somewhat similar condition prevails in Canada. Ellis and Shafer (20) report chernozems in South-Western and South-Central Manitoba with 8 to 12 per cent organic matter, the A horizon extending to depths varying from 7 to 20 inches.

In table 42, data are presented on the C:N ratio of two profiles. Even the B horizon shows a ratio much higher than 10:1. It is also apparent that the higher humic acid and the lower uronic acid contents are found in the organic matter of regular chernozem. In the degraded chernozem (the more humid regions), the reverse is true.

In the chernozems of Canada, the C:N ratio is lower. This may be due to erosion, evidence of which may be detected in the shallow A horizon. It is also probable that the Canadian chernozems represent cultivated soils which have a lower C:N ratio than virgin soils.

According to Tyurin and Gutkina (Ch. 7, 75), the humins of chernozem which can not be dissolved in cold NaOH, when oxidized with cold HNO_3, 5.0N, for 15 minutes, followed by heating to 60°C. for 1 hour, become vulnerable to the action of NaOH, 0.1 N, shaken for 2 hours. After several extractions, the humins go into solution. This method of extracting humins has been worked out by Fuchs (Ch. 7, 12). The humins of chernozem are characterized by a stable bond of the humic acid with the fulvic acid. Tyurin considers the humins as types of complex esters which have lost a portion of their acid function, having a high degree of polymerization and condensation. Essentially, the humins in solution, upon precipitation with acid, are analogous in composition to humic acid of original chernozem samples. The organic substances of the light colored filtrate, after the precipitation of the humic acid, represent the fulvic acid. Kravkov points out that humification in an alkaline or neutral medium does not produce crenic and apocrenic acids (fulvic acid) in any appreciable quantities.

Tyurin (91) investigated a series of chernozems, brown forest soils, and genuine podzols by the hydrolysis method used in plant analyses. The soil was extracted with ether in Soxhlets for 10 to 16 hours, followed by hot alcohol. The residue was treated with 80 per cent H_2SO_4 in the cold for 2.5 hours (50 gm. of soil in 50 cc. of acid). Next, 375 cc. of water were added, and the diluted acid mixture was heated in flowing steam for 5

Table 42

Composition of organic matter in chernozem

(Analyses by Gutkina and Natkina; from Tyurin)

Soil	Horizon	C (organic)	N	C:N	Carbon content, per cent of total C in:	
					Humic acid	Uronic acids
	cm	*per cent*	*per cent*	*ratio*		
Degraded chernozem	A: 0-10	4.27	0.280	15.2	42.7	9.8
	B:45-65	2.10	0.170	12.3	44.2	10.0
Ordinary chernozem	A: 5-25	6.14	0.460	13.4	39.0	12.3
	A-B:25-60	4.15	0.320	12.9	29.3	11.2

Organic matter in chernozem of South-Central Manitoba, Canada

(After Ellis and Shafer)

Soil type	Depth in profile	C (organic)	N	C:N
	inches	*per cent*	*per cent*	*ratio*
Waskada, heavy loam	0-2	7.09	0.62	11.26
	2-6	6.63	0.51	12.98
	6-12	1.93	0.22	8.82
	12-18	.68	0.08	7.82
Darlingsford clay loam	0-2	7.33	0.59	12.38
	2-14	6.27	0.53	11.68
	14-20	1.55	0.17	8.91
	20-31	0.73	0.09	7.69
Hilton, clay loam	0-4.5	6.98	0.61	11.43
	4.5-7	3.55	0.34	10.26
	7-11	2.19	0.27	8.11
	11-19	0.48	0.07	6.32
Holland, clay loam	0-9	6.31	0.51	12.18
	9-18	2.88	0.27	10.67
	18-27	1.04	0.10	9.90
	27-36	0.65	0.10	6.5

hours. This treatment dissolved the carbohydrates, leaving behind a residue to lignin or lignin-humus, on which the C and N are determined.

The results in table 43 show that the C and N are higher in the chernozem residue than in any other upland soil type, which indicates the stability of the organic matter. This is especially true for the N complexes, of which more than half (59.4 per cent) is tied up. Thus, the N in chernozem is less mobile than in any other soil type. The immobility of N in chernozem is ascribed by Kudryavtzeva (50) to the stable melanin form, which is not hydrolyzable to any great extent.

Mattson (57) has shown how a protein, the chief source of nitrogen in humus, forms proteinates of Al, Fe, etc., as well as protein humates, silicates, etc. In the former, the protein serves as the anion — the acid — with a negative charge, and in the latter, as the cation—the base—with a positive charge. When alumina, which is isoelectric at pH 8.1 (and becomes more positive with a decrease in pH), is mixed with casein, which is isoelectric at ph 4.8, "a considerable quantity of protein is required to lower the isoelectric pH of alumina while, conversely, small amounts of alumina cause a considerable increase in the isoelectric pH of the protein."

The protein humates are isoelectric at a lower pH than the original protein. An increase in the protein fraction in the mixture shifts the isoelectric pH to a higher value, whereas an increase of humate shifts it to a lower value.

It is within the sphere of reactions of the isoelectric precipitation of colloids that a solution to some of the complex phenomena of the stability of humus is to be sought. Unquestionably, the introduction of the strongly positive Ca and Mg ions into the colloid system of chernozem shifts the pH range of the isoelectric precipitation of the colloids. It is in this direction that the work of Mattson may help to elucidate the reactions which are responsible for the qualitative differences between the organic constituents of the chernozem and those of other soil types.

Inorganic Constituents.—Some reactions and behavior of the inorganic constituents in the chernozem profile are specific. They have been, in part, discussed in the section on the process of chernozem formation, and are, in part, repeated at this point for emphasis.

Calcium and Magnesium.—The data in tables 44-45, as well as other data examined, clearly reflect the mobility of Ca and its reactions in the chernozem profile. No further elaboration is necessary on the accumulation of this element in the B horizon. Moving as it does in combination with various anions, the Ca ends up as the carbonate. Besides this phase of Ca

Table 43

Hydrolysis of organic substances from the surface horizon of a chernozem, podzol, and brown forest soil

(After Tyurin)

Type of soil	Depth of sampling	C and N content in original soils			C and N in residue after hydrolysis. Per cent of original		Ratio C:N in residue
	cm.	*per cent* C	*per cent* N	*ratio* C:N	*per cent* C	*per cent* N	
Chernozem	0-10	8.05	0.57	14.0	71.9	59.4	16.9
Peat podzol	10-15	13.38	0.62	21.6	67.9	38.9	37.6
Brown forest	5-8	4.86	0.29	16.7	65.2	48.6	22.4

activity, its combination with humates and fixation of these are to be considered.

A comparison of the Ca and Mg contents in the profile, calculated on the basis of milliequivalents, shows that in general the Ca is only slightly higher in the surface portion of the A horizon where fixation of Ca-humates is highest. With depth, down to the horizon of lime accumulation, the Ca decreases and the ratio of Ca:Mg becomes less than 1. The increase in Mg, except perhaps for the B horizon, is relative. From the data in table 44 on the Armenian chernozem, calculated on the organic matter—water—carbonate free basis, it is clear that Mg moves but little. In table 45, data are presented showing the behavior of Ca and Mg when the analyses are recalculated on basis of milliequivalents.

An examination of the composition of the colloidal fractions of the chernozems in Armenia, table 48, shows that the Mg content is much greater than that of Ca. This situation is due to the Mg-bearing montmorillonitic clay minerals inherent in chernozem.

Sodium and Potassium.—Sodium is leached from the A horizon, but does not accumulate in the B horizon. It is to be remembered that, whereas K and Ca return to the surface soil and throughout the root zone upon the death of plants, Na is generally not considered in the same way. We do know of some plants that take up much Na. The phase on the translocation of Na through plants needs more definite data. The data on the colloidal fractions of the Armenian chernozems corroborate the loss of Na from the surface layers.

As to K, it has been established that K is fixed in the surface layer of the A horizon because of the drying effects of the high temperatures that chernozem is subjected to during the summer. Undoubtedly, the K fixation is associated with the montmorillonite of these soils. It is also possible that the high P content of the surface layer has something to do with the fixation of K (41).

R_2O_3.—Not much can be added on the reaction of these constituents to what has been said in the discussion on the process of the chernozem type of soil formation. Generally speaking, there is little movement of the R_2O_3, due to the high pH and the presence of alkaline earth bases. There is, however, an intake of the R_2O_3 by plants, especially Mn and Al. These elements return to the surface soil upon the death of the plants, and hence an occasional slight increase of these elements in the A horizon. The data

Table 44

Analysis of chernozem in Armenia, per cent of total

(After Mirimanyan)

Depth in cm	Organic Matter	CO_2	SiO_2	Al_2O_3	Fe_2O_3	TiO_2	MnO	CaO	MgO	Na_2O	K_2O	P_2O_5	SO_3
0-13	5.89	0.07	53.95	18.92	6.17	0.92	0.06	4.34	2.47	2.44	1.60	0.19	0.51
13-36	5.10	0.03	4.09	18.27	6.86	0.93	0.06	4.06	2.67	2.30	1.93	0.20	0.57
36-65	3.29	0.03	55.00	18.17	7.40	1.00	0.05	4.21	2.61	2.27	1.51	0.12	0.37
65-100	1.00	11.04	39.44	14.45	4.97	0.71	0.03	17.88	2.38	2.01	1.16	0.17	0.38
100-120	—	—	57.64	18.90	5.41	0.93	0.05	5.68	2.56	2.50	2.60	0.36	0.38
Parent material	—	—	58.72	18.18	5.66	1.08	0.05	5.28	2.42	3.35	2.63	0.43	0.32
0-20	6.60	0.14	55.13	16.35	6.78	1.02	0.06	3.60	2.75	2.08	1.45	0.19	0.46
20-37	5.50	0.26	38.72	17.31	7.33	1.06	0.06	3.91	2.90	2.12	1.36	0.16	0.37
37-65	2.71	11.20		12.41	4.92	0.73	—	18.50	2.84	1.62	0.89	0.14	0.53
0-14	5.67	0.21	50.37	13.98	5.92	—	—	7.08	3.89	3.30	2.69	—	Trace
35-60	4.93	0.38	50.80	14.38	6.22	—	—	7.24	4.25	3.07	2.01	—	″
90-145	—	10.25	40.24	11.68	4.81	—	—	18.55	3.52	2.58	1.72	—	″

Analyses (per cent) of the mineral portion of chernozem in Armenia; on carbonate, organic matter, and water free basis

Depth in cm	SiO_2	Al_2O_3	Fe_2O_3	TiO_2	MnO	CaO	MgO	Na_2O	K_2O	P_2O_5	SO_3	$\dfrac{SiO_2}{Al_2O_3}$	$\dfrac{SiO_3}{Al^2O^3 + Fe^2O^3}$
0-13	59.91	21.01	6.85	1.02	0.06	3.66	2.74	2.70	1.78	0.21	0.57	4.85	4.01
13-36	59.81	20.20	7.58	1.03	0.06	3.34	2.95	2.54	2.13	0.22	0.63	5.03	4.06
36-65	60.11	19.86	8.08	1.09	0.05	3.46	2.85	2.48	1.65	0.13	0.41	5.15	4.10
65-100	56.71	20.77	7.15	1.02	0.04	5.64	3.42	2.89	1.67	0.24	0.55	4.66	3.81
100-120	58.95	19.33	5.53	0.09	0.05	5.81	2.62	2.56	2.66	0.37	0.39	5.48	4.40
Parent material	58.93	18.25	5.68	1.08	0.05	5.30	2.43	3.36	2.64	0.43	0.32		4.58
0-20	62.39	18.62	7.72	1.16	0.06	3.12	3.13	2.37	1.65	0.22	0.52	5.71	4.51
20-37	60.92	19.12	8.10	1.17	0.06	3.27	3.20	2.34	1.50	0.18	0.41	5.42	4.28
37-65	58.52	18.76	7.44	1.10	—	5.53	4.23	2.44	1.35	0.21	0.80	5.30	4.23
0-14	57.05	16.08	6.89	—	—	7.85	4.8	3.80	2.00	—	Trace	6.15	4.82

Table 45

Ca and Mg in typical chernozem soil profiles, organic matter free basis

(Compiled and calculated from Marbut's (Ch. 8, 20) data)

Barnes soil series				Moody soil series				Holdrege soil series			
Depth in profile	Ca	Mg	Ca:Mg	Depth in profile	Ca	Mg	Ca:Mg	Depth in profile	Ca	Mg	Ca:Mg
inches	m.e.*	m.e.		*inches*	m.e.	m.e.		*inches*	m.e.	m.e.	
0-2.5	70	50	1.4 :1	0-2.5	56	50	1.12:1	0-6	64	45	1.42:1
2.5-8	53	50	1.06:1	2.5-11	53	55	0.96:1	6-16	60	55	1.09:1
8-23	43	55	0.78:1	11-22	40	60	0.66:1	10-28	60	60	1:1
23-47	40	15	3.33:1	22-30	50	70	0.71:1	28-43	125	80	1.56:1
				30-57	35	15	2.33:1				

*m.e. = milliequivalents per 100 grams of soil.

on the colloid fractions of the Armenian chernozem seem to bear out this observation.

Gemmerling (27a) reports an increase of R_2O_3 in the horizon of illuviation. Bolyshev (Pedology (1947) No. 11, p. 666) substantiates the findings of Gemmerling. It seems that under certain conditions, not clarified as yet, appreciable quantities of R_2O_3, especially Mn, does move in some of the chernozem soils.

Phosphorus and Sulfur.—The relatively high Ca and N contents of the A horizon are responsible for the high P content in this layer. It is the proteins of the organic matter that furnish the P. As the organic phosphorus compounds are mineralized, the P released ties up primarily with the Ca.

The accumulated organic matter in the A horizon retains appreciable quantities of S. Its rapid circulation through dying plants and precipitation keep up the supply in the surface layer in spite of the ease of leaching of sulfates. Of course, large quantities of S in the A horizon persist in the form of organic complexes.

Ratios of $SiO_2:Al_2O_3$, $SiO_2:Fe_2O_3$, and $CaO+K_2O+Na_2O:Al_2O_3$:— Marbut (Ch. 8, 20, p. 21) recognized what has been known but often not taken into consideration: apparent gains or losses in the profile, as a result of the movement and translocation of soil constituents, are not always absolute. He points out that "a better expression of the changes which have taken place in the horizons through the processes of soil development is obtained by determining the molecular ratio of silica to alumina in each of the horizons after calculating analyses to a mineral basis (free from volatile and combustible matter)." This ratio, designated by Harrassowitz by the letters *Ki*, is named by Marbut *sa* ratio. Another ratio used by Marbut is the molecular $SiO_2:Fe_2O_3$ ratio, designated by him as *sf*. "This ratio has not hitherto been used in the interpretation of tables of chemical analyses of soils, but it seems to be of considerable value." A third ratio, "the sum of the molecules of CaO, K_2O, and Na_2O to those of alumina in the same material by the letters *ba*." This ratio serves as an expression of the amount of leaching that has taken place.

In the words of Marbut, "these ratios are used to compare between the several horizons of the soil profile rather than between the rock and the products of its decomposition. In the latter case, the extent to which the removal of material has taken place is measured."

Marbut also used data on "the molecular equivalent composition of SiO_2, Fe_2O_3, and Al_2O_3 (from these the *sa* and *sf* ratios may be calcu-

lated: J.), and in some cases of the combined alkalies and alkaline earths. . .
In the processes of soil development, the most significant changes in the
materials concern the sesquioxides, silica, and the alkalies and alkaline
earths. . . The significant matter with regard to them is the relations of
these figures for *each substance* in the *several horizons* of the soil and not
the interrelations of substances themselves."

To illustrate the method used by Marbut, table 46 is presented. It
reproduces the data as given by Marbut. His reasoning in interpreting
the data is of interest:

The ratios show clearly that no shifting of sesquioxides has taken place from
an A to a B horizon similar to that in the podzolic soils. The occurrence of the apparent concentration of sesquioxides in the layers of the soil where the carbonates are
high could not be due to the concentration of carbonates alone, since this concentration
would affect both sesquioxides and silica alike in all the layers and would not, therefore, change the relationship of the ratios in the several layers after the carbonate
concentration from what it was before.

In view of the fact that the Ca and Mg accumulations are clearly
brought out by the complete analyses, the *ba* ratio has been omitted in the
voluminous analyses presented by Marbut. In calculating the *ba* ratios for
chernozem, Marbut used the sum of Ca and Mg in place of the sum of
Ca, K, and Na.

pH.—The reaction of chernozem is generally neutral to alkaline. In the
zone of lime accumulation, the pH is never below 8.2, the pH of calcium
carbonate. It goes up to 8.6, probably as a result of an admixture of
magnesium carbonate, or sometimes because of some sodium in the exchange complex.

Ellis and Shafer (20) report the pH values of H_2O and KCl extracts
of 18 chernozem profiles in South-Central Manitoba, Canada. In texture,
these soils vary from clay loams to loamy sands. In all the profiles, except
one, the pH values of the surface layer varies from 7.4 to 8.4; of the B
horizon—from 8.2 to 8.8. The pH values of the Armenian chernozem,
table 51, show about the same range of the pH values. Bailey (8) reports
the pH values on 14 profiles of chernozem in the United States. The pH
values vary from 6.2 to 7.4 in the upper layer to 7.9-8.7 in the parent material and the lime zone.

Ion Exchange and Colloidal Properties.—The exchange capacity, per
unit substance, is higher in the organic than in the mineral fraction of chernozem soils, brought out in the data of table 47. Dividing the millequivalents
by the percentage composition of the two fractions, we get approximately 2

Table 46

Composition of Barnes silt loam, free from volatile and combustible matter, per cent of total soil

(After Marbut)

Horizon	Depth in inches	SiO$_2$	TiO$_2$	Fe$_2$O$_3$	Al$_2$O$_3$	MnO	CaO	MgO	K$_2$O	Na$_2$O	P$_2$O$_5$	SO$_3$
1	0-2.5	77.10	0.62	4.93	11.65	0.15	1.98	1.01	2.25	1.08	0.27	0.31
2	2.5-8	75.55	0.68	4.91	12.78	0.16	1.50	0.97	2.03	1.12	0.23	0.30
3	8-23	75.49	0.64	4.82	12.42	0.26	1.21	1.14	2.12	1.23	0.11	0.15
4	23-47	68.39	0.45	3.89	10.10	0.17	10.81	2.83	1.70	1.08	0.17	0.18
6	60-66	70.26	0.50	4.09	10.59	0.20	8.20	2.76	1.78	1.00	0.17	0.14

Depth in inches	Ratios			Molecular equivalent composition			Percentage calculated to a total of 100			Percentage calculated to constant percentage of CaO and MgO		
	ba	sf	sa	SiO$_2$	Fe$_2$O$_3$	Al$_2$O$_3$	SiO$_2$	Fe$_2$O$_3$	Al$_2$O$_3$	SiO$_2$	Fe$_2$O$_3$	Al$_2$O$_3$
0-2.5		41.24	11.25	1.278	0.0308	0.1140	82.30	5.26	12.43	77.10	4.93	11.65
2. 5-8	0.530	40.77	10.05	1.253	0.0307	0.1250	81.02	5.26	13.70	75.55	4.91	12.78
8-23		41.50	10.33	1.252	0.0301	0.1215	81.41	5.20	12.39	75.49	4.82	12.42
23-47	2.308	46.59	11.51	1.134	0.0243	0.0988	83.90	4.40	12.26	76.93	4.37	11.36
60-66	1.843	45.52	11.28	1.165	0.0256	0.1036	82.70	4.81	12.46	76.75	4.46	11.56

Table 47

Exchange capacity and exchangeable bases in chernozem.

(After Gedroiz)

Horizon	Depth	Absorbed cation in milliequivalents		Exchange capacity	Relative quantity of absorbed cations	
		Ca	Mg		Ca	Mg
	cm.	*m.e.*	*m.e.*	*m.e.*	*per cent*	*per cent*
A	0-15	46.5	6.8	53.3	87.2	12.8
A	15-30	46.5	4.7	51.3	90.8	9.2
B	30-45	36.0	5.0	41.0	88.0	12.0
B	45-60	34.7	5.2	39.9	87.0	13.0
B	60-75	34.6	5.4	40.0	86.5	13.5
B	75-90	33.0	4.1	37.1	89.0	11.0
C	90-105	32.1	4.7	36.8	87.2	12.8

(After Tyurin)

Horizon	Depth	Exchangeable cations				Total capacity exchange	Proportion of Ca	Ca:Mg*
		Ca	Mg	K	Na			
	cm.	*m.e.*	*m.e.*	*m.e.*	*m.e.*	*m.e.*	*per cent*	*ratio*
A_1	2-14	42.50	9.0	0.15	0.48	52.13	81.5	4.72:1
A_1	20-35	36.46	5.5	0.11	0.48	42.55	85.7	6.60.1
B_1	60-73	24.28	5.3	not determined		29.58	82.1	4.50:1
B_2	100-115	21.78	6.5	not determined		28.28	77.0	3.30:1

Cation exchange capacity of mineral and organic fraction in a chernozem soil

(After Tyurin)

Depth	Organic matter	Clay fraction	Exchange capacity of organic matter	Exchange capacity of clay fraction	Total exchange capacity: clay and organic matter	Exchange capacity determined on soil
cm.	*per cent*	*per cent*	*m.e.*	*m.e.*	*m.e.*	*m.e.*
2-14	11.50	67.20	21.39	26.88	48.27	52.13
20-35	7.54	68.07	14.02	27.23	41.25	42.55
60-73	3.31	64.03	6.16	25.61	31.77	29.58
100-115	1.04	69.31	1.93	27.72	29.65	28.28

*Similar ratios may be found in the work of Mirimanyan (60)

m.e. per unit of the organic fraction and 0.4 m.e. per unit of the mineral fraction. The higher the organic matter content, the higher the exchange capacity. As to the exchangeable bases in chernozem, it is clear from the data of Gedroiz and Tyurin that more than 80 per cent of the exchange capacity is made up of Ca. A glance at the ratios of Ca:Mg shows that these vary somewhat, from as high as 8 (in the data of Gedroiz) and as low as 3.3 to 1. If we compare these ratios with those in the chestnut and brown soils, we find that they are much higher in chernozem soils.

In table 48, analyses of two colloidal fractions of a chernozem profile are given.

A slight decrease in SiO_2 is apparent in the finer fraction. The reverse is true for the R_2O_3. The meaning of these facts is not clear. The decrease in the ratio of $SiO_2:Al_2O_3$ in the fine fraction is undoubtedly affected by the montmorillonitic nature of the colloid. The practically even distribution of R_2O_3 in the profile corroborates the data on the total soil analyses.

A significant feature of the colloid fractions is the higher Mg than Ca content, a decrease of Ca with an increase in dispersion, and a practically constant content of Mg in the different fractions. (See also Ivanov's results, table 49). These phenomena are undoubtedly associated with the montmorillonitic nature of the chernozem colloids.

Nothing of significance may be inferred from the data on the other constituents. Why the uppermost layer of the coarse fraction should have such a low P content is not clear. The low Na content in the fine fraction and the high Na content in the coarse fraction is probably associated with the composition of the parent material. The coarser fraction undoubtedly carries some of the original minerals.

The data also show that the colloid complex of the average chernozem is saturated and, therefore, carries no potential acidity. This condition imparts stability to the chernozem colloids. The change from a dry to a wet state causes little swelling of chernozem despite the montmorillonitic nature of its colloids which have an expanding lattice structure and are, therefore, amenable to swelling. However, the dominance of the Ca ions in the colloid complex cuts down the swelling. The high cation sorptive capacity of the montmorillonitic type of clay minerals and the high circulation of Ca in the process of chernozem formation help to saturate the complex with the stabilizing and non-swelling effects of the Ca ions.

In connection with the colloid properties of chernozem, the data on the Saratov chernozem, table 50, are of interest. The HCl extract dissolves practically all of the Fe and Mn, and only one half of the Al. Apparently, the clay minerals are Al-silicates of the montmorillonitic type, with very

Table 48

Analyses of the colloidal fraction of chernozem in Armenia, per cent of total
(After Mirimanyan)

Depth in profile	Hygroscopic water	Loss on ignition*	SiO_2	Al_2O_3	Fe_2O_3	TiO_2	MnO	CaO	MgO	Na_2O	K_2O	P_2O_5	SO_3
cm													
Fraction <2μ													
0-13	5.57	18.34	47.55	18.59	8.35	1.23	0.04	1.22	2.42	1.35	1.80	0.04	0.18
13-36	5.67	17.56	47.67	18.97	8.12	1.34	—	1.21	2.27	1.26	1.44	0.29	0.38
35-65	5.52	15.55	49.42	19.41	8.06	1.12	—	1.15	2.78	1.10	1.83	0.29	0.32
65-100	7.80	16.47	47.49	19.19	8.75	0.78	Trace	2.86	3.17	0.87	1.04	0.39	0.36
Fraction <0.2μ													
0-13	8.42	17.10	46.26	22.14	9.93	0.92	Trace	0.41	2.42	0.29	0.83	0.22	0.38
13-36	7.66	16.85	46.21	22.48	9.87	1.02	Trace	0.34	2.61	0.32	1.03	0.22	0.23
36-65	8.12	16.37	46.91	22.45	9.88	1.00	0.02	0.35	2.67	0.35	0.97	0.23	0.29

Analyses of the mineral portion of the colloidal fraction of chernozem in Armenia, per cent of total

Depth in profile	SiO_2	Al_2O_3	Fe_2O_3	TiO_2	MnO	CaO	MgO	Na_2O	K_2O	P_2O_5	SO_3	$\dfrac{SiO_2}{Al_2O_3}$	$\dfrac{SiO_2}{Al_2O_3 + Fe_2O_3}$
cm													
Fraction <2μ													
0-13	58.06	22.70	10.19	1.50	0.05	1.49	2.95	1.65	2.20	0.05	0.22	4.35	3.38
13-36	57.73	22.97	9.83	1.62	—	1.46	2.75	1.52	1.74	0.35	0.46	4.27	3.36
36-65	55.25	21.70	9.01	1.25	—	1.28	3.10	1.23	2.04	0.32	0.35	4.34	3.44
65-100	56.65	22.89	10.44	0.93	—	3.41	3.78	1.04	1.24	0.46	0.43	4.21	3.10
Fraction <0.2μ													
0-13	55.60	26.61	11.93	1.10	—	0.49	2.90	0.35	1.00	0.26	0.45	3.61	2.81
13-36	55.36	26.93	11.84	1.22	—	0.41	3.12	0.38	1.23	0.26	0.28	3.50	2.73
36-65	56.01	26.80	11.80	1.19	0.02	0.42	3.19	0.42	1.16	0.27	0.35	3.88	2.74

*Includes CO_2

Table 49

Composition of ash of colloid fraction $<0.25\mu$, recalculated from original data on millimolar basis

(After Ivanov)

Location and name of soil	Sample	Loss on ignition	Organic matter	Ash	SiO_2	Al_2O_3	Fe_2O_3	CaO	MgO
	gm	per cent	per cent	gm			Millimols		
Voronezh, chernozem sod	1.0846	16.3	4.53	0.9078	8.30	1.1	0.66	0.11	0.85
Voronezh, slightly degraded chernozem	0.8956	18.4	3.72	0.7331	6.69	1.81	0.52	0.10	0.70
Orlov Station, chernozem sod on slope	0.8546	16.38	—	0.7146	6.56	1.77	0.50	0.07	0.66
Orlov Station, chernozem, fallow	1.0750	15.64	—	0.9068	8.30	2.1	0.66	0.19	1.05

little Fe in them. The fact that not all of the Mg is extracted points in the same direction.

Water Extract of Chernozem.—Data on water extracts of chernozem, tables 50-52, show a relatively low soluble salt content. The loss on ignition shows that less than half of the dry residue is organic in nature. It is important to remember that loss on ignition may include loss of water of hydration. Whereas Ca is practically constant throughout the profile, Mg increases with depth.

Table 50

Solubility of chernozem from Balashev County, Government of Saratov,
in a 10 per cent HCl solution; per cent of dry soil

(After Zakharov)

Horizon	Depth of horizon	Al_2O_3	Fe_2O_3	Mn_2O_3	CaO	MgO	K_2O	Na_2O
	cm.							
A_1	0-30	7.98	4.09	0.07	1.78	1.23	0.78	0.06
A_2	30-55	7.83	4.55	0.08	1.82	1.19	0.84	0.07
B_1	55-80	8.53	4.68	0.09	1.34	1.65	0.88	0.08
B_2	80-100	7.72	4.28	0.10	5.63	1.52	0.80	0.06
C	100-	8.37	4.15	0.09	9.90	1.26	0.68	0.08

PHYSICAL PROPERTIES OF CHERNOZEM*

True and Apparent Specific Gravity and Porosity.—In table 53, data are presented on chernozem soils of several localities. It is to be noted that, despite the high organic matter content, the average specific gravity is relatively not so low; it fluctuates between 2.5 and 2.6. The apparent specific gravity or volume weight of chernozem, as compared with other soil types, is not high. In general, it varies from 1 to 1.2 and increases with depth.

The pore space in the upper layer is higher than 50 per cent; in some cases, it is as high as 60 per cent. In the more sandy varieties of chernozem, the pore space decreases. It also decreases with depth. Data on porosity and volume weight of a number of profiles in the chernozem zone of the United States are reported by Smith and Rhoades (82).

*This section is modeled after Kossovich (Ch. 2, 40, pp. 214-223).

Table 51

Composition of water extract of chernozem, per cent of dry soil

(After Mirimanyan)

Depth in profile	pH	Bicarbonate	Dry residue*	Loss on ignition	CaO	MgO	SO₃	Cl
cm								
0-10	8.06	0.0299	0.0780	0.0318	0.0166	Trace	None	0.0046
30-40	8.13	0.0396	0.0853	0.0377	0.0178	0.0094	Trace	0.0046
55-65	8.30	0.0454	0.0718	0.0286	0.0143	0.0185	"	0.0045
80-90	8.72	0.0401	0.0719	0.0228	0.0146	0.0184	"	0.0082
0-10	7.71	0.0229	0.0716	0.0393	0.0099	0.0045	"	0.0008
20-30	7.46	0.0344	0.0857	0.0349	0.0190	0.0036	"	0.0038
40-50	8.18	0.0413	0.1417	0.0780	0.0190	0.0068	"	0.0146
70-80	8.3	0.0421	0.0620	0.0172	0.0107	0.0060	"	0.0051
0-13	8.10	0.0284	0.0953	0.0449	0.0190	0.0042	"	Trace
13-38	8.15	0.0319	0.0892	0.0319	0.0173	0.0088	"	0.0010
38-60	8.27	0.0405	0.0608	0.0108	0.0146	0.0144	"	0.0021

(After Zakharov)

Depth	Color of extract	Bicarbonate	Dry residue	Loss on ignition	CaO	SiO₂	SO₄	Cl
10-25	Golden Yellow	0.020	0.073	0.037	0.016	0.005	0.0050	0.006
30-80	Colorless	0.024	0.064	0.036	0.014	0.004	0.0017	0.006
80-150	Colorless	0.039	0.064	0.026	0.015	0.003	0.0024	0.004

*In a paper by Koposov (47), data on profiles of 5 varieties of chernozem show a fluctuation between a low 0.059 and a high 0.098 per cent dry residue.

Table 52

Solubility of organic matter from the various chernozem subtypes

(After Tumin)

Chernozem subdivision	Per cent of total humus at various depths			
	1-5 cm.	40-45 cm.	80-85 cm.	120-140 cm.
Degraded	0.383	0.600	1.333	1.562
Northern leached	0.365	0.512	0.637	0.555
Deep	0.250	0.335	0.342	0.433
Southern	0.239	0.303	0.323	0.526
Ordinary	0.226			

Temperature Relationships.—No data are available on the thermal capacity (the ratio of the specific heat of $H_2O=1$, to that of the substance) of chernozem, but it is probably around 0.25. Theoretically, it should be higher than in the other soil types because of the high heat capacity of the organic matter (0.472) which is twice the thermal capacity of the mineral fraction (0.19-0.23).

Table 53

True and apparent specific gravity and porosity of chernozem

(After Kossovich)

Location	Depth of soil	True specific gravity	Apparent specific gravity	Pore space, Volume of total
	cm.			per cent
Mariumpol County, Government of Jekaterinoslav	Surface	2.60	1.10	58
	10.25		1.20	54
	25.50		1.30	50
	50-75	2.65	1.35	49
	75-00		1.40	47
Poltava plateau	——	2.57	1.19	58
Poltava valley	——	2.62	1.36	48
Clay chernozem from Shatilov Experiment Station	12.5-25	2.60	1.00	61.8
	37.5-50	2.68	1.00	59.2
	62.5-75	2.74	1.34	51.0
	87.5-100	2.71	1.40	48.5
On loess, Orlov Government	——	2.46	0.81	67.0

The volume thermal capacity is about the same for the various kinds of chernozem as it is for all other types of soil; it fluctuates around 0.5 because the volume thermal capacity of the mineral constituents and that of the organic matter are almost similar, to wit, 0.512-0.576 and 0.651

respectively. With the increase in the volume weight of the soil, the volume thermal capacity increases.

Adamov (1) determined the property of heat conductance of chernozem by the changes in temperature at various depths in relation to the fluctuations in the air temperature. He found the heat conductance of chernozem to be lower than that of the other soil types. It took 7 to 8 hours to conduct heat from the 10 cm. depth to the 25 cm. depth and 18 to 20 hours to the 50 cm. depth. The increase in temperature to a depth of 10 cm. seldom exceeded 1° in 24 hours and to a depth of 50 cm., it hardly reached 0.1 to 0.2° C.

The low heat conductance of chernozem is readily understood since this soil type is usually of fine texture and high in organic matter. It should increase with the decrease in organic matter and with the increase in the coarseness of the parent material. Such a tendency is indicated by the work of Petrov (70). It is to be noted from the data in table 54, that coarse-textured soils which show a low hygroscopicity have a higher heat conductance.

Moisture Relationships.—The hygroscopicity of chernozem is high because of its organic matter content. It fluctuates between 4 and 8 per cent, but may be higher. In table 55, the hygroscopicity of a series of chernozems is given. The relation of the hygroscopicity to the organic matter content is clearly brought out. Lein (51) discusses the effects of sorbed cations, (Na, Li, K, Mg, Ca, Ba, Al, and Fe) on hygroscopicity and size of total surface of two chernozems and a podzol.

The data of Smith and Rhoades (82) on the hygroscopic coefficients of a series of profiles in the chernozem zone of the United States show that, in general, the coefficients increase with depth. Of course, this increase is due to the heavier texture of the lower horizons.

The moisture holding capacity of chernozem has not been investigated to any great extent, but it is known to be high—58 to 67 per cent. With depth, this capacity decreases. Again, it is the organic matter content and texture that control this property.

The percolation properties of chernozem soils in their natural habitat have been studied but little. Kravkov (48) investigated the speed with which rainwater penetrates a clay chernozem under fallow, sod, and virgin conditions. The results presented in table 56 show that the water penetrated the soil slowly, at the rate of less than 1 cm. per hour. Izmailskii (38) studied the penetration of the spring rains into a chernozem soil. He found that over a period from March to May, it reached a depth of

Table 54

Heat conductance and hygroscopicity of several chernozem soils
(After Kossovich)

Variety of chernozem	Specific gravity	Hygroscopic moisture	Increase in temperature through a depth of 10 cm. after 6 hours
		per cent	*°C*
Sandy loam	2.56	2.21	5.18
Sandy loam	2.63	2.55	5.08
Ordinary chernozem	2.67	6.29	4.65
Ordinary chernozem	2.54	8.81	4.41
Ordinary chernozem	2.58	11.25	4.38

Table 55
Hygroscopicity of chernozem
(After Kossovich)

Description of soil	Hygroscopicity of air-dry soil	Maximum hygroscopicity	Humus
	per cent	*per cent*	*per cent*
Tula Government; loam; plowed layer	4.49	8.02	9.88
Tula Government; loam; sub-plowed layer	4.18	7.92	6.97
Tula Government; loam; parent material	3.25	6.53	0.94
Another Tula chernozem; loam; plowed layer	4.25	8.55	7.39
Another Tula chernozem; loam; sub-plowed layer	4.02	8.23	7.17
Another Tula chernozem; loam; parent material	3.36	7.06	1.11
Voronezh chernozem; sandy texture	4.38	5.90	5.59
Penza chernozem	6.64	8.78	6.42
Jekaterinoslav chernozem	8.23	9.29	5.84
Orlov chernozem	5.16	8.20	9.01

Table 56
Penetration of water through a clay chernozem
(After Kossovich)

Virgin soil		Sod		Fallow	
Time elapsed after rain	Depth of penetration	Time elapsed after rain	Depth of penetration	Time elapsed after rain	Depth of penetration
hours	*cm.*	*hours*	*cm.*	*hours*	*cm.*
1	5.2	1.5	6.0	1.75	8.2
4	9.0	4.5	10.1	4.75	18.0
24	15.1	24.5	17.4	24.75	24.0
				48.0	38.0

140-210 cm. Similar investigations were conducted by Vysotskii (Ch. 2, 84) and Rotmistrov (77). The latter pointed out that, on heavy soils, the speed of water penetration equaled about 20 cm. a month.

No data are available on the lifting power—capillary rise—for water in the chernozem under natural conditions. Some laboratory data on chernozem soil material is to be found in table 57, which also contains information on its other properties.

Smith and Rhoades (82) present data on the plasticity constants of a number of chernozem profiles. "The lower plastic limit represents the moisture content at the change from a friable to a plastic consistency. It is, then, the minimum moisture percentage at which a soil can be puddled. The liquid limit is the moisture content at which thick films permit the soil mass to flow under a small applied force. The plasticity index (the difference between the liquid limit and lower plastic limit) is an indirect measure of the force required to mold a soil."

Smith and Rhoades point out that the higher figures for the lower plastic limit of the A_1 horizons in the Filmore and Scott profiles is due to the high organic matter content of these.

CHERNOZEM SUBDIVISIONS

In view of the extensive geographic distribution of the chernozem type of soil formation, the soils of this belt cannot be identical all over the area. All of them possess the cardinal features of this type of soil formation, but the variations in the two chief elements of climate-rainfall and temperature—and to some extent, in the type of grass vegetation introduce definite divisional attributes which serve as a basis for the subdivision of chernozem into several varieties. Accordingly, Tumin (88) divided the chernozem soils into five subdivisions, as shown in table 58.

Degraded Chernozem.—In Tumin's classification the degraded chernozem appears as a distinct division. Both the northern and leached chernozems were incorporated by Glinka in this division in which the process of podzolization is very much in evidence. Glinka (Ch. 2, 27, p. 358) stated: "In the degraded chernozem, the horizon of effervescence is separated from the humus horizon by a more or less compact brownish horizon which is nothing more than the starting point of the illuvial B_1 which is so typical for the degraded loams. Beginning with the deep chernozem, this brownish illuvial horizon disappears, and one should, therefore, look at this point for the true chernozem attributes. In the degraded chernozem, one may find elements indicating the transition to the podzol type."

Table 57

Physical properties of some Russian chernozem

(After Kossovich)

Lab. No.	Specific gravity	Weight of a liter of soil	Crushing re- sistance	Height of rise of water after different time intervals							
		gm.	gm.	10 min. cm.	20 min. cm.	30 min. cm.	1 hour cm.	3 hours cm.	6 hours cm.	12 hours cm.	24 hours cm.
1	2.48	1176	4420	3.9	5.5	6.3	—	—	19.3	27.2	—
2	2.33	1152	2450	4.6	6.2	6.8	—	—	20.6	28.3	—
3	2.56	1314	1500	8.5	11.0	10.8	—	—	—	—	—
4	—	—	—	2.9	3.9	4.4	5.3	7.4	9.8	12.7	16.9
5	—	—	—	4.2	5.3	6.2	7.9	11.9	15.8	20.8	26.7
6	2.37	1179	4342	2.4	3.2	3.9	—	—	11.5	—	—
7	2.57	1246	2349	3.0	4.8	6.2	—	—	14.4	—	—
8	—	—	—	8.4	9.8	10.8	—	18.0	2.0	—	—
9	2.64	—	—	—	—	—	13.1	—	23.5	25.8	—
10	2.65	—	—	—	—	—	12.5	—	20.0	35.0	—
11	2.38	1220	12000	6.5	—	9.2	11.0	15.0	17.5	32.5	23.7
12	2.49	1280	5700	6.2	—	10.5	13.2	19.5	22.5	20.0	—
13	2.62	1410	10100	7.7	—	11.7	16.5	26.0	—	27.0	—
14	2.50	1205	—	7.5	9.5	11.3	14.5	—	—	—	—
15	2.55	1352	—	8.0	10.5	12.2	15.5	—	—	—	—

Table 57 (*Continued*)

Lab. No.	Time period to lift water 30 cm.		Time period for water to penetrate 18 cm. deep		Moisture holding capacity	Maximum hygroscopicity	Hygroscopic moisture of dry soil
	hrs.	*min.*	*hrs.*	*min.*	*per cent*	*per cent*	*per cent*
1	15	30	21	15	45.52	7.8	2.8
2	14	25	16	15	55.35	9.0	4.11
3	4	35	6	—	40.40	5.8	2.7
4	118	20	5	—	—	—	5.7
5	33	—	3	—	—	—	6.6
6	22	10	2	11	43.73	5.3	—
7	19	10	3	—	38.46	3.6	—
8	23	25	—	—	—	—	4.2
9	—	—	—	—	—	—	8.53
10	—	—	—	—	—	—	6.47
11	78	—	—	—	42.90	—	7.87
12	22	—	—	—	39.40	—	4.82
13	4	—	—	—	31.90	—	3.37
14	—	30	1	23	48.16	—	4.90
15	—	5	—	11	41.93	—	3.83

Table 58

Chernozem subdivisions

(After Tumin)

Variety name	Depth of A horizon and color	Depth of A and B	Point of effervescence	Extent of SiO₂ sprinkling (Pepper and salt effect)	Structure of the clay varieties
1. Northern chernozem	*cm.* 45-25 gray to dark gray	*cm.* 100-70	*Horizon C*	Entire profile; very distinct	Granular to nutty and nutty-lumpy, deeper in the profile
2. Leached chernozem	55-45 dark gray	65-75 100-90	C or at junction of B and C	Entire profile	Granular to nutty and lumpy, deeper in the profile
3. Deep chernozem	34-54 dark	100-120	B or at junction of B and C	Horizon A and part of B	Granular to granular lumpy, deeper in the profile
4. Ordinary chernozem	20-35 dark	40-55 65-85		Surface 5-10 cm.	Lumpy-granular to lumpy, deeper in the profile
5. Southern chernozem	10-25 grayish	40-70	A and B	None	Lumpy, irrespective of mechanical composition

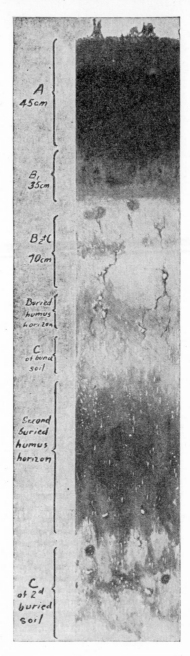

PLATE 21
A degraded chernozem loam on loess-like loam with a buried humus horizon
(After Kassatkin and Krasyuk)

Tumin extended the northern limits of the chernozem belt into the gray forest soils which at present have no forest cover. Other Russian pedologists, especially the Moscow group, separated the degraded and northern forestless gray forest soils into a forest black belt. A discussion of this subdivision was given by Filatov (22). These soils might be identified with the so-called forest steppe region where the forests have invaded the steppe or the steppe has "driven back" the forests. It would seem that the forest steppe soils should be looked upon as a transition or interzonal belt, since there can be no sharp line of division between the various zones. A review of this problem is presented by Zakharov (97).

A characteristic feature of the degraded chernozem is the "pepper and salt" effect. It has been variously interpreted, but the general opinion seems to be that it is the result of the disruption of the silicates with the separation of SiO_2. With the advance of the process, the sprinkling becomes more pronounced, and a coating of SiO_2 appears over the structural units. This gives the characteristic bleached appearance of the A_2 horizon in the mature podzols. From this point of view, one would be prone to consider the degraded chernozem as a type with distinct podzolization tendencies. And there is other evidence to substantiate the podzolic nature of the degraded chernozem, such as reaction, movement of bases and R_2O_3, mobility of organic matter, and formation of a compact horizon of illuviation. It is noteworthy that the line of effervescence in these soils has been shifted to the C horizon which, before the degradation process set in, was a part of B horizon, the horizon of lime accumulation. In this connection, the investigations of Tumin (Ch. 5, 104) on the experimental chernozem plots at the Kamennaya Steppe Experiment Station, inaugurated by Dokuchaev, are of interest. Strips of forest plantings were made in the treeless steppe region to follow up the effect of forest on chernozem. After 40 to 50 years of forest cover, the line of effervescence in the profile was lowered, an indication of the degradation process.*

Extensive investigations on the process of chernozem degradation have been reported by Florov (24). For an extensive bibliography on all types and varieties of chernozem, the reader is referred to Glinka (Ch. 2, 27) and to Kossovich (Ch. 2, 40), the latter being available in German. In the United States, the prototypes of degraded chernozem are the soils of the prairie region (see p. 316).

*Silviculturists will be interested in the remarks made by Tumin on the opinion of foresters that the stability of the forest plantings in the steppe region depends on the speed of the degradation process.

Deep Chernozem.—The depth of the A horizon determined the early establishment of this chernozem subdivision. It is to be looked upon as an artificial separation, as an aid in the study of the extensive chernozem belt. As a matter of fact, after this subdivision was established, a belt of chernozem in the region of the Azov sea was found that is just as deep as, and even deeper, than the regular deep chernozem.

Glinka (Ch. 2, 27, p. 359) described the deep chernozem profile as follows:

The A_1 horizon is of a homogenous dark almost black color, varying in depth from 35 to 55 cm., of a clear-cut granular structure with rounded pea-like ends. Horizon A_2 may hardly be differentiated from A_1. It is uniformly colored to the very bottom. The structure is granular, becoming lumpy at the bottom. Effervescence occurs at the bottom of A_2 or immediately below it. The carbonates usually occur in the form of pseudo-mycelium with vertical veins deeper in the profile. And still deeper, even concretions of CaCO3 may be found.

It is noteworthy that the B horizon of the deep chernozem is normally not compacted. In this respect, it differs sharply from the degraded chernozem. Whatever compactness is noted in the deep chernozem is undoubtedly due to the solonetzic process.

The composition of a typical deep chernozem is given in table 59. It will be noted that both A_1 and A_2 are high in organic matter content—14.85 and 11.38 per cent, respectively. There is no shift of the R_2O_3 in the profile and there is a definite accumulation of $CaCO_3$ in the B horizon.

No adequate studies have been made on the chernozem soils of the United States and Canada to separate a belt of deep chernozem. In the opinion of Afanasiev (2), Tyurin (90), and Vilenskii (93) who based their observations while on the excursion with the First International Congress of Soil Science in 1927, the deep or genuine chernozem is to be found in North Dakota and in the Canadian provinces of Alberta, Saskatchewan, and Manitoba.* South of this region, the chernozems are to be looked upon as of the southern variety of Russian chernozem, of which more is to be said presently. The data of Ellis and Shafer (20) show that the A horizon of the chernozem in Manitoba, Canada, is deeper than the corresponding horizon in the chernozem of the United States, south of Manitoba.

In the so-called "ordinary chernozem", the total depth of A_1 and A_2 does not exceed 85 cm.; the A_2 horizon may be differentiated from the A_1, and the color of the latter is not as dark as that of the deep chernozem. The structure is granular to lumpy, but the granulation is not so well ex-

*A review of the papers by these authors is to be found in a paper by Joffe and Antipov-Karataev (40).

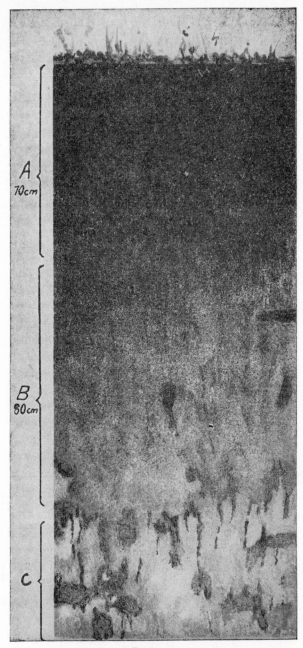

PLATE 22
A chernozem on a heavy loess-like loam
(After Kassatkin and Krasyuk)

Table 59

Analysis of a loam chernozem, from Balashev County, Government of Saratov; per cent of dry soil

(After Zakharov)

Texture of material	Horizon	Depth of horizon	Humus	Loss on ignition	Mineral constituents	Chemically combined water	CO_2	$CaCO_3$ as calculated from the CO_2 data
		cm.						
Loam	A_1	0-30	14.85	16.20	83.80	1.35	0.05	0.11
Loam	A_2	30-55	11.38	12.76	87.24	1.38	0.07	0.16
Loam	B_1	55-80	8.70	9.73	90.27	1.03	0.08	0.18
Loam	B_2	80-100	6.16	7.63	92.37	1.47	3.57	8.11
Loam	C	100-	3.54	4.44	95.56	0.90	7.55	17.17

Texture of material	Horizon	P_2O_5	SO_3	SiO_2	Al_2O_3	Fe_2O_3	Mn_2O_3	CaO	MgO	K_2O	Na_2O
Loam	A_1	0.22	0.01	44.35	15.80	4.52	0.07	1.97	1.55	2.27	0.71
Loam	A_2	0.19	0.00	55.84	14.84	5.16	0.08	2.05	1.49	2.37	0.58
Loam	B_1	0.17	0.00	57.88	15.75	5.20	0.09	1.54	1.93	2.34	0.84
Loam	B_2	0.16	0.00	54.32	14.61	4.83	0.10	5.82	1.76	2.27	0.88
Loam	C	0.15	0.00	48.21	14.75	4.63	0.09	10.00	1.47	2.03	0.86

pressed as in the deep chernozem.   Lime accumulates in B in the form of coatings, veins, and spots known as "white eye" spots.

Southern Chernozem.—A characteristic feature of the southern chernozem is the drop in percentage of organic matter and the consequent departure from the true black color of the ordinary chernozem to a dark gray with a brownish tinge or to dark brown.   When wet, however, this soil is black.   The profile is not as deep as in the ordinary chernozem; its structure is less granular and more powdery and lumpy.   The zone of effervescence is just below the surface and, infrequently, at the top.   The lime accumulates in the form of "white eye" spots, concretions, and even as entire layers. Frequently, gypsum is found below or at the zone of lime accumulation.   A rather extensive investigation of these soils was made by Nikiforov (62), who described them as follows:

A :   The humus horizon, which may be divided into A_1 and A_2, the latter being more compact and of a somewhat darker brownish tinge, is dark gray or dark brownish in color, black when wet, 40-45 cm. deep, with a sharp line of division in color and structure from the layer below.   It varies in structure from a condition somewhat laminated at the top to lumpy granular at the bottom, and when plowed becomes powdery and lumpy.   The horizontal cracking at the surface accentuates the laminar structure, giving the appearance of a layered formation.

The horizon immediately below, i.e., the horizon of illuviation, is more compact, ranging in thickness from 60 to 80 cm., and is divided into B_1, B_2, and B_3.

B_1: Compact, 15 to 20 cm. deep, cracked vertically and horizontally, forming prismatic lumps.   The cracking extends through the next horizon of carbonate accumulation and even below that, and also to the top through the A horizon.   On the walls of the structural prismatic units, glistening coatings of humus are noted.   The humus follows the cracks in the profile giving it a characteristic appearance of dark streaks, splotches, and tongue-like projections.

B_2:   It is the visible layer of lime accumulation, 25 to 30 cm. deep.   The lime spots are round in shape, 1 to 2 cm. in diameter, varying in consistency from soft to hard, and occur in large numbers so that from the distance it appears as a solid layer.

B_3:   A layer of gypsum, occasionally with some soluble sulfates, is found in this horizon.   It occurs in the form of incrustations, irregular in shape, soft or hard, dirty yellowish in color.   Below the gypsum layer, just within the mellow parent material, black specks, usually soft but infrequently of concretionary nature, are noted, probably manganese compounds.

The B horizon, because of the streaming effects of the humus and the distribution of lime and gypsum, is not uniform in color.   Generally, the color is yellow-brown. This horizon is sharply differentiated from C although the line of demarcation is not as well marked as that between B and A.   Toward the bottom of this horizon the material has a tendency to crumble.   In contrast to other divisions of chernozem in the U.S.S.R., the southern chernozem has but few crotovinas.

In table 60, partial analysis of two southern chernozem profiles are given.

Commenting on the analyses, Nikiforov stated: "The high organic matter content, about 2.5 per cent, in B_1 at a depth of 50 to 60 cm. is significant.   It may be explained by the abundance of cracks filled with

Table 60

Partial analysis of two southern chernozem profiles

(After Nikiforov)

Horizon	Depth	Hygroscopic moisture	Humus	Chemically combined water	Loss on ignition	CO_2	SO_3
	cm.	per cent	per cent	per cent	per cent	per cent	per cent
I. In Khoper district, RR Station Panflovo							
A_1	2-8	7.00	7.10	2.75	9.85		
A_1	10-15	5.89	7.41	3.50	10.91		
A_2	25-35	6.86	3.75	3.16	6.91		
B_1	45-55	6.08	2.49	3.09	5.58	4.28	
B_2	70-85	4.50	1.10	3.23	4.33	8.18	
B_2	90-100	4.57	0.89	2.72	3.61	8.33	
B_3	105-165	4.47					0.173
B_3	190-200	6.73					7.049
II. In Ust' Medveditzk district, at the source of the river Buzuluka							
A_1	1-10	6.94	7.60	2.87	10.47	1.17	
A_1	15-25	6.98	5.42	2.92	8.34	5.08	
A_2	30-40	6.52	4.10	3.07	7.17	8.13	
B_1	50-60	5.90	2.46	3.55	6.01	8.33	
B_2	70-80	4.52				5.47	
B_3	100-110	4.42					
B_3	170-190	4.60					

material from A_1." Thus, the movement of organic matter through the profile is purely mechanical in the southern chernozem, whereas in the degraded chernozem it is in solution. Naturally, one should expect a difference in the composition of the organic matter in the B horizon of the two respective chernozem subtypes, but no analytical data are available. Tumin's data (table 52), compiled by Glinka (Ch. 2, 27, p. 366), were recalculated on a percentage basis showing the difference in solubility of organic matter in the profile of various chernozem subdivisions. It will be noted that the degree of the dispersion increased from the deep to the degraded chernozem. It also increased with depth in the profile, especially in the degraded chernozem.

Azov Chernozem.—Northwest of the Caucasus, northeast of the Azov Sea, another distinct type of chernozem has been distinguished by the Russian pedologists. As described by Prasolov (73), it has a deep humus horizon (up to 140 cm. and even deeper), is dark gray or dark brown in color, but is not of such intensity as the deep chernozem. Its organic matter content is also lower than in the other varieties of chernozem. The structure is of peculiar nutty-lumpy nature, and yet it easily becomes powdery and mellow. The profile is permeated with fluffy needle-shaped crystals of $CaCO_3$. "White eye" spots of $CaCO_3$ are found deep in the profile, usually not above the 100 cm. mark. Tracks of earthworms may be easily traced in the humus horizon, beyond which they appear as black lines on the brown background.

The rainfall of the region is equal to that of the central portion of the great chernozem belt, to wit, 300 to 500 mm. annually. The average temperature, from 5.7 to 9.4° C., is higher than that in the chernozem belt, with moderate summers and mild winters. In evaluating this variety of chernozem, the effect of the Azov Sea on the climate of the area has to be considered. No details of this effect have as yet been worked out.

The following is a description of a typical chernozem profile, as given by Prasolov:

A_1: 0-20 cm. Black with a dark brownish-gray tinge; the soil breaks into regular lumps and is easily crushed into a powdery, finely divided granular mass; effervesces from a point 8 cm. below the surface.

A_2: 20-55 cm. Grayish black, friable and granular at the top, more of a nutty structure at the bottom with irregular protrusions on the surface of the structural units.

B_1: 55-90 cm. A gradual transition from grayish-brown to a motley spotted coloration pattern; in structure, it is a similar to that of the bottom of A_2 with units larger in size; a white delicate effloresence of $CaCO_3$ crystals is noted on the edge of the structural units.

B_2: 90-105 cm. Rapid disappearance of the humus dark brown color with a transition to a yellow-brown; it is honeycombed with crotovinas; a white efflorescence is apparent, and at the bottom "white eye" spots appear.

C_1: 105-108 cm. Yellow-brown clay with humus streaks and spots, "white eye" spots irregularly scattered.

C_2: 185-240 cm. Yellow-brown homogenous clay with black lines of root passages; scattered spots of lime are found; no gypsum.

No counterpart of Azov chernozem has been reported for the United States. It would seem that this type of chernozem might be found in South-Western Texas and Mexico, where the Gulf of Mexico might have an effect.

Chernozem in Vertical Zonation.—In mountain country of the arid region, we have the vertical distribution of the zonal soils, the so-called vertical zonation (see Index). At altitudes with a climate conducive to the formation of chernozem, a special mountain chernozem type of specific features is encountered. A detailed description of this variety of chernozem is given in chapter XVI.

PRAIRIE SOILS

Bordering the eastern edge of the meridianal belt of chernozem soils in the United States, another meridianal belt of soils known as *prairie soils* extends eastward to the forest soils. It covers the southern half of Minnesota, extending into eastern South Dakota, occupying almost all of Iowa, a great portion of Illinois, eastern Nebraska, northwestern Missouri, eastern Kansas, and eastern Oklahoma, and protruding farther south through east-central Texas.

The German workers associate the prairie soils with *Wieseböden*— meadow soils. *Wiesenböden* implies the influence of moisture, the great external agency in soil formation. This, however, does not convey the internal characteristics of these soils, for they are neither well defined nor known for the Wiesenböden itself. On the other hand, the *degraded chernozem* concept, suggested by the Russian pedologists, associates the prairie soils with a series of definite internal characteristics. Stremme (86) upholds the view, without giving any evidence, that prairie soils are Wiesenböden. He believes that the treeless condition of the prairie is due to the thorough grazing by the numerous animals which at one time inhabited it. Glinka (Ch. 2, 27, p. 353) questioned Krasnov's assertion that the grasslands of the Middle Amur (Eastern Siberia) were prairie soils. He considered them as true meadow "soils that have nothing in common with chernozem."

As yet the position of the prairie soils in the genetic scheme of soil classification has not been fully established. Investigations on the origin of the prairie have not uncovered much that would be helpful in solving the genetic problems of the soils in this vast region.

Woodard (96) made a study of the Illinois prairie and pointed out that prairies in general have xerophytic vegetation. The main part of the prairie province is found in typical "grassland climate." In some sections, like Illinois and neighboring states, the prairie is found in a "forest climate" and the forests are invading the prairie. The prairies remain because "the conditions prevent a rapid invasion, and the time since the origin of the prairies has been too brief for their complete occupation by forests."

Woodard associates the origin of the prairie in Illinois with the Post-Glacial period. "When the last ice sheet retreated, the bare area which it left was invaded by the tundra, and the tundra was invaded by other plants. In the plains region, prairie grasses invaded the adjoining tundra and moved east, occupying all the level country from which trees were excluded by the desiccating action of the strong winds. It is probable that all the level country as far east as Ohio became prairie early in Post-Glacial times. Fires may have checked the invasion of forests into prairies, but prairies never originated by the destruction of forests by fire."

Norton and Smith (64), discussing the origin of the Illinois prairie, come to the conclusion that the treeless condition of the prairie is "due chiefly to soil immaturity and lack of subsurface drainage or to the existence of a continued high water table."

Weaver and Thiel (95) investigated the prairie near Minneapolis, Minnesota, and Lincoln, Nebraska. They show that prairie soils lack available moisture to a depth of 30 cm. during the growing season. This, together with the great amount of evaporation, gives a clue, they claim, to the absence of trees on the high prairies. Conditions of this sort are sufficient cause for the xerophytic character of the vegetation; they also are unfavorable for the establishment of trees in grassland and may explain their absence from the prairies.

Pool, Weaver, and Jean (72) confirmed the ideas of Weaver and Thiel. They point out that "the high saturation deficit and the low soil moisture of the prairie sites in eastern Nebraska constitute barriers over which forest trees can scarcely pass. This gives probably the most ready explanation of why natural Nebraska woodlands are confined to the moist slopes of rather narrow valleys and also the most probable answer to the question of the treelessness of the prairies in general." Campbell (15), in his discussion of the origin of the prairies in Canada, adheres to the view that fire was the immediate cause of the treelessness of the prairie. Hanson (31) from a study of the prairie inclusions in the deciduous forest climax in southeastern Nebraska, concluded that the factor chiefly responsible for this phenomenon is the xerophytic environment produced in midsummer as a result of the great evaporating power of the air which causes a lack of soil moisture.

A vivid description of the prairie is given by Shively and Weaver (80). They report on the quantities of underground plant material furnished by different plant species in 5 areas of the grass country, starting with one in Iowa (33 inches precipitation) and ending with one in Colorado (14.5 inches precipitation).

In the light of pedogenesis, the data available on the nature and origin of the prairie are significant insofar as they show clearly that the prairie soils have developed under a grass cover, in a climate intermediate between humid and subhumid. With the accumulation of more data on the profile characteristics of these soils, interpretation of their mode of formation and hence of their place in the scheme of soil types of the world will be simpler. As it is, the standards of the known types have been applied, and by the comparative method some of the characteristics of the prairie soils have been elucidated.

Typical representatives of prairie soils are the Marshall, Carrington, Clarion, Cherokee (tables 61, 62) and other series. Marbut (56) gives the following account of a typical Marshall profile: "The surface horizon is very dark brown, and the material is normally well granulated. In the upper 12 inches the granules are small, but downward, in what may be described as the B horizon they are larger but somewhat rounded. They are well defined, the material falling into the individual structure particles very readily when in optimum moisture condition. The dark color in the A horizon penetrates the soil particles completely so that the crushed material is practically as dark as the broken material. In the B horizon, the dark color consists of a coating on the outside of the structure particles, the thickness of the coating decreasing downward so that in the upper part the crushed material is dark brown in color, in the lower part brown, and finally the dark coating disappears entirely at a depth of about 5 feet."

In the Grundy* soil of Nebraska, described by Hayes (32)

the surface layer consists of a structureless mulch, dust-like when dry, ranging in thickness from a mere film to about 12 inches, and varying in color from light grayish brown to dark grayish brown. The second layer is very dark grayish brown or almost black; it is usually as dark as, or darker than, any horizon above or below. The soil aggregates resemble disk or plate-like forms which overlap one another in such a manner as to give the characteristic laminated or platy appearance (evidence of podzolization: J.) to the horizon. Material from this layer breaks into more or less flattened granules to which the roots cling tenaciously. This horizon, averaging about 3 inches in thickness, is followed by the zone of granulation, which varies in thickness from 10 or 12 inches up to 2 feet. This layer usually contains an abundance of well-rounded

*Areas of Grundy soils are also associated with true chernozems under the name Hastings. The Grundy described by Hayes shows some solonetzic properties in the B horizon.

Table 61

Composition of Cherokee silt loam, Kansas, organic matter free basis; per cent of total

(After Marbut)

Horizon	Depth	SiO₂	TiO₂	Fe₂O₃	Al₂O₃	MnO	CaO	MgO	K₂O	Na₂O	P₂O₅	SO₃	N*
	inches												
A₁	0-6	89.61	0.71	2.95	4.83	0.07	0.73	0.44	0.94	1.10	0.07	0.08	0.113
A₂	6-16	87.22	0.77	3.57	5.98	0.09	0.67	0.50	1.02	1.19	0.07	0.07	0.090
B	16-28	74.71	0.79	4.99	16.17	0.02	0.83	1.15	1.29	1.18	0.10	0.19	0.134
C	28-40	71.53	0.76	5.12	17.54	0.02	0.84	1.20	1.17	1.10	0.12	0.24	0.089

*This figure is based on weight of soil before the organic matter was removed.

worm casts. Borings, or twisted rod-like forms, probably representing old filled-in insect or worm holes, are common throughout the horizon and are often very numerous in the lower portion. Grass roots are abundant in the granular zone, the rootlets clinging to the finer granules. The color, although dark, is lighter than that of the laminated horizon. In the lower portion, the darker shades are less pronounced but stand out clearly in the lighter colored matrix.

In the B horizon of the Grundy soil one may find a zone of maximum compactness resembling a clay-pan. Its depth is normally 15 to 24 inches though often deeper. It is denser than in the Marshall series. The structure is sometimes columnar-like with many vertical and horizontal cracks, and the soil breaks into more or less prismatic units. The color is grayish brown. Dark intrusions are to be found in the upper zone. Scattered rusty brown iron stains and soft iron concretions are usually encountered throughout the horizon. In some localities the brown and grayish color of the clay-pan zone gives way to extremely dark brown or dense black, apparently due to the accumulation of soluble humus.

There is a definite lime zone in the Grundy and Marshall soils just below the layer of compaction at a depth of 3 to 4 feet below the surface, and varying from 6 to 8 inches to as much as 4 feet in thickness. It occurs in finely divided powder-like form all through the silty loess-like material but may be concentrated along old root-hair channels and in insect and worm holes, assuming in places a dendritic arrangement. The basic color varies from grayish brown to yellowish brown, but it may occur as a thin white film in the small seams and cracks of the soil. It may also be in the form of soft concretions, hard concretions, or soft cencretions with indurated centers. Concretionary forms subspherical in shape, with rough surfaces and varying from 0.05 to 0.25 inch or more in diameter, usually dominate. Below this horizon of lime accumulation iron stains occur at a depth 7 to 8 feet below the surface.

In his "Soils of the United States", Marbut points out that in the northern end of the Marshall belt the soils have not been degraded, whereas in the southern end they have. "The colloids are still saturated with bases, the organic matter is not yet being dissolved rapidly and eluviation has not taken place. Most of the prairie soils, however, have been slightly and some of them strongly degraded (Ch. 8, 20, p. 64)."

Hayes (32) states: "Similar conditions, in reference to lime distribution, are thought to exist in two Grundy areas north of the Platte River, but our knowledge of these is confined to only three profile descriptions, and does not warrant any definite conclusion. We do know, however, that a similar method of distribution is characteristic of nearly all the mature upland and terrace soils of eastern Nebraska including those of the Marshall, Waukesha, and Carrington series."

Rost (76) considers the Minnesota prairie soils as degraded chernozem, a conclusion not fully borne out by the data in table 63. They look more like those of a typical chernozem. Most of the constituents, especially the R_2O_3, show no translocation. On the other hand, the Ca and Mg data do not indicate sufficient accumulation at a depth of 25 to 37 inches to warrant a designation of a true chernozem.

Hayes and Roberts (33) describe the soils of Saline County, southeastern Nebraska, as being in the tall-grass prairie region; they report lime accumulation at a depth of 4 to 5 feet below the surface. The entire profile

Table 62

*Chemical composition of Marshall silt loam, Case County, Nebraska,
and Edgerton, Missouri; per cent of total*

(After Robinson and Holmes)

Constituents	Depth in inches			
	0-14	14-18	0-15	15-36
SiO_2	72.06	70.22	73.61	71.43
TiO_2	0.67	0.71	0.71	0.77
Fe_2O_3	3.66	4.73	3.54	4.28
Al_2O_3	11.18	12.91	9.67	13.44
MnO	0.05	0.10	0.12	0.104
CaO	0.90	1.03	1.08	1.40
MgO	0.66	1.12	0.77	1.28
K_2O	2.66	2.29	2.28	2.03
Na_2O	1.02	1.14	1.03	0.63
P_2O_5	0.21	0.30	0.22	0.16
Loss on ignition	6.94	5.42	7.44	5.56
N	0.23	0.10		

Table 63

Composition of Carrington loam, per cent of total

(After Rost)

Constituents	Depth in inches			
	1-6	8-12	14-24	25-37
SiO_2	72.89	73.62	75.24	73.65
Al_2O_3	10.46	10.87	11.35	12.13
Fe_2O_3	2.99	3.21	3.42	3.81
MgO	0.72	0.74	0.88	1.21
CaO	1.24	1.18	1.24	2.08
Na_2O	1.39	1.35	1.33	1.31
K_2O	1.66	1.74	1.86	1.87
TiO_2	0.50	0.52	0.54	0.53
P_2O_5	0.18	0.17	0.14	0.11
N		0.33		

is permeated with worm casts and borings. Goke and Brown (30) report lime accumulation in the Moody soil series, Dixon County. Orrben, Gray, and Boatright (65) report a zone of lime accumulation in the profile of Marshall silt loam in Sac County, Iowa, at a depth of 3 to 4 feet.

From the reports cited, and they could be augmented with many more, it is clear that the soils in the prairie province, especially in the western section, exhibit the characteristic features of chernozem; namely, a deep humus horizon, with the organic matter content decreasing gradually with depth; granular structure; and uniform texture. A closer examination of the observations reported and of data in table 38 reveals the translocation of R_2O_3 constituents, the compactness of the B horizon (the compactness of the B horizon might be attributed to the mechanical movement of the finer particles during the dry periods in the late summer when the soil cracks to a considerable depth), and the presence of a zone of lime accumulation in the lower part of the B horizon. Since these characteristics point to the degradation process, one cannot help but place the prairie soils into the subdivision of the degraded chernozem, the inherent nature of which is a somewhat leached condition with all its accompanying effects, among which are the shifting of the lime zone deeper into the profile and its ultimate disappearance as the podzol process of soil formation predominates. Whether or not the prairie soils that show no lime zone will ever become more podzolic is a debatable question. A solution to the problem lies in establishing the balance between the outgo and the return of bases, in the alkaline earths in particular. A practical approach to the experimental solution of this problem has been suggested (Ch. 5, 59) in connection with a discussion of the status of some podzolic soils in the great podzol zone. The lysimeter methods of studying the leachings and an analysis of the incoming materials are the salient features of this approach.

Data on prairie soils are limited. Those presented in the tables are on soils that have been sampled at depths which do not always seem to correspond to horizon depths. It is, therefore, difficult to trace the distribution of the soil constituents. Of the more recent data, one may cite the description and some analyses of the Fillmore, Crete, and Butler profiles, by Smith and Rhoades (82). An examination of these proves definitely the degradation elements in these soils, especially of the Fillmore profile.

A few other points about the prairie soils command our careful deliberation and critical analysis. They are prompted by the scholastic treatment of the prairie soils by no less an authority than Marbut (Ch. 8, 20) who states:

The paradox in the prairie soils consists in the fact that the A horizon has the characteristics of semiarid soils. The B horizon, however, has the characteristics of humid soils. The characteristics of the surface soil of the degraded chernozem have at least the incipient characteristics of humid soils, while those of the B horizon are still those of semiarid soils. The prairie soils were developed under the influence of a high rainfall. They were developed, so far as our present knowledge is concerned, under exactly the same climatic conditions as the forest soils in the region east of the prairies, in the region of Ohio and Indiana. They were developed also on essentially the same topography as the forest soils in the latter two states and from almost identically the same parent material. The parent material is identical not only in character but also in the process by which it was accumulated. It is in both cases glacial material and also highly calcareous. It is apparent that the only important factor influential in the development of the prairies soils not influential in the development of the forest soils of central Indiana is that of the natural vegatation.

Since the characteristics of the surface soil in the prairies are similar to those of the surface soil in the semiarid region, the question arises as to whether this could have been brought about by any change in climatic character. In other words, does this character of the surface soil signify a change of climate that has affected the surface only? If so, the change, so far as our present knowledge of climatic effect on soils will permit us to decide, must have been a change from more humid to less humid. It would have to mean that the climate is less humid now than at some time in the past. Whether that be the case or not, the climate is at the present time undoubtedly humid, and being so it is unthinkable to postulate that this semiarid condiion has been produced by a humid climate even though that humid climate may be less humid than some other climate that affected these soils in the past. Furthermore, so far as is now known, no soil has yet been found in which regradation has taken place by a change in climate from humid to arid. No part of the soil bodies of the world, at least those having any significantly wide distribution, have been described as regraded soils, or soils which were formerly subjected to a humid climate but later were subjected to a semiarid climate.

If the semiarid character of the prairie soils cannot be explained on the ground of climatic change, it would seem that, on the basis of geographic correlation, we are limited to the single factor of difference in natural vegetation. The prairies soils have developed under grass cover. The forest soils adjacent to them on the east have developed under identically the same conditions in all respects except that of a timber cover. Can the difference between the two soils be explained as the product of the different effect of the two kinds of natural vegetation? Or, stated in another way, can semiarid character of the surface soil of the prairies be explained on the ground of what is known to be the characteristic influence of a grass cover on soil development?

Marbut was not decided as to where to place the prairie soils. In his introduction to this volume he takes issue with the author on the prairie soils. He states: "the prairie soils are not degraded." He also reiterates the specific characteristics of the process of soil formation in the prairie:

The existing soils of the prairies are the normal product of the factor in the soil developing environment, the biological factor of the American prairies being the first large area of the world in which the relationship of climate to plant is such that the specific quality and effectiveness of the plant in soil development can be measured for the first time. It is shown that it is by far the dominant factor.

In his monumental work on the "Soils of the United States" Marbut states:

The typical prairie soil profile has a very dark brown or black surface horizon, the blackness being caused by the presence of a high percentage of organic matter. The structure is granular with rather fine grains. This layer is underlaid by a brown horizon which is little if any heavier in texture than the surface horizon, but differs from the surface layer in the much lower percentage of organic matter and in the brown color. The material in this layer usually falls, on exposure, into particles ranging up to about half an inch in diameter, larger than the granules in the upper part.

The profile just described is the ideal and somewhat theoretical profile. The soil over most of the area is less dark than the typical soil, is slightly acid at the surface; the colloids at the surface are slightly deflocculated, and very slight eluviation has taken place. The soil is in the earliest stages of podzolic development. In soil survey work a soil in the prairies is accepted as a member of the prairie group if the surface horizon has a well defined dark color and is 8 or more inches thick. Most of the prairie soils are slightly degraded.

We are confronted with the presence of a grass vegetation in the prairie and with the fact that such presence is the characterizing attribute of a prairie. Just as the brown, chestnut brown, and undisputed chernozem soils of the steppe region are endowed with certain characteristics because of the steppe (grass) vegetation, so are the X, Y, or Z soils of the prairie region—no more, no less—for natural forces and agencies are universal in their reactions, varying in degree, but not in kind, because of certain side reactions. If we accept the genetic point of view that the soil body as an object in nature is the product of the combined forces of climatic elements and biosphere, we must expect, if not the same, at least very similar results in the steppe and prairie regions. It is probable that the biosphere, which in itself is a resultant of the climatic forces, is more active in the prairie region. We are aware of the meadow podzol in the forest zone where the grass vegetation, which is a resultant of the climate, especially of the moisture element, is a dominating factor in forming this type of podzols.

But why a grass vegetation? Why should not a timber cover develop in the prairie if it is true that the climatic conditions in this region are similar to those of the adjacent forest country? The fact that forests seem to be unable to invade the prairie indicates that there must be some fine differences in climate, not as yet discerned, which are responsible for the phenomenon. Thus far, as pointed out earlier in this discussion, the origin of the prairie has been explained by such factors as fires, grazing, and moisture regime, the last being the only climatic element.

There is one other suggestion the author wishes to make. From studies conducted by lysimeter leachings in the podzol zone, it was noted that the highest amount of organic matter comes through during the late summer and fall. During this period, as pointed out (Ch. 5, 49), the electrolyte content increases appreciably and the reaction shifts toward alkalinity from pH 4.8-5.6 in winter, spring, and summer, to 6.4-6.8 in fall. An examination of the climate in the prairie shows that one of its characteristic features is frequent droughts during the summer and a dry period in the late summer. Undoubtedly, this climatic feature is responsible for the stabilization and accumulation of organic matter in the otherwise humid or subhumid prairie region in the same manner as in the chernozem region. With the high ash content of the grass vegetation, the electrolyte content and the pH must be high during the late summer. It is during this period that most of the tree seeds are carried to the prairie, and it is not at all improbable that the soluble organic substances, the high electrolyte content, and the increased alkalinity contribute in a large measure to the destruction of the seeds. At the same time, these conditions provide an ideal environment for the germination and growth of grass seeds. The well-known luxuriant vegetation in the prairie in the spring gets its successful start in the fall. All of this is inimical to the germination of tree seeds. At the border of the forest region and the prairie, a struggle ensues between the forests and grass vegetation, and in favorable localities the forests invade the prairie. Ordinarily the prairies are confined to the smooth watershed ridges and plateaus between the streams, whereas the forests occupy the hilly belts adjacent to the streams.

The prairie soils have developed under conditions either more humid or more arid than those of the present day. Which of these two conditions once prevailed is still a *terra incognita,* although evidence to prove either has been advanced.

Granting that a more humid climate prevailed, the prairie soils are to be looked upon as secondary meadow soils. If that were the case, we should find ample evidence of the podzolization process: accumulation· of R_2O_3, cases of ortstein formation, gleiing effects, and the other remnants of the meadow podzol type of soil formation. Of course, with the advent of a more arid climate, the podzol process would have been reversed, and, with the lowering of the water table, higher evaporation, capillary rise of salts, change to xerophytic type of vegetation, and all the other phenomena accompanying the more arid climate, a semiarid, chernozem process of soil formation would have ensued. Phenomena pertaining to the reversal from one to another type of soil formation have been reported in the pedological literature. Lundblad (54) cites the reversion of a brown forest soil into a genuine podzol through the change of forest type.

If the climate in the prairie region had been more arid* than it is now, then the prairie soils must have developed under conditions of a semiarid or chernozem process of soil formation. As they are found now, the prairie soils exhibit a number of typical chernozem attributes; to wit, dark color, relatively high humus content which decreases gradually with depth, granular structure, and deep A horizon. A more detailed analysis of the morphological and chemical characteristics of the prairie soils reveals that in the western section, like eastern Nebraska, and even in the central section, like Iowa, there is a zone of lime accumulation in the prairie soil profile. It appears in the B horizon in the western section and, as we move eastward toward the forest region, it is lowered deeper in the profile until it finally disappears altogether (more information on the depth of the zone of effervescence is highly desirable). Another characteristic of the prairie

---

*For further proof on the probable aridity of the climate in Post-Glacial time see the discussion: "Vilenskii's Views on the Evolution of Saline Soils" in chapter XIV.

soils is the release of some bases, the movement of R_2O_3 constituents, and the formation of a compact brown or yellowish brown illuvial horizon. All of these characteristics are attributes of chernozem degradation.

Another link in the chain of evidence as to the chernozem-like nature of the prairie soils is the presence of the climatogenically subdued soil types inherent in the zonal type. Nikiforov (63) found in the Minnesota portion of the Red River Valley, which is in the prairie province, a number of areas of typical solonchak and solonetz among the normal Fargo and Bearden soil series and he justly remarks: "Many prominent authors who have developed systems of soil classification have constantly emphasized that solonetz is a constant associate of definite zones, namely the chernozem zone and the zones south of it in the geographic distribution of the climate in Europe and Asia (In the United States it would be west of the chernozem zone: J.). Therefore, according to this, the occurrence of a solonetz within the Red River Valley would indicate indirectly that the normal soils of this region belong to the chernozem type of soil formation." *We must therefore accept, until otherwise proved, the view that the prairie soils belong to the subdivision of degraded chernozem.*

Florov (24), in his numerous researches on the steppe soils, concludes that the widespread phenomenon of degradation indicates a change of climate in the direction of more humid conditions. He is of the opinion that during the interglacial periods of the ice age, arid and humid conditions alternated.

Analyzing the profile characteristics of the soils in the vicinity of Kansas City, Florov states: "It is clear that we are dealing with criteria of degradation and I maintain that we have here the phenomenon of the invasion of the forest in the prairie with all the typical features of degradation." In this connection, Florov quotes Marbut: "The prairie plains are not entirely treeless. The treeless areas are confined to the smooth or rolling lands within the prairie plains belt, the hilly areas being covered with forest growth. Not only is there forest growth in the hilly areas, but in many cases the forests have invaded localities with smooth surface reliefs where the soils are very shallow."

In the many descriptions of the prairie soils in the U. S. Soil Survey reports, there is frequent reference to the zone of effervescence appearing in the C horizon. This only goes to show that the climate in this region was at one time perhaps less humid than it is now. With an increase in humidity, greater leaching ensued, resulting in the lowering or even the disappearance of the lime zone and in a movement of the R_2O_3. On the other hand, Marbut points out that from evidence obtained on the characteristics of buried soils in Nebraska there is no justification in assuming a more arid climate for this region in earlier times.

The color of the B horizon in the northern section of the degraded chernozem in the United States is grayish brown. In the southern section it is reddish brown. *In the northern section, we have the transition from the chernozem to the podzolized forest gray soils in an environment of a temperate climate; in the southern section, the transition is towards the podzolized yellow and red soils in an environment approaching the subtropical climate.*

General Remarks

The outlying borders of the chernozem belt touch other zonal types. At the points of contact, the influence of the chernozem and of the respective zonal soil types is reciprocal. Thus, at the forest steppe transition zone, we find elements of the process of podzolization making inroads into the chernozem. The color of the profile, expressing the physical, the chemical, and, undoubtedly, the biological characteristics of the processes involved, changes toward a gray with the prominent pepper and salt effects. There is a specific mode of distribution of the organic matter through the profile; it is concentrated in the surface A_1 horizon and diminishes rapidly with depth. There is a translocation of the sesquioxides and organic compounds which gives to the B horizon its compactness, a typical feature of the podzol process of soil formation.

In the more temperate region, the chernozem comes in contact with the brown forest soils; closer to the humid subtropics, with the yellow earths and red loams; and in the less humid subtropics, with the "terra rossa." In every case, a definite change in color takes place. There is also a decrease in the quantity of organic matter, greater or lower, a loss or gain of bases, and a differential translation of R_2O_3, depending on the transition zone. Because of these circumstances, we have the so-called varieties of chernozem. In the U. S. Soil Survey reports, it has been repeatedly mentioned that with the shift toward the south, as in southern Kansas, Oklahoma, and south-central Texas, the soils are dark-brown chocolate rather than black in color, with a reddish subsoil and a high accumulation of carbonates. Color alone is, however, not the characteristic that could be relied upon in differentiating soil types, subtypes, or subdivisions.

Baldwin, Kellogg, and Thorp (9, p. 990) discarded Marbut's geographic designation of northern and southern varieties of prairie, chernozem, and other soils. Instead, they have introduced descriptive terms, such as reddish brown, reddish chestnut, and reddish prairie. This approach violates the pedologic principle of the geographicity of soil distribution in nature. Actually, the geographic designation given by Marbut (north and south) imparts specific attributes, of which color is but a minor one, and permit the separation of varieties within the zonal type. Indeed, the color difference is probably a remnant of the color of the parent material, the result of the process of laterization that occurred sometime during the Post-Wisconsin glacial time. Some of these varieties of steppe soils may be looked upon as regraded, the transformation having been brought about by a change in climate. Pedologic evidence (30) seem to indicate that immediately after the last glaciation, the areas south of the glacial retreat have enjoyed a humid temperate climate, followed by an arid lateritic, humid lateritic or vice versa, and the present day climate.

References

1. Adamov, N. 1904 Fertility factors of Russian chernozem (Russian), pp. 1-191. See also his papers on "Temperature of chernozem" in *Pochvovedenie* (Pedology) No. 2 and 4, (1900) and No. 2, (1901).

2. Afanasiev, Ya. N. 1928 On the soil zones of North Ameria. *Pedology* (U.S.S.R.) No. 3-4: 170-218.

3. Afanas'eva, E. A. 1946 On the problem of the origin and evolution of chernozem. *Pedology* (U.S.S.R.) No. 6: 379-384.

4. Agafonov, V. 1924 Some properties of loess. *Comp. Rend. Acad. Sci.* 178: 103-105.

5. Agafonov, V. and Malychev, V. 1929 Loess and loam in the Villejuif plateau. *Extrait de Bull. de la Soci. geolog. de France,* 4 ser. v. 29: 109-145.

6. Agapitov, ? ? To the problem on the origin of chernozem, Izv. *Vostoch. Sibirsk. Otd. Imp. Geogr. Obshch.* XI, No. 3-4 (From Glinka).

7. Amer. Jour. of Sci. (1945) v. 243, No. 5: 225-303.

8. Bailey, E. H. 1944 Hydrogen-ion concentration of the important soils of the United States in relation to other profile characteristics: I. Pedocal soils. *Soil Sci.* 57: 443-474.

9. Baldwin, M., Kellogg, Ch.E., and Thorp, J. 1938 Soil classification. Soils and Men. *Yearbook of Agriculture.* U.S. Dept. of Agriculture.

10. Barbot-de-Mart, and Karpinskii. 1873 Geolog. investigations in Volyn government. Nauch. Istorich. Sbornik Gorn. Inst. (From Kossovich).

11. Benningsen-Förder, Rudolph von. 1863 Das nordeuropäische und besonders das vaterländische Schwemmland in tabellarischer Ordnung seiner Schichten and Bodenarten. Ein geognostisch-geographisch. Versuch. Berlin.

12. Berg, L. S. 1927 Loess as a product of weather and soil formation. *Pedology* (U.S.S.R.) No. 2: 21-37.

13. Berg, L. S. 1946 Loess fauna (Russian). *Trudy Inst, Geografii,* Acad. Sci. (U.S.S.R.) No. 37: 225-240.

14. Bogdanov, M. 1871 Birds and beasts in the chernozem belt of the Volga region and the valley of the middle and lower Volga. St. Petersburg (Russian).

15. Campbell, R. H. 1921 Why the prairies are treeless? *Canad. Forest Magaz.* 17, No. 1: 5-8.

16. Chamberlin, Th. Chrowder, and Salisbury, Rollin D. 1885 Preliminary paper on the driftless area of the Upper Mississippi Valley, *Ann. Rpt. U.S. Geol. Surv.* 6: 199-322.

17. Denisov, N. Ya. 1944 Theoretical considerations and experimental evidence of the soil hypothesis of loess formation. *Izvest. Akad. Nauk,* Ser. Geol. (U.S.S.R.) No. 2: 15-21.

18. Durand, E. J. 1878 Les Pluies de poussiere des deserts de l'Asie central. *Comp. Rend. Assoc. franc. avan sci.* 7: 474-479.

19. Eichwald, Ed. 1850 Paleontology of Russia. (Russian). St. Petersburg.

20. Ellis, J. H. and Shafer, W. H. 1940 Soil survey South-Western Manitoba. *Dominion Dept. of Agr., Univ. of Manitoba, Soil Report* No. 3. See also *Soil Report* No. 4 (1943) on South-Central Manitoba.

21. Fallou, Fr. Alb. 1867 Uber den Löss, besonders in Bezug auf sein Vorkommen im Königreiche Sachsen. *Neues Yahrb. Min.* 143-158.

22. Filatov, M. 1923 The genetic scheme of the chief soils of the world. (Russian). Moscow.

23. Florov, N. 1927 Uber Lössprofile in den Steppen am Schwarzen Meer. *Ztschr. für Gletscherkunde,* v. 15.

24. Florov, N. 1929 Zur Frage der Degradierung der dunkelfarbigen Böden von Nordamerika. *Soil Research* (Suppl. to the Proceed. Inter. Soc. Soil Sci.) 1: 200-224.

25. Free, E. E. 1911 The movement of soil material by the wind. U.S. Dept. of Agr. Bureau of Soils, Bul. 68.

26. Gedroiz, K. K. 1927 The mobility of soil constituents as influenced by calcium. Nosov. Sel-Khoz. Opuit. Stan., Bul. 43.

27. Gedroiz, K. K. 1929 On the adsorption properties of soils, ed. 2. Moscow-Lenigrad. (Russian or German).

27a. Gemmerling, V. V. 1936 The genesis of soils in the steppe type of soil formation. *Pedology* (U.S.S.R.) No. 4: 530-539 (Extensive English summary).

28. Gerasimov, I. P. 1939 On the genesis of loess and loss-like deposits. *Izvest. Acad. Nauk* (U.S.S.R.), Geografich. ser. 97.

29. Gerasimov, I. P. and Markov, K. K. 1939 Quaternary geology. Moscow-Leningrad.

30. Goke, A. W. and Brown, L. A. 1929 Soil Survey of Dixon County, Nebraska. U.S. Dept. of Agr. Bureau of Chem. and Soils, series 1929, No. 4.

31. Hanson, H. C. 1922 Prairie inclusions in the deciduous forests climax. *Amer. Jour. Bot.* 9: 330-337.

32. Hayes, F. A. 1927 The Grundy soils of Nebraska. *Amer. Soil Sur. Assoc. Bul.* 8: 112-123.

33. Hayes, F. A. and Roberts, R. C. 1928 Soil Survey of Saline County, Nebr. U.S. Dept. of Agr. Bur. of Chem. and Soils, No. 12.

34. Il'in, R. S. 1935 The origin of loess in the light of the teachings on the zones in nature becoming displaced in time and space. *Pedology* (U.S.S.R.) No. 1: 80-100 (See also his paper: Proc. 2nd Inter. Cong. Soil. Sci. (1932).

35. Il'in, R. S. 1936 The fundamental rule in the distribution of surface rocks and soils according to the topography (age) and sculptured valleys. *Pedology* (U.S.S.R.) No. 4: 588-601.

36. Ivanov, D. V. 1926 The absorption complex of chernozem. *Nauchno--Agron. Zhurnal* (U.S.S.R.) 3, No. 4: 268-288.

37. Ivanov, D. V. 1928 The solubility of the solid phase of the soil mass in salt solutions and a new method for determining absorbed bases in the soil. Azerbaidzhan. Tzentr. Sel-Khoz. Opyt. i Selektz. Stan., Agrochim. Otdel, Bul. 1.

38. Izmailskii, A. S. 1894 Soil Moisture and the Ground Waters, etc. Poltava. (Russian).

39. Joffe, J. S. 1941 Climatic sequences of the Post-Wisconsin glacial age as revealed in the soil profile. *Proc. Soil Sci. Soc. Amer.* 6: 368-372.

40. Joffe, J. S. and Antipov-Karataev, I. 1929 American soils as seen by Russian investigators. *Soil Sci.* 27: 159-166.

41. Joffe, J. S. and Kolodny, L. 1936 Fixation of potassium in soils. *Proc. Soil Sci. Soc. Amer.* 1: 187-192.

42. Joffe, J. S. and Levine, A. K. 1946-47 Fixation of K in relation to exchange capacity of soils: I. *Soil Sci.* 62: 411-418; II. *Soil Sci.* 63: 151-158; III. 241-247; IV. 329-335; V. 407-416.

43. Johnson, W. H. 1867 Report on journey to Ilchi, the capital of Khatan, in Chinese Tartary. *Jour. Roy Geog. Soc.* 37: 1-47.

44. Kassatkin, V. G. and Krasyuk, A. A. 1917 Ukazaniya k proizvodstvu polevykh pochvennykh izsledovanii. (Manual for soil investigations in the field). Petrograd.

45. Kingsmill, Th. W. 1871 The probable origin of deposits of loess in North China and Eastern Asia. *Quart. Jour. Geol. Soc.* 27: 376-84.

46. Kontkevich, 1881 Geolog. invest. in the granite belt of Novo-Russia on Eastern Bank of the Dniepr. (Russian). (From Kossovich).

47. Koposov, I. P. 1937 The possibility of artificial structure formation in chernozem soils. *Pedology* (U.S.S.R.) No. 2: 184-221.

48. Kravkov, S. 1901 Investigations on several physical properties of virgin chernozem soil. Trudy Opyt. Lesnich. Derkul'skoe Lesnich., p. 43.

49. Krokos, V. I. 1927 Loess formation of the Ukraine. Contributions to the study of the soils of Ukraine, No. 6. *Reports to the First Inter. Cong. Soil Sci.*, pp. 1-13 (English).

50. Kudryavtzeva, A. 1924 The conversion of the forms of N in the soil and nitrification. *Nauch.-Agron. Zhur.* 1: 297-311.

51. Lein, Z. Ya. 1931 The influence of absorbed bases on the surface of soil particles. *State Inst. for Tobacco Culture* (Russian). Bul. 78: 39-49.

52. Leverett, F. 1899 The Illinois glacial lobe. Monogr. U.S. Geol. Surv. 38.

53. Longwell, C. K., Knopf, A. J., and Flint, R. S. 1939 Textbook of Geology. Wiley and Son, New York.

54. Lundblad, K. 1924 Properties and degradation of the soils derived from brown earth types in southern Sweden. *Meddel. Statens Skogsförsöksanst.* Hafte 21, No. 1: 1-48.

55. Makhov, G. 1927 The fundamental moments of the genesis and geography of loess soils of the Ukraine and their relation to cartographical and agricultural work. Contribution to the study of the soils of Ukraine. No. 6. *Report to the First Inter. Cong. Soil Sci.*, pp. 25-65 (English).

56. Marbut, C. F. 1928 The excursion. *Proceed. and Papers of the First Internat. Cong. Soil Sci.* 5: 41-88.

57. Mattson, S. 1932 The laws of soil colloidal behavior: VII Proteins and proteinated complexes. *Soil Sci.* 33: 41-42.

58. McGee, W. J. 1891 The Pleistocene history of Northeastern Iowa. *Ann. Rpt. U.S. Surv.* II, I: 199-577.

59. Mills, James E. 1889 Quaternary deposits and quaternary or recent elevation of regions and mountains in Brazil with deductions as to the origin of loess from its observed conditions there. *Amer. Geol.* 3: 345-61.

60. Mirimanyan, Kh. P. 1940 The chernozem of Armenia (Russian). Acad. of Sci. (U.S.S.R.) Moscow-Leningrad.

61. Murchison, G. 1849 A geological description of European Russia and the Ural Divide. (Russian). pt. II.

62. Nikiforov, K. K. 1916 A morphologic description of the chernozem in the northern section of the Don province. *Trudy Dokuchaev. Pochv. Komiteta,* No. 4, 86 p.

63. Nikiforov (ff), C. (K) C. 1930 Solonetz and solonchak soils of the Red River. *Amer. Soil Survey Assoc. Bul.* 11: 141-150.

64. Norton, E. A. and Smith, R. S. 1931 The relationship between soil and native vegetation in Illinois. *Ill. State Acad. of Sci.* 24, No. 2: 90-93.

65. Orrben, C. L., Gray, A. L., and Boatright, W. C. 1928 Soil Survey of Sac County, Iowa. U.S. Dept. of Agr. Bur. of Chem. and Soils, No. 24.

66. Orth, A. 1877 Die Schwarzerde u. ihre Bedeutung für d. Kultur. *Die Natur.* No. 3, p. 37.

67. Pallas, P. S. 1799 Bemerkungen auf einer Reise in die südlich. Staathalerschaften des Russischen Reich. I.

68. Pavlov, A. P. 1911 The place of Lomonossov in pedology. *Pedology* (U.S.S.R.) No. 4: 1-12 (A complete German translation).

69. Petrov, B. F. 1937 On the origin of loess in the Biisk forest steppe. *Pedology* (U.S.S.R.) No. 4: 584-591.

70. Petrov, V. 1893 On the heat conductance of several soils. *Materialy po izuchen, russkikh pochv.* 8: 28-56.

71. Petzholdt, A. 1851 Investigations on the chernozem of southern Russia (1850). *Bul. Sci. de l'Acad. des Sci. de St. Petersburg,* IX, p. 75.

72. Pool, R. J., Weaver, J. E., and Jean, F. C. 1918 Further studies in the ecotone between prairie and woodland. *Univ. Nebr. Studies* 18, No. 1-2: 7-53.

73. Prasolov, L. I. 1916 About the chernozem of the Azov steppes. *Pedology* (U.S.S.R.) No. 1 : 23-46.

74. Pyaskovskii, B. V. 1946 Loess as a deep soil formation. *Pedology* (U.S.S.R.) No. 11 : 686-696.

75. Rode, A. A. 1942 A few words on loess formation. *Pedology* (U.S.S.R.) No. 9-10 : 16-24.

76. Rost, C. O. 1918 Parallelism of the soils developed on the gray drifts of Minnesota. Dissert. Univer. of Minn., pp. 1-68.

77. Rotmistrov, V. 1904 The movement of water in the soils of the Odessa Exp. Station. *Zhur. Opyt. Agron.* 4, p. 631.

78. Russell, R. J. 1944 Lower Mississippi Valley loess. *Bul. Geol. Soc. of Amer.* 55 : 1-40.

79. Scheidig, A. 1934 Der Löss und seine geotechnischen Eigenschaften. Steinkopff. Dresden.

80. Shivley, B. S. and Weaver, J. E. 1939 Amount of underground plant materials. Nebraska Conserv. Bul. No. 21, Univ. of Nebr. (Extensive bibliography).

81. Smith, G. D. 1942 Illinois loess variations in its properties and distribution. A pedologic interpretation. Ill. Agr. Dept. Sta. Bul. 490 : 138-184.

82. Smith, H. W. and Rhoads, H. F. 1942 Physical and chemical properties of soil profiles of the Scott, Fillmore, Butler, Crete, and Hastings series. Res. Bul. 126, Univ. of Nebraska Agr. Expt. Sta. See also Res. Bul. 139 (1945).

83. Sobolev, S. S. 1937 On loess formation. *Pedology* (U.S.S.R.) No. 4 : 580-583.

84. Sokolovskii, A. N. 1927 Properties of the absorbing complex of Ukrainian loess as a proof of its origin. Contributions to the study of the soils of Ukraine, No. 6. *Reports to the First Inter. Cong. Soil Sci.,* pp. 15-23 (English).

85. Sokolovskii, A. N. 1943 The role of soil forming processes in the genesis of loess. *Bul. Acad. Sci.* (U.S.S.R.) ser. Geol. No. 6: 125-144; see also *Pedology* (U.S.S.R.) No. 9-10 (1943) : 3-23.

86. Stremme, H. 1930 Die Prärieböden. Blanck's *Handbuch der Bodenlehre* 3 : 287-294.

87. Tanfiliev, G. I. 1928 Zur Entstehung des Tschernozembodens und der südrussischen Steppen. *Pedology* (U.S.S.R.) No. 1-2 : 5-23.

88. Tumin, G. M. 1915 The soils of the Tambov government. Vol. I and II (Russian). Quoted from Neustruev's "Elements of Soil

Geography" (Ch. 2, 50).

89. Tutkovskii, P. A. 1899 On the mode of loess formation. *Zem-levedenie* v. 6. (A list of over 300 references is given).

90. Tyurin, I. V. 1928 About the soils of North America. *Uchennye Zapis. Kazan. Gosudarst. Univ.* 58: 27-48.

91. Tyurin, I. V. 1933 Kurs pochvovedenrya (A text book in Pedology). Moscow-Leningrad.

92. Vangengein-von-Kvalen, F. 1854 On the chernozem in Russia. *Trudy Imper. Vol. Ekonom. Obshches.,* III. (From Glinka).

93. Vilenskii, D. 1928 The principal features and the distribution of soils and vegetation in the United States and Southern Canada. *Pedology* (U.S.S.R.) No. 1-2: 99-138.

94. Vilenskii, D. G., and Germanova, V. N. 1934 Experimental investigations of the problem of structure formation. *Pedology* (U.S.S.R.) No. 1: 34-60 (Extensive English summary).

95. Weaver, J. E., and Thiel, A. E. 1917 Ecological studies in the tension zone between prairie and woodland. *Univ. Nebr. Bot. Survey of Nebr.* (n.s.) No. 1: 1-60.

96. Woodard, J. 1924 Origin of prairies in Illinois. *Botan. Gazette* 77: 241-261.

97. Zakharov, S. A. 1935 A struggle between forests and steppe in the Caucasus. *Pedology* (U.S.S.R.) No. 4: 501-545.

CHAPTER X.

PODZOL TYPE OF SOIL FORMATION:
THE PROCESS OF PODZOLIZATION

Introduction.—The name *podzol* has its root in the Russian word *zola* which means ash, a reminder of the ash-gray color of the A_2 horizon in soils of vast areas in the forest regions of the humid temperate climate. This name is common among the Russian peasants in the provinces of Smolensk and Moscow. In other sections of Russia, this soil type has been described by names conveying ash-gray color characteristics.

Geographic Distribution.—The podzol type of soil formation dominates probably the largest habitable area of the earth's surface. According to Glinka's "Soil Map of the World," published by Prasolov (Ch.2, 59), these soils extend from the subarctic region, at the boundary line of forest vegetation, through the temperate zone, to a few degrees north of the Mediterranean in Europe, to about the parallel 50° north latitude in Asia (at the Pacific coast it extends south to the parallel 40°) and North America (at the Atlantic coast it extends south to the parallel 40° north latitude). According to estimates of the Russian Bureau of Soils (53), more than 10 million of the 21 million square kilometers of area in the U. S. S. R. are classified as podzolized. This does not include almost a million square kilometers of forest steppe soils which are transition type of podzols. Afanasiev (Ch. 2, 2), in his schematic "Soil Map of the World," includes the brown forest and yellow soils in the podzol type of soil formation. No genuine or mature podzols, as a zonal soil, are mapped by either Glinka or Afanasiev for Africa, South America, or Australia. In the United States, the area of the zone of podzolization is 614,000 square miles. Podzols are common in the mountain regions the world over in the scheme of vertical zonation. Mohr (Ch. 13, 69) and Senstius (Ch. 13, 90) describe podzols and podzolic soils in the mountains of Java. Hardon (Ch. 13, 34) reports podzols in the tropical lowlands of Borneo.

Climate.—According to Glinka (Ch. 2, 27, p. 464), the climatic conditions of the podzol zone in European Russia, when a wide range of meteorological data is averaged, are 500 to 570 mm. precipitation, with a mean annual temperature of 3.6°C. Within this zone, any temperature rise is accompanied by a rise in the annual precipitation, and similarly any drop in temperature is accompanied by a lowering in the annual precipitation. In North America, we find podzols in sections where the rainfall runs up to 1,100 mm. annually, with a mean annual temperature as high as 10°C.

In Europe and Asia, the podzol zone follows in general the forest zone of the temperate climatic belt. It reaches the edge of the forest zone in the north and fades out in the steppe with the disappearance of the forests in the south. In North America, where the rainfall decreases from east to west and increases from north to south (especially in the eastern half), the limits of podzol soils border the forest region of the subtropics where the lateritic process of soil formation begins. Generally, the podzol zone is to be identified with the humid-temperate climate.

Genesis of Podzols

Historical.—Long before the true nature of podzols was established, the bleached layer just a little below the surface of the soil was observed and noted. Sprengel (Ch. 2, 72) described what we know now as podzol soils. Scandinavian and German foresters and geologists also noted and described podzols. Müller (Ch. 5, 70) mentioned the views held by some Danish geologists, particularly Selmer, that the ash-gray to white horizon in some of the forest soils in Scandinavia did not form *in situ,* but was brought in by the winds or laid down by water. They considered the bleached horizon as an independent geologic stratum. Müller and Ramann (Ch. 2, 60) refuted this idea, but they failed to explain the origin or the process responsible for the *white sand formation.* Not until the Dokuchaev school of pedology revealed the genetic relationship of the soil horizons in the profile was it possible to elucidate the mode of formation of the bleached layer. As a mater of fact, Dokuchaev (Ch. 2, 12) began his soil studies on the podzols of the Smolensk region in Russia, but it was Sibirtzev (Ch. 2, 71) who separated these into a special type.

Ever since the classical researches of Dokuchaev, podzol soils have been studied in great detail, and a wealth of information has accumulated on the process of podzolization. Close to 200 papers were cited by Glinka (Ch. 2, 27) merely on the soils in the podzol zone within the boundaries of the U. S. S. R. Since then, the literature on the subject has been augmented by studies in Russia and other parts of the world, as may be judged from the list of references in this and the chapter following.

Theories on the Process of Podzolization.—Studies on the process of podzolization have been linked with the organic acids and organic matter of the soil in general. Ramann, Dokuchaev, Sibirtzev, Glinka (in his early work), and a number of other investigators stressed the role of the organic acids in the process of podzolization. They were under the influence of Mulder (Ch. 7, 42) and of Detmer (Ch. 7, 6), who subdivided the soil humus into neutral and slowly moving ulmin and humin and into slightly soluble humic acids and easily soluble crenic and apocrenic acids.

Dobrovol'skii attempted to differentiate types of organic matter in 1900 and systematized the data in tabular form. On the basis of these and his own work, he reached the following conclusions:

"The upper horizons are high in total SiO_2 because the other constituents are leached out. In general, podzols are rich in Fe and poor in Ca. The P content of the A horizon is lower than that of the B. When wet, the bleached horizon is a sticky, smeary mass, which upon drying hardens and when crushed becomes powdery and silt-like, especially in the loams."

Dobrovol'skii attempted to differentiate types of organic matter in the profile. An $(NH_4)_2CO_3$ extract of the A_1 horizon gave a dark brown solution; of the A_2 bleached horizon, a red-yellow solution. When neutralized with acid, humic acid settled out from A_1 but not from A_2. The filtrate of A_1 resembled in color the extract from A_2. The filtrate of A_1 and A_2 extracts, upon addition of $CuSO_4$, gave a precipitate of a dirty green color (crenic and apocrenic acids). In the bleached A_2 horizon, there was little apocrenic acid; it was mostly the less oxidized state — the crenic acid. The lack of humic acid in this horizon, in the opinion of Dobrovol'skii, caused the white or ash-gray color.

Williams (Ch. 3, 72), whose views on the processes of soil formation are at some variance with the orthodox Dokuchaev school of pedology, stressed the differential role of the various organic acids in the process of podzolization. As pictured by him, the crenic acid formed in the decomposition process of the forest litter reacts first with the carbonates of calcium, liberating CO_2 and forming soluble calcium crenate. Not until all the lime has disappeared does the crenic acid react with the other elements of the parent material. Iron and manganese are attacked next, forming crenates of these elements that are also soluble and are, therefore, carried downward. The loss of iron and manganese causes the whitish or gray color. After the leaching of the sesquioxides which, according to Williams (Ch. 3, 72, p. 116), are . . .

always present in the parent material in a very fine state of division, the kaolin or the hydrate of alumino-silicic acid ($H_2Al_2Si_2O_8.nH_2O$) is disintegrated by the crenic acid, giving rise to free sols of silicic acid and aluminum crenates. The latter and part of the silica sol move downward in colloidal state. The rest of the silica turns into gel, loses water, and in an amorphous state fills the interspaces in the parent material, imparting to it the white color and a structureless condition. Such is the complexity of phenomena which results in the formation of the podzolized horizon in the upper layer of the parent material."

An interesting observation was made by Williams on the microbiological condition of the A_2 horizon:

Neither bacteria, because of the acid medium due to the crenic acid, nor fungi, because of the crenic acid which is a waste product of the fungi, may develop. It thus becomes a "dead" horizon where only mineral reactions take place.

Kossovich (Ch. 2, 40), in discussing the processes of soil formation, sums up the podzol process as follows:

It takes place under conditions of sufficient or excess of moisture. The organic acids, carbonic, nitric, and perhaps sulfuric act on the mineral constituents and liberate the bases. The finely divided organic substances in colloidal state also enter into a series of reactions. During periods of saturation, ferrous salts might be produced and leach out. Primarily, however, aerobic conditions exist, and the iron probably moves as the sol protected by the organic colloids. Silica is usually left behind. Because of the leaching of bases, the horizon of eluviation is acid. The horizon of illuviation is enriched with electrolytes, causing the precipitation of the iron and aluminum which serves as cementing material for the ortstein formation or incrustation. Some of the fine clay particles are caught in their downward movement in the layer of incrustations of ortstein formation, identified as the B horizon, which becomes compact even if the parent material is not of clay origin.

The processes descrbed are responsible for the formation of a grayish-white horizon just below the humus accumulative layer. It is poor in bases, iron, aluminum, and colloidal substances and is acid in reaction. In soils poor in organic matter or in sandy soil, this layer is practically free from organic matter, poor in bacteria, and rich in fungus mycelium. This process prevails in the northern part of the temperate zone. At the northern and southern limits of this zone, the so-called intrazonal gradations of podzols are found. Within the zone, one finds regions of true podzols, strongly podzolic, medium podzolic, and weakly podzolic.

The conditions described by Kossovich for sandy soils have been found to prevail in the sandy soils of the Coastal Plain of New Jersey, known under the name Lakewood sandy soils.

Zakharov (73) analyzes the process of podzolization with reference to the moisture regime as influenced by the macro- and microrelief of the region. He outlines the development of the various types of podzols, from a slightly podzolized soil to a peat podzol and finally to a peat-glei. His conclusions are similar to those of Tumin (Ch. 2, 82) who divides the podzol zone of Russia into five belts: in the center of the zone, there is a belt of genuine podzols; to the north* and south of it are the two belts

---

*In reality, the belts do not run north and south, but northeast and southwest.

of podzolic soils; and north and south of these are the two belts of
weakly or slightly podzolized soils. The difference in the analogous belts
— north and south of the belt of genuine podzols — consists of the following: in the north, more organic matter and conditions for a higher

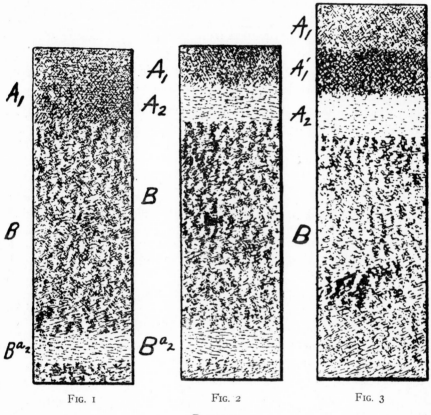

FIG. 1   FIG. 2   FIG. 3

PLATE 23

Schematic presentation of podzol profiles

(After Tyurin)

reducing activity (due to more frequent saturation) are encountered; in
the soils of the northern belts, there is a bleached whitish horizon below
B; this is not found in the southern belts. In figure 1 and 2 of plate
23, reproduced from Tumin (Ch. 2, 82, p. 324), a podzolic and a genuine
podzol soil with a bleached horizon (B^{a_2}) below B are represented
Tumin points out:

> The diminution in degree of podzolization in the southeastern direction takes place
> under conditions of lower rainfall and higher temperature; in the northwestern direc-

tion it takes place under conditions of higher rainfall, lower temperature, and decreased aeration.

The amount of humus in the soils of the podzol type varies as follows: at the extreme northeast and southwest, there is an increase in the humus content; from these extremes toward the central portion of the zone, the humus content decreases.

Tumin (62) disagreed with Sibirtzev (Ch. 2, 71, p. 257) who, in his pioneer work on podzols, correlated podzolization with the separation of SiO_2 in the bleached horizon. According to Tumin, the process of podzolization is related to the formation of the light colored humus substances, crenic acid, and the dark colored humic acid. The preponderance of the former in the A_2 horizon determines the podzol features of the profile.

According to Tumin (Ch. 2, 82), "The distribution of podzols, podzolic, and weakly podzolic soils, as outlined above, is true for loams on a level plain topography. Otherwise, the morphology of each belt in the podzol zone is closely related to the relief and mechanical and chemical composition of the parent material." These points are brought out schematically in table 64. Commenting on the data, Tumin states: "Changes in the degree of podzolization, in connection with fluctuations in relief, take place in the direction from a higher elevation to depressions. The degree of podzolization will change as we advance to the northwest. In the southeastern zone (first belt), the podzolization of loams, sandy loams, and sands increases in the direction of the depressions, where true podzols are to be encountered. In the central portion of the zone (third belt), the podzolization of loams in the depressions decreases and increases in the sandy loams and sands. With the transition towards the depressions, the deoxidation processes are stimulated, causing an accumulation of organic matter (peat formation) in the upper soil horizons. In the depressions, the depths of some of the horizons increase. A new sub-horizon A_1', darker in color than A_1 appears, peat accumulates, the A_1' is converted into a deep A_0 layer which eventually replaces the A_1, as illustrated in plate 24."

Glinka (Ch. 2, 27) has shown experimentally that upon ignition the soil material from the bleached horizon darkens, indicating carbonization of the light colored humus substances. Neustruev (Ch. 2, 50), in discussing the relationship of the organic acids to the process of podzolization, justly remarks; "No one has proved the presence of crenic acid, and its existence and properties are thus hypothetical."

Gedroiz (Ch. 9, 27) interprets the process of podzolization in the light of cation exchange reactions. Whenever conditions are favorable for the replacement of bases with hydrogen ions in the exchange complex

Table 64

Variations in the degree of podzolization due to the mechanical composition of parent material

(After Tumin)

Portion of the zone	Belts	Soils on loams	Soils on sandy loams	Soils on clay loams	Lower bleached horizon (below B)
Northwestern portion	5	Weakly podzolized	Podzolized	Podzols	Present
	4		Podzols	Podzolized	
Central portion	3	Podzols	Podzolized	Weakly podzolized	Is disappearing
Southeastern portion	2	Podzolized	Weakly podzolized	Weakly podzolized	Absent
	1	Weakly podzolized	Weakly podzolized	Weakly podzolized	

(mineral or organic), podzolization takes place. Such conditions prevail in the regions of moderate rainfall where the percolating waters exclude the accumulation of soluble salts.

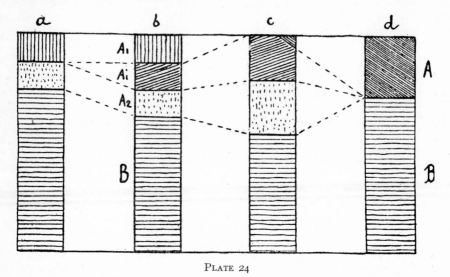

PLATE 24

A diagramatic presentation of the influence of micro-relief on the gradual replacement of the A_1 horizon by the A_i subhorizon and finally by the A_0 horizon (peat formation)

a, level place; b, slight depression; c, a slightly deeper depression; d, a peat depression
(After Tumin)

Pure water, upon dissociation, gives at 22°C., 10^{-7} gm. of hydrogen ions per liter. In the presence of carbonic acid, the amount of hydrogen ions appreciably increases, since the dissociation constant of this acid is 3×10^{-7}. A still greater increase in the concentration of hydrogen ions takes place in the presence of organic acids, the products of organic matter decomposition. The processes of nitrification and sulfur oxidation introduce into the soil solution the highly ionized nitric and sulfuric acids. Thus, the concentration of hydrogen ions in the soil solution may reach at times a magnitude of considerable moment.

The energy of replacement of hydrogen is higher than that of Ca, Mg, K, and Na. This means that the replacing power of the H ion, when compared with an equimolecular or ionic quantity of Ca, Mg, K, Na, or a combination of these in solution, is greatest. On the other hand, the total concentration of the other cations — Ca, Mg, K, Na — either individually or in combination, may supply enough energy of replacement to suppress the activity of the H ions.

Gedroiz (p. 66) points out that

. . . water circulating in the soil, when saturated with CO_2 under pressure of one atmosphere, will contain 10^{-5} gm. of H ions per liter; under the same conditions, the solubility of $CaCO_3$ will bring into solution about 5×10^{-1} gm. of Ca per liter, i.e., its concentration will be 50,000 times higher than that of the H ions. It is perfectly clear that in the presence of calcium and magnesium carbonates, or any other more soluble salt, the processes which take place in the parent material and in the soils will not tend to produce an unsaturated complex.

Thus, the formation of an unsaturated soil complex and hence of a soil unsaturated with bases is possible only when almost all of the easily and difficultly soluble salts have been leached out and carried down to a depth from which the capillary rise of moisture cannot bring them to the surface horizons.

The replacement of the bases with hydrogen and the formation of an unsaturated complex (organic and mineral) are not the only effect of the action of water on the soil. To quote Gedroiz (p. 68) :

Water affects the soil alumino-silicates (and humates) not only through ion replacement. Simultaneously, it disintegrates them into simpler compounds and partly decomposes them into the oxides of iron, aluminum, and silica. The action of water on the aluminum silicates and humates unsaturated with bases is a good deal more effective than on the silicates which have not reached that stage.

To give some idea of the greater activity of water on soils unsaturated with bases, analyses are presented in table 65. A 100-gm. portion of natural chernozem saturated with Ca and Mg and a 100-gm. portion of the same chernozem, from which the bases had been removed and replaced with hydrogen, were each mixed with 500 cc. of water. Both mixtures were kept for 3 days and the water extracts analyzed.

From the data in table 65 it is apparent that . . .

Table 65

Water extract analyses, per cent of total soil
(After Gedroiz)

Soil	Dry residue		SiO_2	$Al_2O_3 +$ Fe_2O_3	CaO	Organic matter (by titration)
	Ordinary drying	Igniting				
Original chernozem	0.0575	0.0095	0.0095	0.00	0.0107	0.0360
Chernozem saturated with H	0.1140	0.0504	0.0430	0.0055	0.00	0.0605

The soil loses not only the bases, but also the colloidally dispersed organic matter and the complex mineral components which decompose into silicic acid, hydrates of the oxides of aluminum and iron, and colloidally soluble organic matter. In this way, the process of degradation and podzolization lead, on the one hand, to the formation in the soil of insoluble compounds unsaturated with bases, and on the other hand, to their decomposition.

According to Gedroiz (p. 69), the process of podzolization consists of two stages:

First stage: The hydrogen ions of the water replace the absorbed bases of the absorbing complex which is not protected by the presence of minute quantities of simple salts against the entry of these ions.

Second stage: The portion of the complex unsaturated with bases begins to be energetically disintegrated by the water. The colloidally dispersed humates are carried downward, and the aluminum silicate portion of the unsaturated complex is decomposed into silica and oxides of iron and aluminum.

In the scheme of Gedroiz, the decomposition process is one of the essential features. Besides, Gedroiz postulates the formation of aluminum silicates anew in the B horizon through the mutual coagulation of the positive Al and negative SiO_3 sols.

In the light of Mattson's theories (Ch. 4, 45-48), the process of podzolization is related to the conditions of acid hydrolysis which exist in the zone of the humid temperate climate. The net result of acid hydrolysis is the release of bases from A and their replacement with H ions, whereby a partial disruption of the silicate complexes takes place and sesquioxides are set free. Depending on the pH environment, which is periodically shifted away from the isoelectric point, the sesquioxides move downward leaving behind SiO_2. Some of the iron and aluminum silicate complexes, saturated with H, become colloidally dispersed. Under certain conditions, some SiO_3 may be replaced by the humates and other anions, giving rise to iron and aluminum complexes of silicates, phosphates, humates, and other anionic chains, all of which possess definite isoelectric points of precipitation. As these complexes, as well as other colloids, like free iron, aluminum, manganese, titanium (as oxides or hydrated oxides), humic, crenic, apocrenic, and other organic acids move through the soil profile, they reach a point where a large portion precipitates, because of electrostatic forces controlled primarily by the pH of the medium and the presence of electrolytes. These are in part the complexes known as "new formations." They all possess the property of ionic exchange which varies with the acidoid-basoid ratio. Thus, a high $SiO_2:R_2O_3$ ratio is indicative of a high base exchange capacity.

The new formations orginate and accumulate in the B horizon because the acid hydrolysis is subdued at that point in the profile. The fine particles which move downward mechanically, together with the new formations, impart to this horizon the compactness typical of the B horizon. An accompanying phenomenon is the formation of concretions, ortstein, and orterde.

Aarnio (2) reviewed the contributions on ortstein and presented valuable data on the composition of such formations in Finland. He conducted a series of experiments on the role of organic matter in the precipitation reactions of Fe and Al in podzol soils. He obtained humic acid from ammonia extracts on two peats by dialyzing these for 5 weeks; he then mixed definite quantities of the extracts with variable quantities of iron and aluminum sols. From analyses on the iron and aluminum coagulates, ratios were obtained for the amount of humus (by weight) necessary to coagulate one unit (by weight) of Fe_2O_3 or Al_2O_3. In the first extract, the ratios of Fe_2O_3 to humus ranged from 1 :2.79 to 1 :090; in the second humus extract the ratios ranged from 1 :2.46 to 1 :0.82. For Al_2O_3, the ratios with the respective humus extracts were: 1 :30.12 to 1 :1.20, and 1 :26.62 to 1 :5.32. These ratios indicate that colloidal iron in its downward movement coagulates faster than aluminum. In other words, since more humus is required to coagulate one unit of Al_2O_3 than of Fe_2O_3, iron is more rapidly fixed than aluminum and the losses of the later should therefore be greater. This point has been substantiated by the analyses on mature podzols presented by Joffe and Watson (27). The validity of this behavior has also been brought out by Joffe (21), in connection with a study on the movement of Fe and Al in the soil. It is shown that the river waters contain more Al than Fe. Aarnio also studied the relation of colloidal SiO_2, SO_4, and PO_4 to the coagulation of iron sols.

Similar to the work of Aarnio is that of Udulft (64) and Simakov (56). The latter studied the mutual coagulation of the sols of Fe_2O_3 and Al_2O_3 by MnO_2 and by Na-saturated soil suspensions. This work, as well as that of Aarnio, would have been more valuable if the pH of the disperse phase had been available, since it is one of the chief factors controlling coagulation and peptization.

A different view on the movement of iron in the podzol profile is held by Nikolich (40). According to him, the leaching of iron is due to the formation of organic iron compounds, the ferrous and ferric humates playing only a minor role in the process. Gallagher (14) ascribes the movement of R_2O_3 to oxalic and other organic acids. He presents some experimental data.

Smirnov (59) attempted to demonstrate experimentally the process of podzolization. Tubes, 5 cm. in diameter, were filled with soil material from a podzol sandy soil. The material from the C horizon was placed on the bottom of the tubes, followed by A_2 and A_1. The B horizon was left out, in order not to hinder percolation. The percolates consisted of distilled water, distilled water saturated with CO_2, and a weak ammonia (1 :100) solution. From time to time, 50 to 60 cc. portions were titrated. The H_2O percolates were yellowish brown and acid in reaction, requiring for neutralization 0.25 to 0.5 cc. of 0.01 N NaOH. The CO_2 percolates were colorless and alkaline for the first 3 days, after which they became acid. The ammonia extract was acid and dark brown, and continuous leaching with ammonia produced under the A_2 material a ring resembling ortstein formation.

Mattson (34), in his investigations on the nature of the soil colloidal complex, observed that the mobility of the ions upon electrodialyzing is fundamentally a function of the pH. After a certain period of electrodialysis, the colloid becomes unsaturated and attains a definite pH known as the *ultimate pH*. Mattson states:

The cations of the insoluble bases, Al, Fe, Mg, and Mn become mobile only after the pH has been reduced to a certain value exactly as under natural conditions. Above these pH values, the compounds in which these ions exist in the soil are too slightly dissociated. Under natural humid conditions, the soluble strong bases (together with silica which ionizes at high pH) are always removed from the soil by the drainage water, whereas Al and Fe become mobile only under conditions of a certain degree of acidity when podzolization sets in.

The electrodialysis of a soil results in a pH gradient within the soil mass from the cathode to the anode membranes. The unsaturation of the soil becomes at first greatest next to the anode membranes. As the pH here is reduced to a certain value, Al and later Fe begin to ionize and to move towards the cathode not as single trivalent ions $Al+++$ and $Fe+++$ (the pH is too high for them to exist) but as complex ions such as $Al+ (OH).(SiO_3H).Al++(SiO_3H)$, or any low multiple of this.* This accounts satisfactorily for the appearance of silica in the cathode chamber. The ions will, however, not migrate directly to the cathode with the speed of the common ions, but will repeatedly be precipitated in zones of higher pH where they will become associated with OH ions and lose their charge only again to become ionized as the pH progressively drops through the soil mass in the direction of the cathode. As the "wave" reaches the cathode membrane, some of the ions will emerge into the chamber where, by precipitation, they produce the aforementioned sediment, whereas others of the ions will precipitate at the membrane itself.

The precipitation of the ions at the membrane builds up a new complex which is richer in sesquioxides and poorer in silica (and humus) than the original soil complex. Its ultimate pH and isolectric point are, therefore, higher and will finally reach a value at which no ions of Al and Fe will be able to penetrate the layer, not even after complete unsaturation. No sediment then appears in the cathode solution but basic material will continue to be ionized within the more acid soil mass and be transported towards the cathode membrane where the amphoteric ions will lose their charge and be precipitated. The colloidal complex near the anode will become more and more acidic while the complex on the cathode side becomes more basic, which is analogous to the development of the A and B horizons in the podzol profile. The pH differs, therefore, greatly in the two parts of the soil upon the completion of electrodialysis.

––––––––––––

*The movement of such complexes is demonstrated by the analyses of lysimeter leachings (24) from a gray-brown podzolic soil.

Such a mobility of Fe and Al takes place in the Mattson 3-compartment electrodialysis cell, the central cell containing the soil colloid on either side of which are located the cathode and anode chambers filled with distilled water.

In order to show that in the progressive building up of an amphoteric layer which has a high isoelectric point and, therefore, a high ultimate pH which causes the precipitation and accumulation of the sesquioxides in the layer adjacent to the cathode membrane, Mattson performed the following experiment:

A fourth compartment, 0.5 cm. thick, was made between the soil and the cathode compartments. This was filled with aluminum hydroxide C.P. (Merck) and electrodialyzed until free from all diffusible ions. The solid compartment was then filled with Sharkey soil and electrodialyzed. All cations released would have to pass through 0.5 cm. layer of $Al(OH)_3$ before reaching the cathode compartment. The $Al(OH)_3$ constituted the amphoteric layer spoken of before, with a high isoelectric point (about pH 8). It represented, so to speak, an artificially interposed B horizon.

The electrodialysis required a long time because of the high resistance of the $Al(OH)_3$, but after 163 hours it was practically complete. The titrable bases amounted to 23.92 m.e. (83.5 gm. of soil were used). The cathode solution remained clear throughout the experiment. Magnesium was present in very small quantities, but Al_2O_3 and SiO_2 were absent, except for traces so small that they might be ascribed to the glassware and the reagents.

On opening the cell, a heavy brownish mottled crust was found on the parchment membrane between the soil and the $Al(OH)_3$. The soil next to this membrane had a brownish color and the otherwise snow-white hydroxide was pitted with a brownish coloration on the side facing the same parchment. The $Al(OH)_3$ had effectually prevented the passage of the alumino and ferric silicate cations.

The pH was then determined at three points in the cell and found to be as follows:

Soil next to the anode membrane .... pH 3.4
Soil next to the cathode membrane .... pH 6.0
Aluminum hydroxide .... pH 8.4

The "podzolization" is therefore in evidence by the difference both in color and in pH of the soil at the two sides of the compartment. The whole soil must have been unsaturated, but, because of the enrichment of the basoid constituent in the complex at the cathode side its isoelectric point and, therefore, its ultimate pH were increased.

By adding electrodialyzed humic acid to a podzolic soil and electrodialyzing the mixture, Mattson increased the mobility of the R_2O_3, as shown in table 66. It was caused by a drop of the ultimate pH from 5.15 to 3.6.

In the light of the investigations of Mattson, the empirical findings of Aarnio, Udulft, and Simakov, already mentioned, on the protective action of humus in the mobility of the R_2O_3 acquire a new interpretation.

In the podzol zone, the mobility of the humus is a well-known phenomenon which, of course, lowers the ultimate pH of the soil mass, bringing about the movement of R_2O_3. In the soil, where the content of the natural cathode and anode chambers are subject to diffusion reactions, "new formations" appear as a result of the interaction of the basoids and acidoids released. The isoelectric point and the ultimate pH are lowered and raised, depending upon the type and quality of basoid or acidoid involved. With a lowering of the ultimate pH, an increase in the mobility of the cations takes place, sending the divalent bases to the ground waters and forcing the R_2O_3 to the B horizon, where they precipitate because of a higher ultimate pH environment.

Table 66

Electrodialysis of a podzolic soil (Sassafras loam) with and without the addition of humic acid

(After Mattson)

	No humic acid	6 gm. humic acid in 100 gm. soil
Alkalinity of cathode solution		
hours	*m. e.*	*m. e.*
1-3	3.3	4.5
3-21	0.4	0.2
21-45	0.2	0.05
Total	3.9	4.75
Sesquioxides and silica in cathode solution		
	gm.	*gm.*
SiO_2	0.0039	0.0660
Al_2O_3	0.0074	0.0969
Fe_2O_3	trace	0.0504
pH after electrodialysis (ultimate pH)		
	5.15	3.6

The theories of Mattson open a new approach in the study of the mechanism of podzolization, and, with the perfection of the methods, the puzzling phases of the problem will find their solution. Those who are interested in following up in more detail the researches of Mattson on the process of podzolization are to consult the series of papers published by him and his collaborators (35, 36). The investigations of Lundblad (31) on podzols and brown forest soils corroborate the theories of Mattson.

A new twist in explaining the process of podzolization has been suggested by Remezov (47). He maintains that the disruption of the colloid complex leading to podzolization can not be attributed exclusively to acid hydrolysis. He claims that because of the impeded nitrification in soils under forest, due to the formation of bitumens, some NH_4 is adsorbed by the colloids causing dispersion and disruption of the colloids. Remezov invokes the aid of NH_4 for dispersing the colloids because he sees a contradiction in having the H-ion, generally considered as a coagulant, cause dispersion.

No experimental data are presented by Remezov to prove the presence of NH_4 in podzolized soils in quantities sufficient to cause dispersion. From his table on the effect of H and NH_4-ions on dispersion, it is clear that unsaturation has caused 1000 per cent increase of soluble humus. This goes to show that the adsorption of H ions by the exchange complex (unsaturation, or as Mattson expresses it "a cationic solvation and eluviation of the soil basoids") does cause dispersion. In the regions of genuine podzols in the Costal Plain of New Jersey and as far south of North Carolina, the author has observed time and again the waters of brooks during the spring being brown in color because of the dispersed organic substances and organo-mineral gels. These colloids are unsaturated and come from a medium highly unsaturated, the pH in some areas being as low as 4.2.

Aaltonen (1) presents chemical and physical data on the profile constitution of soils in young and old moss-forests of Finland, Sweden, Latvia, Estonia, Poland, Czechoslovakia, and Germany. He traces the development of the profiles and reiterates the well known fact that the upward growth of the B horizons is associated with the greater and deeper movement of SiO_2, followed by Al_2O_3, and topped by Fe_2O_3. Aaltonen's graphic presentations have been reproduced by Mattson (35) and Jenny (Ch. 5, 48).

Aaltonen's paper has to be studied to appreciate his interpretations of the pH data on water, KCl, and $H_2C_2O_4$ solutions in relation to the podzol process. He comes to a rather startling conclusion that clay soils are hardly podzolized. This conclusion is not borne out by the Caribou loams of Maine, the clay loams of the Lysino forest in the vicinity of Leningrad, the Ontonagon silt loams of Michigan, and many other soils that have typical podzol profiles.

Tyurin (Ch. 5, 105), in his monograph on soil organic matter, credits the acid soluble organic matter, in a pH medium of 5.0 to 6.0, as the precipitating agents of Al and Fe. This organic fraction accumulates in the B horizon and is of the fulvic acid type. This contention has been substantiated by Tyurin in a later publication (Ch. 6, 71, 72). He states that "the organic substances having the properties of the so-called fulvic acids, especially their stable fraction, play the most active part in podzolization. This fraction is precipitated with the hydroxides of Al at a slightly acid reaction. These organic substances are endowed with the properties of organic oxycarbonic acid formed in A_1 and A_2 in combination with Fe and Al, in very dilute solutions of these." The work of Sallans and associates (54) may throw some light on the movement of organic substances in the podzol profile.

Norman (41) states: "Uronic containing substances are in some degree mobile, since in podzolized soils there seems to be a surprising accumulation in the B horizon. These carboxyl groups are probably in fact the acids which have been so often postulated, but never identified as agents involved in the podzolization process."

Rode (50), in an extensive monograph, gives a review and critical analysis of the world literature on the subject of podzolization. According to Rode, four possibilities have been suggested on the movement of R_2O_3 and organic substances: *first,* in the form of ionic solutions; *second,* in the form of solutions of complex organo-mineral compounds in which the Al and Fe appear as a part of the anionic complex of organic acids; *third,* in the form of organo-mineral sols; *fourth,* in the form of fine clay suspensions protected by humus sols. In the first two cases, it is primarily fulvic acid that combines with the R_2O_3, with the possibility of some humic acid participating. In the third case, it is the humic acid that is supposed to combine with the R_2O_3. In the last case, no specific portion of the organic matter is singled out for combining with the R_2O_3. Rode considers first in order the complex compounds, whereby Al and Fe enter into combination with the anions of organic acids. The next possibility is the migration of R_2O_3 in ionic solution, and lastly, the movement of complex sols with humic acid which takes place in light sandy soils but not in the heavier textural classes.

In summarizing the development of the podzol process of soil formation, Rode points out that it depends on the mineralogical composition of parent material and degree of moisture saturation of the mass.

On loam and clay parent materials consisting of a mixture of primary and secondary minerals, four phases in the development of the p o d z o l process may be recognized.

a)   The first phase is the disintegration of the primary minerals with the simultaneous formation of secondary minerals. Essentially, this phase is not of a soil forming process. This phase is the link between the processes of weathering and soil formation.

b)   The second phase is associated with the development of plant life. Organic residues appear on the surface of the soil, with all that is involved in it, especially the appearance of organic substances of an acid nature in the soil solution.

c)   The third phase consists in the replacement of bases by the H-ions and a simultaneous increase in the disruption of the primary minerals.

d)   The fourth phase consists in disruption of the particles of the secondary minerals in the upper *zone* of the eluvial horizon.

The podzolization stage is ushered in at the moment when the disintergration of the secondary minerals surpasses their synthesis in the zone of the eluvial horizon.

On sandy parent materials, consisting almost exclusively of particles of primary minerals, the process under dry conditions (well drained? J.) follows a different path. The weathering of these minerals is suppressed at first. Therefore;

a) The first phase is identified with the appearance of organic matter in the surface horizons.

b) The second phase (apparently of short duration) consists in the mobilization and removal from the upper horizons those small quantities of secondary minerals which are found in the parent material.

c) The third phase probably begins simultaneously with the second phase and consists in the development of physical weathering of particles of primary minerals. This phase may be illustrated by the fact that in sandy soils the quantity of the finest particles is always at a maximum in the surface horizon.

d) The fourth phase, apparently quite an extensive one, consists in the development of chemical weathering of the primary minerals stimulated by physical weathering. Secondary minerals accumulate in the surface horizons.

e) The fifth phase consists in the disruption of the secondary minerals formed.

In this case, apparently, one has to differentiate two podzol stages which correspond to the second and fifth phases, separated from one another by the third and fourth phases. These phases can not be related to the podzolic stage in view of the prevalence of the synthesis of secondary minerals in the surface horizons while they are decomposed.

One has to study Rode's interpretation of the voluminous data to appreciate his viewpoint. Fundamentally, it is just an extension of concepts expressed before him. Elements of the hydrologic aspects of the process of podzolization stressed by Rode may be detected in the work of Tumin (plate 24). Later, Mattson (36), whose work Rode has criticized and used extensively, presented his "pedography of hydrologic podzol series." In these investigations, Mattson and his associates discuss the elements of the moisture regime modifying the process of podzolization. In a way, these investigations are a version of the catena principle advanced by Milne (37).

Rode stresses the inadequacy of the standard approach in studying the process of podzolization by symptoms and characteristics of the podzol profile. He emphasizes the study of the dynamics of the process. Whereas it may appear that the standard approach and the one advanced by Rode differ radically, a closer scrutiny will disclose very little difference.

Rode's novel approach is the interpretation of the transformation of the primary and secondary minerals in the process of podzolization. Only general aspects of the mineralogic analysis are presented by Rode. He points out that the breakdown of the primary minerals in the surface horizon, whereby fine particles of silt accumulate, is associated with the wide fluctuations in temperature at the surface. In a recent publication on the probable role of vegetation in the process of podzolization, Rode (52) states:

The essence of the podzolization process, from the point of view of the mineral component of the soil, consists of the *complete decomposition of the primary minerals,* except quartz, and the removable of *all products of decomposition.* Besides, the most characteristic feature of the process is the circumstance that even the secondary clay minerals are subject to decomposition. These minerals are the products of weathering that takes place in the thermodynamic systems of the surface of the earth and as such should be more stable. Their instability in the process of podzolization illustrates the principal difference between the process of weathering and soil formation.

In this publication, Rode advances the idea that living plants promote podzolization by acidifying the soil solution through their root system. However, he cites cases of high pH value of forest litter. It is rather strange why Rode does not consider the facts that in the zone of podzolization the free bases of dead plants leach out long before the organic constituents begin to decompose. Upon humification, plant residues supply the host of acids that decrease the pH of the soil.

In a study of the physico-chemical properties of the soluble substances of forest litter, Rode (51) presents data on the soluble organic matter, pH, bases of deciduous and coniferous forest on podzols of similar parent material. Broadfoot and Pierre (Ch. 6, 3) present data on the acid base balance of leaves of 58 species of trees. They also give data on pH, N, Ca, ash, and soluble organic matter.

In analyzing the data on lysimeter leachings under conditions of forests, the author (24) has shown that in the fall the pH of the soil rises as a result of the release of bases, primarily K and Ca, from the freshly fallen leaves. These bases are quickly leached in the late fall, the pH drops sharply, and the forest litter remains acid most of the year.

Rode (50) introduced the concept of the eluviation-accumulative coefficient, EAm, expressing the degree of podzolization. This coefficient represents the "relative loss of the sum of mobile oxides (i.e., the sum of all oxides minus the quartz silica or, in case of its absence, minus the total silica which, by the way, is distorting the value of EAM in the upper zone of the eluvial horizon." Taking the quartz silica as immobile, he calculated the relative gains or losses of the respective elements or their oxides from the data obtained by the tri-acid mixture, H_2SO_4, HCl, and HNO_3. For a discussion on the derivation and mathematical treatment of the EAm, the reader is referred to the papers of Rode (49) on the problem of the degree of podzolization.

Zaitsev (77) reviewed the literature on the relation of the N content of the forest species to that of the organic matter and its effects on the site quality. From the data reviewed, he inferred that the N content of the species had an effect on the degree of the humification of the organic matter, and the soil forming processes should in turn have their effect on the

N content and humification of forest soils. The data in table 67 illustrate the aforesaid. The higher the N content of the species, the higher the humification.

Table 67

Relation of total N and degree of humification to the total Ca of the organic matter of forest podzols

(After Zaitsev)

Group Number	Number of samples analyzed	Total Ca in 100 gm. of organic matter	Total N in 100 gms. of organic matter	N : Ca	Degree of humification; per cent of loss on ignition
		gms.	gms.		
I	7	0.31	1.73	5.5	42.0
2	18	0.56	1.96	3.5	41.0
3	16	0.98	2.58	2.6	46.0
4	9	1.37	2.59	1.9	48.6
5	2	1.86	2.27	1.2	51.7
6	2	2.22	2.78	1.3	53.3
7	2	2.47	2.35	1.0	59.2
8	3	3.00	3.19	1.0	55.8
9	1	4.70	3.22	0.7	52.2

Table 68 shows the relation of the total N and degree of humification on the total Ca in the organic matter. The tendency is for an increase in humification with the increase in Ca. There is also an increase in N with the increase in Ca, but only up to a certain point. From then on (group 5-9) the N content does not follow the Ca.

Morphology of Podzolized Soils

In describing podzolized soils, the degree of podzolization determines their nomenclature: strongly, medium, and weakly podzolic. Morphologically, the degrees of podzolization are delineated by the intensity of the ash-gray color of the A_2 horizon, the strongly podzolic degree giving the genuine distinctive color of podzols.

The A_0 Layer.—In the forest, this layer consists of leaf mould and forest litter in general, about 2 to 3 or more centimeters thick. It is what the foresters call "the F and H layers." In general, one may find in the A_0 layer 3 subdivisions: 1, the undecomposed litter — the latest leaf fall; 2, semidecomposed residues of earlier seasons' forest debris, and 3, strongly humified organic matter which in case of conifers on heavy soils has a strong putrifactive odor sometime during the hot early summer season.

In the meadow podzol, the A_0 consists of a mat of dead grass. In peat podzols, or in places where conditions are favorable for swamping, the A_0

Table 68

*The influence of the soil forming processes on the total N and humification of organic matter of forest soils.**

(After Zaitsev)

Soil forming processes	Spruce		Pine		Deciduous species		Data on forest with no reference to species	
	Total N	Humified substance	Total N	Humified substance	Total N	Humified substance	Total N	Humified substance
	In 100 grams of dry organic matter							
Podzolic	1.74	40.3	2.17	43.4	3.05	50.7	2.32	44.8
Podzolic-bog	1.28	41.8	1.98	45.4	2.38	59.7	1.78	46.8
Marsh	1.20	29.5	3.19	58.3	—	—	2.20	43.9

*The data represent the average of 95 samples. The degree of humification was determined by the Robinson method, oxidation with 6% peroxide.

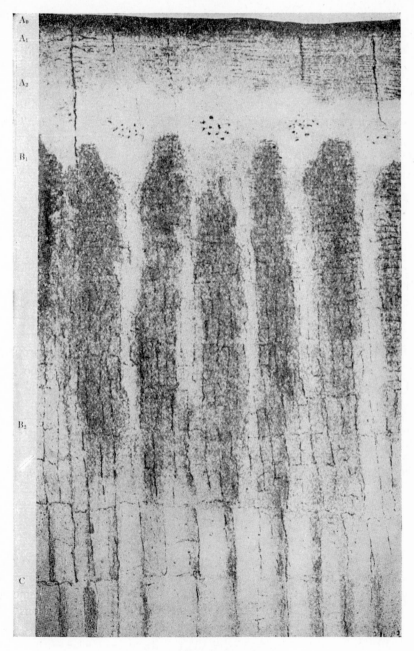

PLATE 25

A typical loam podzol profile
(After Zakharov. Reprinted from Soil Sci. v. 33, p. 237)

may reach a depth of 50-60 cm. In light sandy parent materials which are well aerated, the A_0 layer may be entirely lacking in places.

Romell and Heiberg (Ch. 6, 37) and Romell (Ch. 6, 36) carried out a series of comprehensive studies on forest litter, types of layers of the forest floor, and reactions taking place there. They present a review of the literature and discuss the earlier efforts on the problem of classifying the forest floor debris. The authors retain P. E. Müller's two main groups, *mull* and *duff*. They follow the Scandinavian school in defining the mull group morphologically, such as *crumb mull, grain mull, twin mull*, and *detritus mull*. For the duff group, the specific types listed are: *root duff, leaf duff, greasy duff*, and *fibrous duff*.

The A_1 Horizon.—On the heavier textural materials down to the sandy loams, the surface 3 to 5 cm. layer of this horizon exhibits the influence of the organic matter. It is black, or dark brown to dark gray in color, mellow consistency, and a somewhat pseudo-crumb structure. An abrupt drop in organic matter content follows, and in the case of a mature profile (maturity being associated with a well developed ash-gray to white A_2 horizon) the color changes to gray or brownish gray, extending to a depth of 6 to 10 cm., of a powdery and loose consistency in appearance when wet, with indications of platy or laminated structure. Roots permeate this horizon, but do not make the dense growth noted in the chernozem profile.

In the medium to weakly podzolized soils, the gray color is not expressed as in the strongly podzolic soils (true podzols). The brown color predominates, with an occasional sprinkling of gray, due to the SiO_2 released in the process of podzolization. The intensity of this sprinkling may be taken as an expression of the degree of podzolization.

In sandy soils, this horizon can not frequently be differentiated from the underlying typical ash-gray to white A_2 horizon, except for the surface 1 or 2 cm.

The A_2 Horizon.—This horizon differs from the overlying A_1 horizon in exhibiting more strikingly the degree of podzolization. In the strongly podzolic soils (true podzols), the A_2 horizon is bleached ash-gray to white gray in color. The average thickness of this horizon is 12 to 16 cm. in loamy soils and deeper in sandy soils. Structurally, the soil is platy or laminar (in the heavier soils), powdery when crushed after drying; it is smeary when wet, with little pore space. Sometimes granules of concretions are found in this horizon.

In the medium podzolic soils, the bleached ash-gray color of the A_2 is less pronounced and in the weakly podzolic soils it is not apparent at all. The color is grayish brown and brownish gray. It is very likely that the predominance of the gray is an indication of stronger podzolization, or of poorer drainage.

The B Horizon.—The B_1 is 20 to 40 cm. deep, of a dull brown to brown coloration, with some light and some dark streaks, or veins, pocket-like on top, and extending deeper in tongue shaped fashion. The light colored markings are bleached material from the overlying A_2 horizon, and the dark streaks are the soluble organic materials from the A_0 and the A horizon which precipitate because of a higher pH, concentration of electrolytes at this point of the profile, and perhaps because of the mutual coagulation of the positively charged Al and Fe and negatively charged organic matter.

With depth, the texture becomes heavier and darker brown, due to the movement of clay and hydrated oxide of iron. The structure is definitely laminar, sometimes lumpy, and even prismatic. The last named type of structure is found more in the podzols of the transition zone, from the degraded chernozem to the forest-steppe and forest soils.

In the podzolized soils of North America, in the regions bordering the warm temperate climate where laterization effects are noted, the structure is lumpy with definite platy cleavage. The color is more brown to reddish brown and brownish-red.

The B_2 horizon which begins at the point where the texture is heaviest extends to a depth of 20 to 40 cm. It has none of the contaminations from the A_2, nor any of the streaks of organic matter. With depth, the color becomes a lighter brown and the soil lighter in texture.

Whenever pebbles are found in the B horizon of the podzolized soils, some elements of ortstein (hardpan) are frequently encountered.

At the bottom of this horizon, the texture becomes lighter and the color blends in with that of the underlying parent material, or the C horizon.

In many of the podbolized soils, heavy coatings of Mn are noted. This is particularly true for many of the soils on the unconsolidated materials of the Coastal Plain in the United States. Other coatings may be found, such as SiO_2, organic matter, and oxides of Al and Fe. These coatings are usually found on the faces of the structural units and along paths of roots and cracks. Infrequently, especially in the lighter soils, ortstein, orterde, and concretions form along these paths.

Chemical Properties of Podzolized Soils

The A_0 Layer.—Fresh dead leaves and herbaceous and grass vegetation carry large quantities of alkali and alkaline-earth bases. Upon reaching the surface of the A_0 layer during the early fall, they release the bases after the first few rains causing a pH increase in the soil, being higher than at any other season of the year. The late fall rains leach these bases. In their downward movement, some combine with the organic and inorganic exchange complex of the A and B horizons and others are washed into the ground waters. At that time, the humification process sets in, releasing organic and inorganic acids which impart a low pH to the medium. From then on until next fall, except for a brief period in the spring, the A_0 layer is almost always acid, pH lower than 6.0, the acidity depending on the plant species and on the type of parent material. In the early spring, when the electrolyte content is low, the unsaturated organic and inorganic complexes are subject to dispersion. They move downward carrying the excess acids and acid salts which react with the mineral constituents, decompose the primary minerals, form secondary minerals, decompose some of these, and set off a series of reactions. Thus, the A_0 is the starting point of many reactions. It is the potential source and storehouse of the substances which react with the underlying horizons and impart to the profile the characteristic features of podzols.

One of the distinctive chemical properties of A_0 is its high cation exchange capacity, as compared with the other horizons. In no other soil type is the difference in exchange capacity between the A_0 and the underlying horizons as great as in the podzol zone. Table 69 presents data on the exchange capacity of the A_0 layer of several podzolic soils. For comparison, the exchange capacity of the parent material (horizon C) is given. It may serve as a measure of the exchange capacity of the mineral portion of the soil. As a matter of fact, it is difficult to assign a cation exchange value to the mineral fraction that would be applicable to all horizons in the profile. It is variable because of the dynamic nature of the soil-forming processes. And yet, the data on the A_0 layer and C horizon may illustrate the comparative role of the organic and mineral fractions in the exchange reactions of the soil. The data in table 69 reveal that the seat of the exchange capacity in A_0 lies primarily in the organic fraction.

Mattson (33) prepared, by the Oden method, humic acid having an exchange capacity of 306.4 m.e. per 100 gm. Analyses of 12 A_0 samples (only 4 are given in table 69) record only one case where the cation exchange capacity was equal to 37.2 m.e. per 100 gm. Thus, at best, the organic matter would contain about 12 per cent of the humic acid. We know, however, that the humic acid is not the only organic constituent capable of cation exchange. The state of decomposition has something to do with the formation of many organic complexes in A_0 which influence the exchange capacity. In table 70, data are presented showing the influ-

Table 69

*Some chemical properties of the A₀ layer**

Soil series*	Depth of A₀	Reaction		Base exchange capacity	Unsaturation		Base exchange capacity of Horizon C
		H₂O extract	Neutral salt extract				
	cm.	*pH*	*pH*	*m.e.†*	*m.c. of H*	*per cent*	*m.e.†*
Sassafras loam	3	5.0	3.8	22.3	19.7	88.3	5.2
Penn silt loam	3	5.2	4.3	26.4	18.64	70.6	11.2
Chester gravelly loam ...	3	6.2	5.0	18.5	5.83	31.5	5.3
Washington loam	5	7.2	6.8	37.2	1.98	5.3	5.03

*From paper by Joffe (23).

m.e. is the milligram equivalents per 100 gm of soil.

ence of the stage of decomposition on the exchange capacity of organic materials.

Table 69 brings out another important chemical property of the A_0 layer in podzolized soils, namely, unsaturation; it varies from 5.3 to 90 per cent of the exchange capacity. This wide variation is due primarily to two factors: *parent material* and *vegetation*. In the podzol process of soil formation, the mineralized bases from the A_0 layer move downward. In the B horizon, they are retained temporarily, partly to be adsorbed, partly to

Table 70

Base exchange in decomposing organic materials

(After Muller)

Time	Exchange capacity per gram dry weight		
	Soybeans	Straw	Manure
	m.e.	*m.e.*	*m.e.*
Beginning	0.58	0.00	0.73
After 3 weeks	—	0.22	1.03
After 2 months	0.52	0.30	1.09
After 3.5 months	0.48	0.33	1.11
After 6 months	1.20	0.38	1.45
After 9 months	—	0.59	1.67

be leached, and partly to be picked up by the plant roots. The same thing happens to the bases of the organic matter in the intermediate layers— between A_0 and B. These bases show up in circulation when the leaves, twigs, and branches of the new crop die and are redeposited in the A_0 layer to be decomposed. The richer the parent material in bases, the greater is the circulation of these. The state of unsaturation, therefore, depends on the balance between the outgo and the return of bases. Naturally, soils that have a parent material rich in bases resist podzolization.

The specificity and wide variations in the ash content of plants are factors influencing the rate of podzolization. In evaluating analyses of different species, it is to be noticed that hardwood litter decomposes much faster and more completely than conifer litter. Hardwood forests, by virtue of the high base content of their species slow down the pace of podzolization when compared with conifers. In tables 71-73 ash analyses of wood, bark, roots, and forest litter of a number of hardwoods and conifers are given. For analyses of freshly fallen needle litter and a selected set of reference on the composition of forest litter in general, the reader is referred to the papers by Shuttleworth (55), Chandler (Ch. 6, 6), Plice (43), Coile (6), Polynov (46), Dzens — Litovskaya (10), and Broadfoot and Pierre (Ch. 6, 3).

Table 71

Ash constituents of some forest trees

[Compiled by Joffe (23)]

No.	Species	Ash content in			CaO content in	
		Wood	Bark	Forest litter (old leaves)	Forest litter	Wood
		per cent	*per cent*	*per cent*	*per cent*	*per cent*
1	Yellow pine (*Pinus mitus*)	0.3765	——	——	——	0.163
2	Old field pine (*Pinus mitus*)	0.2620	1.81	——	——	0.113
3	Red pine (*Pinus resinosa*)	——	——	2.30	——	——
4	White pine (*Pinus strobus*)	——	——	2.70	——	——
5	White pine (*Pinus strobus*)	——	——	2.90	——	——
6	Pine (*Pinus sylvestris*)	——	——	1.46	0.59	——
7	Pitch pine (*Pinus rigida*)	——	——	1.29	——	——
8	Black pine (*pine nigra*)	0.2874	——	——	——	0.123
9	Red spruce (*Picea rubra*)	——	——	3.30	——	——
10	Red spruce (*Picea rubra*)	——	——	3.31	——	——
11	Balsam fir (*Abies balsamea*)	——	——	3.08	——	——
12	Larch (*Larix europaea*)	——	——	6.09	——	——
13	Red maple (*Acer rubrum*)	0.2714	3.48	4.40	——	——
14	Red maple (*Acer rubrum*)	——	——	4.08	——	——
15	Sugar maple (*Acer saccharum*)	——	——	11.30	——	——
16	Sugar maple (*Acer saccharum*)	——	——	6.68	——	——
17	Black locust	——	——	11.74	——	——
18	Birch	——	——	4.68	——	——
19	Grey birch (*Betula populifolia*)	——	——	4.10	——	——
20	Grey birch (*Betula populifolia*)	——	——	4.07	——	——
21	Beech (*Fagus grandifolia*)	——	——	4.49	——	——
22	Beech (*Fagus grandifolia*)	——	——	9.26	——	——
23	Beech (*Fagus grandifolia*)	——	——	9.36	——	——
24	Beech (*Fagus grandifolia*)	——	——	7.11	——	——
25	Beech (*Fagus grandifolia*)	——	——	5.57	2.46	——
26	Bird cherry	——	——	7.24	——	——
27	Chestnut (*Castanea vulgaris*)	0.1500	3.43	4.55	——	0.050
28	Hickory (*Carya tomentosa*)	0.6468	3.86	——	——	0.161
29	Red oak (*Quercus rubrum*)	0.7687	6.28	——	——	0.246
30	White oak (*Quercus alba*)	0.3927	5.88	——	——	0.083
31	Post oak (*Quercus obtusiloba*)	0.9224	11.80	——	——	0.301
32	Dogwood (*Cornus Florida*)	0.8029	9.62	——	——	0.223
33	Ash (*Fraxinus americana*)	0.4247	——	10.26	——	0.075
34	Poplar (*Populus grandidentata*)	——	——	3.85	——	——
35	Sycamore (*Plantanus occidentalis*)	1.00	——	——	——	——

Table 72

Ash analyses of plants and forest floor

(After Polynov)

Object analyzed	Ash in 100 gms. of dry matter	In 100 parts of ash										
		SiO$_2$	Al$_2$O$_3$	Fe$_2$O$_3$	MnO	CaO	MgO	K$_2$O	SO$_3$	P$_2$O$_5$	Cl	$\frac{SiO_2}{Al_2O_3}$
Tree roots	2.93	34.72	32.64	6.94	2.71	6.59	4.43	1.60	7.59	2.05	not determined	1.8
Leaves of: Beech	3.09	9.40	6.09	1.71	2.13	14.54	11.68	22.00	24.60	2.58	not determined	2.6
Crab	1.96	13.31	16.33	0.94	3.34	13.14	7.93	16.60	11.22	2.03	not determined	1.4
Chestnut	2.78	2.88	12.67	3.48	3.20	20.94	19.20	22.08	8.58	13.20	not determined	0.4
Rhododendron	3.18	3.92	9.21	4.08	2.23	16.90	4.11	12.80	7.17	11.21	not determined	0.7
Forest floor: Leaf fall	5.46	22.93	15.75	7.49	1.83	23.09	6.18	trace	5.06	1.18	not determined	2.5
Peat	—	46.21	29.84	9.67	trace	2.12	1.82	not determined	5.87	2.12	0.40	2.6

Table 73

Molar ratios of oxides in the ash of plants

(After Dzens-Litovskaya)*

Plant	$\dfrac{SiO_2}{R_2O_3}$	$\dfrac{Al_2O_3}{Fe_2O_3}$	$\dfrac{CaO}{MgO}$	$\dfrac{K_2O}{Na_2O}$
Oak-birch association				
Oak—living leaves	23.57	1.33	3.46	3.40
Oak—wood and bark	3.55	2.00	7.61	2.00
Oak—roots	4.89	1.60	4.20	1.20
Oak—dropping leaves (autumn)	22.50	1.00	3.73	2.11
Oak-aspen association				
Aspen—living leaves	20.00	1.50	2.00	2.70
Oak—wood and bark	5.28	1.33	6.00	2.87
Oak—roots	9.71	2.50	4.74	2.30
Oak—dropping leaves (autumn)	39.00	0.93	3.54	2.30
Oak—living leaves	19.54	1.20	2.34	3.10
Oak—wood and bark	1.28	2.50	6.00	2.50
Oak roots	4.75	3.00	3.52	2.67
Oak—dropping leaves (autumn)	35.40	0.63	4.92	5.41
Aspen-mixed association				
Oak—living leaves	19.00	1.69	1.80	2.54
Oak—dropping leaves (autumn)	22.00	6.67	5.07	0.94
Aspen—living leaves	18.08	2.00	1.55	1.50
Aspen—dropping leaves (autumn)	19.38	2.20	5.36	1.66

*See reference 10.

In a pedologic study of New Jersey soils, Joffe (25) has shown that the Ca and Mg content of the A_0 is relatively high, in spite of the low pH environment. The Ca tends to approach (on percentage basis) the quantity of Mg, even in soils that have a higher total Mg content. This condition is due to the larger quantity of Ca returned to the A_0 by plants and to the insolubility of Ca-humate upon drying. Mg-humates do not become insoluble upon drying.

The effect of the composition of the vegetation on the type of soil formation has been noted by Lundblad (30). Tyurin (63, p. 209) points out that pine, with its surface rooting habits, exhausts the bases from the horizon of eluviation more intensively than any other plant association. It is for this reason that the podzolization effects are more strongly expressed under pine forests.

The A Horizon.—The outstanding chemical characteristic of this horizon, especially that of the A_2, is high acidity. The pH of the A_1 horizon is generally higher than that of the A_2 and lower than that of the B horizon.

This is due to the higher organic matter content of the A_1 horizon (there is an abrupt drop in organic matter below the surface 2 to 3 inches of this horizon) and hence higher cation sorption. As the bases are released from the A_0, some are caught in the A_1 horizon. Table 74, showing the cation exchange capacity of a number of podzolic soils in New Jersey, illustrates the above.

As a result of the prevalence of acid in the exchange complex of this horizon, the primary as well as secondary minerals are being disrupted, releasing aluminum and iron. In the acid medium, the silicic acid hydrolyzes to give H_2O and SiO_2. It is this SiO_2 coating that imparts the ash-gray color to the A_2. Whenever the circulation of bases is sufficient to reprecipitate some of the iron, the bleached layer does not appear morphologically. In the podzolic soils mentioned in table 74, save the Lakewood sand, the A_2 horizon is not bleached, but the SiO_2 content is high just the same. Because of the breakdown of the minerals and release of SiO_2, the texture of the A horizon is lighter than that of the B. It is to be noted that in the process of mineral disintegration some of the fine particles move from the A horizon, leaving behind a coarser texture.

The exchange capacity of the A_2 horizon is lowest, and the exchange capacity of the A_1 horizon is highest, because of the organic matter in the latter.

The solubility and hence the mobility of organic matter in the A horizon is relatively high. According to Kravkov (Ch. 6, 19-20), more than 50 per cent of the 0.08 to 0.1 per cent of solids that may be extracted with water are organic in nature.

An interesting point about the A horizon is its relatively low Ca and relatively high Mg content, particularly in the A_2 horizon. Richard and Chandler (48) have observed the "violent weathering of certain minerals in the A_2 horizon." As to the bases in general, they are released from the profile, even though there is a relative accumulation of the alkaline earths in the B horizon. Some K, Na, Ca, Mg, and Mn are returned to the A horizon by the dying vegetation.

The P content of the A_1, because of the organic forms of P in it, is higher than in the A_2 horizon. In comparison with the B horizon, the A_2 has very much less P.

Pelisek (42) cites data on podzolic soils of Moravia, formed on granite containing 0.01 per cent SnO_2. In the A_1 horizon, the SnO_2 content goes up to 0.05- 0.1 per cent. This indicates the immobility of Sn in the profile under conditions of podzolization. This element can, therefore, serve as a tracer ion in establishing the movement of other elements.

Table 74

Acidity and exchange capacity of a number of podzolic soils in New Jersey

Horizon	Depth of horizon	Reaction		Exchange capacity	Unsaturation (H)	
		H₂O extract	Neutral salt extract			
	cm	pH	pH	m.e.	m.e.	per cent

Sassafras loam

Horizon	Depth	H₂O pH	salt pH	Exch. m.e.	Unsat. m.e.	per cent
A₀	3-4	5.0	3.8	23.30	19.70	88.3
A₁	15	5.2	4.4	5.46	5.14	94.1
A₂	18	5.0	4.4	4.74	4.27	93.6
B	14	5.1	4.4	4.98	4.05	81.3
C		4.9	4.5	5.20	4.05	78.0

Penn silt loam

Horizon	Depth	H₂O pH	salt pH	Exch. m.e.	Unsat. m.e.	per cent
A₀	3-4	5.2	4.3	26.4	18.64	70.6
A₁	12	4.9	4.5	14.1	7.56	53.6
A₂	26	4.8	4.5	10.7	7.56	70.6
B	38	4.9	4.3	11.4	7.56	66.3
C		5.1	4.3	11.2	7.64	68.2

Chester gravelly loam

Horizon	Depth	H₂O pH	salt pH	Exch. m.e.	Unsat. m.e.	per cent
A₀	3-4	6.2	5.0	18.50	5.83	31.5
A₁	12	5.5	4.4	7.19	4.57	63.5
A₂	16	5.4	4.4	6.31	3.46	54.8
B₁	15	5.2	4.4	6.80	4.49	66.0
B₂	43	5.2	4.4	6.61	3.34	50.5
C		5.4	4.6	5.30	2.38	45.0

Washington loam

Horizon	Depth	H₂O pH	salt pH	Exch. m.e.	Unsat. m.e.	per cent
A₀	3-5	7.2	6.8	37.20	1.98	5.3
A₁	21	5.3	4.4	12.00	5.97	50.0
A₂	11	5.1	4.4	8.16	5.37	65.8
B	19	5.3	4.4	6.24	3.19	51.1
C		5.4	4.8	5.03	2.20	43.7

Lakewood sand (normal profile)

Horizon	Depth	H₂O pH	salt pH	Exch. m.e.	Unsat. m.e.	per cent
A₁	13	4.8	4.4	3.00	2.00	66.6
A₂	25	4.8	4.8	0.77	0.55	71.4
B₁	20	5.1	5.0	2.74	2.60	94.8
B₂	35	5.2	5.0	2.74	2.55	93.0
C		5.2	5.2	0.64	0.50	78.1

Lakewood sand (dwarf profile)

Horizon	Depth	H₂O pH	salt pH	Exch. m.e.	Unsat. m.e.	per cent
A₁	5	4.2	3.4	11.5	9.55	83.0
A₂	15	4.6	4.2	1.8	1.05	60.0
B₁	5	4.9	4.6	7.2	6.50	90.0
B₂	7	5.0	4.8	6.6	6.30	95.0
C		5.2	5.0	1.8	1.20	66.0

The B Horizon.—Chemically, this horizon is distinguished by the relatively low SiO_2 content, high sesquioxide content, relative increase of bases and exchange capacity, and lowering of unsaturation. The B_1 horizon frequently contains more organic matter than the A_2 horizon. This horizon has a high clay content which is generally kaolinitic in nature, although in some cases, where the parent material is high in bases, some montmorillonitic-like minerals have been reported. The work of Coleman and Jackson (7) are of interest in this connection. They demonstrate montmorillinite in some of the soils in the zone of podzolization.

The sesquioxide content is also generally highest in the B horizon, although in some soils the accumulation of Al is not absolute, as shown by Marbut (Ch. 8, 13). In the B horizon, some of the R_2O_3 is in combination with organic matter. It is very likely that the organo-mineral gels, as pictured by Tyulin (Ch. 6, 68), hold the bulk of the R_2O_3 that may be extracted by the oxalate method and its modifications, like the one by Jeffries (20). According to Lundblad (30) and Gemmerling (15), the B horizon has the highest amount of gels. The quantity of R_2O_3 in the profile may thus serve as an index of the degree of podzolization, a low content indicating a low degree of podzolization and vice versa.

Limonite and gibbsite are the usual forms of R_2O_3 in the B horizon. They frequently serve as cementing materials for ortstein and concretion formations. Manganese also accumulates in the B horizon and behaves in general like the other R_2O_3 constituents. Udulft (64) has shown that organic matter and negative maganese behave alike towards carbonates and bicarbonates. Winters (69) presents data on ferromanganiferous concretions in some podzolic soils. As to the P, it is known that most of the P that passes the A horizon becomes fixed in the B horizon, primarily as phosphates of R_2O_3. Appreciable quantities of P accumulate in the A_0 layer, primarily in organic forms.

Ortstein, or Hardpan, and Concretion Formations.—Ortstein and concretion formations are usually associated with the B horizon of podzols. Very few podzols, however, show ortstein or concretion formations. Therefore, they are not to be looked upon as inherent to the process of podzolization.

Ortstein has been known for a long time. Müller (Ch. 5, 70) distinguished three fundamental groups: (a) ortstein due to washing in of fine particles, (b) ortstein formed by adsorption of organic matter and iron, and (c) ortstein of a concretional origin. In the last group, Müller placed also a type of bog iron formation. Hilgard (Ch. 2, 30, p. 184) associated hardpan formation with the deposition of iron, clay, and humus. An extensive discussion on ortstein may be found in the work of Weis (68) on the podzols in Denmark. He stresses the point of the high nitrogen content of ortstein. As higs as 0.29 per cent N (an average of 10 profiles) is found in the humus hardpan and 0.06 per cent in iron hardpan.

PLATE 26

Ortstein veins in a podzol soil

(After Krasyuk)

Ramann identified podzols with pan formation. According to him (Ch. 3, 53, p. 69) : "The pan is a layer of the soil cemented together by organic substances and since the podzols are preponderately sandy soils, this is a humus sandstone. Soft, easily friable pans may be termed earthly pans' (Orterde)." He (Ch. 2, 60, p. 167) differentiated three forms of ortstein: (a) *Branderde* which forms a mass rich in organic matter but not cemented together, (b) *ortstein hard as a rock,* dark brown to black, with an average content of organic matter, encountered in the northern part of

Germany, and (c) *a dark brown ortstein, very hard,* containing a small amount of organic matter, usually very thick, and overlain by a softer and lighter layer.

Warrington (67) pointed out that humic acids dissolve the iron which precipitates in its downward movement on sand, forming iron pan. An extensive study of podzols and of ortstein formation was made by Tamm (61). He considers ortstein as unweathered material cemented with colloids, primarily iron (limonite) and organic matter. Ortstein rich in organic matter is soft, whereas that rich in iron is hard.

Chemical analyses of ortstein and orterde are presented by Lundblad (30) in connection with his investigation of the podzols in the coniferous forests and degraded brown earths in the beech forests of southern Sweden. A fact brought out in his work is that the inorganic gel content of ortstein formation is relatively small when compared with the organic colloids.

A discussion of the work of Tamm and Lundblad, as well as of the more important investigations on ortstein formation, is given by Stremme (60). He quotes van Bemmelen, who designated ortstein "as a cementing of the sand particles with colloidal humus, silicic acid, aluminum and iron oxide complexes, and some clay fractions."

According to Aarnio (3), the process of ortstein formation is to be identified with the movement of the sesquioxides and organic matter from the surface horizons into the lower ones. The iron and aluminum move as sols protected by organic substances and by silicic acid sols, as well as by the cations Ca, Mg, K, Na, and the anions SO_4, PO_4 and CO_3. If there is little organic matter, iron-ortstein poor in organic matter forms; with large amounts, the organic matter-iron-ortstein poor in iron forms. The precipitation of sesquioxides is homogeneous throughout the mass of sandy soils. In loam and clay soils, they precipitate in cracks and tracks of roots whereby concretions are formed. The relation between the parent material and ortstein formation has been investigated by Münst (39) and by Helbig (18).

Stremme (60, p. 134) discusses the influence of ortstein formation and podzolization on forest growth and the relationships between podzolization and type of vegetation. He quotes Hazard (17) who shows that under certain conditions ortstein is an asset to the physical conditions of the soil. He also quotes Hausrath (16) in this connection. Tamm (61) concludes that podzol and ortstein formation are of no great significance from the forestry standpoint. An examination of an experimental area of white pine plantations in South Jersey by the author has revealed that the deterioration of many trees could be ascribed to the shallow rooting as a result of hardpan formation.

Emeis (12) attempted to approach the subject of ortstein formation experimentally. He filled several cylinders with quartz sand, added the various constituents which make up the ortstein, and percolated daily a humus extract through it. He succeeded in forming a humus-iron ortstein by the reaction of the sesquioxides, humus, and lime. Filatov (13) passed colloidal solutions of the iron hydroxide through columns of quartz sand with intermediate thin layers of fine quartz (0.05-0.001 mm). He found that only the fine quartz became colored with iron. Intermediate layers of finely ground minerals (orthoclase, biotite) exhibited a still larger retentive power for the iron.

Skeen (57) defined hardpan as "that stratum found at varying depths below the surface composed of 'clay' and sands, more or less cemented by precipitated Fe, Al, and sometimes organic compounds. He correlated hardpan formation with the hydrogen-ion concentration of the medium; he found hardpan in clay soils whenever the pH was 4.8 and conducted experiments showing how $Fe(OH)_3$ precipitated on kaolin at that particular pH. In a second paper, Skeen (58) advanced a theory on the formation of hardpan acid clay soils: if the reaction of the upper layers of the soil were acid enough to bring into solution Fe and Al, hardpan might form.

The limited observations of Skeen should not have been generalized. As a matter of fact, almost all the soils in the podzol zone, except where the parent material is limestone, are sufficiently acid to dissolve some Fe and Al, but still not all podzols, even those of clay texture, have an ortstein or hardpan layer. It is well established now that podzol and ortstein formation do not run parallel.

Summarizing the work of Western European and Russian investigators on ortstein formation. Glinka (Ch. 2, 27, p. 325) points out that "horizon A_2 becomes impoverished of bases and sesquioxides, when compared with the parent material, and ortstein becomes enriched with the sesquioxides and manganese, *but not always with bases, except magnesium.* Ortstein decomposes more rapidly than the parent material in HCl solution. The solubility of alumina in ortstein increases very markedly."

Polynov (44) investigated mineralogically and chemically the new formations in ortstein. He found a mineral of the palygorskite type, a magnesium aluminum silicate. Apparently, this is the source of magnesium which is so frequently encountered in ortstein.

Gemmerling (15) demonstrated the presence of free aluminum hydroxide in ortstein concretions, which is in accord with the theory of Gedroiz (Ch. 9, 27) that in the podzol soils some portions of the aluminum silicate nucleus are decomposed.

At times, ortstein formation appears in the profile, primarily in weakly podzolized soils, as narrow winding bands of a dark brown iron-like color.

These bands were studied by Vysotskii (65,66), who designated them *pseudofibers*.

A review of the problem of pan formation was given by Jones, Trefor, and Wilcox (28). They discused some of the earlier theories and presented some experimental evidence on the process of pan formation. Extractions were made, with dilute solutions of tartaric or oxalic acid, of soils from several podzol profiles. The extract from the A horizon was filtered, a portion sampled for analysis, and the rest used for the extraction of the soil from the B horizon. This was filtered, sampled for analysis, and the remainder used for the extraction of the soil from the C horizon. The data obtained show that the sesquioxides went into solution in the A horizon and precipitated in the B horizon. It was suggested that the sesquioxides enter "into the electro-negative portion of the molecule, since soil organic acids consist largely of hydroxy acids, and these acids dissolve in the sesquioxides to form salts of the type Fe_2R_3. Fe_2O_3. These compounds are then leached through the soil in solution and are ultimately precipitated as basic salts, giving rise to a zone of sesquioxide accumulation and finally to a pan."

Concretions are another type of ortstein. They are usually encountered in clay podzols, at the bottom of the A_2 and on top of the B horizon. They contain variable amounts of organic matter (greater than in the surrounding soil material), iron, and manganese. The paper of Drosdoff and Nikiforoff (9) on iron-manganese concretions is of interest in this connection. The Fe_2O_3 content varies from 8 to 25 per cent and the MnO content—from 0.5 to 6.0 per cent.

According to Tumin (Ch. 2, 82) :

Ortstein is encountered in soils of sandy parent material only; on loams, concretions (iron and maganese) in the form of grains or complexes of grains are apparent. And even on sands ortstein is not always found. The same may be said about concretions on loams. Thus, ortstein and concretions do not accompany all podzolized soils. They appear only under special conditions.

It is of interest that ortstein is always found at the boundary between horizons A and B. This is not true for concretions which are found throughout the profile. In the southeastern portion of the zone (on sands), ortstein is found also in the depressions. In the northwestern portion, orstein gradually appears as we go from the deep depression to the level topography.

In general, the facts indicate that ortstein and concretions have formed by a process of change in the oxidation system of the soil.

Bystrov (4) discusses the process of ortstein formation and presents extensive data on its composition. He accepts the view of the Swedish investigators on the types of ortstein. One is *allochtonic*, a formation similar to bog iron. It is the result of the accumulation of iron oxide moving downward and of ferrous iron moving upward and oxidizing as it strikes the layer above the water table. The second type of ortstein is *autochtonic*, formed exclusively by the downward movement of iron which precipitates in the horizon of illuviation. Bystrov adheres to the theory on the micro-biological origin of the allochtonic type of ortstein.

SANDY PROFILES ON COASTAL PLAIN OF NEW JERSEY

On the sandy soils of the Coastal Plain in New Jersey, mapped under the name *Lakewood sand* (these sandy soils extend all through the Coastal Plain down into the subtropical Florida), typical podzols have developed. Soils of a similar texture in the same geographic-physiographic area, mapped under the name Sassafras sand, have not developed the typical podzol profile. It has been shown by Joffe (22, 23) that the difference be-tween the two soils is the higher Ca content in the parent material of the Sassafras series. In table 75, the total analyses and the exchange properties of two Lakewood profiles are presented.

The podzolic nature of these profiles and the typical chemical character-istics of podzols, as outlined earlier, are very well illustrated by the data. An interesting point to be noted in profile 1 is the more rapid removal and movement of Al in comparison with Fe. This, of course, is due to the higher isoelectric pH of Al, as pointed out by Mattson (Ch. 4, 46). From a slightly different view point this has been brought out by Joffe and McLean (26) and Joffe (21).

The high C:N ratio of the A_1 and A_2 in profile 2 and of A_1 in profile 1 is due, in large measure, to the charcoal prevalent in the pine barrens (Pinus rigida) of New Jersey and other regions of the Coastal Plain fre-quented by forest fires. Charcoal was found in the A_2 of profile 2, but not of profile 1.

An outstanding feature of the organic matter distribution in profile 1 is its increase in the B horizon. This increase is controlled by the presence of other electrolytes and by the pH. Apparently, the pH in B is the isoelectric pH for the precipitation of higher amounts of humates. According to Matt-son (Ch. 4, 46), at lower pH values, a smaller proportion of R_2O_3 is required for high organic matter fixation. An increase in pH should release some humates. This was the case when the soil was treated with a neutral salt at pH 7.0, to determine unsaturation.

True to form, horizon C has a very low organic matter content, but some of the highly dispersed organic materials do move into it. Undoubtedly, some organic complexes become more soluble at increased pH environments, occurring sometimes during the fall season, as pointed out elsewhere (24). These finely dispersed organic materials are high in nitrogen, which perhaps will explain the extremely high N content of the organic matter in horizon

Table 75

Total chemical analyses of Lakewood and profiles

1. Normal profile

Horizon and depth	SiO_2	Fe_2O_3	Al_2O_3	CaO	MgO	K_2O	C	N	C:N
cm.	per cent	per cent	per cent	per cent	per cent	per cent	per cent	per cent	ratio
A_1: 13	97.16	1.3	0.407	0.118	0.0723	0.225	0.750	0.0156	48.3
A_2: 25	98.12	1.1	0.315	0.121	0.0795	0.200	0.118	0.0078	15.2
B_1: 20	93.32	1.9	2.50	0.124	0.1122	0.340	0.550	0.0231	23.8
B_2: 35	93.40	1.9	2.65	0.143	0.1157	0.365	0.430	0.0241	17.8
C :	95.97	1.35	2.09	0.203	0.1447	0.415	0.090	0.0085	10.6
2. Dwarf profile									
A_1: 5.0	90.50	0.72	1.25	0.123	0.119		4.22	0.103	40.9
A_2: 15.0	97.00	0.69	1.07	0.076	—		0.79	0.009	87.7
B_1: 5.0	90.10	1.23	4.02	0.089	0.116		1.33	0.041	32.4
B_2: 7.0	89.00	1.66	4.65	0.054	0.101		1.21	0.044	27.5
C : 61.0*	94.10	1.01	2.88	0.056	0.105		0.27	0.008	33.8

*The light yellow sand rests upon a heavy clay layer.

C. Dispersion may also occur in the spring when the acidity of the soil is at its peak, and the electrolyte content is low.

The A_1 is, as pointed out, contaminated with charcoal. This, of course, makes the total organic matter content appear somewhat higher than it actually is. It also reduces the percentage of N in the organic matter. The low organic matter content in A_2 is resonable, in view of the fact that in this horizon most of the destructive or decomposition reactions take place in the podzol process of soil formation. Morphologically, one could hardly recognize the organic matter in A_2. Charring the apparently white bleached sand turns it black, indicating the presence of organic matter, and the chemical analyses prove this. There is, however, a difference in the type of organic matter in each horizon. This is especially reflected in A_2, where the organic matter is colorless and probably, as suggested by Williams (Ch. 3, 72), of the crenic and apocrenic acid type, which contains 3 to 4 per cent N. This might explain the high N content in the organic matter of this horizon. It is very likely that the organic matter here is highly contaminated with fungus mycelium (fungus mycelium contains from 4 to 6 per cent nitrogen), since the reaction environment is unfavorable for bacterial activity and favorable for fungi.

The high organic matter content in B is accompanied by a high percentage of N. The B_2 is higher in N than the B_1. As explained in connection with the discussion on organic matter in horizon C, it is the degree of dispersion that controls the N content. The more finely dispersed particles are of a higher N content, and, with an increase in depth of the profile through B, there is an increase in the fineness of the particles. Edington and Adams (11) present results showing an enrichment of N in the B horizon of the podzol which they studied.

The total N content of the podzol soil under consideration follow the trend of the R_2O_3 or of the organic matter: it is lowest in A_2, increases in B, and drops in C. The N content of A_1 is comparatively low because of the absence of an A_0 layer which usually increases the total organic matter content of this horizon. Under normal conditions, in the presence of an A_0 layer, the percentage of N in the organic matter is, as a rule, low in A_1, but its total N is high because of the high organic matter content. In this case, the results are obscured by the presence of charcoal, of which mention was made. The high C:N ratio in C of profile 2 is difficult to account for. If we discount the factor of the charcoal in profile 2, the tendency toward accumulation of organic matter in B is also noted in this profile. The same is true if we critically analyze the N content which tends to be high in B, corroborating the analytical results of profile 1. In general, profile 2 shows a higher total organic matter and N content than profile 1. These contituents follow the increase in R_2O_3, which corroborates the point made in this connection in the discussion of profile 1.

Colloid Fraction of Profile 2.—The colloids of the various horizons were extracted and subjected to partial analyses, with the purpose of establishing relationships which might illustrate some reactions in the process of podzolization in a typical mature podzol.

The method of preparing the colloid was practically the same as that of the Bureau of Soils, United States Department of Agriculture. The samples were put through a 2-mm. sieve which allowed almost everything to pass except large woody particles. A 5-kgm. quantity from each horizon was placed into a 3-gallon bottle, 8 liters of distilled water added, and the reaction adjusted, by addition of 0.1 N NaOH, to be alkaline to litmus. The suspension was shaken vigorously and then allowed to stand for 24 hours, after which half of it was decanted, water and NaOH were added again, shaken, left standing 24 hours, and decanted again. This operation was repeated six times. The decanted suspensions were centrifuged, the colloids precipitated with $CaCl_2$, filtered through Chamberlain "F" filters, washed with H_2O, and dried on a steam bath. The dried material was ground in a mortar for analysis.

SiO_2:R_2O_3.—Table 76 gives the analyses on the colloid fraction. As is to be expected, the ratio is highest in the horizon of eluviation and lowest in the horizon of illuviation. The low pH in A indicates a destructive acid hydrolysis, whereby the sesquioxides are lost and the SiO_2 accumulates, as shown in the columns on the SiO_2, Al_2O_3, and Fe_2O_3 content of the colloids.

It is questionable whether the increase in the ratio of SiO_2: R_2O_3 in the colloid should be ascribed entirely to the colloidal complex. Undoubtedly, some of the SiO_2 is not chemically combined with the sesquioxides as in the complex. There must be a certain limit for the quantity of SiO_2 which makes up the highest SiO_2:R_2O_3 ratio beyond which the SiO_2 is free and inactive. In his studies on the relation of cation exchange capacity to the SiO_2:R_2O_3 ratio, Cziky[*] points out that when this ratio passes the value of 7.0, the exchange capacity begins to drop. This may be offered as further proof that there is free SiO_2 mixed with the complex and hence such a high ratio. What apparently happens is that in the decomposition of the clay nuclei, SiO_2 is released, but it remains behind in the A horizon. Some of it, in the process of colloid extraction, appears with the colloid complex, thereby increasing the SiO_2:R_2O_3 ratio.

If we accept the SiO_2:R_2O_3 ratio in C as a basis of comparison, and remember that only small amounts of amorphous SiO_2 penetrate beyond the B horizon, then the ratio in B_1 and B_2 becomes significant. The oppositely charged R_2O_3 and SiO_2 colloids released by the forces of the podzol process

---

[*]Cziky, J. S. 1932. Base exchange studies. Personal communication from author.

Table 76
Colloid fraction of profile 2

Horizon	SiO_2	Fe_2O_3	Al_2O_3	$\dfrac{SiO_2}{R_2O_3}$	N	C	Ignition loss	Organic matter*	$\dfrac{C}{N}$ ratio	N in organic matter	Cation exchange
	per cent	per cent	per cent	molar	per cent	per cent	per cent	per cent		per cent	m.e.
A$_1$	74.00	2.23	14.02	8.15	0.720	18.9	37.0	32.60	27.0	2.2	85.4
A$_2$	79.00	2.06	14.09	8.75	0.259	4.1	44.6	7.10	15.8	3.5	33.6
B$_1$	45.40	11.69	35.81	1.79	0.456	7.1	23.9	12.24	15.6	3.7	65.4
B$_2$	43.20	10.84	21.86	2.55	0.362	7.1	23.4	12.24	19.6	3.0	39.0
C	45.60	10.15	21.67	2.76	0.164	1.36	14.6	2.34	8.3	7.0	21.8

of soil formation meet at B to become discharged and mutually coagulated, giving rise to new formations. The disrupted mineral complexes from A_1 and A_2, because of the same forces, attain colloidal dimensions and move downward to be "filtered" out in B. All of this makes the colloid fraction of the B horizon more representative and less liable to foreign colloidal intrusions, except perhaps for some free Al_2O_3 and Fe_2O_3, and, therefore, the $SiO_2:R_2O_2$ ratio is closer to that of the soil colloid fraction. As we compare the ratios of C and B, we note that in the latter it is narrowing. The limited supply of bases in the soil material and the low pH are conducive to such a medium ratio, becoming narrower as the sesquioxides appear in a medium of a higher base content or of a higher pH.

The low Fe_2O_3 content in A_1 is indicative of the thorough podzolization of the soil under consideration. Itis of interest that less Al_2O_3 than Fe_2O_3 has disappeared from the colloidal complex in A, as compared with C. It is probable that there is some return movement of Al_2O_3 because of the underlying geologic deposits and through the vegetation.

Organic Matter and N Content.—The data on the organic matter of the colloid fraction is more instructive than of the total organic matter, especially of the A_1 horizon where large amounts of charcoal obscure the true picture of the organic matter in the soil. The method used in dispersing the colloids does not in all probability affect the charcoal, and the organic matter content of the colloid fraction is, therefore, more representative.

The data show that the percentage of N in the organic matter of the colloid fraction is high in A_2. What makes the C horizon so high in N is difficult to explain, except that the method of dispersion brings into the extract the very fine particles of the organic matter which are, as a rule, higher in N.

Closely related to the organic matter content is, of course, the C:N ratio which in profile 2 is rather narrow as compared with that of the total soil analysis. The charcoal factor, of course, needs to be considered in this connection. Besides, the method of dispersion does not apparently bring in all of the organic matter but leaves a residue high in carbon and low in N. Only the fine particles that are higher in N enter into play. The narrower C:N ratio seems to prove this.

There is not as close a relation between the organic matter and the R_2O_3 in the colloid fraction, as there is in the total soil analysis. Again, this is probably due to the incomplete dispersion of the organic matter.

The data on the loss on ignition do not compare at all favorably with the data on the total organic matter. This discrepancy must be sought in the errors involved in the procedure of "the loss on ignition" rather than in the factor 1.724 which is used for converting carbon into organic matter and which may be perhaps too low, especially for the colloids where a high amount of organic matter is found. A discussion on the reliability of this factor has been presented by Lunt (32).

The data on the total N in the colloid fraction show the eluviation condition of A_2, the accumulation in B, and the drop again in C. These are characteristic features of the constitution of a mature podzol.

Cation Exchange Capacity.—The cation exchange of the colloid fraction varies in the profile. The tendency is for a decrease in A_2 (the high capacity of A_1 is due to the large amount of organic matter), an increase in B, and a decrease in C. A similar tendency was noted in the analyses of the total soil.

General Discussion

The similarity of the two profiles discussed in the preceding pages consists in their maturity and in the clear-cut differentiation of horizons, with all the characteristic morphological features of a mature podzol. The chemical analyses corroborate the morphological features. There is, however, one distinctive difference between the two profiles: profile 1 is 93 cm. and profile 2 only 32 cm. deep, the soil body being figured from the surface to the bottom of the B horizon. As pointed out, the shallowness of profile 2 is due to the underlying geologic deposits of clay. Here is a case where the parent material inhibited the growth of the soil body. All other factors being equal, with the exception of the clay deposition where profile 2 developed, the forces of the climate and vegetation produced a deep soil body in one case and a stunted soil body in the other.

In speaking of the maturity of the profiles, it is worth while to take notice of the similarity in composition of B_1 and B_2. This similarity indicates an equilibrium condition with respect to the formation of the horizon of illuviation. The natural course of the growth of this horizon is from the bottom up, and the homogeneity, as far as the chemical composition is concerned, is evidence of the completion of the process.

The value of total chemical analyses of soil has been repeatedly questioned. However, from the pedogenic point of view, total analyses are a great aid in elucidating the reactions that take place in the processes of soil formation. This has been brought out in the data on the total analyses of the soils, and has been corroborated by the analyses of the colloid fraction which shed no more light on what is going on in the soil than did the total analyses, except for the important property of the $SiO_2 : R_2O_3$ ratio in the colloid fraction, especially in the B horizon. Probably, if the technique of colloid extraction is improved, the analyses may mean more. As they are, they supplement very effectively the data on the total analyses.

It may be opportune to consider again the role of organic matter in the process of podzolization. Apparently, the process of podzolization is to a large extent intimately related to the speed of decomposition and quantity of organic matter. A too rapid destruction of the organic matter depresses the reactivity efficiency of the split products, since under such conditions the organic acids produced are usually decomposed to the so-called "mineralized state." The result is that the role of the organic acids is reduced to a minimum.

In soils undergoing the process of podzolization, some bases and sesquioxides combine with the humates and move downward to enter again into a reaction (depending on a number of factors, especially the pH) with SiO_3, forming new Al and Fe silicate complexes. The work of Mattson (Ch. 4, 46-48) on the behavior of the anions with respect to the sesquioxides in acid and alkaline media, or rather on the acid and alkaline side of the isoelectric precipitates, promises to uncover the fundamental principles of this process.

In the belts north of the true podzol belt, the organic matter, as a rule, does not undergo such rapid decomposition and does not, therefore, mineralize so fast. Under such conditions, the percolation element of podzolization dominates the process, and, of course, the lighter soils are more thoroughly and efficiently leached. The result is that in these belts, the lighter soils become more rapidly podzolized than the heavier soils.

The considerations presented open the question of the role of organic matter in the process of podzolization from an entirely new angle. We are not concerned so much now with empirical studies of the early investigators on the relative importance of the hypothetical crenic, apocrenic, and humic acids in the soil profile; we are concerned in learning how the various organic substances which form humates behave. The work of Mattson (Ch. 4, 46) on the isoelectric precipitates of the sesquioxides, under various conditions of pH and electrolyte content, and on the anion exchange relation with respect to humates, offers an approach to the study of organic matter distribution in the soil profile of the podzol zone.

Odd Facts on Podzolization.—Moss (38) presents data on a number of podzol profiles in Saskatchewan. These soils have a well developed bleached A_2 horizon, laminar structure at the bottom of it, an accumulation of R_2O_3 in the B horizon. Still, the pH throughout the 5 profiles reported on ranges from 6.5 to 8.1, and in one of the peat podzols it is 7.1, even in the A_2 horizon. True enough, the glacial drift parent material carries debris of limestone origin, but, in the zone of podzolization, this type of parent material with the profile characteristics reported above would have either a low pH, or it would develop into a Braunerde of Ramann or some form of rendzina. It is to be noted that the forest cover persists at an annual precipitation not higher than 15 inches. In short, the anomalies are so outstanding that one is at a loss to explain the podzolic characteristics. There is, however, the possibility of an ancient solodi persisting for one reason or another. More data on the water table and composition of the ground waters, as well as an analysis of the exchangeable cations, would perhaps decipher the puzzle.

An interesting observation was reported by Yarkov (70) on the movement of Fe and Mn. Under conditions of forests, these elements move in the trivalent state, whereas under conditions of meadows, they move in the more soluble divalent state. Both forms of R_2O_3 appear occasionally in either one of the environments.

The circulation of calcium controls in a large measure the pH of the medium, and the two in turn influence the level of organic matter in the profile. Among the more recent publications on this subject are those of Chandler (5) and Zaitsev (72).

An experimental approach in the study of the process of podzolization has been attempted by Kachinskaya (29). She removed the podzolized horizon and replaced it with material from other zonal soils. After 12 years, definite changes in the direction of podzolization were noted.

An interesting contribution on the time required for podzol profile formation is that of Chandler (Ch. 5, 13). He studied soils exposed 15, 90, 250, and 1000 years by the receding Mendenhall glacier near Juneau, Alaska. The weak point of this study is the assumption that the variations in texture are primarily due to the age of the soil. The peat-like podzol character of the soils examined is not brought out and its possible significance not evaluated.

Summary Statement.—In general, the process of podzolization results in the depletion of the alkali and alkaline earth bases from the A_1 and more so from the A_2 horizon. The reason for the difference is due to the higher organic matter content of the A_1 horizon and hence a higher cation adsorption capacity. On parent material rich in bases, the return of these through the vegetation contributes to the differential distribution of the bases in the profile. Some recent developments on this phase are discussed by Ivanova (19). The type of vegetation, whether rich or poor in bases, may also be a factor.

With the depletion of bases, the sesquioxides and clay particles enter into circulation, move downward and accumulate in the profile to form the

Table 77
Podzol on stony loam
(After Rode)

Horizon and depth	Organic matter	Percentage composition of mineral portion				
		SiO_2	$Al_2O_3 + P_2O_5$	Fe_2O_3	CaO	MgO
cm.	*per cent*					
A$_1$ 5-10	6.05	84.53	8.88	1.88	0.60	0.40
A$_2$ 20-25	0.23	85.03	8.92	1.70	0.66	0.34
B$_1$ 30-35	0.18	80.83	10.45	3.40	0.63	0.68
B$_2$ 40-45	0.16	78.12	11.99	4.66	0.62	1.03
B$_2$ 60-65	0.10	77.38	11.98	4.33	0.79	0.98
C 95-100	0.09	77.09	12.48	3.85	0.90	0.95

(Continued on page 382)

Table 78

Strongly podzolized soil on clay

(After Rode)

Horizon and depth	Organic matter	Percentage composition of the mineral portion									
		SiO₂	SO₃	P₂O₅	Al₂O₃	Fe₂O₃	CaO	MgO	K₂O	Na₂O
cm.	*per cent*									
A₁ 5-10	4.31	75.58	0.02	0.10	13.36	4.30	0.90	1.27	2.94	1.17
A₂ 15-20	0.92	75.12	0.02	0.05	13.34	4.60	0.85	1.42	3.10	1.21
B₁ 25-30	0.39	71.83	0.02	0.06	18.27	5.62	0.82	1.71	3.28	1.20
B₂ 40-45	0.30	66.59	0.03	0.01	18.10	7.16	0.91	2.06	3.45	1.26
B₂ 50-60	0.16	65.67	0.02	0.01	18.79	7.17	1.27	2.31	3.50	1.21
C 80-90	0.10	65.25	0.02	0.01	18.88	7.27	1.35	2.34	3.50	1.42

(Continued on page 382)

Table 77
(*Continued*)

Podzol on stony loam

(After Rode)

Particles <0.01 mm.	Absorbed cations, m.e. per 100 gms.				pH
	H	Ca	Mg	Exchange capacity	
34.08	18.40	0.32	0.35	19.07	4.01
30.59	1.60	0.29	0.35	2.24	4.96
——	2.30	0.71	0.30	3.31	5.13
37.59	3.50	3.22	1.90	8.62	5.15
——	1.90	6.39	3.30	11.59	5.37
37.81	0.50	5.32	2.55	8.37	6.91

Table 78
(*Continued*)

Strongly podzolized soil on clay

(After Rode)

Particles <0.01 mm.	Absorbed cations, m.e. per 100 gms.				pH
	H	Ca	Mg	Exchange capacity	
per cent					
67.87	5.50	7.42	6.30	19.22	5.65
70.51	0.80	3.50	2.45	6.75	5.67
——	1.00	4.00	3.25	8.25	5.71
78.85	0.40	9.04	8.15	17.59	6.39
——	0.40	13.49	8.95	22.84	——
80.41	0.40	13.49	8.70	22.59	7.26

B horizon and give it its characteristic properties. The absorptive power of the clay causes the retention of some alkaline earth bases which in turn enhance the precipitation of the sesquioxides.

Tables 77 - 78, taken from the voluminous data of Rode's papers (49-52), give a summarized picture of the process of podzolization as presented in the foregoing pages.

References

1. Aaltonen, V. T. 1939 Zur Stratigraphie des Podsolprofils. II *Communicak. Inst. Forestalis Fenniae* 27, 4: 1-133.
2. Aarnio, B. 1913 The precipitation of iron in podzol soils. *Inter. Mitt. Bodenk.* 3: 131-140.
3. Aarnio, B. 1915 The precipitation of the oxides of iron and aluminum from sandy and gravelly soil of Finland. *Pochvovedenie* (Pedology) 17 (2): 1-50.
4. Bystrov, S. V. 1936 Contributions on the process of podzolization. Trudy Pochven. Inst. imeni Dokuchaeva 13: 163-211 (Extensive English summary).
5. Chandler, R. F. 1937 A study of certain calcium relationships and base exchange properties of forest soils. *Jour. For.* 35: 27-32.
6. Coile, T. S. 1937 Composition of leaf litter of forest trees. *Soil Sci.* 43: 349-355.
7. Coleman, R. and Jackson, M. L. 1945 Mineral composition of several Coastal Plain soils of southeastern United States. *Proc. Soil Sci. Soc. Amer.* 10: 381-391.
8. Dobrovol'skii, M. 1900 The nature of origin of podzols according to our present knowledge of soil science. *Materialy po izuchenii rushkikh pochv.* Bul. 13: 1-48.
9. Drosdoff, M. and Nikiforoff, C. C. 1940 Iron manganese concretions in Dayton soils. *Soil Sci.* 49: 333-345.
10. Dzens-Litovskaya, N. N. 1946 Ash composition of the forest vegetation of the Savalsk forest-steppe. *Pedology* (U.S.S.R.) No. 4: 209-216.
11. Edington, S. and Adams, J. R. 1925 Distribution of N in the podzol profile. *Soil Sci.* 20: 177-179.
12. Emeis, C. 1908 Die Ursachen der Ortsteinbildung und ihr Einfluss auf die Landeskultur in Schleswig-Holstein. *Vereinsblatt des Heidekultur-Vereins für Schl.-Holstein,* 9-20 (Quoted from Zakharov).
13. Filatov, M. 1922 On the problem of the genesis of ortsand. *Russki pochvoved.* No. 1-3.
14. Gallagher, P. H. 1942 The mobile colloidal humus of podzolic soils and its relationship to the process of podzolization. *Proc. Royal Irish Acad.* 48B: 213-229.

15. Gemmerling, V. V. 1922 Some data which characterize podzol soils. *Russkii pochvoved.* No. 4-5.

16. Hausrath, H. 1907 Der Deutsche Wald. Leipzig.

17. Hazard J. 1907 (?) Bericht über eine Anfang des Sommers 1907 behufs bodenkundlicher Untersuchungen nach Nordwestdeutschland unternommenen Reise (Unveröffentlicht: Quoted from Stremme (60, p. 101)).

18. Helbig, M. 1909 Uber Orstein in Gebiete des Granits. *Naturw. Zeitschr. Forst. u. Landw.* pp. 1-8 (Quoted from Stremme).

19. Ivanova, E. N. 1946 On the separation of subzones in the podzol zone of the Pre-Urals. *Pedology* (U.S.S.R.) No. 3-4: 162-174.

20. Jeffries, Ch. D. 1946 A rapid method for the removal of free iron oxides in soil prior to petrographic analysis. *Proc. Soil Sci. Soc. Amer.* 11 :211-212.

21. Joffe, J. S. 1930 Experiments on the movement of Fe and Al in the soil. Paper presented before the 2nd Commission, Second Inter. Cong. Soil Sci. *Proc. of the Second Inter. Cong. Soil Sci.* 2: 136-145.

22. Joffe, J. S. 1931 Soil profile studies: III. The process of podzolization. *Soil Sci.* 32: 303-323.

23. Joffe, J. S. 1932 Soil profile studies: IV. Morphological and chemical evidence of podzolization. Soil Sci. 33: 217-237.

24. Joffe, J. S. 1932 Lysimeter studies: II. The movement and translocation of soil constituents in the soil profile. *Soil Sci.* 35: 239-257.

25. Joffe, J. S. 1937 A pedologic study of some soils in New Jersey. *Soil Sci.* 43: 221-238.

26. Joffe, J. S. and McLean, H. C. 1928 Colloidal behavior of soils and soil fertiilty: IV. Anion effect on the precipitation reactions and degrees of dispersion of Fe and Al hydroxides. *Soil Sci.* 26: 47-59: V. The distribution of soluble and colloidal iron and aluminum in soils. *Soil Sci.* 26: 317-325.

27. Joffe, J. S. and Watson, C. W. 1933 Soil profile studies: V. Mature podzols. *Soil Sci.* 35: 313-331.

28. Jones, H. Trefor, and Wilcox, J. S. 1929 Studies in soil genetics: I. *Journ. Soc. Chem. Indus.* 48: 304T-308T.

29. Kachinskaya, E. S. 1937 On the speed of the soil forming process under conditions of the podzol zone. *Pedology* (U.S.S.R) No. 7: 721-728.

30. Lundblad, K. 1924 See reference 54, Ch. 9.

31. Lundblad, K. 1934 Studies on podzol and brown forest soils. I. *Soil Sci.* 37: 137-155, II. 41: 295-313 (1936).

32. Lunt, Herbert A. 1931 The carbon-organic matter factor in forest soil humus. *Soil Sci.* 32: 27-36.

33. Mattson, Sante. 1932 The laws of soil colloidal behavior: VII. Proteins and proteinated complexes. *Soil Sci.* 33: 41-72.

34. Mattson, Sante. 1933 The laws of soil colloidal behavior: XI. Electrodialysis in relation to soil processes. *Soil Sci.* 36: 149-163.

35. Mattson, S. and Gustafson, Y. 1934 The chemical characteristics of soil profiles. I: The podzol. *Ann. Agr. College,* Sweden. v. 1: 33-68; II. The mutual interaction of podzolic materials, v.2: 1-30 (1935); III. (in collaboration with Nilsson) The podzol complex. v.2 (1935) : 115-

36. Mattson, S. and Lönnemark, H. 1939 The pedography of hydrologic podzol series. I. Loss on ignition, pH and amphoteric reactions. *Ann. Agr. College,* Sweden, v.7: 185-227; II (in collaboration with Lönnemark and Wiklander). The loss on ignition and the reacaction of the Annerstad series, v.8 (1940): 183-207; III (in collaboration with Larsen) : Loss on ignition and pH of the Dala brown earth series, v.9 (1941) : 222-238; IV (in collaboration with Bengtsson and Karlsson): The distribution of Si, Fe, Al, Ti, Mn, Ca, and Mg in podzol and brown earth series, v.11 (1943): 172-189; V The distribution of K and P and the Ca/K ratios in relation to the Donnan equilibrium, v.12 (1944): 119-130; VI (in collaboration with Karlsson): The composition and base status of the vegetation in relation to the soil, v.12 (1944): 186-203.

37. Milne, G. 1935 Some suggested units of classification and mapping, particularly for East African soils. *Soil Res.* (Inter. Soc. Soil Sci.) 4, No. 3. See also: *Trans. Inter. Cong. Soil Sci.* 1: 345-347 (1935).

38. Moss, H. C. 1938 The morphology and composition of Saskatchewan podzolic soils. *Sci. Agr.* (Canada) 18: 708-718.

39. Münst, M. 1916 Ortsteinstudien im oberen Murgtal. *Mitt. Geol. Abt. Kg. Württenb. Stat. Landesamtes* (Stuttgart) S: 30. (Quoted from Stremme).

40. Nikolich, S. 1930 Chemical researches on podzolized soils and their improvement. Thesis, Univ. Tolouse, pp. 80, figs. 10. (Original not seen; quoted from Expt. Station Rec. v. 64, no. 6, pp. 522-523).

41. Norman, A. G. 1942 Problems in the chemistry of organic matter. *Proc. Soil Sci. Soc. Amer.* 7 : 7-15.

42. Pelisek, J. 1942 The occurrence of the microelement Sn in West Moravian soils. *Sbornik Cezkoslov. Akad. Zemeled.* 17 : 46-49.

43. Plice, Max J. 1934 Acidity, buffering and nutrient content of forest litter, etc. Cornell Univ. Agr. Expt. Sta. Memoir 166.

44. Polynov, B. B. 1915 Secondary minerals of ortstein horizons. *Izvestia Dokuchaev. Pochv. Komit.* 3, No. 2 ; 125-138.

45. Polynov, B. B. 1927 The sands of the Don region. Reprint from the *Trudy pochven. imeni Dokuchaeva,* pt. 2, 1-128.

46. Polynov, B. B. 1944 The crust of weathering in red earths and their soils. *Pedology* (U.S.S.R.) No. 1 : 20-28.

47. Remezov, N. P. 1937 On the theory of the podzol process of soil formation. *Pedology* (U.S.S.R.) No. 8 : 1139-1159.

48. Richard, J. A. and Chandler, R. F. 1943 Some physical and chemical properties of mature podzol profiles. *Proc. Soil Sci. Soc. Amer.* 8 : 379-383.

49. Rode, A. A. 1936 The problem of the degree of podzolization. *Trans. Dokuchaev Soil Inst.* 13 : 113-161 ; for an extensive English summary see : Studies in the Genesis and Geography of Soils. *Dokuchaev Soil Inst.,* Academy of Sci. U.S.S.R. (1935), pp. 55-70.

50. Rode, A. A. 1937 The process of podzolization (Russian). Acad. of Sci. Moscow-Leningrad, pp. 454 (A resume of this monograph is given by Rode in *Pedology* No. 6 (1937) : 849-862.

51. Rode, A. A. 1941 Data on the physico-chemical properties of soluble substances of forest litter. *Pedology* (U.S.S.R.) No. 3 : 103-128.

52. Rode, A. A. 1944 On the possible role of vegetation in the process of podzolization. *Pedology* (U.S.S.R.) No. 4-5 : 159-179.

53. Russian Bureau of Soils. 1928 Pedology at the service of agriculture. Sel'sko-Khoz. Opyt. Delo. U.S.S.R. 1917-1927. State Inst. Expt. Agron., Leningrad, pp. 16-43.

54. Sallans, H., Snell, I., Mackinney, H., and McKibbon, R. 1937 Water soluble substances in the raw humus of podzol soils. *Canad. Jour. Res.* 15B : 315-320.

55. Shuttleworth, A. E. 1896 Composition of ashes of the wood of Canadian trees and small fruits. Ontario Agr. College Rpt. p. 24-26.

56. Simakov, V. N. 1929 More data on the problem of the mutual effect of colloids encountered in soils. *Pedology* (U.S.S.R.) No. 1-2 : 22-123.

57. Skeen, John R. 1925 A critical pH for the formation of hardpan in acid clay soils. *Soil Sci.* 20 : 307-311.

58. Skeen, John R. 1927 Effects of some electrolytes on kaolin and the probable relation to the soil. *Soil Sci.* 23: 225-242.

59. Smirnov, V. P. 1912 Experimental data on podzol formation. *Ezhegod. Geolog. i Miner. Rossii* 14: 206-210.

60. Stremme, H. 1926 Grundzüge der praktischen Bodenkunde. Gebrüder Borntraeger, Berlin.

61. Tamm. O. 1930 The brown forest soils in Sweden. *Ztschr. Schwed. Forstvereins* 28: 1-41. See also Ref. No. 97, ch. 5.

62. Tumin, G. M. 1911 Podzolization and leaching of bases. *Zhur. Opyt. Agron.* 12: 1-19.

63. Tyurin, I. V. 1933 Kurs pochvovedeniya (A course in pedology). Moscow-Leningrad.

64. Udulft, Hans. 1924 Geological chemical investigations on the behavior of $Fe(OH)_3$ and MnO_2 and humus sols towards carbonates, bicarbonates, and clay. Kolloid Ztschr. 34: 233-237.

65. Vysotskii, G. N. 1905 Glei. *Pochvovedenie* (Pedology) 7: 291-327.

66. Vysotskii, G. N. 1913 Soil-forming processes in sands. *Izvestia Russk. Geograph. Obshches.* 47 (Quoted from Neustruev).

67. Warrington, R. 1900 Lectures on some of the physical properties of the soil. Oxford, England.

68. Weis, Fr. 1929 Physical and chemical investigations on Danish heath soils—podzols. *Det. Kg. Danske Videnskab. Selskab. Biolog. Meddelelser* VII, 9, pp. 199 (Exgensive English summary) See also: Further investigations on Danish heath soils and other podzols. *Biologiske Meddelelser* 10, 3 (1932), pp. 201.

69. Winters, E. 1938 Ferromanganiferous concretions from some podzol soils. *Soil Sci.* 46: 33-40.

70. Yarkov, S. P. 1942 The classification of soils in the zone of sod podzols in the light of the theories of Williams. Sbornik Pamyati Williamsa. *Acad. of Sci. (U.S.S.R.), Dokuchaev Soil Inst.,* pp. 103-119.

71. Zaitsev, B. D. 1937 Total N and degree of humification of organic substances of forest podzols. *Pedology* (U.S.S.R.) No. 10: 1442-1453.

72. Zaitsev, B. D. 1945 The relation of calcium to the accumulation of organic matter in podzolic soils. *Pedology* (U.S.S.R.) No. 8: 413-420.

73. Zakharov, S. A. 1910-1911 On the problem of the influence of the macro- and micro-relief on the soils in the podzolized region. *Pochvovedenie* (Pedology 12 (1910): 339-366: 13 (1911): 49-72.

CHAPTER XI

SUBTYPES AND TRANSITION TYPES OF SOILS
IN PODZOL ZONE

Introduction.—The degree of podzolization varies in the soils of the broad zone of podzols because of the variations in the moisture-temperature relationships. It is natural, therefore, to expect that in areas adjoining the true podzols there should be soils of the podzolic type, with subdued activity of the podzolization process.

In the United States, the belt of true podzols extends through northern parts of the New England States, the Upper Lakes region, and the St. Lawrence basin. Diverging lines, drawn from any point in the belt of genuine podzols to the west and southwest, will follow a course covering practically all the climatogenic soil types, except those of the humid subtropics, tropics, and desert tropics. We pass from the humid northern temperate climate through the humid, subhumid, semiarid, and arid temperate to the subtropical arid climate; in other words, from a high rainfall with a low temperature to a gradually diminishing rainfall with a gradually increasing temperature. In terms of chemical reactions active in the soil-forming processes, we go from a degree of hydrolysis in an acid medium (genuine podzols) through a lesser degree of acid hydrolysis (podzolic soils) toward a hydrolysis in an alkaline medium (chernozem, chestnut brown, and gray soils).

As the meridianal lines from east to west cross the diverging lines, they produce soil belts running north and south which increase in extent as the divergence increases, reaching a limit at the Rocky Mountains, where they are broken up by the natural forces of vertical zonation. It is of interest that the isohyetal lines through these belts also run almost north and south, with the isotherms cutting them almost perpendicularly. We should, therefore, find between the isotherms, within these belts, varieties of the zonal soils. And in the soil map of the United States, prepared by Marbut (Ch. 8, 13), we do find zonal belts running north-south, with the isotherms dividing them into varieties, like northern and southern chernozem.

If we follow the climatic elements from the northern points, where the true podzols are found, toward the south along the Atlantic Coast and the Gulf of Mexico, through the eastern climatic province, we find this: all along this region, where the continentality of the climate is slightly modified by

388

the oceanic influences, there is little change in the rainfall, except for such Gulf states as Louisiana, Mississippi, Alabama, and Florida, where it is higher. The temperature, however, varies considerably, increasing gradually from north to south. In this broad region, we have the great belt of podzolic soils, varying from true podzols in the north to the less podzolized soils in the south. As a matter of fact, the conditions for podzolization become depressed from north to south in the same degree as in the region along the diverging lines from east to west and southwest. There is, however, this difference: in the direction from north to south we have a decreasing degree of acid hydrolysis, with the bases and silica leaching out, a low organic matter content and rapid mineralization which, together with the high isoelectric pH of the accumulating Fe and Al, suppress the exchange capacity and unsaturation. As we move along the diverging lines, from the east (in reality from the northeast) toward the west and southwest, we go toward a region of less rainfall where leaching is impeded. The bases, therefore, remain behind, as does the silica, thereby increasing the exchange capacity and decreasing the acid hydrolysis which, in turn, is conducive to the fixation of organic matter complexes. We reach a similar decrease in acid hydrolysis as we move northward, from the true podzols outside of the forest zone and approach the treeless tundra where leaching processes are at a low ebb.

Because of the reactions mentioned, we pass along the diverging lines from the true podzols to brown forest soil then to forest gray brown soils, and finally to the degraded chernozems or chernozem-like prarie soils. On the other hand, as we move from north to south, we start with the true podozols, pass through brown forests, in some places forest gray brown and into yellow soils, and finally into red soils.

Pedologists generally agree that all soils in the podzol zone have some morphological and chemical attributes which place them in this zone. Some pedologists, however, believe that the soils within the zone which do not show clear-cut morphological evidence of podzolization are simply transitional, that such soils as the rendzina, Braunerde of Ramann, gray forest soils, and degraded chernozem are merely temporary conditions which eventually will give way to the forces of podzolization and cause true podzols to form. No attempt, so far as the author is aware, has been made to prove or disprove the validity of this contention. Is it not possible that the soils mentioned will remain in their present condition as long as the present climatic and biotic conditions prevail?

In its final analysis, the natural development of true podzols is based on the depletion of bases and the unsaturation of the exchange complex. These conditions, in turn, bring about the final breakdown of the kaolin nuclei, with the splitting off of SiO_2. If there were a source of bases to prevent the aforementioned reactions, one would logically expect that the process of podzolization in its highest degree would be hindered and would never attain the genuine podzol state. The entire question thus hinges on the balance between outgo and return of bases. This phase should lend itself to experimental verification.

An approach to a study of this kind may be made by the lysimeter method on a virgin soil, without disturbing the natural distribution of the horizons in the soil profile. Such a type of lysimeter has been in operation at the New Jersey Station (Ch. 5, 49). The leachings from such lysimeters furnish data on the outgo of bases and other constituents. This represents the debit side of our balance sheet. Analyses of the leaves, twigs, herbaceous growth, and other forest debris over an area adjacent to the lysimeter plot furnish the credit side. To the former we have to add the constituents which are locked up annually in the growth increase of the forest stand.

Let X represent the quantity of bases percolated with the leachings, and Y the quantity mobilized and returned by the forest debris, then if $X > Y$, the process of podzolization is still going on; if $X = Y$, the soil has reached a definite equilibrium which can only be disturbed by a shift in the climatic and biotic conditions or by the interference of men; if $X < Y$, there is a reversion from the process of podzolization, in which case a true podzol may go to a forest gray or brown forest soil. If any of the transitional sub-types or even some of the intrazonal soils should show that they have reached a condition where $X = Y$, it is futile to expect these soils ever to become true podzols. It would seem better to assign to them an independent status in the family tree of zonal soil types.

There is another approach to the experimental study of the podzolized soils with a view to establish the dynamics of the podzol process, namely, an analysis of the $SiO_2 : R_2O_3$ ratio in soil colloids of the respective subtypes. From the work of Byers and Anderson (9), Mattson (26, p. 231) computed the average ratio of silica to sesquioxides in the colloids from the soils in the humid region of the Atlantic seaboard. From table 79, it is clear that a lowering of the $SiO_2 : R_2O_3$ ratio takes place in the colloids as we move from north to south, with the lowest ratio for the lateritic Nipe. The computation of the ratios would have been more significant if they had been confined to the A_2 horizon. In the B horizon, the ratio is apt to be obscured because of the new formations, such as the gibbsite-like minerals, limonite, argil-laceous hematite, palygorskite, and others. Grouping the colloids of C with those of other horizons is still less justified, for the parent material may be an old B horizon.

Mattson (26) has shown that the so-called Al and Fe hydroxides, "when precipitated from the chlorides, are isoelectric at pH 8.1 and 7.1 re-

Table 79

*The ratio of silica to sesquioxides in soil colloids from different latitudes
of humid regions*

Colloid	Locality	Numbers of analyses	$\dfrac{SiO_2}{Al_2O_3 + Fe_2O_3}$
Nipe	Cuba	3	0.30
Cecil	Alabama	3	1.27
Cecil	Georgia	9	1.33
Cecil	North Carolina	9	1.44
Davidson	North Carolina	4	1.44
Cecil	Virginia	3	1.60
Chester	Maryland	22	1.61
Leonardtown	Maryland	12	2.01
Podzols:			
Beckett	Massachusetts	5	1.74
Emmet	Michigan	3	2.93
Superior	Wisconsin	4	2.94

spectively. Aluminum silicate can, therefore, begin to form at a higher pH than ferric silicate." With the introduction of various anions in the system, the isoelectric pH at which new formations are built up may be lower. The case of the pure Al and Fe hydroxides simply serves as an aid to formulate the fundamental theoretical basis, from which it follows that Fe silicates hydrolyze at a lower pH than Al silicates. As a consequence, we have the precipitation of the Fe colloids as the oxides, and the more favorable the conditions for such hydrolysis—and this is the case we move along the meridianal lines from north to south along the Atlantic seaboard— the farther we depart from the process of podzolization and the closer we come to the process of laterization.

The theory of acid and alkaline hydrolysis, and the actual facts in nature with respect to the SiO_2:R_2O_3 ratio supplement each other. In the yellow earths, a lower ratio (as compared with the true podzols) persists, and in the red earths it is still lower. A larger number of analyses on the SiO_2:R_2O_3 ratio of the colloids and on the lysimeter leachings on the soils in the podzol and adjacent zones along a meridianal profile would clarify the dynamics of the various soil types.

Areas may be found within the podzolic subtypes where the process of podzolization is favored. Thus, the composition of parent material may favor the formation of a podzol outside the belt of true podzols. Topography, local climate, and drainage conditions may favor a high organic matter accumulation which would tend to produce a podzol because of a shift toward a more acid hydrolysis of the humic acids.

In summarizing, we may say that, from the two angles of experimental investigations (determination of X and Y and complete data on the SiO_2 : R_2O_3 ratio of the colloids in the respective horizons, especially in the A_2 horizon of the transitional soils), it should be possible to answer the question whether or not the so-called podzolic soils will ever become podzols.

In New Jersey and all through the Coastal Plain region, we have within the broad zone of podzolized soils some local areas with true podzols. They are known under the series names: Lakewood, St. John, Leon, Portsmouth, and others. What was responsible for the development of a *true podzol* state on the Lakewood and other series in the midst of the *podzolic soils,* like the Sassafras, Collington, and other series, is a question to be answered.

An inkling of the factor responsible for the through podzolization and hence maturity of the Lakewood soils may be obtained by comparing them with the Sassafras soils of a similar texture. In table 80, analyses on the mineral consituents of the two soils are presented. It is to be noted that both soils are texturally about the same, containing between 93.5 and 97 per cent SiO_2. Geologically, they are also of the same age. There is, however, a difference in the sesquioxides, especially in their distribution in the profile. They are higher in the Sassafras, as shown by the analyses of the material from the C horizon. And yet, there is relatively more R_2O_3 accumulation in the B horizon of the Lakewood soils than in that of the Sassafras. The cause of this to be sought in the conditions responsible for the mobility of the R_2O_3, namely, the pH of the medium and the nature of the electrolytes, especially the anions present. Both of these conditions influence the isoelectric point of precipitation of the sesquioxides and other soil colloids and hence their mobility. A comparison of the analyses of these two soils shows that the pH of the Sassafras soil is higher than that of the Lakewood, except for the B_2 horizon, and in a less degree the B_1, where the accumulation of the R_2O_3 takes place in connection with the increase in Ca and Mg which suppress the H-ion concentration. A glance at the table shows that the Ca content in the Sassafras is higher throughout its profile. It has been shown by Mattson (26), that a soil complex possessing a high SiO_2 content (or acidoid in general), more than the R_2O_3 content can normally hold in combination, "can be stable only as long as it is saturated with divalent cations." This condition prevails more in the Sassafras soil than in the Lakewood, because the former contain more Ca. The Mg content in this case does not play such an important part, for it probably forms less dissociated ionogens than Ca. Polynov (29) isolated from the B horizon the mineral palygorskite,

Table 80

Mineral constituents in the sandy soils of th e Lakewood and Sassafras series

Soil series	Reaction	SiO₂	Fe₂O₃	Al₂O₃	CaO	MgO
	pH	per cent	per cent	per cent	per cent	per cent
			A_1 horizon			
Lakewood	4.8	97.16	1.30	0.407	0.118	0.0723
Lakewood	4.2	90.50	0.72	1.250	0.123	0.119
Sassafras	4.9	94.92	2.90	0.022	0.342	0.079
			A_2 horizon			
Lakewood	4.8	98.12	1.10	0.315	0.121	0.0795
Lakewood	4.6	97.00	0.69	1.070	0.076	0.070
Sassafras	5.0	96.40	3.07	0.652	0.280	
			B_1 horizon			
Lakewood	5.1-	93.32	1.90	2.50	0.124	0.1122
Lakewood	4.9	90.10	1.23	4.02	0.089	0.116
Sassafras	5.3	94.32	3.91	0.642	0.346	0.086
			B_2 horizon			
Lakewood	5.2	93.40	1.90	2.65	0.143	0.1157
Lakewood	5.0	89.00	1.66	4.65	0.054	0.101
Sassafras	5.1	93.32	4.62	0.78	0.322	0.099
			C horizon			
Lakewood	5.2	95.97	1.35	2.00	0.203	0.1447
Lakewood	5.2	94.10	1.01	2.88	0.056	0.105
Sassafras	5.4	93.42	5.13	0.40	0.342	0.059

a magnesium aluminum silicate which probably inactivates the Mg. Thus, the stability of the Sassafras soil and its resistance to podzolization is due in a large measure to the Ca ion. The lack of Ca in the parent material of the Lakewood soil is in the same measure responsible for its through podzol condition.

Based on the foregoing appraisal of the transition types and subtypes of soils affected by the process of podzolization, a number of pedologic classification units or designations have been recognized.

Gray Forest Soils

As the name implies, these soils, also known under the name *forest steppe* soils, have formed under forest cover. In general, these soils are looked upon as chernozems that have been invaded by forests or the steppe has advanced on the forests for one reason or another. Zakharov (Ch. 2, 91) recognizes two subtypes of gray forest soils: 1, primary, formed directly on a variety of parent materials; 2, secondary, formed on degraded chernozem. The history of the problem of these soils has been discussed by Tyurin (45). He classified the different views on the problem of the genesis of the gray forest soils into the following three trends:

1. Gray forest soils, formed under the influence of deciduous forests (oaks, etc.) as a transitional belt between the steppe (chernozem) and the taiga-forest (podzol) zone. This was the view held by Dokuchaev.

2. These soils formed by the degradation of the former steppe chernozem, under the influence of the forests invading the steppe. This view, proposed by Korzhinskii (20), has a strong following.

3. Their origin is to be sought in the changes occurring in the podzol soils that formed under a dense forest cover which was gradually replaced by a herbaceous turf vegetation, first into a soil with less dense forest and finally into gray forest soil. This was the view held by Williams (Ch. 3, 72) who approached most of the processes of soil formation from the standpoint of the so-called "turf or sod process of soil formation."

The salient features of Tyurin's comprehensive analysis of the last two views (the Dokuchaev view is discussed only in passing) are as follows:

It has been established that the humidity at the upper soil horizon is higher in the forests than in the neighboring steppe; the percolation is also more effective. For these reasons, the organic matter of the forest soil becomes unsaturated and mobile and consequently its content decreases; in other words, the degradation process sets in. Experimentally, this has been proved by Kostychev (21) and Kravkov (22). Kostychev reduced the organic matter content of a chernozem from 8.5 to 2.5 per cent by washing it with water. Kravkov obtained similar results by washing various soils

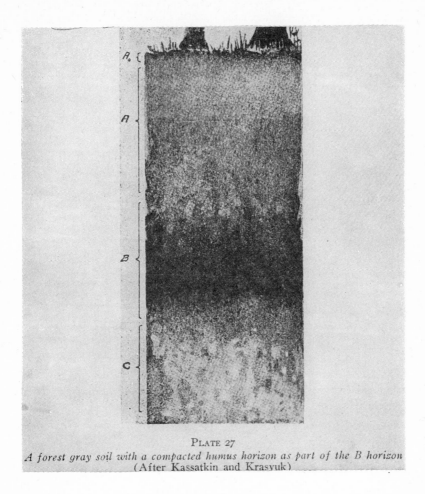

PLATE 27

A forest gray soil with a compacted humus horizon as part of the B horizon
(After Kassatkin and Krasyuk)

with solutions containing organic matter. Further evidence in support of the degrading action of forests on chernozem was obtained by studying the changes produced in a chernozem by the artificial introduction of a forest cover.

Tkachenko (43) studied the effects of artificial plantings of oaks, firs, and larch on a chernozem in the Tula government. His conclusions were that the greatest degradation takes place under dense oak plantings, less degradation under fir, and very little under larch. The age of the forest stand was about 40 years at the time Tkachenko studied the degradation process.

Gorshenin (15) studied the influence of forest plantings (a 15-year old stand) on the chernozem near Omsk in Western Siberia. His conclusions were as follows:

Upon the forestation of chernozem, an increase in the organic matter content takes place at first. Later its content decreases, primarily in the lower portion of the upper horizon. With the initial increase in organic matter, there is an increase of the adsorbed calcium. Later, however, this also decreases at a rate greater than that of the organic matter. In the early stages, the Ca is leached from the surface, then it is pushed deeper into the profile. Simultaneously, there is a lowering of the carbonate zone. With the entrenchment of the forest, an energetic translocation of the R_2O_3 from the A horizon takes place. In general, the process of degradation proceeds at a fast rate.

Tumin's investigations (44) on the experimental plots at the Kamennaya Steppe Experiment Station, mentioned in the discussion on "Degraded Chernozem," corroborated fully the results of Gorshenin.

Tyurin is not fully satisfied that forests will, under all conditions, give rise to a state of podzolization. He cites the Braunerde as an example of a forest soil which, in typical cases, shows very faint signs of podzolization. He also cites observations of Polynov (30) that no indications of degradation were noted under pine forests in the southern portion of the chernozem belt.

Whether the forests advanced on the steppe or the reverse process prevailed, Tyurin is inclined to disagree with Korzhinskii's view that the former took place. He cites the work of Taliev (36) and Krylov (23) who believed that besides the natural factors, such as fires and cyclic climatic varitations, man has entered as a factor in deforesting the region at the edge of the steppe, thereby favoring the meadow steppe vegetation. This view has been upheld by Gordyagin (14), Keller (19), and a number of other geobotanists.

Williams (Ch. 3, 72) considered the advance of the meadow (turf) and herbaceous vegetation as the starting point of deforestation. An accumulation of organic matter takes place in the "turfy podzolic soils," to use the terminology of Williams. Tyurin points out that "at a certain stage of development, it will not be difficult to find the common gray forest soil in the transitional forest steppe belt, or, to be more exact, in the southern portion of the forest zone."

In further support of the views of Taliev, Krylov, and Williams on the advance of the meadow or steppe vegetation on the forests, Tyurin cites the theories of Marbut (Ch. 2, 45) on the role of the vegetation in the formation of the prairie soils.

Morphological Characteristics.—Whatever is the true origin of the gray forest soils, all agree that, by and large, they are a transitional type between the true chernozem and forest podzol soils. The gray forest soil receives its name from its distinctive color and, because of variations in color, three subdivisions are recognized: gray, dark-gray, and light gray. The higher the organic matter content, the darker gray the soil is. Levchenko (25) lists a number of gray forest soils varying in organic matter content from 2 to 8 per cent.

The following is a description of a typical gray forest soil, as presented by Zakharov:

A_0: 5 cm (0-5 cm), forest litter consisting of semi-decomposed leaves, twigs, fruit, etc.

A_1: 20 cm. (5-25), humus-rich, gray in color, silty crumb structure, sometimes platy, somewhat compact constitution, with a network of roots.

A_2: 20 cm. (25-45 cm.); nutty,* slightly podzolized layer; the nut-like structural units are small, colored irregularly gray or brownish gray, with a sprinkling of silica (pepper and salt effect) on the surface; this layer is more mellow than A_1.

B_1: 45 cm. (45-90 cm.); large nutty structure, turning into prisms at the bottom, brown in color, more compact and sticky, it is the horizon of illuviation of R_2O_3. (In some profiles because of the prismatic structure at the bottom of this horizon, a sub-horizon is separated.)

B_2: 50 cm. (90-140 cm.); prismatic structure not clearly pronounced, slightly cracked constitution, brownish-straw colored, with dark brown and gray tongue-like projections from material of the horizon above; it is illuviated with carbonates which sometimes occur in the form of light veins.

C: Parent material, usually a loess-like formation, uniformly colored.

---

*Because of the distinctive structure of the gray forest soils, Dokuchaev named them originally *nutty soils.*

Table 81

Comparative partial analyses of soils — from chernozem to gray forest

(After Tyurin)

Name of soil	Horizon	Depth	Organic matter	Sorbed bases		pH
				Ca	Mg	
		cm.	*per cent*	*m.e.* *	*m.e.*	
Leached chernozem loam; plowed land	A	0-10	10.23	41.7	5.0	6.62
	A	20-30	8.95	43.9	5.0	6.79
	B_1	45-55	3.30	27.5	4.0	6.72
	B_2	75-85	0.89	24.6	4.0	7.13
Degraded chernozem loam; plowed field	A	0-10	13.47	——	—	6.36
	A	20-30	12.45	——	—	6.39
	B_1	55-65	5.13	——	—	6.24
	B_2	80-90	1.15	——	—	6.76
Gray forest loam; oak forest	A	0-12	7.75	23.5	2.0	6.47
	A	15-20	3.47	20.0	2.0	5.85
	B_1	30-40	2.24	23.2	4.0	5.81
	B_2	45-55	1.35	——	—	5.75
Podzolized gray forest soil; oak forest	A_1	2-10	6.90	21.7	1.5	6.40
	A_2	12-19	2.64	8.6	1.0	5.66
	A_2/B_1	20-30	1.92	13.2	3.0	5.67
	B_2	40-50	0.61	19.7	4.0	5.70

*m.e. = milliequivalents per 100 gms. of soil.

Table 82

Analyses of degraded chernozem and gray forest soils

(After Levchenko)

Soil	Depth	Humus	SiO_2	R_2O_3	Fe_2O_3	CaO	MgO	K_2O	P_2O_5	$CaCO_3$
	cm.	per cent	per cent	per cent	per cent	per cent	per cent	per cent	per cent	per cent
Degraded chernozem	0-30	4.75	74.25	16.74	3.52	1.31	1.23	2.20	0.13	....
	60-115	2.79	73.70	16.61	3.88	1.25	1.24	2.29	0.10	....
	135-200	0.97	71.42	18.09	3.98	2.57	0.71	2.08	0.09	5.79
Light gray forest loam	0-15	1.97	81.70	12.94	3.85	0.91	0.54	2.17	0.08	....
	60-123	0.65	77.39	16.68	4.31	0.96	1.05	2.24	0.07	....
	123-170	0.60	.76.31	15.10	3.93	2.11	0.27	2.09	0.13	....
Light gray forest loam	0-20	1.93	88.90	0.89	2.00	1.07	0.29	....	0.11	....
	20-38	0.43	90.13	8.24	1.02	1.02	0.30	....	0.09	....
	80-100	0.22	85.74	14.51	4.30	1.13	0.43	....	0.18	....
	110-170	0.19	87.09	11.89	2.43	1.19	0.48	....	0.08	12.50

Table 83

Mechanical composition of a number of gray forest soils

(After Levchenko)

Soil	Depth	>0.25	0.25-0.05	0.05-0.01	0.01-0.005	<0.005
	cm.	*per cent*	*per cent*	*per cent*	*per cent*	*per cent*
Gray loam.	0-15	0.27	2.03	32.58	52.14	12.98
	65-80	0.52	2.12	23.39	57.17	17.80
Podolia	200-220	0.39	2.50	34.28	50.13	12.14
Gray loam.	0.15	0.62	3.84	44.12	44.14	7.28
	75-90	0.51	4.80	38.10	46.25	10.34
Kiev	200-220	0.30	6.28	45.12	43.20	5.10
Gray loam.	0-15	0.45	4.63	38.65	45.91	10.36
	60-80	0.14	5.22	32.67	47.36	14.61
Poltava	200-220	0.80	7.20	37.45	44.45	10.10
Gray loam.	0-15	1.38	6.30	50.60	27.90	13.90
	80-90	1.17	5.00	52.32	30.19	11.43
Voluin	240-250	0.73	4.22	53.10	29.11	12.84
Light gray	0-20	0.15	10.50	60.25	24.60	4.50
loam.	80-100	0.12	7.57	56.68	30.00	5.63
Voluin	140-170	0.06	5.02	66.29	21.57	7.16
Dark gray	0-10	12.60	12.76	31.34	43.30	
loam.	30-36	10.32	9.91	28.14	51.63	
Ryazan	150-160	23.55	17.24	13.37	44.84	

Chemical Characteristics.—The data in tables 81-85 show that we are dealing with soils having attributes of the chernozem, as well as of the podzol types of soil formation. The organic matter content is fairly high, but not as high as in chernozem. This fact is clearly brought out by Tyurin in table 81, where the composition of two chernozems and two gray forest soils are compared. An interesting feature is the low Ca and Mg content in the A_2 of the podzolized soil and the low pH of the forest gray soils. The sharp drop of organic matter in the lower horizons is another indication of the podzolic character of these soils.

Table 84

Mechanical composition of Clermont silt loam

(After Conrey)

Depth	Fine gravel	Coarse sand	Medium sand	Fine sand	Very fine sand	Total sand	Silt	Clay	Moisture equivalent
inches	per cent	per cent	per cent	per cent	per cent	per cent	per cent	per cent	per cent
0-8	1.0	1.9	3.4	2.4	22.8	31.4	53.3	13.5	22.2
8-14	1.3	1.4	3.1	2.2	20.3	28.8	57.1	14.0	22.7
14-22	1.0	1.1	2.4	1.8	18.4	25.0	54.3	20.0	23.5
22-28	0.3	0.6	1.5	1.1	12.9	16.2	43.9	30.9	28.0
28-36	0.4	1.0	2.4	2.1	17.9	23.8	38.2	38.1	27.5
36-48	0.6	1.4	3.0	2.3	24.2	31.5	37.8	30.4	31.4
48-60	0.6	1.4	3.3	2.7	27.2	35.3	32.9	31.7	30.3
60-72	0.7	1.6	4.1	3.2	31.1	40.7	28.0	30.5	23.8
72-108	1.8	2.8	5.4	3.7	24.4	38.1	26.4	35.4	24.1
108-120	5.1	5.5	6.7	4.0	26.9	48.2	32.4	19.0	16.4

Table 85

Chemical composition of Clermont silt loam

(After Conrey)

Depth	SiO₂	Al₂O₃	Fe₂O₃	MnO	CaO	MgO	K₂O	P₂O₅	N	Organic carbon	pH
inches	*per cent*	*per cent*	*per cent*	*per cent*	*per cent*	*per cent*	*per cent*	*per cent*	*per cent*	*per cent*	
0-8	82.36	8.76	1.08	....	0.45	0.57	1.52	0.040	0.054	0.83	5.22
8-14	86.18	12.68	3.07	0.026	0.33	0.78	....	0.025	0.025	....	4.06
14-22	82.44	13.81	4.00	0.026	0.32	0.59	....	0.022	0.027	....	4.06
22-28	74.70	14.30	5.18	0.013	0.41	0.85	....	0.025	0.030	....	4.82
28-36	71.46	17.89	6.06	0.026	0.33	1.06	....	0.028	0.026	....	4.95
36-48	72.33	13.11	5.50	0.130	0.55	0.71	1.62	0.041	0.022	0.11	5.51
48-60	72.33	12.05	5.19	0.040	0.55	0.40	1.48	0.043	0.022	0.11	7.35
60-72	73.78	13.11	5.19	0.075	0.66	0.17	1.74	0.045	0.025	....	7.47
72-108	71.02	12.29	5.68	0.010	0.31	0.14	1.68	0.024	0.028	....	7.75
108-120	50.70	7.35	5.50	0.075	9.84	3.84	1.62	0.109	0.024	....	8.44

The nitrogen content of the gray forest soil is not as high as in the chernozems but the organic matter content is extremely high in the lower horizon, indicating a movement of the finely dispersed organic constituents, rich in nitrogen. This is in accord with the podzol process of soil formation, as pointed out in the preceding chapter. Another feature of the position of this soil, midway between the chernozems and podzols, is the carbonate content which is very low in the horizon of illuviation.

Zakharov noted (Ch. 2, 91) an interesting relation in the distribution of P_2O_5 in the gray forest soils. In the dark gray soils, because of the high organic matter content, P_2O_5 accumulates in the surface horizon, a chernozem attribute. In the light gray soils, P_2O_5 accumulates also in the B horizon, an attribute of podzolization. Zakharov also noted that the K in the zeolitic portion of these soils was lower than in the chernozem, 0.2 to 0.4 per cent, decreasing from the dark gray to the light gray soils. Levchenko (25), who compiled analytical data of a number of investigators, clearly brought out in table 82 that the podzolic characteristics were far advanced in the light gray forest soils.

Mechanical Composition.—A characteristic feature of the profile of the gray forest soils is the distribution of the mechanical fractions; there is a shift of the fine particles, 0.001 mm., from the horizon of eluviation into the horizon of illuviation, another property of the podzol process of soil formation, and an increase of silt in the upper horizon. The mechanical analyses of a number of gray forest soils (table 83) prove the aforesaid. The only exception to the rule is the gray loam from Volyn. As pointed out by Levchenko, this soil "is still very closely related to a chernozem."

What appears to be a gray forest soil is the Clermont silt loam described by Conrey (10). Its mechanical and chemical analyses are presented in tables 84-85. The data show a gradual increase of the clay fraction with depth, an increase in R_2O_3 in the layer of clay accumulation, and a general distribution of the other chemical constituents, as previously outlined for the typical gray forest soils. The relatively poor drainage of the Clermont series within the environment of the prairie has undoubtedly influenced the invasion of the forest, with the consequent podzolization effects.

It is very probable that some gray-brown podzolic soils (Marbut's designation of the huge belt of soils bordering the genuine podzols to the north the yellow-red soils to the south, and the prairie soils to the west) adjoining the prairie soils are on the order of the gray forest soils. The Russian pedologists describe the B horizon of these soils as being brownish in color. It is noteworthy that the Miami soil series of the Little Corn Belt

(Central Indiana and west-central Ohio) is being described in the United States Soil Survey publications (33, p. 1040) as being gray-brown in color and possessing a nutty structure. This description fits well the characteristic properties of the gray forest soils. As yet, no gray forest soils, as described by the Russian pedologists, have been reported in the American literature. As hinted earlier, these soils undoubtedly do occur in the United States.

Braunerde of Ramann and Brown Forest Soils

According to Ramann (Ch. 3, 53) :

Brown earths develop under the influence of a temperate climate which fluctuates greatly; in some years they are wet and others — dry, so that the leaching of the soil varies with the season. The rainfall is not sufficient during the warm season to form seepage water in soils covered with vegetation. In warm and dry years, slightly arid conditions prevail, whereby the ascent of the ground waters is effective. This effect is prominent whenever the soil is enriched with calcium carbonate. In general, deposits of calcium carbonate are rare, or are only found in soils having an abundant water supply, as in loess. Leaching preponderates in most of the brown earths; the soluble salts and the alkaline earth carbonates are washed out, while the phosphates and sesquioxides are retained in the soil . . . In no other soil formation does the parent rock exercise such a great influence as in the brown earths . . . The soil has normally a neutral or slightly alkaline reaction; hence readily dispersed humus bodies are not found.

Glinka (p. 340) considered the brown earth as a variety of podzol, forming on parent materials rich in lime. He stated that "all the participants of the excursion (in connection with the soil conference in Hungary) who happened to study the brown earths in their respective countries have agreed with me that those examined by us represent one of the varieties of the podzol type of soil formation on carbonate loams. It is to be noted that the brown soils in most cases contain carbonates in the lower horizon." Glinka (p. 343) also suggested that "the brown earths of western Europe represent, so to speak, the last stage of the podzol type of weathering; they are transitory to the more southern yellow and red earths." Prasolov (31) agreed with Glinka that the brown earths were, a transition stage from yellow and red soils of the southern regions into podzols. Antipov-Karataev and his collaborators (2) described the brown earths of Crimea and found no effervescence in the B horizon. Tamm (40, 41) and Lundblad (Ch. 9, 54) associateed brown earths with beach forests. Analyses taken from Glinka's (Ch. 27, p. 30) work show that the percentage of ash is high in beach forest litter (5.57 per cent against 1.46 per cent in pine) and that the ash is high in CaO (2.46 per cent against 0.59 per cent in pine). The Ca and other bases, in their circulation through the soil profile, exert a definite influence on the process of soil formation. They are gathered by the plants from the horizons of root distribution, to be redeposited as dead plant residue in the humus-accumlative A_0 layer where they are mineralized and sent into circulation through the profile. In the case of the beech litter, the replenishment of leached bases is high and, therefore, hinders the process of podzolization. Extensive data on brown forest soils are presented by Lundblad (25a) in a series of papers. They supplement his earlier reports on the problem.

Tamm (40) divides the brown forest soils of southern Sweden (the average annual temperature in the region is 7°C.; and the rainfall 900 mm.) into two subtypes: climatic and aclimatic. The former are soils formed on parent material poor in calcium under a beech and oak forest; the latter are soils formed on parent material rich in lime or by infiltration of calcium from seepage waters (Braunerde). The climatic brown forest soils are readily podzolized whenever the vegetation changes to a coniferous or heath type. The aclimatic soils are more stable and support a heavy stand of conifers and a rich flora in general. Tamm postulates the regradation of a brown soil from a podzolized soil through a change in vegetation. He cites an example where a podzolized soil under beech has changed gradually into a brown soil through the introduction of birch, grass, and herbaceous vegetation. Appreciable quantities of organic matter intermingle with the mineral constituents, form a mull 8 to 10 cm. thick, and finally a brown soil.

In a more recent publication, Tamm (41) expresses the view that "there is no general tendency, as some believe, towards the podzolization of brown forest soils. The reverse is much in evidence . . . The brown forest soil as a climatic type is very apt to persist; it belongs to the medium humid temperate climate where deciduous forests represent the natural vegetation."

Smolik (32) points out that the organic matter of the Braunerde in Moravia is rich in lipoids, to the extent of 0.4 to 0.9 per cent. The chief humus components are iron humates and some calcium humates. In most of these soils, a carbonate zone is present which varies in its position in the profile, depending on the parent material or the seasonal variations in rainfall. There is no wide difference in the distribution of the R_2O_3 in the profile, except that the layer immediately above the carbonate zone is richer in R_2O_3. The colloidal complex of these soils has a higher Mg content than the complex of podzols. It is saturated primarily with Ca, varying from 36 to 85 per cent. As to the color, the Moravian Braunerde varies as follows: the A horizon is light brown; the B_1, dark brown; and the B_2, rusty brown. In structure, these soils are more or less crumbly.

Stebut (34, p. 353) agrees with Glinka and Prasolov that the Braunerde is a transition between the podzols and laterites. He points out (p. 439) that in the Balkans, the brown forest soils are subject on one hand to the process of podzolization and on the other hand to the process of red earth formation. At the border of the red earths, the brown forest soils find their highest expression, morphologically and chemically. "The brown forest soil is adapted to the warmer southern climate rather than to the northern cold and humid climate. There is no doubt that in a climatic region where acid humus forms, no Braunerde may form. It is the higher temperature that paralyzes the formation of acid humus." According to Stebut, Braunerde cannot form under conifers, for the latter require a high moisture content which is inimical to Braunerde formation.

The following is a morphological description of what Stebut calls a "typical brown forest soil" (Braunerde) in Serbia (p. 444):

A_0: 2 cm. deep, primarily forest litter.

A : About 30 cm. deep, with no differentiation into the conventional A_1 and A_2 horizons, homogenous in appearance, brown in color, and with a large crumb structure (2 to 3 cm. in diameter).

B_1: Usually about 50 cm. deep, lighter brown on top and darker brown or chocolate color on the bottom. Veins and streaks of a lighter color are encountered. It is more compact than A, in places extremely hard, of a cloddy structure, and effervesces at the bottom.

B_2: More open structure, due to the accumulation of lime. At some point in this horizon, there is a darker layer where the products of illuviation precipitate. At the bottom, the lime content is fairly high.

Tyurin (45) identifies the brown forest soils with the so-called "disguised" or "concealed" podzolic soils. In other words, these do not show any morphological characteristics of podzols, but a careful analysis reveals some podzolic features. As described by Tyurin, these soils have a "simple morphological constitution. On the surface is a layer of forest litter, followed by a rather shallow humus A horizon, 15 to 25 cm. in depth, which retains the basic color of the parent material, slightly darkened by the organic matter. The B horizon shows slight effects of illuviation and blends into the C horizon. Chemically, these soils are distinguished by a neutral or slightly acid reaction of the A horizon, with a slight degree of unsaturation. The organic matter content of loams runs from 3 to 5 per cent, and lower in the lighter textured soils."

Tyurin, following the schemes of Polynov, differentiates thermal subtypes, such as the "brown forest soils of the cool, temperate, temperate-warm, and warm climates." The last-mentioned subtype is favored by the rapid decomposition of organic matter, without the lingering of the intermediate organic acid compounds in the profile. This characteristic brings it closer to the lateritic type of soil formation.

The analyses of a brown forest soil, presented in table 86, show a higher Ca content in the A than in the B horizon. Apparently, the organic matter is saturated with Ca. This is further corroborated by the high content of the exchangeable Ca. There is also very little translocation of the R_2O_3 and no movement of the fine particles.

Ballenegger (4) followed Treitz in naming the Ramann Braunerde of Hungary "brown forest soils." In table 87, reproduced from Stremme (35), the analyses of two profiles are given. It will be noted that the soil from the plowed field shows a higher degree of podzolization than the one from the beech forest. Even the latter shows distinct podzolic features, namely, an accumulation of R_2O_3 in the B and a low P_2O_5 in the surface horizon.

An extensive comparative study of the brown forest and podzol soils of southern Sweden has been made by Lundblad (Ch. 9, 54). Nine profiles were investigated. No. 1 was a typical and No. 2 a slightly less typical Braundrde under beech forest; Nos. 3 and 4 were degraded Braunerde, the degradation having been brought about by a beech raw humus layer and a fir planting respectively; No. 5 was a normal podzol; No. 6 was also a degraded Braunerde under a mixed forest, grown on an old beach forest soil; No. 7 was a Braunerde under oak forest; Nos. 8 and 9 were two typical podzols, one of which had an ortstein formation.

Lundblad judged the state of degradation of the Braunerde by the quantity of inorganic gels extracted with acidified NH_4-oxalate, the Tamm (38) method. The curves in plate 28 show the percentage of inorganic gels (SiO_2, Fe_2O_3, and Al_2O_3) extracted. Only slight variations in gel content at the various depths in the profile are apparent in the Braunerde. The podzols show the highest quantity of gels in the B horizon, and the one with ortstein formation exceeds even this. The degraded Braunerde take a middle position. The curves also show that the brown forest soils lack the bleached A_2 horizon, which for the true podzols shows a drop in gel content. Thus, the Braunerde suffers no deep seated decomposition of the silicate complexes as is the case with the podzols. As a result, there is a relatively uniform distribution of R_2O_3 in the brown forest soil profile, with no well-defined illuvial horizon. Lundblad describes the typical brown forest soil as having a crumb structure and a loose consistency even in the B horizon. These studies on brown forest soils have been elaborated upon by Lundblad (27a) in another series of papers.

An elaborate study on 6 profiles of Braunerde in Switzerland is presented by Geering (13).

Aarnio (1) describes a brown forest soil in southwestern Finland under a stand of hazel (*Corylus avellana*). A comparison of this soil with the ones described by Lundblad shows a great similarity. Both the Swedish and the Finnish brown forest soils have a high organic matter and CaO con-

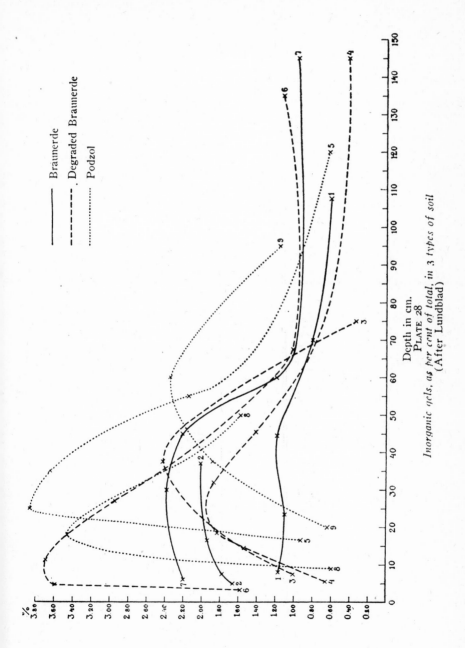

Depth in cm.
PLATE 28

Inorganic gels, as per cent of total, in 3 types of soil
(After Lundblad)

——— Braunerde
- - - - Degraded Braunerde
·········· Podzol

Table 86

Chemical composition of a Braunerde from the Black Sea Coast of the Caucasus

(After Tyurin)

Horizon	Depth	Hunus	SiO₂	Al₂O₃	Fe₂O₃	CaO.	MgO	Particles <0.01 mm.	pH	Exchangeable Ca
	cm.	per cent	per cent	per cent	per cent	per cent	per cent	per cent		m. e.
A	1-4	5.43	60.00	17.94	11.40	2.70	5.33	90.90	5.35	8.1
A	17-20	4.45	59.97	17.61	11.30	2.16	5.30	90.25	5.37	7.2
B	36-40	1.42	58.67	17.77	11.44	1.71	6.07	89.62	5.98	8.5
B/C	78-82	0.61	55.05	21.21	12.31	1.64	5.08	88.00	6.8	13.2

Table 87

Chemical composition of Braunerde from Hungary, HCl soluble

(After Ballenegger)

Constituent	From a beech forest			From a plowed field		
	A:0-10 cm.	B:40-50 cm.	C:80-90 cm.	A:0-22 cm.	B:50-60 cm.	C:140-150 cm.
	per cent	per cent	per cent	per cent	per cent	per cent
SiO₂	3.41	4.90	4.66	3.68	4.48	4.70
Al₂O₃	4.14	7.16	4.25	5.71	8.86	6.39
Fe₂O₃	2.91	4.06	3.11	3.49	5.88	4.41
MgO	0.70	1.21	2.52	0.83	1.41	2.36
CaO	0.49	0.58	12.43	0.46	0.50	5.42
Na₂O	0.30	0.29	0.34	0.11	0.16	0.46
K₂O	0.48	0.77	0.52	0.65	0.70	0.67
SO₃	0.03	0.01	0.01	....	....	....
P₂O₅	0.05	0.06	0.12	0.05	0.04	0.05
MnO	0.11	0.00	0.06	0.02	0.04	0.02
Humus	1.64	0.11	....	1.86	0.43	....
insoluble in HCl	81.27	72.19	57.27	79.47	70.93	65.78

tent, as shown in table 88. The significant feature of the relatively high organic matter content is its gradual decrease with depth. To some degree, these characteristics may be ascribed to the high Ca content of the deciduous species. In this respect, these particular soils approach, in a small measure, the chernozem type of soil formation. More data would be necessary to establish this point.

In the chain of evidence presented on the role of biotic elements in changing a brown soil to a podzol, the Ca, in one way or another, enters into the soil reactions and influences the pH of the medium, thereby controlling the stability and mobility of the R_2O_3 and other colloid complexes in the soil.

As far as the author is aware, no well defined Braunerde of Ramann have been reported in the United States. One would expect, perhaps, to

Table 88

Organic matter and CaO distribution in a Swedish and Finnish brown forest soil

Sweden (After Lundblad)			Finland (After Aarnio)		
Depth	Humus	CaO	Depth	Humus	CaO
cm.	*per cent*	*per cent*	*cm.*	*per cent*	*per cent*
3.13	9.69	1.70	0-7 (A)	10.51	2.18
15-32	3.96	1.46	7-13 (B₁)	5.49	1.70
100-115	1.08	1.87	20-30 (B₂)	2.60	2.10
			50-60 (C)	0.47	1.80

find some among the gray-brown podzolic soils of Marbut, in the regions adjoining the southern belt of the prairie. It is also likely to be found in the forest soils of the Pacific Coast.

Krusekopf (24) distinguishes the group of brown soils as "regional, the limits of which are not well defined. These include large areas of the North-Central States, Michigan, Wisconsin, Indiana, Ohio, New York, Pennsylvania, Kentucky, Tennessee, Missouri, and portions of the surrounding states. To the north, the gray forest or true podzol soils occur; to the south, the yellow and gray soils of the more humid regions are found; to the west there is a blending with the dark prairie soils." The brown forest soils described are not typical Braunerde. They are members of Marbut's gray-brown podzolic soils.

Krusekopf points out that the "prevailing color is some shade of brown, and this prevails in both soil and subsoil." He differentiates an A_2 horizon, 3 to 10 inches in thickness, in which, in the lower portion, there is segregation of iron and an accumulation of clay. Apparently, this lower portion is a part of B_1. Most of the brown soils are, according to Krusekopf, acid in reaction, "but the acidity may not be higher than that for the black (prairie) soils."

The Miami and Russell series of soils seem to be good examples of brown forest soils. Baldwin (3) gives the following characteristics of the profile:

The surface has a covering of leaf litter from deciduous trees underlain by a very thin layer of nearly black leaf mold. The upper mineral horizon A is dark grayish-brown or grayish-yellow below; the texture is silty or silty loam; structure is single grain or, in the upper portion, soft granular; there is a roughly horizontal or platy breakage; reaction is generally acid, acidity increasing downwards (in the A horizon); the thickness varies with the composition of the parent material, up to 18 inches in the very sand material, down to 6 inches in very heavy soils. The B horizon is brown or yellow-brown in color, higher in clay content than A; the structure is prominent, the mass breaking readily into angular lumps; reaction is generally acid; thickness ranging from 1 to 2 feet.

In table 89, the chemical composition of a Miami silt loam is given.

Table 89

Chemical composition of Miami silt loam

(After Baldwin)

Depth	0-2 in.	2-5 in.	5-12 in.	16-32 in.	32-36 in.	36-
Horizon	A_1	A_2	A_3	B_2	B_3	C
	per cent	*per cent*	*per cent*	*per cent*	*per cent*	*per cent*
SiO_2	71.82	77.08	77.35	69.52	65.64	47.93
TiO_2	0.57	0.65	0.65	0.65	0.60	0.39
Fe_2O_3	2.91	3.08	3.22	5.92	5.60	3.34
Al_2O_3	9.06	9.50	10.09	14.06	14.73	8.56
MnO	0.127	0.144	0.119	0.077	0.133	0.069
CaO	0.81	0.63	0.53	0.70	1.57	13.59
MgO	0.62	0.64	0.62	1.20	1.97	6.05
K_2O	2.02	2.03	2.19	2.38	2.64	1.93
Na_2O	1.06	1.02	1.16	0.97	1.39	0.85
P_2O_5	0.13	0.10	0.08	0.09	0.12	0.09
SO_3	0.13	0.07	0.06	0.05	0.05	0.05
N	0.334	0.153	0.104	0.053	0.069	0.029
pH	5.78	5.07	5.10	5.16	7.21	8.21

It will be noted that there is an accumulation of R_2O_3 in B, and yet there is a higher CaO content in what Baldwin designates "the A_1 horizon," indicating that the organic matter is somewhat saturated with Ca. There is a fairly high N content which does not decrease very rapidly in the profile. An accumulation of P_2O_5 in the A horizon is also significant. In general, the A horizon (A_1, A_2, and A_3) is homogeneous in composition, an attribute of a brown forest soil. The definite accumulation of R_2O_3 in B indicates their translocation, a distinct podzolic feature which generally links the brown forest soils with the podzols. The "roughly horizontal or platy breakage" is a definite attribute of the podzolization effects. According to Marbut (Ch. 2, 45), these soils belong to the gray-brown forest soils. The U. S. Soil Survey workers (33, p. 1029) describe a group of *brown podzolic* soils. It is questionable whether the separation, made purely on color characteristics, is justified. These soils, located in the Northeastern states, may just as well be incorporated in the gray-brown podzolic soils. In this connection, the work of Brown and Thorp (8) on the Miami catena is of interest.

From detailed studies by the author on some of the so-called brown podzolic soils in New Jersey (Ch. 10, 23) and general observations on these soils in adjacent states, it seems that we are dealing with soils of various degrees of podzolization. Color is not necessarily a distinctive attribute of the state of podzolization. Other factors enter into play, e.g., parent material (the Triassic red shales give rise to red soils), drainage history (the chocolate brown color of the Bermuda soil series) lithogenic-orogenic (the reddish brown Montalto soil series). On the other hand, soils on parent material rich in lime, such as the Hagerstown, Washington, and Dover series, approach the characteristics of Braunerde. It looks as if we shall have to differentiate *the true Braunerde as an independent type and the more podzolized brown forest soils as a subtype of podzols.*

SECONDARY PODZOLIZED SOILS

As the name implies, these soils have developed on an early well defined soil type. In this respect, they are related to the gray forest soils. Indeed, Il'in (17) considers the secondary podzolized soils a variety of the forest steppe. However, according to Dranitsyn's (11) exhaustive studies, these soils are specific in their morphology, their distinctive characteristic being a profile with an upper and a lower humus (organic matter) A horizon, formed on bog-meadow dark colored chernozem-like soil after the invasion of forests. As a rule, the upper humus (organic matter) layer has by far a higher organic matter content. In the second humus layer, below A_2, the color is darker than that of A_1, although the percentage of organic matter is much lower. These soils have been found to be widespread in western Siberia, in the Ob'-Irtysh watershed (Narymsk region). As postulated by Dranitsyn, the bog-meadow soils have originated from chernozem solonchak as a result of a shift of the zone of podzolization towards the south. This shift implies a change in climate. Glinka (Ch. 2, 27) sees the possibility of the change in plant association, from meadow to forest, without a change in climate. An improvement in the drainage of the bog-meadow may bring about forest vegetation and podzolization.

A review of the problem on the origin of the second humus horizon of the podzolized soils of Western Siberia and additional data on the subject have been presented by Petrov (28). Ivanova and Dvinskikh (18) made a study of these soils and corrobrated the views of Dranitsyn and Petrov on the shift of the zone of podzolization as a result of a change in climate. They extracted the different horizons with 5 per cent KOH and demonstrated the presence of amorphous SiO_2, an indication of solodization. Other evidence, such as Cl content and presence of carbonates in the subsoil, corroborates the solonetzic character of the soil at some earlier time. A description of one of the profiles of the soils analyzed by these authors might help in recognizing a typical secondary-podzolized soil.

A_0: 0-2 cm.; sod and forest litter.
A_1: 2-10 cm.; dark gray heavy loam, clumps.
A_2: 10-17 cm.; gray, platy, heavy loam.
A_3: 17-30 cm.; black clay, granular-nutty, with a grayish sprinkling.
B_1: 30-50 cm.; grayish-brown, clay, small nuts, with a SiO_2 sprinkling
B_2: 50-80 cm.; dark-brown, large nuts, clay.
BC: 80-120 cm.; light brown sandy clay, with dark blotches of humus along the roots.
C: 120 cm.; light brown sandy slightly prismatic clay, with carbonates.

It is very probable that the Clermont soil series referred to as a gray forest soil should be classified with the secondary podzolic soils.

Thermal Subtypes

In line with the principles of pedology, differences should appear in the detailed features of the soil profiles in the widely separated temperature belts of the forest regions. Such differences have been noted by Tumin from the point of view of the organic matter content in relation to the geographic position—north and south of the soils. Tumin's separation of 5 belts of podzolized soils was based on differences in organic matter content with reference to the belt of genuine podzols, north and south of it. With the refinements attained in the soil classification schemes, some factor or factors of soil formation have served as a basis for separating subtypes and varieties of any one zonal type. In the case of the zone of podzolization, thermal subtypes have come into use. In the zone of podzolization of North

America, extending from the artic regions of Canada to the southern states of the United States, the thermal subtypes may easily be separated.

Northern or Arctic Podzolized Soils.—Not much information is available on the soils at the edge of the forest zone bordering the arctic region in general and still less on their profile characteristics. The thermal subtype of the so-called tundra podzols is characterized by a shallow podzolized layer and profile. These soils have been designated as dwarf podzols. The author described a dwarf profile (see table 74) located in the southern part of New Jersey on sandy material underlain by a heavy clay. Thus, dwarf profiles are not limited to the thermal belt of the subarctic. It would, perhaps, be more proper to call the soils of these regions as northern or arctic podzolized (we do speak of artic forests).

The precipitation in this thermal belt is low. In the regions of Cook Inlet, including the Kenai Peninsula, and of the valleys of the Yukon and Tanana, Alaska, the precipitation varies from 10 to 14.5 inches, the greater part of which falls in the summer and fall. It is to be remembered, however, that the evaporation in these regions is low. For more information on the soils of Alaska, the papers by Bennett and Rice (6) and others (33) are to be consulted.

Tatarinov (42) investigated the soils of Middle Karelia. In table 90, chemical data on two profiles are given. They show that the process of podzolization, while very evident, is subdued because of the low temperature (9.7°C average in the warm season and -7.7°C during the period from late October to April 17) and poor percolation (about 320 mm. of precipitation). The profiles are dwarfed, 42 and 33 cm. respectively for the light loam and the sandy loam. The data, on the basis of moisture and organic matter free soil, clearly bring out the relative accumulation of R_2O_3 and other attributes of podzolization. It is to be noted that the organic matter content of the soil was high and that it accumulated in the B horizon. This phenomenon and the deep A_0 layer indicate that these soils are related to the poorly drained subtypes in the zone of podzolization. The high organic matter content of the B horizon is also an indication of a possible ortstein formation, as pointed out by Tyurin (Ch. 10, 63, p. 204). In discussing this subtype, Tyurin states: "The podzolized type of soil formation in the cold regions is of a transitional character towards bog formation. This condition is enhanced by the presence of ever-frozen lower horizons."

Southern Podzolized Soils.—Another thermal subtype has been reported in the southern belt of the humid temperate climate bordering the subtropics. The distinctive feature of the soil forming process in this belt is the superimposition of the process of laterization on the process

Table 90

Analyses of Northern podzolized soils

(After Tatarinov)

Horizon	Depth cm.	Ash	Organic Matter	Per cent of dry soil-dried at 105°C							Exchangeable	
				SiO_2	Al_2O_3	Fe_2O_3	CaO	MgO	K_2O	P_2O_5	CaO	MgO
Strongly podzolic light loam												
A_0	0-4	35.3	63.2	29.3	3.9	0.54	1.2	0.49	0.93	0.18	0.692	0.126
A_1	4-6	92.1	7.1	76.3	9.8	1.81	1.8	0.49	1.74	0.10	0.120	0.063
A_2	6-12	98.8	1.0	82.5	6.4	1.44	1.4	0.28	1.63	0.09	0.024	0.009
B	12-24	93.7	5.0	63.6	14.5	4.52	2.0	0.69	1.80	0.19		
C	55-65	99.3	0.4	78.8	9.9	3.24	2.3	0.61	2.06	0.14		
Strongly podzolic sandy loam												
A_0	0-2	62.2	32.3	49.1	7.1	0.56	2.6	0.96	0.72	0.33	0.326	0.065
A_1	2-4	91.9	7.2	75.9	9.0	2.90	1.7	0.51	1.21	0.19	0.118	0.042
A_2	4-11	99.0	0.6	81.1	7.7	7.17	1.7	0.45	1.40	0.17	0.016	0.010
B	11-33	97.7	1.6	69.3	13.1	4.39	2.4	1.16	1.20	0.15		
C	60-70	99.3	0.3	77.7	10.6	2.15	2.6	0.96	1.18	0.15		

Table 90 (*Continued*)
Analyses of Northern podsolized soils
(After Tatarinov)

Per cent of soil after ignition						
SiO_2	Al_2O_3	Fe_2O_3	CaO	MgO	K_2O	P_2O_5
Strongly podzolic light loam						
82.8	10.9	1.5	8.5	1.4	2.6	0.51
82.9	10.6	2.0	1.9	0.5	1.9	0.11
83.4	6.5	1.5	1.4	0.3	1.7	0.09
68.2	15.6	4.8	2.2	0.7	1.9	0.20
67.8	10.0	3.3	2.3	0.6	2.1	0.14
Strongly podzolic sandy loam						
79.5	11.4	0.9	4.3	1.8	1.2	0.51
82.5	9.8	3.2	1.9	0.6	1.3	0.20
81.9	7.9	7.2	1.7	0.5	1.4	0.17
71.0	13.8	4.4	2.5	1.2	1.2	0.16
76.3	10.7	2.2	2.7	1.0	1.2	0.15

of podzolization, or the simultaneous effects of these two processes of soil formation. Rodrigues and Hardy report the presence of podzolized soils in Trinidad, and Hardon describes podzols in Borneo. (See Chapter 13 for a discussion of these reports).

Because of the favorable high temperatures and abundant precipitation in the climatic belt under consideration, decomposition of organic matter is enhanced. The A_0 layer is rapidly mineralized, releasing bases that precipitate the R_2O_3 in the A horizon. Percolation is highly effective, causing the removal of the reaction products of the processes of humification and mineralization and of the solubilized products of the native minerals and rocks. As a result of this type of reaction, the soil profile becomes depleted of the alkali and alkaline earth bases, with relatively little movement of R_2O_3. Whenever the parent material is poor in R_2O_3 and rich in SiO_2, there is a chance for the development of an A_2 bleached horizon. Such soils have been encountered by the author in Tennessee on the Cumberland plateau. With an abundance of iron, the red color of the oxides masks the SiO_2 in the A_2. A number of these soils have been described by Marbut (Ch.8,13) in connection with the presentation of the yellow and red soils of the southern states in the United States.

Yellow Forest Soils or Yellow Earths.—There is no definite understanding among pedologists about the group of yellow forest soils encountered in the humid warm climate, in proximity of the subtropics. From the reports available, these soils do not, as a rule, occur in massive areas. Here and there, they are found among the southern brown forest soils and also among the red soils of the subtropics.

Glinka (Ch.2,27,p. 311) states:

From the cursory observations on the way from Paris to Bordeaux and farther south to the border of Spain, and also on the way to Lyons, the yellow soils seem to form on all kinds of parent material, including limestone. The small quantities of organic matter, as judged by the color of the A horizon, and the appreciable quantities of R_2O_3 connect these soils with the red earths (krasnozem). However, these soils seem to have something in common with the podzolic soils. As pointed out by Bogoslovskii (7), there seems to be some evidence of the translocation of the R_2O_3. Soils of this group are apparently widespread also in Japan. France and Japan would seem to offer the best opportunity for the study of these soils. In both countries, the soils of the continental zones seem to be lacking, and it is therefore possible to follow up all the transitions from the podzols to the red earths. Similarly, such transitions may be noted in Hungary and Jugoslavia. It is probable that some of the brown forest soils, which are in general a complex group, may be associated with this group.

The term "yellow earth" has been used by Wohltmann (49) who contributed a great deal to our knowledge of the tropical and subtropical soils. He indicated that, with the retreat from the hot tropical zone toward the north and south of the equator, the laterites change into the red and yellow earths.

Lang (Ch. 5, 29), in his soil classification scheme, places the yellow earths in a region having a rain-factor—the annual rainfall over the average annual temperature—of about 60, the border-line for Braunerde. Thus, the yellow soils in France are found in a region of 600 to 750 mm. of rainfall, with an average annual temperature of 12 to 14° C.

Harrassowitz (16) points out that "red loams and yellow loams are related soil types. In neither of these is the iron being removed. *The iron hydroxide of the yellow loams is highly hydrated,* which gives it the color. Chemically, the yellow loams are characterized by a relatively high SiO_2 content. According to Lang, the figures run from 60 to 80 per cent. With this as a distinct chemical attribute, no soil with a SiO_2 content below 60 percent should be named a yellow soil." Harrassowitz found that in the subtropical and southern temperate climate yellow soils are found on parent materials rich in the silicates of calcium, whereas on a pure limestone the red soils seem to prevail. According to him, a soil having a *ki* value, the molecular ratio of SiO_2 to Al_2O_3, below 2 should be classed with the yellow earths.

Marbut (Ch.8,13) postulates that the yellow soils on the Coastal Plain are those "which until a relatively short time ago, geologically speaking, were poorly drained. The yellow soils have a well developed profile, have a gray surface, the grayness being to a considerable extent due to their sandy texture and, therefore, to the color of the sand, a pale yellow subsurface and a deep yellow B horizon, each horizon throughout its entire thickness being uniformly colored. There is no longer any evidence of waterlogging in the A or B horizons, and both of them are well developed."

In his classical work "Soils of the United States" (Ch.8,20, p. 40), Marbut discusses at greater length the yellow soils and cites a series of analyses related to these soils. Tyurin (Ch.10,63, p. 205) cites the analysis of a southern thermal subtype of yellow soils along the Black Sea in the Caucasus. He quotes Afanasiev who considers these soils as yellow podzolic.

ELUVIAL-HYDROMORPHIC, HYDROMORPHIC, AND PHYTOMORPHIC SUBTYPES

Soils of the zonal types are characterized chiefly by the broad fundamental and specific process of soil formation. For the well drained soils, the process of eluviation is the basis of soil formation. It is the release, movement, translocation, distribution, and loss of constitutents that determine the soil type. These soils are, therefore, referred to as *the eluvial series* of soil formation. Whenever the hydrologic elements interfere with normal eluviation, the *eluvial-hydromorphic* series are recognized; and whenever the eluviation process is supressed, and the soil forming process is controlled chiefly by the hydrologic elements, the *hydromorphic* series is recognized. The last two series are associated with profile characteristics determined by varying degrees of poor drainage.* Besides, there may be some *phytogenic-hydromorphic* and, perhaps, purely *phytogenic* series.

The enumerated series may constitute independent soil types, subtypes, or varieties of these. A number of subtypes and varieties of the series mentioned may be recognized in the podzol type of soil formation. Some elements of the hydromorphic series can be detected in the secondary podzolized soils described.

Glei Formation

Within the soils of the podzol zone, at the northern edge of the forest region where the tundra appears, the meadow and marsh or bog type of soil formation comes in. It is the beginning of the true marsh-tundra type. There are meadows in places where forests have disappeared, either because of fires or because of improper lumbering. There are even primary meadows, where, for some reasons not definitely established, no forests have grown. In the tundra region, the marsh type of soils dominates, giving rise to the zonal marsh-tundra type. There is one other type closely related to the marsh type, namely, the *glei* which is influenced primarily by *phytogenic-hydromorphic* and, perhaps, purely *phytogenic* series.

---

*There is another hydrologic series whereby a high water table (not accompanied necessarily with poor drainage) in the initial stages is the primary soil forming process and is followed in later stages by a change in hydrologic conditions. This series, of which the saline soils are the representative, is known as *hydrogenic*.

a rising water table, but not in such a high degree as is the marsh type. In the latter, we have the formation of a deep A_0 and an accumulation of large quantities of organic matter known as *peat* or *muck*. There is no radical change in the biosphere whenever the gleiing effects set in. Of course, there is some change in the flora, but not so much as in the marsh type, where frequently there is a complete change in the flora from forests towards mosses, sedges, etc.

In Russia, the popular understanding of glei, according to Vysotskii (46), is "a more or less compact, sticky loam or clay parent material which is not, however, as sticky as the usual loam or clay, frequently with a more or less clearly pronounced light greenish-blue tinge." Glei formation is typical for marshes and conditions of a high water table. The waterlogged state of the glei horizon (G) brings about anaerobic conditions which favor reducing reactions and minimizes leaching effects. Besides, the ground waters rise by capillary forces and enrich the glei horizon with bases, if such are in solution, and impart to it an alkaline reaction. In the reduction process, the ferric iron gives rise to the ferrous iron, and in the case of the hydroxide, the weak base changes into the stronger ferrous iron base. One should, therefore, expect a higher pH in the glei horizon, party because of this. Data on the reaction in the glei horizon bear this out. With the receding of the level of the water table, the ferrous iron is oxidized and the pH must naturally drop. This, perhaps, is the reason why some glei horizons show a lower pH than others. The downward and upward movements of the substances in solution bring about a unique condition with respect to the iron. When reduced, it becomes soluble and moves downward. Simultaneously, the rise of substances in solution by the capillary forces brings back some iron to precipitate as soon as it comes in contact with the air. We thus find an ocherous layer on the top of the glei horizon. This is probably the chief factor in the process of bog-iron formation. Whereas the upper layer of the glei horizon becomes enriched with iron, the lower layer becomes impoverished of iron. It is in this layer of the glei horizon that we find the mottling effects with the characteristic gray-bluish green tinge of the material.

Bog-iron formations are not restricted to the glei formations of the northern regions. In the Chatsworth area of New Jersey, extensive deposits of this type of iron ore were worked during the Civil War. They are located 12 to 16 inches below the surface. Some of these formations at the B-G horizon contain as much as 65 per cent Fe_2O_3, chiefly limonite (5). Vysotskii (46) reports the presence of the glei formation in the southeastern sector of the Precaspian steppe.

Glei has been studied primarily in the podzol zone and has, therefore, been associated with it. Whenever glei formation is found on a podzol soil, it is the C or B horizons which undergo the respective changes. The A₂ horizon, as a rule, remains intact, i.e., the rising waters do not reach this horizon.

Frosterus (12), in his work on the podzols, discussed the question of glei. An extensive study of glei in the podzol zone was made, under the direction of the late Glinka by Zavalishin (50). In table 91, the reaction. of a number of soils with a glei horizon is given.

In table 92, the soluble and total organic matter is recorded. With depth, the soil becomes less acid, and the glei horizon reaches the neutrality

Table 91

Reaction of soils with a glei horizon

(After Zavalishin)

Soil	Horizon	Depth	Reaction
		cm.	*pH*
Clay marsh	A₀ A₁ A₂ G G G	0-8 8-18 18-29 29-42 41-61 61-75	6.2 6.5 6.5 5.9 6.5 7.4
Clay marsh	A₁ A₂ G	0-10 10-25 25-60	5.8 5.8 7.3
Clay marsh	A₀ A₁ G	0-8 8-22 31-61	5.7 6.2 6.5
Podzolic-glei	A₁ A₂-G G	0-20 20-28 28-40	5.8 6.4 6.5
Podzolic with a glei horizon	A₁ A₂ B-G G	3-14 14-36 36-56 56-65	5.4 5.8 6.8 7.0

point. There is not much organic matter in the glei horizon, but the quantity of soluble organic matter increases with depth and is higher in the G than in the overlying A horizon, which has a higher total.

Table 92

Water soluble organic matter in soils with a glei horizon

(After Zavalishin)

Soil	Horizon	Total humus	KMnO$_4$ used for water-soluble humus	Soluble humus
		per cent	*cc.*	*per cent*
Peat podzol; podzolic glei	Humus ortstein (bog-iron)	2.25	2.55	0.00033
Peat podzol; podzolic glei	G (upper portion)	1.35	7.11	0.00093
Glei marsh	G	0.23	5.10	0.00066
Podzol, with ortsand	Humus ortsand	4.19	4.40	0.00057
Peat podzol	Lower portion of humus ortsand	2.16	10.20	0.00132
Peat podzol	G$_1$	0.51	8.15	0.00105
Peat podzol	G$_2$	0.41	8.35	0.00108
Peat marsh	G	0.34	7.85	0.00102

An interesting attribute of the glei horizon is the saturation of its exchange complex with bases. As indicated in table 93, the glei horizon differs but little from the parent material, except that it contains slightly less Ca. The Mg in the G horizon is retained more tenaciously than the Ca and is less mobile. In the other horizons, the Ca is higher than the Mg. In regions where the ground waters are rich in K and Na, the glei horizon is more sticky and in a poorer physical condition than ordinary glei. A case of this nature was described by Wityn (47-48) who found the acid and normal carbonates in the glei horizon. It is of interest that the horizon overlying the glei horizon is relatively high in absorbed Ca and Mg, probably because of the capillary rise of substances in solution.

Table 93

Exchange complex of glei soils

(After Zavalishin)

Soil	Hori-zon	Absorbed cations			Mg in terms of Ca	H in terms of Ca	Total cations in terms of Ca
		Ca	Mg	H			
		Per cent of dry soil					
Clayey marsh on a heavy loam	A₁ G₁ G₂	2.15 0.36 0.30	0.16 0.11 0.12	None None None	0.27 0.16 0.19	— — —	2.42 0.62 0.49
Podzolic glei sandy loam	A₁ A₂ G	0.12 0.05 0.07	0.02 0.005 0.007	0.0006 None None	0.03 0.01 0.01	0.012 — —	0.16 0.06 0.08
Podzolic soil with a close glei horizon	A₁ A₂ B G	0.17 0.06 0.14 0.18	0.04 0.02 0.06 0.10	0.0008 None None None	0.06 0.03 0.10 0.17	0.016 — — —	0.25 0.09 0.24 0.35
Weakly podzolized with a close G horizon on a heavy loam	A₁ A₂ B-G G	0.76 0.23 0.24 0.24	0.23 0.04 0.12 0.15	— — — —	0.38 0.06 0.20 0.25	— — — —	1.14 0.30 0.44 0.49
Weakly podzolic glei loam A normal loam	A₁ A₂-G G C	0.38 0.13 0.18 0.16	0.08 0.05 0.08 0.09	— — — —	0.13 0.08 0.13 0.15	— — — —	0.51 0.21 0.31 0.31

Another interesting attribute of the glei soils is its SiO_2 and Al_2O_3 content soluble in the $0.05N$ HCl (Gedroiz acid) and in 5 per cent KOH solution (Gedroiz method). From table 94, it is clear that the SiO_2 content extracted with the $0.05\ N$ HCl increases with depth. Practically none, however, is found in the filtrate from the podzolized A horizon, even though

Table 94

Al_2O_3 and SiO_2, extracted from glei podzols with 0.05 N HCl and 5 per cent KOH

(After Zavalishin)

Soil	Horizon	On replacing the bases by extracting with a 0.05 N HCl		5 per cent KOH extract		Molar ratio of Al_2O_3: SiO_2 from KOH extract
		Al_2O_3	SiO_2	Al_2O_3	SiO_2	
		per cent	*per cent*	*per cent*	*per cent*	
Clayey marsh on a heavy loam	A_1	1.10	Traces			
	G_1	0.40	0.12	0.36	0.44	1 :2.09
	G_1	0.46	0.13			
Clayey marsh loam	A_1	0.30	0.028			
	G	0.18	0.025	0.38	0.63	1 :2.83
Podzolic glei loam	A_1	0.30	0.012			
	A_2-G	0.16	Traces			
	G	0.16	0.020			
Podzolic glei sandy loam	A_1	0.15	Traces			
	A_2	0.08	Traces			
	G	0.10	0.01			
Podzolic loam with a close G horizon	A_1	0.18	Traces			
	A_2	0.056	Traces			
	B	0.16	0 04			
	G	0.40	0.14			
Weakly podzolized with a close G horizon on a heavy loam	A_1	0.54	—			
	A_2	0.16	Traces			
	B-G	0.30	0.08			
	G	0.38	0.24	0.42	0.81	1 :3.1

its total SiO_2 content is highest, as compared with the other horizons. The same is almost true for the A_1 horizon. The highest quantity of SiO_2 goes into solution from the glei horizon after the Ca has been replaced. To appreciate more fully the significance of the data, we must consider the figures presented by Zavalishin on the SiO_2 extract from other soils by the same method. "The B horizon of a sandy podzol from the Leningrad district gave 0.06 per cent SiO_2; the B horizon of a loam from the same district, 0.03 per cent; an ortsand of a sandy podzol from the Valdai county, 0.01 per cent; an ortstein from Pavlovsk, 0.08 per cent; the B horizon of a red soil from the Bengaza steppe desert, 0.32 per cent; an ortstein of a podzol sandy loam in the Murman region on the river Tuloma, 0.18 per cent."

As a rule, the HCl soluble SiO_2 of genuine podzols or of podzolic horizons lags behind that of the glei horizon. Apparently, there is some decomposition of the base exchange complex in the glei horizon. Zavalishin adds "that probably some amorphous SiO_2 is carried to the glei horizon from the upper horizon and from the ground waters."

As to the HCl soluble alumina, Zavalishin points out:

In the glei horizon, it is higher than in A_2 and in most cases lower than in A_1. In the B horizon, the soluble aluminum is even higher than in the A_1 horizon.

Turning our attention to the results of the alkali (5 per cent KOH) extract, it is to be noted that in the soils investigated the molar ratio of $Al_2O_3:SiO_2$ fluctuates between 1:2.09 and 1:3.8. Thus, there is a slight excess of SiO_2. This indicates the probability of the splitting off of SiO_2 by the action of the ground waters.

Another important feature in the geliing process is the presence of ferrous iron in the glei horizon. Zavalishin investigated a series of soils and presented his findings in a series of tables. A summary of these findings follows:

1. No water-soluble ferrous compounds have been found in the soils investigated. 2. The lower hydroxide makes up the bulk of FeO found (as determined on H_2SO_4 extract). Some ferrous compounds of phosophoric acid are encountered. Small quantities of ferrous compounds of sulfur are found. 3. The highest quantity of FeO found in the G horizon of the clayey marsh loam soil (1.4 per cent), the smallest in the transition horizons A_2G and B-G of the podzolic soils with a close glei horizon. 4. The quantity of ferrous iron does not go beyond the limit of 20 per cent of the total iron. 5. The solubility of the FeO compounds varies in the different horizons when subjected to the gleing process; it is highest in the upper parts of the glei horizon, in A-G and B-G. 6. Not all the forms of FeO compounds in the soil are easily oxidized in the air.

In table 95, Zavalishin presents data on the total constituents of a number of glei profiles. He makes the following remarks:

Although the data show no sharp fluctuations in the composition of the different horizons, a number of points are worthy of notice. Of all the constituents, the Al_2O_3 seems to be the most mobile. It is clear that A_2 becomes impoverished and B enriched with Al_2O_3, while the least mobility takes place in the glei horizon. The iron does leach slightly from the G horizon, but in these samples it is weakly expressed. In the podzol sandy types, the glei horizon occupies a position intermediate between the true podzol horizon and the parent material, suffering, however, a definite loss of iron. The latter goes into solution only either at the outset of the gleing process or periodically when the horizon becomes saturated with water enriched with organic substances and primarily with carbonic acid. This phenomenon finds its corroboration in the separation of iron formations in the form of bog ore at the lower points of the clayey and peat-glei bogs. In these places, the ground waters, as they reach the surface, become enriched with organic matter and their products of decomposition.

Table 95

Total analyses of several glei podzol soils

(After Zavalishin)

Soil	Horizon	On basis of dry soil			On basis of mineral portion of soil				
		Hygroscopic water	Chemically combined water	Humus	SiO$_2$	Fe$_2$O$_3$	Al$_2$O$_3$	CaO	MgO
		per cent	per cent	per cent	per cent	per cent	per cent	per cent	per cent
Podzolic loam with a close glei horizon	A$_1$	4.93		12.69	73.28	3.82	16.85	2.28	1.84
	A$_2$	1.25	1.19	1.28	77.48	3.40	13.86	1.84	1.52
	B-G	1.29	2.53	0.40	72.18	2.50	18.44	2.62	1.65
	G	1.75	1.47	0.30	75.10	3.15	15.42	2.84	1.50
Podzolic loam with a close glei horizon	A$_1$	3.56		10.64	74.24	3.05	14.85	2.76	1.94
	A$_2$	2.02		4.50	77.35	3.08	13.40	1.88	1.46
	B	2.65	2.20	0.42	74.25	5.25	14.27	2.00	1.50
	G	2.30	1.88	0.20	74.50	3.18	16.30	1.92	1.64
Podzolic sandy soil with a close glei horizon	A$_2$	0.10			93.42	0.48	6.08	0.30	0.09
	G	0.25			92.55	0.62	7.25	0.50	0.14
	C	0.30			89.92	1.20	7.85	0.80	0.25
Weakly podzolic sandy soil with a glei horizon	G	0.20			91.25	0.70	6.90	0.50	0.13
	C	0.30			90.01	1.00	7.15	0.60	0.11

The bases leach but slightly from the G horizon, a great deal less than from A_2. In general, there is not much loss of the alkaline earths, the Mg being particularly stable.

Thus, the total analyses seem to to indicate a certain similarity between the glei and the podzolized horizons. The decrease of hygroscopic and chemically combined water in the glei horizons points in the same direction. The similarity, however, is slight; thus, chemically the glei horizon resembles more the parent material than the podzol. Fluctuations in the total analyses of the glei horizon are, of course, probable. These depend in a large measure on the movement of the moisture which brings about the gleiing effects, i.e., the rapidity with which the solution introduces changes in the soil. It is therefore clear that a sandy loam glei, because of the aforementioned, will change more than a clay. And incidentally, the process of removing substances in the gleiing reaction is a secondary phenomenon. The primary phenomenon — the change from the higher to the lower states of oxidation — is more prominent in clays than in sands. It is well to remember that other sooil horizons, even the A_2, may be subject to the gleiing process with the change in the level of the water table. A chemical analysis of such a horizon may lead to wrong interpretations.

The Oxygen Factor in Glei Formation.—Tamm (39) investigated the oxygen tension in the ground waters of a number of soils affected by a high water table. His results, compiled in table 96, bring out a number of points bearing on the problem of glei formation.

A comparison of the oxygen content in the ground waters of moraine soils with that of open bodies of water, springs, and streams shows that the former contain less dissolved oxygen. However, if we compare the dissolved oxygen content of moraine soils with that of soils containing a deep organic matter layer with spots of peat and a moss cover, we find that the moraine soils are fairly rich in dissolved oxygen. In the peat areas bordering the extensive marshes, the ground waters are rich in oxygen, except at one point, at a depth of 66 cm. On the other hand, the ground waters of the fringes of the marsh, having a thin layer of peat, are free or very poor in oxygen. Similarly, the ground waters of the belt of soils bordering the marsh which has a layer of peat 15 to 25 cm. thick show a very low oxygen content. According to Tamm, the apparent discrepancies are due to the movement of the ground waters. Whenever there is a free movement of the ground waters from the dry areas through the marsh, there is oxygen even under the peat. In the case of stagnant waters, the oxygen as it penetrates the peat is utilized, and the ground waters show a low oxygen content. Tamm points out that rainwater percolating through peat loses its oxygen, whereas through a normal A horizon it is carried downward. Zavalishin (50) cites areas of the latter type, with poor stands of pine under which the soil has undergone the effects of gleiing.

Tamm also shows that in cases where the ground waters from a marsh, because of topographic and geologic conditions, flow through coarse textured strata, ortstein formations appear which ultimately clog the underground channel. Apparently, the reduced iron compounds in the marsh waters oxidize, precipitate, and accumulate an *allochtonic* ortstein, using Tamm's nomenclature.

Table 96

Oxygen content of ground waters in soils related to the marsh or bog type of soil formation

(Compiled from Tamm's data)

Source of sample	Depth	Oxygen per liter of water	Source of sample	Depth	Oxygen per liter of water
	cm.	cc.		cm.	cc.
Open body of water		8.05	Edges or fringes of marshes with a thin layer of peat	120	0.00
				120	0.08
Open body of water		8.35		55	0.12
				55	0.12
				100	0.34
Moraine soil in neighborhood of open body of water	245	3.21		100	0.35
	245	3.72			
	245	3.80			
		3.96	An island of dry soil in a marsh	80	4.39
				120	2.15
				185	0.42
				225	0.00
	30	1.61			
Under soils with a deep humus layer with spots of peat and a moss cover	30	0.28			
	105	2.53			
	105	2.78	Belt of soil bordering the marsh, with a 15-25 cm. peat layer	30	0.32
	30	0.00		40	0.05
	30	0.00		60	0.54
	85	3.04		100	1.30
				130	2.20
	63	3.99			
	95	4.68			
Areas of peat bordering the extensive marshes	95	5.82			
	66	0.00			
	85	1.98			
	70	2.21			
	95	2.70			

Zavalishin (50) infers from Tamm's results and his own observations that the "oxygen determinations of the ground waters may explain the frequent failures of forest stands in certain areas, the formation of ortstein in such areas, and the formation of the glei horizons. According to Tamm, water percolating through a peat horizon, 40 to 50 cm. deep, loses its oxygen. Coming in contact with the ground waters that are saturated with oxygen, a new hydrological system forms whereby the two sources of water are not related hydrostatically. This may explain why the more bluish glei horizons free from iron concretions are always encountered under the clayey or peat-clayey horizons A_0 and A_1. There are least penetrable by the oxygen. At any rate, no ortstein formations are found under clayey or peat horizons."

Zavalishin sums up the discussion on glei as follows:

The glei horizon appears in the form of a sandy or clay material of a light gray or gray color, with a bluish hue, or sky-blue tinge. The color is not uniform; it depends on the intensity of gleiing and on the mechanical composition of the material. Usually, the gray-blue background is mottled with large red spots and veins. These spots, found more frequently with clays, are associated with cracks and root paths. Around the roots, the spots may be of two kinds. If decomposed organic substances are present in the root path, a light gray-bluish glei formation with a reddish band on the outside develops. If, on the other hand, the gleiing has proceeded very far and the root path is nothing more than a tube through which air passes, then a red ring forms around it on a light gray-bluish background. When the gleiing is very strong, the material is of a homogenous gray-blue coloration without any spots or veins. Glei horizons, especially sandy, at times resemble podzols; the bluish tinge and the red spots identify it, however, as glei.

Usually, the glei horizons are without structure, more or less compact, sticky, smeary, and appear to be more clayey than the adjoining parent material. A suspension of glei formation does not settle out and is highly dispersed.

The humus content is higher in the upper layer of the glei horizon than in the lower. The solubility of the humus increases with an increase in gleiing. With that, the reducing property of the glei increases and this in turn influences the reducing reactions with respect to the iron compounds.

According to Tyurin (Ch.10,63, p. 222), the G horizon is frequently enriched with Mn in the form of spots and concretions. As the water table rises and the increased depth of the A_0 layer supplies soluble organic matter, the iron formation at the G horizon becomes enriched with humic substances. Whenever the water table reaches the surface, "the ochre-iron glei horizon disappears and the illuvial horizon is distinctive with its accumulation of humus."

Tyurin (p. 224) describes five varieties of glei, differing in their profile characteristics because of the variability in the intensity of the hydrologic elements:

1. Podzol with iron-ocherous ortstein.
   A_0 (forest litter), A_1, A_2, B(Fe), G, C.
2. Peat-podzol with a humus-iron ortstein:
   A_0 (peat-like), A_1, A_2, B(h), B(Fe), G. C.
3. Peat podzol with humus ortstein:
   A_0 (peat-like), A_1, A_2, B(h), G. C.
4. Peat-podzolic-glei soil:
   A_0 (peat-like), A_1, A_2, G. C.
5. Peat-glei soil
   A_0(peat-like), A_1, G. (C).

"The depth of the peat-like layer in the peat-podzolic soils is generally not more than 25-30 cm. With a greater depth of this layer, the soil loses its attributes of the eluvial series of soil formation, and changes into a typical marsh (No. 5), and finally into a peat deposit."

In his excellent monograph on the soils of South Africa, van der Merwe (27, p. 174) presents data and a discussion on some glei-podzolic soils. A valuable adjunct to the descriptions are the fine illustrations (in colors) of the glei profiles.

A Glei-Like Podzol in New Jersey.—A study has been made on the effect of a high water table in a podzol sandy soil of the Collington series in New Jersey. The profile is located on the Freehold Area of the Soil Survey of New Jersey, between the parallels 40° 16'-18' north latitude and between the meridans 70° 8'-10' longitude. The profile cut was made in a wooded section just about where the road running north and south in the particular sector crosses the Hockhocken Brook. The topography of the section is level, with microrelief features. Geologically, it belongs to the Coastal Plain Province which consists of formations of unconsolidated, almost horizontal beds of gravel, sand, sandy clay, and marls, with a slight dip to the coast. The formations are chiefly Tertiary, the upper Miocene. The climate is characterized by the relatively narrow daily and monthly ranges of temperature. The rainfall is rather heavy, averaging about 50 inches annually, with a minimum of about 40 and a maximum of over 70 inches. The mean annual temperature is about 50° F., with an absolute minimum of —11°F. and an absolute maximum a little over 100°F. During the winter, the ground freezes, occasionally a few inches deep, but these frosts do not last very long and are alternated by mild weather which quickly thaws out the frozen ground. The humidity is relatively high, except during some periods in the fall. An important feature of the rainfall is its relatively even distribution.

The vegetation consists of a stand of second growth hardwoods, 20 to 50 years old; red maple, black and white oak, sweet gum, gray birch, and iron-wood. Of the more prominent herbaceous vegetation noted are: smilax, carex, cinquefoil, and star flower.

Morphological Characteristics.—The morphological features of the profile under consideration are as follows:

A_0: 0 to 2 cm. deep; forest debris of dead leaves and twigs, some slightly decomposed and some still fresh.

A_1: 10 cm. deep; dark gray, with a sprinkling of silica; structureless; sandy texture; charcoal found in upper portion.

A_2: 25 cm. deep; light brown; sandy texture but heavier at the bottom; structure tending toward lamination; poor in organic matter.

B : 15 cm. deep; reddish brown (coffee color); slightly heavier than A_2; iron incrustations found in the upper portion; the structure is more distinctly expressed.

G :   A typical glei formation; color grades into a bluish gray; dark iron concretions are scattered through the horizon; tongues of iron formation penetrate it; greensand marl is found below a depth of 65 cm.; the water table, at the time of examination, was at that depth.

Chemical Characteristics.—The outstanding feature of the chemical data, presented in table 97, is the high acidity of the soil. Both the pH and the unsaturation clearly shows that with depth the acidity increases. This is not in accord with the findings of Zavalishin and the other Russian investigators who claim that the G horizon, as a rule, is less acid than the overlying horizon. Apparently, the composition of the ground waters enters as a factor in determining the reaction of the glei horizon. In this particular case, the ground waters from the adjoining areas have proved to be acid, pH 5.2 and even lower.

If it were not for the absence of a morphologically apparent A_2 horizon, this profile could be interpreted chemically as a genuine podzol. The high SiO_2 content in A_2 and the accumlation of R_2O_3 in the B horizons point in this direction. There are, however, a few departures from the true chemical features of a podzol. Thus, for instance, the Ca content is not higher in the B than the A_2 horizon, the *usual* case in podzols. Neither is the pH of the B typical for a true podzol, in which it is usually higher than in the A_2 horizon. Morphologically, the B horizon has also been affected by the gleiing process. Instead of being 40 to 50 c. thick, as in the adjacent normal podzols (the Lakewood soil series), it is only 15 cm. The slight variations in the chemical composition of the B and G horizons may be attributed to the gleiing effects. It is of interest to note that the Mg accumulates in the G horizon, a typical attribute of the gleiing process. The high K content is probably due to the glauconite in the greensand marl parent material.

General Statement.—The profile under consideration is located at the fringe of a swamp area; there are indications that the water is coming in from a higher level contains appreciable quantities of dissolved oxygen. The orstein veins, the orterde concretions, and the tongue-like iron formation projections in the G horizon are ample evidence of the high oxygen content in the ground waters which tends to obliterate some of the gleiing effects.

We may thus look upon this soil as a glei-like podzol, a sort of transition to the peat podzol which adjoins this particular area. After all, the process of gleiing and the marsh type of soil formation, of which the peat podzol is one of the subtypes, are closely related.

Phytomorphic and Hydromorphic Varieties.—The biosphere, as discussed earlier (Ch. 5), is a factor of soil formation dependent upon the climate. There are, however, situations where the plant association leaves its mark on the profile constitution of the zonal type and introduces a vari-

Table 97

Chemical composition of a glei podzol sandy soil in New Jersey

Hori-zon	pH		SiO₂	Al₂O₃	Fe₂O₃	CaO	MgO	K₂O	N	Base exchange capacity	Un-saturation (H-ions)
	Water extract	Neutral salt solution extract	per cent	per cent	per cent	per cent	per cent	per cent	per cent	m. e.	m. e.
A₁	5.2	4.2	84.79	1.38	2.1	0.264	0.190	0.360	0.173	14.38	13.17
A₂	5.4	4.6	90.69	1.73	3.5	0.216	0.272	0.485	0.0485	6.36	3.67
B	5.1	4.4	83.82	2.55	6.23	0.189	0.282	0.420	0.0745	9.56	6.55
G	4.9	4.6	84.23	3.08	5.15	0.185	0.363	0.545	0.0855	9.92	8.45

ety of soils. Beech forests in Sweden, developed on a podzol change it to a brown forest soil, or vice versa, conifers developed on brown forest soils change it to a podzol; these phenomena are an expression of *phytomorphic* reactions.

Meadow podzols within the gray-brown podzolic soils, podzols, or gray forest soils represent a *phytomorphic-hydromorphic* variety of the podzolized soil type. River valley meadows, mountain, solodi, and watershed meadows are subject to this variety of podzols. In their morphology, these podzols resemble the glei podzols, inasmuch as they sometime show ortstein formation. Generally, however, they are darker in color (dark gray to black) then the glei podzols, especially in the A_1 horizon. The bleached A_2 is usually well developed. The B horizon is usually mottled, wth streaks of brown along the paths of the roots. These soils are sometime referred to as sod-podzols.

Peat and muck podzols are also hydromorphic varieties. These soils also resemble glei podzols, but need not necessarily have cemented hardpan. A coffee-brown layer approaching the consistency of hardpan is frequently encountered. The A_2 layer is usually very acid and has a low R_2O_3 content in comparison with the B and C horizons. They are also poor in Ca, Mg, and K. Of course, the composition of the water table has its influence on these soils.

Sandy parent materials, subject to seasonal waterlogging, give rise to a variety known as *sandy podzols*. They have a shallow A_1, grayish in color, with some organic matter of the A_0 interdispersed. The A_2 is a deep bleached layer, resting on slightly heavier material of the B horizon which shows coffee-brown coloration. In some of these soils, the coffee-brown material attains the consistency of hardpan. The St. John and Leon series of soils in the Coastal Plain of the United States are typical representatives of this podzol variety.

References

1. Aarnio, B. 1925 Brown earths in Finland. *Proc. Inter. Soc. Soil Sci.* n.s. 1 : 71-77.

2. Antipov-Karataev, I. N., Antonova, M. A., and Illuvier, V. P. 1929 The soils of the Nikitskii gardens. Otdel Pochvoved. Gosudarstv. Inst. Opyt. Agron. Bul. 4: 1-241.

3. Baldwin, M. 1928 The gray-brown podzolic soils of the eastern United States. *Proc. and Papers Inter. Soc. Soil Sci.* 4: 276-282.

4. Ballenegger, R. 1920 Über die chemische Zusamensetzung ungarischer Bodentypen. *Jahresber. Kgl. ungar. geol. Reichsanst.* für 1916. 509-601 (After Stremme).

5. Bayley, W. S. 1910 Iron mines and mining. v. 7. Final report ser. of State Geologist, *Geol. Sur. of New Jersey,* 25-32.

6. Bennett, H. H. and Rice, Th. D. 1919 Soil reconnaissance in Alaska with an estimate of the agr. soil possibilities. *U. S. Bureau of Soils Field Operations* 1914, *Rept.* 16: 213-236.

7. Bogoslovskii, N. 1902 Observations on the soils of western Europe. *Pochvovedenie* (Pedology) 4: 357-368.

8. Brown, I. C., and horp, J. 1942 Morphology and composition of some soils of the Miami family and the Miami catena. Tech. Bul. No. 834, U. S. Dept. of Agriculture.

9. Byers, H. G. and Anderson, M. S. 1931 The composition of soil colloids in relation to soil classification. *J. Phys. Chem.* 36: 348-66.

10. Conrey, G. W. 1927 A study of the profile of Clermont silt loam. *Amer. Soil Sur. Assoc. Bul.* 8: 1-8.

11. Dranitsyn, D. 1914 Secondary podzols and the transfer of the zone of podzolization towards the southern Ob-Irtysh watershed (Russian). *Izv. Dokuchaev. Pochv. Komiteta* No. 2.

12. Frosterus, B. 1913 Soil formation on clays of humid regions. *Inter. Mitt. Bodenkunde.* 3: 99-130.

13. Geering, J. 1936 Beitrag zur Kenntnis der Braunerdebildung auf Molasse in Schweizerischen Mittleland. *Landw. Yahr. der Schweiz.* 50: 136-207.

14. Gordyagin, A. Y. 1900 Contribution to the study of the soils and vegetation of Western Siberia. *Trudy Obshches. Estestv. pri. Kazan. Universit.* 34, No. 3; 35 (1901), No. 2; also: Vegetation of the Tartar Republic, Kazan (After Tyurin).

15. Gorshenin, K. P. 1924 The influence of forest plantings on the chemical and morphological constitution of chernozem. *Pochvovedenie* (Pedology) No. 3-4: 41-48.

16. Harrassowitz, H. 1930 Gelberden oder Gelblehme. Blanck's *Handbuch der Bodenlehre* 3: 182-193.

17. Il'in, R. S. 1927 On the problem of the border between the podzol and forest steppe zones. *Pedology* (U.S.S.R.) No. 3: 5-26.

18. Ivanova, E. N., and Dvinskikh, P. A. 1944 Secondary podzolized soils of the Urals. *Pedology* (U.S.S.R.) No. 7-8: 325-344.

19. Keller, B. A. 1916 On the problem of classifying the Russian steppes. *Russkii Pochvoved.* nos. 16-18 (after Tyurin).

20. Korzhinskii, S. 1891 The northern boundary of the chernozem steppe region of the eastern belt in European Russia, etc. *Trudy Obshches. Estestv. pri Kazanskom Universit.* 22, no. 6: 1-204; also v. 18, no. 5.

21. Kostychev, P. 1883 On the chernozem belt in Voronezh, etc. *Sel'skoe Khozyaistvo i Lesovodstvo,* no. 4 and 5. (After Tyurin). See also *Trudy St. Peterb. Obshches. Estest,* 20: 123:168. (After Glinka).

22. Kravkov, S. P. 1912 Investigations on the role of the dead vegetation layer in the process of soil formation. *Materialy po Izucheniyu Russkikh Pochv.* 21: 1-170; 22: 1-98.

23. Krylov, P. N. 1915 On the problem of the fluctuation of the border line between the forest and steppe regions. *Trudy Botan. Kabineta Imper. Akad. Nauk,* No. 14: 82-130.

24. Krusekopf, H. H. 1925 The brown soils of the No.-Central States *Amer. Soil Sur. Assn. Bul.* 6, 2: 146-148.

25. Levchenko, F. I. 1930 Gray soils of the forest steppe in the European part of the U.S.S.R. *Pedology* (U.S.S.R.) No. 3: 49-72.

25a. Lundblad, K. 1934 Studies on podzols and brown forest soils. I: *Soil Sci.* 37: 137-155; II: (1936) 41: 295-313; III: 41: 381-394.

26. Mattson, S. 1932 The laws of soil colloidal behavior: IX, Amphoteric reactions and isoelectric weathering. *Soil Sci.* 34: 209-240.

27. Merwe, van der, C. R. 1941 Soil groups and subgroups of South Africa. *Science Bul.* 231, Dept. of Agr. and Forestry, Chem. Ser. No. 165, pp. 316, Pretoria, S. Africa.

28. Petrov, B. F. 1937 On the question of the origin of the second humus horizon in the podzolized soils of Western Siberia (Russian). *Trudy Tomsk. Gosud. Univers.* 92, ser. G. (Quoted from Ivanova and Dvinskikh).

29. Polynov, B. B. 1915 Secondary minerals of ortstein horizons. *Izv. Dokuchaev. Pochv. Komit.* 3, no. 2: 125-138.

30. Polynov, B. B. 1915 Soils of the Dniepr and Don sand terraces within the boundaries of the chernozem steppe belt. *Izv. Dokuchaev. Pochv. Komit.,* no. 3. (After Tyurin).

31. Prasolov, L. I. 1929 The brown earths of Crimea and the Caucasus. Priroda. no. 5 (From *Proc. Inter. Soc. Soil Sci.* (1930), 5 (2): 125).

32. Smolik, L. 1928 The pedochemistry of Moravian soil types. Cesko- sloven. Akademic Zemledelske. Prague. (Quoted from *Proc. Int. Soc. Soil Sci.* 4: 113-119).

33. Soils and Men. 1938 U. S. Dept. of Agr. Yearbook. Washington, D. C.

34. Stebut, A. 1930 Lehrbuch der allgemeinen Bodenkunde. Gebrüder Borntraeger, Berlin.

35. Stremme, H. 1930 Die Braunerde. Blanck's *Handbuch der Boden- lehre* 3: 160-182.

36. Taliev, V. 1902 Pressing problems of botanical geography. Estestven. Nauka i Geograph. (After Tyurin).

37. Tamm, O. 1920 Soil studies in the needle forest region of Northern Sweden. *Meddel. Statens Skogsförsöksanst.* 17: 49-300. (German Summary 279-300).

38. Tamm, O. 1922 Om bestämmung av de ôorganiska komponenterna i markens gelkomplex. *Medd. fr. Statens Skogsförsöksanst.* 19: 385-404 (After Lundblad).

39. Tamm, O. 1925 Ground water movement and stagnation processes explained by oxygen analyses of the ground waters of North Swedish moraines. *Medd. Statens Skogsförsöksanst.* 22, no. 1 (From Internat. Rev. Sci. and Pract. Agr. 4: 347).

40. Tamm, O. 1930 The brown forest soils in Sweden. *Ztsch, Schwed. Forstvereins* 28: 1-41.

41. Tamm, O. 1932 Der braune Waldboden in Schweden. *Proc. and Papers, Second Internat. Cong. of Soil Sci.* 5: 178-189.

42. Tatarinov, S. F. 1938 The nature of podzolized soils of Middle Karelia. *Pedology* (U.S.S.R.) No. 9: 1145-1161.

43. Tkachenko, M.E. 1908 The forest in soil formation. *Izv. Imper. Lesnogo Inst.* No. 18: 1-144.

44. Tumin, G. M. 1930 The influence of forest strips on the soils of the Kamennaya Steppe. Kamenno-Steppe. Opyt. Stan. im. Dokuchaeva (Lenin Acad. Agr. Sci.), Voronezh, pp. 1-40.

45. Tyurin, I. V. 1930. Genesis and classification of forest steppe and forest soils. (English) *Pedology* (U.S.S.R.) 25, no. 5: 104-141. See also his Pochvy Lesostepi (Forest steppe soils). Pochvy U.S.S.R. v. 1 (1939).

46. Vysotskii, G. N. 1905 Glei. *Pochvovedenie* (Pedology) 7: 291-327.

47. Wityn, J. 1924 Die Hauptphasen des Podsolbildungsprozesses. Riga.

48. Wityn (Vitins), J. 1934 The glei process. Reprint of the Proc. IX Agron. Congress in Latvia, Riga (Latvian and German) pp. 1-14.

49. Wohltmann, F. 1891 Über den Kulturwert der tropischen Lateritboden. *J. Landw.* 39: 149-159.

50. Zavalishin, A. A. 1928 Some obesrvations on the study of soils with a close glei horizon. Pamyati K. D. Glinka (K. D. Glinka: A memorial). Leningrad Sel'sko-Khoz. Inst., 45-90.

CHAPTER XII.

TUNDRA TYPE OF SOIL FORMATION

The word tundra has its origin in the Finnish word *tunturi,* a flat barren plateau. In popular Russian language, the term *tundra* implies every kind of muck. As described by the arctic explorers, the tundra is a treeless waste bordering on the Polar Sea. It is a vast treeless plain in the arctic region projecting into the forest zone, making a rather sinuous and irregular border line.

Geikie (4) states:

In America, these tundra wastes are known as barren grounds. They form plains of immense extent, but of very unequal width from north to south. In Eurasia, they lie for the most part north of the Arctic circle, while in N. America they range upon the whole considerably further south . . . When the flat lands are exposed to the full sweep of the northern blasts, tundra conditions advance far to the south, invading the forest zone in narrower or broader stretches. Indeed, even within the region of arctic forests, isolated patches and wider areas of tundra are encountered. In other places, more sheltered from the fierce winds coming from the Polar Sea, the arctic forests in their turn encroach upon the tundras, so as nearly to reach the shores of the frozen ocean.

According to estimates made by Prasolov, the tundra zone in European Russia alone occupies an area of about 243,000 square kilometers. Its area in Siberia is many times greater than that.

Perpetually Frozen Ground.—By far, the largest portion of the tundra region conincides in its distribution with the area of the perpetually (perennially or ever) frozen ground, *permafrost,* in the language of U. S. Army engineers who have investigated the regions of the Alaskan interior during World War II.

Nikiforoff (18,19) who investigated the frozen areas of Siberia summarized his own work as well as that of Sumgin (27) as follows:

The phenomenon of a perpetually frozen subsoil extends over a vast region in Asia covering more than three million square miles, almost as large an area as the United States and Alaska together. On the north, it reaches in the Arctic Ocean and, at several places near the coast, ice has actualy been found on the bottom of the sea. Its southern boundary is very irregular. Beginning on the west in European Russia near the town of Mesen, on the coast of the White Sea, it closely follows the 65th parallel of latitude, eastward to the Yenisei River in Siberia, where it turns sharply southward and continues in this direction to a point about 150 miles west of Lake Baikal, in south central Siberia. There it crosses the Chinese boundary and extends for some distance into Mongolia, to about the 49th degree of latitude, corresponding to the southern boundary of Canada west of the Province of Ontario. To the north and east and extending to the Arctic and Pacific Oceans, the subsoil of Siberia is continously frozen below a depth of 4 to 10 feet from the surface, except for a relatively narrow strip along the Sea of Japan and the Sea of Okhotsk, consisting of the district between Vladivostock and Khabarovsk, the lower part of the Amur River basin and the southern portion of

436

the Kamchatka peninsula. This vast area extends more than two thousand miles from north to south and several thousand miles from east to west.

The depth to which the soil thaws during the warm but short summer does not depend entirely upon the latitude, but rather upon the character of the vegetation and the physical properties of the upper layers of the soil. Close to the ArcticCircle and on the 55th parallel of latitude, it is more or less uniform. The mosses, especially sphagum, offer the best protection against melting. During the whole summer, ice and frozen soil are commonly found a foot or two beneath the moss and sometimes even within a few inches of it. The sands and other drier soils, especially if they are not covered by a thick growth of grasses, thaw out to greater depths, varying from six to ten feet, while the loams and clays do not thaw to more than three to five feet.

In general, the thickness of the frozen layer varies from north to south, being thicker in the north, where it reaches hundreds of feet. Exact measurements have not been made as to the maximum thickness. At the city of Yakutsk, which is situated on the Lena River, several deep wells were dug in the hope of securing a supply of good drinking water. One of these wells was 382 feet deep and the temperature of the ground near the bottom of it was -3°C. From computations based upon temperature determinations throughout the whole depth of this well, it is concluded that the general thickness of the frozen layer at Yakutsk must be between 550 and 650 feet. Towards the southern boundary, the thickness gradually decreases, several points have beeen found between the 50th and 55th parallels, where the frozen layer was only from 100 to 250 feet thick.

Taber (29) estimates that the total area in perennial frost in North America is 2 million square miles. "In Canada, ground is perennially frozen north of a line extending from the vicinity of the Yukon-British Columbia boundary (lat. 60°N) to a point south of Flinton (lat. 54° 45′N) and thence eastward toward James Bay where the line is perhaps 1° or 2° farther south. Over most of the perennially frozen ground of Alaska, annual precipitation is less than 15″. Forests cover about half of the area of perennially frozen ground; tundra vegetation—most of the remainder. The trees are: spruce, birch, poplar, aspen, willow, alden, and tamarack. Spruce is the most widley distributed. In tundra, lichens, mosses, sedges, grasses, berries, low bushes, and dwarf species of birch and willow predominate. Because of the frozen ground, swampy conditions prevail . . . The tundra vegetation covers much of the forest floor."

In table 98, compiled from Middendorf's (17) work as reported by Sumgin, the temperature variations to a depth of 382 feet in a perpetually frozen soil are given. At a depth of 7 feet, the highest temperature,—3.8°C., occurred in September. Seven feet away from the wall of the well-shaft, the temperature for the same month was slightly lower. The lowest temperature at this depth and at the 15-foot depth occurred not during the real winter months, but toward the spring. Nikiforoff (18,19) points out:

The annual minimum temperature in northeastern Siberia occurs in January. The minimum in the well at a depth of 7 feet, minus 14.1°C., was found in March and April, and at 20 feet in May. According to the ten-year meteorological records oof the Bomnak Experiment Station, in the province of Amur, at a depth of 2.8 meters, the mean annual temperature is -9°C, the maximum usually occurring in January and the minimum in the early part of May. Thus, at this depth both the annual maximum and the annual minimum occur approximately five months later than at the surface.

Table 98

Observations on soil temperature in the Shergin shaft of a well at Yakutsk

(From Middendorf's work as reported by Sumgin)

Depth in feet

	7		15		20		50		100		150		200		250		300		350		382	
	1*	7*	1	7	1	7	1	7	1	7	1	7	1	7	1	7	1	7	1	7	1	7
	°C.		°C.		°C.		°C.		°C.		°C.		°C.		°C.		°C.		°C.		°C.	
1845																						
Junet	−8.0	−8.5	−10.7	−11.4	−11.8	−12.0	−9.6	−8.3	−6.6	−6.5	−5.9	−5.8	−5.0	−5.2	−3.3	−4.1	−3.1	−4.0	−3.2	−3.4	—	−3.0
July	−6.4	−7.1	−10.0	−10.7	−11.8	−11.0	−10.1	−8.3	−6.7	−6.5	−5.9	−5.8	−5.1	−5.2	−3.3	−4.3	−3.1	−4.0	−3.2	−3.4	—	−3.0
August	−4.8	−5.6	−8.7	−9.3	−12.5	−10.1	−10.2	−8.4	−6.7	−6.5	−6.3	−5.9	−5.2	−5.4	−3.5	—	−3.2	−4.0	−3.2	−3.4	—	—
September	−3.8	−4.9	−7.3	−8.4	−12.6	−9.2	−10.0	−8.3	−6.6	−6.4	−6.4	−5.9	−5.1	−5.3	−3.5	—	−3.3	−3.9	—	−3.4	−3.1	—
October	−4.3	−4.0	−7.3	−7.5	—	−8.5	−10.0	−8.3	−6.6	−6.4	−6.4	−5.8	−5.1	−5.5	−3.5	—	−3.3	−4.0	—	−3.4	−3.1	—
November	−6.0	−4.1	−8.5	−7.9	—	−8.1	−10.3	−8.4	−6.7	−6.4	−6.5	−5.8	−5.1	−5.6	−3.5	—	−3.1	−4.0	—	−3.4	−3.1	—
1846																						
February	−16.4	−16.0	−10.9	−9.9	—	−9.6	−10.5	−8.3	−6.8	−6.6	−6.5	−5.8	−5.2	−5.6	—	—	−3.2	−4.0	—	−3.4	—	−3.1
April	—	−14.9	—	−12.8	—	−11.6	—	−8.3	—	—	—	—	—	—	—	—	—	—	—	—	—	—
May	—	−11.7	—	−12.2	—	−12.2	−11.7	−8.3	—	—	—	—	—	—	—	—	—	—	—	—	—	—

*These numbers indicate the depth into the soil from the wall of the shaft

#The data for each month are averages of from two to four observations, as given in the original publication. The temperature data have been converted to Centigrade scale from Reamur scale.

In the regions of deep permafrost, the temperature remains constant throughout the year beginning with the 50-foot depth. While the constancy is maintained, the numerical constant decreases, i.e., the temperature increases with each succeeding depth, although it still remains negative even at the depth of 382 feet, as shown in the table.

Leffingwell (11) cites Scandinavian sources on a tunnel of a coal mine in Spitzenbergen running 500 to 1000 meters into the mountainside. The end of the tunnel may lie 100 to 200 meters below the surface of the ground. At the inned end of the shaft, the temperature was —4.5°C. Leffingwell also reports on his investigations of the Canning River region, northern Alaska. Johnston (9) reports on the frozen ground in the glaciated parts of northern Canada. Geikie (4) states that "in North America the arctic forests straggle down the valleys of the Mackenzie and other rivers to beyond the Arctic Circle. Mosses and lichens form the prevailing vegetation of the tundra. We find cases of trees in the tundra."

The most recent contribution on the perennially frozen ground in Alaska is the one by Tabor (29) mentioned earlier. Any one interested in a bibliography on this subject will find it in Taber's paper. Polytseva and Ivanova (20), in their extensive report on the Khibinsk tundra give 194 references.

Nikiforoff (19) sums up the two principal hypotheses, climatic and glacial, on the origin of the perpetually frozen subsoil as follows:

Climatic Hypothesis. — The southern boundary of the region coincides more or less closely with the line north of which the mean annual temperature is everywhere considerably below 0°C., as shown in plate 29. In fact, it is not higher than -2°C., and over a large area, as for example at Yakutsk, it is as low as —10°C. The supporters of this hypothesis maintain that the excess of annual cold cannot disappear without any effect, and that the volume of the ground which is frozen by the severity of the winter's low temperature cannot be wholly melted by the limited amount of the summer's heat. Accordingly, every year some residue of this cold must remain, such "frozen residues" accumulating year after year and the frozen layer generally increasing in thickness. This hypothesis was first proposed by Wild (34, p. 99).

Glacial Hypothesis. — According to this hypothesis, the ever-frozen ground is an inheritance from the glacial period. It is known that very little of Siberia was covered by ice at the peeriod of the Great Glaciation, and because of this the supporters oof the second hypothesis hold that the area unglaciated, and so left unprotected by ice, was at that time frozen to a great depth.

The principal argument in favor of the second hypothesis has been provided by the discovery in the frozen ground of bodies of ancient mammoths and rhinoceroses, many of which were so well preserved that the natives used the grease obtained from them (34, p. 65). The stomachs of these animals contained undigested food which was in such good condition that it was possible to determine the species of plants that the animals had eaten just before their death (26). It is evident that the bodies of these animals could have been thus preserved during many thousands of years only under the protection of permanent frosts. It means that at the time these animals succumbed, the subsoil was already frozen and has so remained up to the present.

It appears probable that each hypothesis is partly correct and partly incorrect. There is no question that the existence of the ever-frozen ground at the present time depends upon the contemporary climate and that the annual excess of the loss of heat

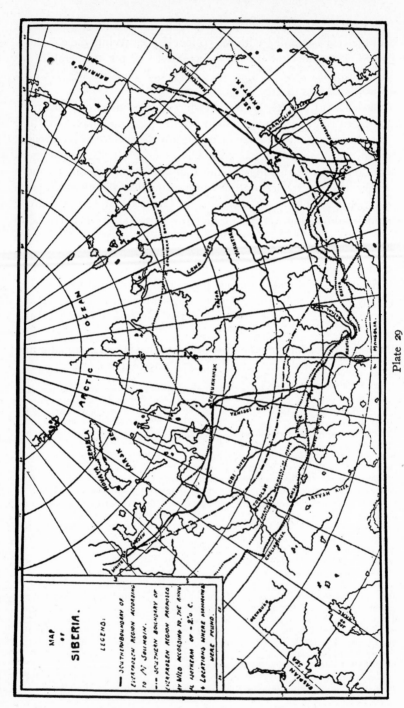

Plate 29

Map of Siberia showing boundary of the portion in which the everfrozen layer has been found
(After Nikiforov)

from the surface into the atmosphere over the amount of heat annually received by the same surface from the sun has a definite significance. Although it is true that the discovery of the bodies of mammoths proves that the ground has been frozen for a long time, it does not dispose of the role played by pre-existing climatic conditions. Probably, the conditions prevailing during the glacial period were more severe, and the freezing was considerably more rapid than at present, but even so the appearance of the frozen subsoil then or later must be regarded as a function of the climate.

If the origin of this phenomenon is dependent upon the absence of protecting glacial ice in eastern Siberia during the glacial period, and if the Great Glaciation in Europe and North America occurred simultaneously with the forming of the ever-frozen ground of Siberia, then the question may be asked as to why the ice sheets were melted while the frozen ground of Siberia, the so-called "continental facia" of the glacial period, remains to the present time. This, of course, must be explained by a change of climate in the glaciated areas of western Europe and northern North America with little or no change in that of Siberia. It means that the present climate of much of Siberia is favorable for the existence of the ever-frozen ground.

There is no reason to assume that the climate during the Glacial Period was not more severe than the contemporary one, even in Eastern Siberia, in parts of which a temperature of -62° to -59°C. is a common phenomenon of every winter, but it may be pointed out that there are no reasons for minimizing the contemporary climate's role in the development of ever-frozen ground, even if it be accepted that the ever-frozen ground is a geological formation.

A very interesting deduction has resulted from the discovery of the mammoths at the different places indicated in plate 29. The finding of at least thirty of these has been reported up to the present, but not in all cases have entire bodies been found, some of the finds reported being of only parts of a body — the head, or a leg with flesh, skin, and hair attached. The circumstances under which the animals died have been contributing factors to the state of preservation. In several cases, the investigators had an opportunity to re-establish in every detail all the circumstances under which the animal had perished. As an example, reference may be made to a part of an article written by the geologist Vollossovitch (27, p. 220) in which he describes the discovery of the Sanga Yurakh mammoth. His statement regarding this follows:

"The mammoth perished in the summer, because it had a thick wool-hair on its hide. As he approached the river bank, where the frozen ground with incrustations of ice was under the mud, he became stalled in this mud. For a long time he kept trying to raise his right hind leg in an attempt to free himself, but without success. Finally he fell down with his left side exposed. Little by little the mud covered his body, but before it became totally concealed the savages removed as much of the carcass as they could. Those parts of the body which were nearest the frozen layer from the very beginning were preserved in the best condition."

In connection with the various discoveries of these mammoth remains, it should be emphasized that not one was made as the result of any special search, but every one was more or less accidental and made usually by natives and not by scientists. The scientists usually heard of a discovery only indirectly and so only after considerable time had elapsed from the finding of the carcass or part of one. The occurrence of these bodies clearly indicates the magnitude of a rich field of paleontological research. The ever-frozen subsoil contains, of course, not only the bodies of mammoths, but the remains of many other prehistoric animals.

Taber (29) notes 4 hypotheses on the origin of perpetual freezing: 1, deposits formed during a warmer climate and subsequently frozen as a result of climate prevailing now; 2, simultaneous deposition and freezing under prevailing climate; 3, Pleistocene climate formation; 4, simultaneous freezing and deposition during Pleistocence.

Nikiforoff states:

It is probable that the question as to the origin of the ever-frozen ground can be best answered by investigations undertaken in northern Canada, most of which, at least, was covered by the great ice sheet during the Glacial Period. If no permanently frozen ground were found in this glaciated region with a climate now similar to that of eastern Siberia, it certainly would prove that the ice sheet served as a protective cover and that the severity of the contemporary climate is not sufficient to bring about the formation of this perpetually frozen subsoil. On the other hand, if the ever-frozen ground should be found in this glaciated area, it would support the hypothesis that freezing took place after the deposition of the drift and the recession of the ice, that the absence or presence of glaciation did not influence the development of this phenomenon, and that its origin is not necessarily associated with the Glacial Period.

For the latest reports on the characteristics and distribution of the ever-frozen ground, the reader is referred to the Russian investigators. In a special publication *Merzlotovedenie* (the Science of Ground Frost), Meister (166) discusses the problem on the depth of permafrost. Tumel (32) presents a map on its distribution in the U.S.S.R. and summarizes the Soviet research in this field. Leontiev (12) takes up the characteristics of the ever frozen layer in the region of Norilsk, and Saks (23) offers some data on permafrost in the basin of the river Pyasna. Anyone interested in the problem of ever frozen ground should consult the Sumgin (27) monograph as a standard reference on the subject. His paper, in collaboration with Demchinskii (28) on the conquest of the north, gives additional valuable information. A review of the problem of perennial freezing to soil formation is presented by Tsyplenkin (31).

Soils in the Tundra

Nikiforoff points out that the rapidity with which the soils thaw during the summer depends upon their texture and the character of the protecting vegetation. During the warmer portion of the year, therefore, the upper surface of the frozen layer is very uneven. The water cannot percolate through it because the first water reaching it seals with ice all cracks in the frozen subsoil. All water derived from rain and snow and the thawing of the subsoil accumulates above the ever-frozen layer, often in such quantities as to form a liquid layer under the dry thawed surface. Such a condition favors the extensive development of swamps not only in the lowlands but upon the mountain slopes as well.

Often in the summer, a layer of water was found under the firm and apparently dry crust of the surface soil, and frequently it was found creeping down into the lower levels. Sometimes, the pressure exerted was so great that the water would crack the dry crust and the liquid mud would then pour out over the surface. In other cases, a process, genetically similar to this, caused the development of a formation of another kind. The layer creeping down was too dense to pour but after bursting through the surface soil it formed small convex mounds, which under foot were resilient like elastic cushions. This phenomenon is known in the Russian literature as a "suffosion process" and has been examined by Prokhorov (21) in the province of Trans-Baikal. They describe a very unusual soil complex which occupies a large gentle slope in this region.

The soil is mostly peat which is covered with hillocks of carex. Numerous hummocks of subsoil penetrate through the surface in the form of convex mounds. The

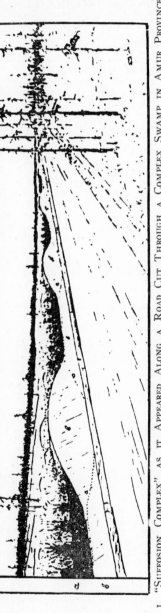

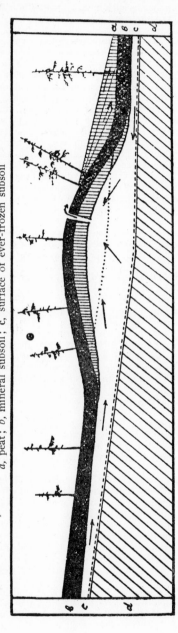

Fig. 1. "Suffosion Complex" as it Appeared Along a Road Cut Through a Complex Swamp in Amur Province

a, peat; *b*, mineral subsoil; *c*, surface of ever-frozen subsoil

Fig. 2. Cross-section of a Soil Blister

a, accumlation of clear ice, both on the surface and under the r ised frozen surface soil; *b*, frozen surface soil; *c*, water in liquid form; *d*, ever-frozen subsoil

Plate 30

Suffosion complex and cross section of a soil blister in the tundra zone

(After Nikiforov)

total surface covered by these mounds is frequently more than one half the surface of the whole area. They do not rise on the average more than two feet above the level of surrounding swamp and usually have very irregular shapes, as shown in fig. I of plate 30. The most recent suffosion knobs are almost bare of vegetation, while even the oldest are but very slightly podzolized. The bare surface of the suffosion convexes hastens the melting of the subsoil and therefore causes marked irregularities of the surface of the ever-frozen layer beneath the complexes. For each convex occurs a corresponding shallow depression in the frozen surface. Because of this, it can be readily understood that any attempts at farming these soils would meet with great difficulties.

Soil Blisters and Ice Caverns. — In the autumn and winter, after the soil has frozen at the surface, the water layer is found lying between this frozen surface crust and the ever-frozen subsoil. Under the influence of the very low temperature, a high pressure is created by the expansion of the freezing water and this exerts such a force that in places the surface layer is raised like a gigantic water blister, with all the buildings and trees that may be on the surface. The author observed mounds of this kind which were more than twenty feet high, all being full of water (fig. I, plate 31). Under the pressure, fissures are formed and the water spurts out in geyser fashion. In several mounds, the surface was intentionally punctured near the base thus allowing the water to escape. After this, the mounds were found to contain large caverns beneath the soil which was supported by massive vaults of clear ice (fig. 2, plate 31; also plate 32). The caverns were so large that one could walk upright within them without difficulty. Some of them were as much as six or seven feet high and almost thirty feet in diameter. The ice caverns were covered with a layer of soil two or three feet thick bearing large larch trees, standing at right angles to the rounded surface of the mound and not vertical, as they were before the sudden growth of this little hill (18, pp. 50-74).

Winter Regimen of the River Valleys. — The streams and rivers of this region frequently freeze to the bottom, and the ice forms dams across the river bed. In such cases, the water coming from the upper parts of the river seeks outlets through the soil adjacent to the stream and often appears on the surface of the ground far away from the banks of the river. These places are very dangerous to travellers in the Siberian taiga (northern forest) in winter, because of the deep water, and in summer because of the blocks of ice remaining. In winter, when the temperature often reaches -45° and -50°C, such places are full of water. The lower the temperature, the higher will be the pressure in the water layer above the ever-frozen subsoil and consequently more and more water will be forced to the surface. In order to escape the treacherous water-soaked snow, which frequently covers several square miles, it is very common for travellers to go many miles through deep snow, breaking paths through the virgin forest.

An investigation of the Academy of Science, G. Maidel, who visited the northeastern part of the Yakutsk province in 1868-1870, in his report described in detail one of these formations, which covered more than forty square miles and in some places was more than seven miles in width. It was caused by the Kyra and Bekharan rivers and their tributaries.

During the long winter, the water freezes little by little, forming layers of ice, one above the other, which are pushed together, forming almost impassible barriers. The summers are not long enough and the heat from the sun's rays is not sufficiently penetrating to melt entirely all the ice that has accumulated during the winter, with the result that varying amounts of ice remain until the following winter. In several places, at the middle of August, the author saw huge blocks of transparent blue ice which were more than ten feet thick and walked along these for more than a quarter of a mile. These summer fields of ice, or "taryn," as the natives call them, form one of the most fantastic and contrasting pictures in the landscape of eastern Siberia.

Podyaknooff, a mining engineer, who first studied the dynamics of this phenomenon offered the following formula, which shows the relation between the energy of the phenomenon (R) and the attributed natural conditions:

$$R = P\frac{c}{d} - Q\frac{a}{M+N}$$

FIG. 1

Typical soil blister with the slopes still covered with ice formed from the water which has spurted out

FIG. 2

View of ice-lined cavern

Plate 31

(After Nikiforoff)

PLATE 32

Exposure of soil ice, 2 meters thick, on the left bank of the river Vitim, Siberia
(After Sumgin)

where P = the force of the frost, c = heat capacity of the alluvium, d = thickness of
the snow layer, Q = quantity of liquid water (unfrozen) in the river bed and unfrozen
deposits, a = width of the valley, N = the cross-section of the open river bed, and
M = the cross-section of the unfrozen deposits in the valley, through which the water
is pressed from the bed (27, p. 275).

Tundra Process of Soil Formation

Not much is known about the tundra process of soil formation, except that it has certain elements of similarity with the bog or marsh type of soil formation, which is a hydromorphic type. There is, however, this fundamental difference: in the process of the bog or marsh type of soil formation, there is an upward and downward movement of the products of the reactions, whereas in the tundra the downward movement is impeded by the frozen subsoil and by the prolonged period of the frozen conditions of the soil as a whole. As to the upward movement, of which more is to be said presently, the following is important. In the tundra, we frequently get a movement of materials (outside of the mechanical movement which takes place by the process of blistering, to which reference has been made) from the point of the frozen subsoil to the upper layers. In the marsh type of soil formation, either the upward movement goes to the G horizon or, if the water table comes to the surface, we have the typical marsh, bog, or swamp. There is also a difference in the biotic elements. In the tundra region, the growing season is short; the type of vegetation is different, the quantity of organic matter available for mineralization is relatively low, and moreover, the microbiological activities are suppressed. In consequence of all these specific conditions, which in turn are the result of the climate in the tundra region, we have a retardation of the processes of eluviation and illuviation. Together with the slow and ineffective decomposition of rocks in this region, to which reference has been made in the chapter on weathering, we are confronted with a minimum of reactivity of the factors of soil formation.

In discussing the tundra zone, it is well to keep in mind the characteristic features of the tundra climate. The winters are long, with long nights and extremely low temperatures. In eastern Siberia, the average annual temperature ranges from —12° to 17°C., with an average annual rainfall from 300 to 200 mm. and even less. Thus, the rainfall in the tundra does not exceed that of the desert steppe. The treeless condition of the tundra, however, is not due to the moisture factor, but to the proximity of the perpetually frozen layer to the surface. The strong dry winds during the winter blow away and sublime the snow cover from the slightly elevated portions of the landscape. As a result, the surface soil dries out and cracks, leaving large bare spots, free from vegetation. This type of landscape is known as the *bold* or *spotty tundra*. The strong desiccating winds also contribute to the treeless condition of the tundra. At the border of the forest and tundra zones, we do find forests whenever the frozen layer is buried deeper in the subsoil. This gives rise to the so-called "forest tundra transition belt."

Grigoriev (7), in discussing the peculiarities of the tundra process of soil formation makes the following remarks:

All agree that tundra soils are related to the marsh type of soil formation. The bone of contention is whether the tundra soils should be separated as a special subtype distinguished by definite pecularities of their soil-forming process, or whether there is no sound basis for such a separation. Without attempting to s o l v e the question raised, I call attention to several details of the tundra process.

It is known that the rainfall in the tundra zone is low; the free play of the winds, which at times blow with great force, strongly influences the evaporation, making up the (evaporation) deficit which would otherwise occur because of the meager heat from sunlight. Consequently, the snow cover here cannot be prominently deep. Furthermore, in the early spring before the snow has disappeared, its evaporation, or rather its sublimation, must be quite intense because of the combined forces of the sun and wind. One might not expect, therefore, large quantities of water from the thawing snow. The major portion of the water runs off and is not available for percolation through the soil which is in a frozen condition. On the other hand, a lot of water is being absorbed and transpired by the lichens and mosses, something which they are capable of doing while the roots of the more highly organized plants are still inactive. Thus, the utilization of the vernal waters by the plant cover in the tundra begins relatively early.

By the time the tundra soil, with its low heat-conducting moss-lichen cover and thin peat litter layer, begins to thaw out, most of the thawing waters have run off. Only a small portion of these waters penetrates the soil, thereby influencing the soil-forming processes. Coming in contact with the layer of perpetual freezing, these waters partially freeze, but at the same time exert a thawing effect on the layer of perpetual freezing. The waters produced by the partial thawing do not hinder the incoming water from penetrating into that frozen layer, since the thawing out process, which involves a change from the solid to the liquid phase, produces a decrease in volume, making room for the incoming water. Moreover, the frozen layer is not devoid of porosity, which depends on the amount of w a t e r present in the soil at the time of freezing. It is natural, however, to find the soils saturated with w a t e r during the spring.

However, this period of saturation does not last long, because the supply of thawing waters is limited, the rainfall in the tundra is low, the evaporation during the nightless period is considerable, and, as mentioned, the mosses and lichens take up a lot of the rainwater before it has chance to reach the soil. Because of the drying out effect of the surface horizons, there sometimes must be established an upward movement of water. This u p w a r d movement may change again to a downward movement after heavy rains.

As a result of that, the moisture in the soil, even though there is enough of it during the summer, exists as film water which allows good aeration. Towards the fall, the upper horizon quite frequently dries out completely. Thus, according to Kertzelli (10), a dry layer, 10 to 25 cm. thick, may be found in the Bolshezemel tundra during the fall overlying a water-saturated layer.

Thus, the soil processes in the tundra do not take place under conditions of constant saturation of the soil with water. The frequent alternation of the downward and upward movement of the water is an important factor. In the beginning of the summer, the downward movement of moisture prevails, followed by an alternation of downward and upward movement during the summer, and by an upward movement during the fall. Naturally, the warmer and drier the summer, the more important becomes the upward movement for the tundra process of soil formation. On the other hand, the milder the winter and the higher the snowfall, which prevents the supercooling of the frozen layer, the faster and deeper proceeds the thawing and the more effective are the percolating waters.

Thus, a series of factors seem to direct the soil-forming processes of the subarctic tundra and of the northern forest belt into one and the same channel. They are, however, tied up with the duration of the thawing out period in the tundra and the lowering of the temperature during the summer. Whenever the latter phenomenon occurs, the parallelism of the soil-forming processes between these two zones come to naught. It is therefore imperative to differentiate the conditions of soil formation prevailing in the southern portion of the subarctic tundra zone and those of the northern portion, keeping in mind the transitions from one to the other.

To bring out more clearly the mode of the movement of water in the soils of the tundra zone, Grigoriev compares his observations on the loamy spots in the tundra with the findings of Dranitsyn (2) who investigated such a loamy spot and described it as follows:

The entire soil depth is slightly laminated and porous, with streaks of iron oxide. At the surface, a dry thin crust is an outstanding attribute. A test with acid showed the presence of carbonates throughout the profile, while the neighboring areas covered with vegetation effervesced only at a certain depth in the frozen mass of eluvium. The areas free of vegetation thaw out more rapidly than the adjacent areas covered with vegetation. For this reason, there is more evaporation from the bare spots and as a consequence, the infiltration waters from the thawed out soil enrich it with salts.

Occasionally, Grigoriev had also encountered on the surface crust-like formations described by Dranitsyn. In some cases, the surface was found strewn with loamy-like pellets. Below the surface, the material showed a porous constitution, becoming more compact with depth and showing a lumpy structure, the size of the lumps increasing with depth. The yellow coloration of the surface horizon changed into a dark brown, the color of the parent material. "Rust streaks were not noted in the porous horizon, neither was the soil effervescing, notwithstanding the presence of carbonate rich rock fragments and stone in the parent material. The porous condition of the surface horizon clearly indicates the upward movement of moisture during the dry period. The absence of salinization, on the other hand, indicates that the polar solonchak described by Dranitsyn is not a general phenomenon for the polar region."

One of the important considerations in the analysis of the tundra type of soil formation is the texture of the soil material. Grigoriev (7) points out that since loamy and clayey materials freeze to greater depths than sand, less moisture is apt to percolate through them. This subdues the podzol effects on these materials. Sandy materials, however, are subject to more through leaching, and on them a well expressed A_2 horizon is usually found. Grigoriev cites an example of a soil cut which has a 50 to 75 cm. layer of peat on a sand which shows evidence of podzolization. It appears, however, that whenever the conditions are favorable for the movement of waters, the typical marsh or bog type of soil formation also develops in the tundra.

Shulga (24) describes a sandy textured profile examined on the island of Koloueva, typical for a sloping topography:

1. A sod layer consisting of lichens and mosses, 0 to 8 cm. deep.
2. A layer of sand or clayey sand, slightly colored with humus substances, giving the mass a grayish tinge, somewhat podzolized, 2 to 6 cm deep.

3. Slightly lighter in color than the layer over it, with indications of a weakly expressed podzolic feature, usually in the form of scattered spots, o to 10 cm. deep.

4. Light-brownish in color, with scattered spots and veins of ortstein formation, o to 5 cm. deep.

5. Subsoil, usually sand, or sand with an admixture of clay and stones.

On the level topography of this island, the soil is covered with a layer of peat 100 to 150 cm. thick, and the frozen layer is found at a depth of 35 to 45 cm. below the surface. On the sloping areas, the frozen layer is 100 to 150 cm. below the surface; in these areas, podzolization features were noted by Shulga.

Reports by Malyarevskii, as quoted by Grigoriev for the soils in Novaya Zemlya, mention no podzols in this area of the arctic region.

For the Kola Peninsula, in the neighborhood of Murmansk, data are available from the investigations of Markus (13). They corroborte, in general, the data cited by Shulga. Mazyro (14) points out that in this peninsula there is no eternally frozen layer, and the soils are podzolized.

Summing up the investigations on the tundra in Europe, Grigoriev states:

1. In the European forest tundra and in the tundra proper, the phenomenon of tundra soils of the bog type is possible only under definite conditions of topography which would lead to swamping in the same manner as in the northern portion of the forest zone.

2. On the sandy and clayey sand parent material, the weakly podzolic soils extend far into the north, into the tundra proper. On the loams, the process of soil formation is reduced to a minimum and does not attain the bog character, at any rate in places where the runoff of water is not hindered. Apparently, the concealed and weakly podzolic soils and the reduced development of soils on the loams are typical for the European portion of the tundra. The tundra soils of the bog type, even though quite extensively distributed in places, are just as much intrazonal there as in the forest belt.

Among the different varieties of the tundra landscape is one known as the *hillock bog*. These hillocks may have a diameter of 5 to 25 m. and a height of 3 to 5 m. They are separated by depressions 5 to 15 m. wide which are filled with water, and the perpetually frozen layer is within 40 cm. of the surface. Such a tundra variety has been described by Tanfiliev (30) for eastern Lapland. The prevailing vegetation is lichens and mosses.

In the forest tundra of the Great Plain of western Siberia, Gorodkov and Neustruev (6) observed obscured or concealed podzolic soils replacing the weakly podzolic soils of the northern forest belt. To the north of the forest tundra, they noticed the gradual replacement of the morphologically concealed podzolic soils by dark colored bog-like soils. Even though the process of podzolization on the loams of the forest tundra in western Siberia is subdued, it is still prominently expressed on the sand. These authors state:

In the forest tundra, one may encounter typical shallow podzols under larch and pine stands in the river valleys. The podzolic sands, frozen to great depths, undoubtedly exist under favorable conditions also in the tundra proper, but it is doubtful whether they extend very far into the north.

Sukachev describes a profile cut of a soil in the tundra region between the rivers Kara and the Lower Ob as follows:

A_0: 3 cm. deep; humus accumulative layer, grayish brown, the plant materials in places being only slightly decomposed.

A_1: 2 to 3 cm. deep; yellowish brown, in places grayish brown ocherous loose loam

A_2: 8 to 10 cm. deep; dark bluish-gray homogeneous sticky viscous loam, flowing when dug out, liquid like when in a monolithic box; there is a sharp line of separation between this and the overlying horizon.

B_1: 2 to 3 cm.deep; brownish yellow (ocherous) loam, similar to A_1 but m o r e compact.

B_2: 25 to 30 cm. deep; compact, dark brownish-gray loam; in the lower portion of this horizon black spots (humus) and rock fragments are found; at a depth of 79 cm. below the surface, the frozen subsoil is encountered but still the character of the described horizon does not change even deeper.

According to Zakharov (Ch.2,91, p. 352), "the soil described resembles morphologically a somewhat weakly podzolic soil with several attributes of swamping." In table 99, the chemical analysis of the soil described is given. In the light of the data, it is difficult to reconcile the view of Zakharov that the soil is podzolic in nature. The most reliable index of the podzol process of soil formation, the movement of R_2O_3, does not seem to support this view. The uniformity in composition of the various horizons is very striking. If anything, this soil shows immaturity.

Ratmanov (22) examined the soils of the western coast in the central part of the island of Novaya Zemlya at parallel 74° northern latitude between the meridians 56 and 57. He gives a schematic map of the soils examined and points out that the soils are generally feebly developed, as indicated by the profile. He records, however, the presence of some gleimarsh and weakly podzolic soil types.

Gorodkov (5), in his latest publication, denies the existence of a specific tundra type of soil formation. Basing his views on studies made in the Siberian tundra by himself and others, he considers these soils primarily as subtypes of the podzol process of soil formation, with some peatmarsh soils, glei podzols, and peat podzols. As an example of the podzolic nature of the tundra soils he describes a sandy clay soil from one of the many sandhills as follows:

A_0: 3.5 cm. deep; primarily lichens, peat-like at the bottom.

A_1: 1.5 cm. deep; dark brown humus horizon.

A_2: 3.2 cm. deep; brownish-gray.

B : 5 cm. deep; yellowish-brown, spotty wet sand, with a few rusty looking spots; the frozen layer is found at a depth of 60 cm. below the surface.

In table 100, partial analyses of the soil described are presented.

Table 99

Chemical analyses of a tundra soil described by Sukachev

(After Zakharov)

Horizon	Depth from the surface	Hygroscopic moisture	Loss on ignition	Mineral substances	Mineral substances soluble in HCl	Mineral substances insoluble in NaOH and HCl	Mineral substances soluble in HCl and NaOH	SiO_2 soluble in NaOH	Al_2O_3	Fe_2O_3
	cm.	per cent	per cent	per cent	per cent	per cent	per cent	per cent	per cent	per cent
A_0	0-3	5.26	17.55	82.45	10.67	58.02	24.43	9.21	3.85	3.56
A_1	3-6	2.46	3.03	96.47	8.63	78.65	18.32	7.94	3.12	3.56
A_2	6-15	2.09	2.69	97.31	8.03	79.27	18.04	8.94	3.26	3.02
B	15-17	2.26	2.69	97.31	8.37	79.33	17.98	8.43	3.14	3.43
C	20-30	2.25	2.32	97.62	8.28	79.30	18.38	8.89	3.30	3.15

Table 100

Partial analyses of a sandy clay soil in the tundra of the western Siberian plain

(After Gorodkov)

Horizon	Depth	Hygroscopic moisture	pH	Loss on ignition	Humus	SiO₂	Clay <0.01 mm.
	cm.	per cent		per cent	per cent	per cent	per cent
A₁	1-1.5	4.55	4.91	24.40	15.67	72.75	39.75
A₂ + G₁	5-6	2.60	5.64	7.55	1.56	73.88	45.75
G₂	14	2.30	5.86	4.67	1.61	73.01	45.00
C	—	2.55	6.77	4.42	1.30	—	47.25

Gorodkov considers the sharp drop in the humus content of the A_2 horizon as the outstanding feature of the podzol effect. On the other hand, one may point out that the pH of A_2 is not lower than that of A_1, which indicates a relative accumulation of bases. The sharp rise of the pH in the glei horizon is an indication of the upward movement of bases sometime during the dry period in the summer. Neither is there much translocation of the clay fraction. All other constituents are uniformly distributed in the profile, except in the A_1 horizon which is high in organic matter. It appears, therefore, that the meager data presented by Gorodkov are not comprehensive enough to indicate that in the tundra we are dealing with the feebly podzolized or concealed podzolic soils. As pointed out earlier in the discussion, we are confronted in the tundra with a different type of movement and percolation of moisture from that in the podzol zone. This, together with the other points discussed, seems to corroborate the view of the majority of investigators as to the specificity of the tundra type of soil formation. Undoubtedly, this type is closely related to the podzol and podzol-marsh type of soil formation, but the podzols and podzolic soils encountered in the tundra are simply varieties in the zonal tundra type of soil formation.

Since subdued activities of chemical and biochemical weathering in the arctic region are not conducive to the kaolinization of the native rocks and minerals, one would expect a low mineral colloid content in the tundra soils. The exchange capacity, therefore, should also be low. Even the organic materials, which are inherently collodial in nature, show a low exchange capacity because of the impeded humification.

A number of other interesting features about the tundra soils are discussed by Griegoriev (7). He points out that on the exposed spots of the tundra, traversed by the Yenissei river, carbonates are found on the surface. In his words:

Even though this phenomenon may be related to the presence of lime in the parent material it deserves to be emphasized, for it is possible only under the specific conditions of the continentality of the climate.

In eastern Siberia, the podzolic soils and the polar limits of forest stands extend farther north than in western Siberia. In this respect, the conditions are similar to those of the tundra soils in Europe. And yet, even on the sandy areas of eastern Siberia, the tundra soils replace the podzolized soils of the "forest islands" and the loams of the forest tundra sections which are not influenced much by the soil-forming processes. Such a replacement is not apparent in the European tundra where the change is gradual. And besides, in the Yenissei tundra we encounter for the first time evidence of a new intrazonal soil, namely, the polar solonchak. Dolenko (1) discovered solonchak among the podzolic soils at the latitude of the city of Yakutsk.

Thus, the tundra of Eurasia may be divided, in the sense of the soil cover, into not less than four provinces. This corresponds in a general way to the four climatic provinces into which the region may be divided. It is clear that in the eastern portion of the continent, with its remarkably warm marine climate, which is related to the high temperatures of the sea which bathes this continent, the podzolized soils are extensively developed and the tundra soils are less widespread. The temperature conditions are conducive to chemical, as well as microbiological, activity and to the circulation of soil waters. It is known that in this portion of the continent, the summer temperatures are more or less even throughout the day, the soil does not freeze so deeply during the winter, there is more snow and not such severe frosts, and the vegetation period is rather long.

In the western Siberian tundra, the specific type of marine polar climate lowers the summer temperatures, diminishes the mildness of the winter, causes the soil to freeze more extensively, and impedes the thawing. All these factors are unfavorable for the process of podzolization and favorable for the development of the tundra soils. And finally, eastern Siberia with a maximum expression of the continental climate is characterized by a scant rainfall throughout the year, by extremely low temperatures during the winter, and by a relatively warm, but very short, summer. Because of the latter condition, the process of podzolization extends into the far north, but there a sudden break takes place. The processes of soil formation come under the dominating influence of the exclusively cold winter temperatures, whereby the influence of the summer temperatures is suppressed. The podzolized soils are replaced by tundra soils. The aridity of the climate finds expression in the process of salinization, provided the conditions of the subsoil are favorable.

And finally, the coast of the Bering Sea provides a still different climatic condition. The winters are very cold, with little snow, and the summers are wet. An evaluation of the influence of these conditions on the processes of soil formation is a problem of the future.

In his latest monograph, Griegoriev (8) presents a critical review on the tundra type of soil formation and a summary of his own extensive researches.

A rather comprehensive discussion of the arctic region, the perpetually frozen subsoils, the processes of weathering, and some data on the soils in that region is presented by Meinardus (15).

A paper on soils from North American arctic regions was published by Feustel, Dutilly, and Anderson (3). Dutilly, a Catholic clergyman, has been visiting annually for many years the regions under discussion. Besides his professional duties, Dutilly has shown himself to be a good geologist, botanist, and keen observer. He collected soil samples (in the agronomic sense) from widely separated areas ranging from a latitude of about 50° north at Churchill, Manitoba, to as far north as Craig Harbour, Ellesmere Island, in a latitude of about 76°. No profile development was observed. Indeed, one would not expect such in the orogenic-lithogenic environment of the points where the soil samples were taken. "Surface material to a depth of 6 inches or less were usually collected." These samples are described in great detail. Analyses are given on the C:N ratio of the organic matter, the chemical composition of the ash of peat and other organic materials, and of the colloidal fraction. It is obvious, from the data presented in the original publication, that we are dealing with weathered rock material supporting the tundra type of vegetation.

It may be appropriate, in conclusion, to elaborate on the influence of rivers on the tundra. With the waters carried to the Arctic Ocean, rivers bring huge quantities of heat units gained at their headwaters that are usually located in the temperate regions. Shostakovich (25) calculated the thermal units carried by the Siberian rivers into the Arctic Ocean and made some inferences of their effects on the tundra. Tanfiliev (30) discussed the extraordinary drainage effects of the rivers on the northern marshes and tundra. Efficient removal of surplus water from the drainage basin reduces the extent and depth of the perpetual layer of underground ice. This change in the hydrologic conditions of the landscape modifies the vegetation and soil cover. Along the river valleys, a fairly rich meadow flora develops and meadow-bog soils make their appearance. Protected somewhat from the winter winds and favored by a deeper thawed out layer, the river valleys harbor some forests, some extending as far north as the coasts of Arctic Ocean. These forest soils do not belong strictly to the tundra climate. They are, as pointed out, earlier, a subtype—forest tundra, with attributes of podzolization strongly developed. These soils may be classed with the climatogenically subdued types.

References

1. Dolenko, G. I. 1916 The sections of the Lena-Vilyui watershed in Yakutsk province. Predvarit. otchet ob organizatzii i ispolnenii rabot po issledovaniyu pochv. Aziat. Rossii V. 1914 (After Grigoriev)

2. Dranitsyn, D. A. 1916 The north Yenissei expedition. Predvaritelnui otchet ob organizatzii i ispolnenii rabot po issledovaniyu pochv. Aziat. Rossii. (After Grigoriev)

3. Feustel, Irving, C., Dutilly, A., and Anderson, M. S. 1939 Properties of soils from N. American arctic regions. Soil Sci. 48:183-199.

4. Geikie, J. 1898 The tundra and steppe of prehistoric Europe. Scottish Geogr. Magaz. 14: 281-294, 346-357.

5. Gorodkov, B. N. 1929 Tundra soils. Priroda 18, No. 7-8: 703-707.

6. Gorodkov, B. N. and Neustruev, S. S. 1923 The soil regions of the Ural province. "Ural", tekhniko-ekonom. sbornik, No. 5 Jekaterinburg (After Grigoriev.)

7. Grigoriev, A. 1925 The soils of the subarctic tundra and forest tundra of Eurasia in connection with the observations in the Bol'shezemelskaya tundra during 1921. Pedology (U.S.S.R.) No. 4: 5-32.

8. Grigoriev, A. A. 1945 Subarktika (Subarctic). Acad. Sci., U.S.S.R. Moscow-Leningrad.

9. Johnston, W. A. 1930 Frozen ground in the glaciated parts of N. Canada. Proc. and Trans. Royal Soc. Canada, 3rd ser. v. 24, sec. IV, 33-40.

10. Kertzelli, S. V. 1911 On the Bol'shezemel. tundra with the nomads. Arkhangelsk.

11. Leffingwell, E. de K. 1919 The Canning River region of Northern Alaska. U. S. Geol. Sur. Prof. Paper 109, 179-243 (An extensive bibliography).

12. Leont'ev, A. V. 1945 Characteristics of the ever frozen layer in the region of Norilsk. *Norilsk, byulet. technich. informatzii.* No. 3-4: 31-36.

13. Markus, E. A. 1922 The podzol-bog soils of the middle part of the Kola Peninsula. Rabotui organizovan. Geog. Inst. V. 1920 g. Kolskogog pochven.-botanich. otryada Severnoi Nauchno-Promuislennoi Ekspeditz., Bul. II (after Grigoriev).

14. Mazyro, M. 1936 Pochvy Khibinskikh tundr (Soils of the Khibinsk tundra). Acad. Sci., U.S.S.R. Moscow-Leningrad.

15. Meinardus, W. 1930 Böden der kalten Region: (a) Arktische Böden, Blanck's Handbuch der Bodenlehre 3:27-96.

16. Meister, L. A. 1946 On the depth of eternal freezing. (Russian) *Merzlotovedenie,* No. 1. 29-30.

17. Middendorf, A. von 1848 Reise in den aussersten Norden und Osten Sibiriends, Band I, Theil I. St. Petersburg.

18. Nikforoff, C. C. (or K. K.) 1912 the dynamic processes in the soil of ever-frozen land. *Pochvovedenie* (Pedology) No. 2: 49-74.

19. Nikiforoff, C. C. 1928 The perpetually frozen subsoil of Siberia. *Soil Sci.* 26. 61-81.

20. Polyntseva, O. A. and Ivanova, E. N. 1936 The complexes in the spotted tundra of the Khibinsk mountain chain and their evolution in relation to the evolution of the soil and plant cover. *Trans. Dokuchaev Soil Inst.* 13: 213-265 (An extensive English summary).

21. Prokhorov, N. 1913 Northern part of the Amur province. *Trudy Amur. Ekspeditz.* No. 14. St. Petersburg (After Glinka).

22. Ratmanov, G. E. 1930 The soils of Novaya Zemlya. *Trudy Pochven. Inst. imeni Dokuchaeva* No. 3-4: 145-149.

23. Saks, V. N. 1945 Some data on eternal freezing in the basin of the river Pyasna. *Trudy gorno-geol. upravl.* No. 21: 29-45.

24. Shulga, I. A. 1904 The nature of the soils on the Kolguev Island. *Pochvovedenie* (Pedology) No. 2: 177-180.

25. Shostakovich, V. B. 1911 The temperature of Siberian rivers and the quantity of heat carried by them into the Arctic Ocean. Zapiski po gidrografii No. 33. St. Petersburg.

26. Sukachev, V. N. 1911 On the problem of the influence of perpetual freezing of the soil. *Izvestiya Akademii Nauk* (Ser. 6) 1 : 51-60.

27. Sumgin, M. 1927 Everfrozen Soils in the Boundaries of the U.S.S.R. Dal'nevostoch. Geofiziches. Observat. Vladivostok, pp. 1-369 (A new edition was published in 1937).

28. Sumgin, M. I. and Demchinskii, B. N. 1939 Conquest of the North. V oblasti Vechnoi Merzloty (In the region of eternal freezing). Acad. of Sci. popular series. Abstract in *Pedology* No. 10 (1939).

29. Taber, Stephen, 1943 Perennially frozen ground in Alaska: its origin and history. *Bul Geol. Soc. of America* 54, No. 10: 1433-1548.

30. Tanfiliev, G. I. 1911 The forest limits of polar Russia according to the investigations in the tundra of the Timan Samoeds (Russian). Odessa.

31. Tsyplenkin, E. I. 1946 Perennially frozen ground and soil formation. *Pedology* (U.S.S.R.) No. 12: 709-718.

32. Tumel, V. F. 1946 Map showing the distribution of ever frozen regions in the U.S.S.R. (Russian) *Merzlotovedenie* No. 1: 5-11.

33. Tumel, V. F. 1946 Some geographic summary results of Soviet research in the domain of ever frozen regions. *Izdanie Akad. Nauk. Ser Geographii i geophisiki,* No. 2: 205-212.

34. Wild, G. 1882 The Air Temperatures in the Russian Empire. St. Petersburg. (Quoted from Sumgin, p. 99).

CHAPTER XIII.

LATERITES AND LATERITIC TYPE OF SOIL FORMATION

The reactions associated with the genesis of soils in the humid tropics and subtropics may be summarized as follows:

1. Rapid disintergration and decomposition of the parent rock in the direction of the end-products of weathering. 2. Release and removal of SiO_2. 3. Separation of sesquioxides and their fixation in the profile. 4. Non-accumulation of organic matter, notwithstanding the luxuriant vegetation. 5. Distinctive red color of the soil.

The specific process of soil formation under which the reactions enumerated take place is known as *laterization*. It gives rise to the type of soils known as laterites and their subtypes and varieties. The degree of laterization serves as the criterion for the respective subdivisions. A succession of these subdivisions may be followed on the American continent, beginning with lateritic soils along the seaboard of the United States, from Maryland to the extreme South, and continuing with true laterites in Cuba and in the tropics and subtropics of Central and South America.

LATERITES

The term *laterite* (from the Latin word *later,* brick) was introduced by Buchanan (20). The brick-red color of typical laterites is due to enrichment of the material with Fe_2O_3 of various degrees of hydration. According to Glinka, it is the mineral *turgite* which imparts the color. Neustruev (Ch. 2.50) cites a laterite containing as high as 86 per cent Fe_2O_3. Bennett and Allison (16) present analyses of Cuban soils, some of which contain as high as 71.8 per cent Fe_2O_3 with only 1.8 per cent of SiO_2, whereas the parent material of these contains only 7.8 per cent of Fe_2O_3 and 41.0 per cent SiO_2. Besides Fe_2O_3, laterites show an accumulation of Al_2O_3 and oxides of Mn and Ti. Fermor (24) proposed to restrict the term *laterite* to soils containing from 90 to 100 per cent of the oxides of Fe, Al, Ti, and Mn, some of these being more or less hydrated. Soils containing from 50 to 60 per cent of these oxides were designated as *siliceous laterites,* and those containing from 25 to 50 per cent as *lateritic.* A similar classification, with slight modifications, was proposed by Lacroix (55) as a result of his studies in Guinea. Marbut (62) designated *as true laterites* the soils that correspond in their composition to Fermor's first group; the others he designated as *lateritic red loams.*

459

Pendelton and Sharasuvana (75) reiterate the earlier stand taken by Pendelton (74) who champions the utterances of Mohr (69) to restrict the term laterite "to the more or less indurated, illuvial, quarryable horizon in the soil resulting from the accumulation of ferric oxides." This definition is in conformity with the one given by Buchanan who looked upon the formation as iron ore. However, in the course of time, the term laterite has lost its original meaning, and is generally used now to designate the mature stage of the dominant soils in the tropics and subtropics.

There seems to be no definite understanding among pedologists of the various subtypes that may be recongized in the zone of laterization. Harrassowitz (39) states:

Ever since the days of Buchanan, surface formations with cellular concretions were considered as laterites, but in later years this concept has been overlooked. Notwithstanding the clear-cut classification of laterites made by von Schenk, one may show that, in general, there is still some confusion. The widespread red colored soils of the tropics have, therefore, been designated as laterites. Walther recognized the red color as the criterion for laterites, and in recent times his pupil Freyberg concurred. But the classical researches of Bauer brought out the important point that the characteristic feature of the weathering process responsible for the formation of laterites is an accumulation of large quantities of free alumina. This offered an exact chemical index. It was then established that not only could the surface slag-like formations be characterized by the presence of large quantities of alumina, but even the deep lying native rock affected by the weathering processes contained some free alumina.

An examination of older soil maps reveal the most widespread distribution of laterite as a weathering product. The entire region of tropical Africa and South America is occupied by it. The reason for such a generous mapping of laterites is the immediate recognition of a laterite among the surface formations is frequently impossible wherever red loam prevails. Macroscopically, no differentiation is possible between a lateritic and a non-lateritic red loam. Only when the surface of the red loams are enriched with the aforementioned products (iron and alumina) does the laterite become distinctive. In the early stages, an enrichment of iron hydroxide takes place in the form of spots, followed later by the formation of bean-shaped concretions which eventually consolidate into iron crusts. To be sure, these crusts are to be considered as lateritic only when enriched with free alumina. One may encounter in the tropics surface formations rich in iron which, however, have no relation to true laterites and yet are identified as such. This confusion, of course, has been reflected in the description of the laterite profile which represents one of the deepest formations known, attaining a depth of as much as sixty meters. (See Campbell's statement on depth of profile: J.).

With reference to the red loam, it is to be noted that frequently it contains inclusions of the deeper lying rocks. These appear irregularly shaped and strongly decomposed. Sometimes, they are coated brown with iron, giving the appearance of concretions. This, however, is not the case. A number of samples from German East Africa examined by the author show that these materials are in reality *Zersatz* which upon further weathering is converted into red loam.

From the descriptions of Fox (27, 28) and Lacroix (55), Harrassowitz reconstructed the profile characteristics of laterites, in terms of his nomenclature, as follows:

A Profile From Lower India

Material		*Depth*	
Orange-red or yellow loam ....About	3.0		m.
Iron crust with alumina gels		0.3 to	2.5 m.
Zone of mottling: with evidence of iron enrichment			
siallitic-like decomposed basalt		2.5 to	7.5 m.
Zersatz* or leached zone		4.4 to	15.0 m.

10.2 to 25   meters

A Profile From Madagascar

Iron crust	1 m.
Red loam rich in concretions	2 m.
Zersatz: allitic siallit ....8 -	10 m.

8 to 13 meters

In some cases, a humus horizon overlies the iron crust. This has been described by Lacroix for the Madagascar profile. In other cases, regular sand formations are encountered. Mention has also been made of a brown-humus-soil as a surface cover. These variations are due to the age of the laterite profile and to its mode of formation. It is conceivable that any profile, be it one in the process of formation or mature, having a vegetation cover will form a humus layer. *In a mature profile formed under present conditions there should be no humus accumulation.* It has been shown repeatedly that with a highly developed iron crust formation vegetation is impeded.

The mature profile we designate as the C formation, examples of which abound in Lower India, Africa, Sumatra, and Australia. The iron crust may reach a depth of several meters, and no red loam is to be found.

Many of the profiles from Madagascar are distinguished by the lack of either iron or aluminum crusts and by a highly dispersed red loam on the surface. This formation, which seems to be very widespread, we designate as the B formation. It represents, as compared with C, a profile not fully matured.

Finally, we find regions where the surface consists of the zone of *Zersatz.* Inasmuch as this is not a humus soil, it represents an undeveloped profile. It is either in the early stages of laterization, or what is more probable, it is an eroded profile. This is called formation A.

As stated above, laterite is distinguished by the formation of appreciable quantities of free alumina, as shown for the first time by Bauer. The hydrate of aluminum is located in two places in the profile, in the *Zersatz* which in many instances appears as *Siallit* (kaolin), or more generally at *Allit*, i.e., primarily free alumnina. Alumina

---

Zersatz, as interpreted by Harrassowitz, consits of rocks which suffered a chemical change but retained their physical appearance. It is also known as the *Bleichzone,* the bleached zone, from which the SiO_2 and bases were removed. *Allit,* another term used by Harrassowitz, is a formation the primary composition of which is a hydrated Al_2O_3 complex with an admixture of SiO_2, Fe_2O_3, and H_2O. Technically, it is a bauxite-like rock. It is notoriously low in SiO_2, not exceeding the 12 per cent limit. Harrassowitz differentiates a monohydrallit and a tri-hydrallit. The latter is most prominent in the laterites. *Siallit,* as used by Harrassoyitz, is the coating on the original rock consisting of the hydrated aluminum silicate approaching the makeup of kaolinite. Acording to Lacroix, the zersatz is the *zone de depart* which, in the interpretation of Campbell, is a *bleached* layer overlying the bed-rock,

is also found in the zone of enrichment. In both cases, it is generally spoken of as laterite. But, whereas in the deeper lying strata the alumina is found in conjunction with disintegrating rock, in the zone of enrichment it forms concretions upon precipitation from solution as the result of the upward movement of the aluminum and the iron.

Harrassowitz's bulky volumes on laterites are a good review of the subject. However, one would expect a clearer blending of the major contributions of the older masters, such as Lacroix, Harrison, and Campbell, without diluting these with his own viewpoint. Harrassowitz's neglect of the pedologic approach (his work was done at a time when the Dokuchaev school of pedology was known in Germany) is inexcusable.

Marbut (61) described the laterites of Africa and presented a good account of the history of the problem. A selected bibliography may be found in the publication of the Imperial Bureau of Soil Science (48) and a more extensive bibliography—in the work of Harrassowitz. Baeyens (8) cites more than 800 general references in his volume on the soils of Central Africa, with special reference to Belgian Congo. This volume (in French, with English summaries after every chapter) contains a wealth of information on tropical soils. Martin and Doyne (64) investigated laterites in Sierra Leone, Africa, formed from a basic rock (norite), under a rainfall of 100-150 inches. The SiO_2 content of 49.6 per cent in the native rock was reduced to 7.2 per cent in the laterite. Similar observations were made by Bauer (11, 12) in the Seyschelles and Madagascar, Arsandaux (6, 7) in French Sudan and Congo Basin, Lacroix (55) in New Guinea, Holmes (44) in Portuguese East Africa, Adams (1) in Ceylon, and Harrison (41) and Hardy and Follett-Smith (37) in British Guiana.

Harrison states that "basic and intermediate rocks weathering below the soil surface in humid tropical climate, with free drainage, rapidly lose most of their combined silica in solution, together with most of their alkali and alkaline earth bases; the residium, which is termed *primary laterite,* has gibbsite and limonite for its principal constituents." An extension of Harrison's excellent contribution is that of Campbell (22), whose work of more than 30 years ago (at the time of this writing) is still the clearest and most scholarly presentation of the subject. A few excerpts from his papers are given to stimulate the quest of the reader to consult his original papers.

According to Campbell (p. 67) :

Laterization is the process by which certain hydroxides, principally those of ferric iron, aluminum, and titanium are deposited within the mass of a porous rock near the surface. Unless a rock near the surface contains uncombined alumina in the form of hydroxide, it can not be regarded as lateritic. Lateritic constituents are deposited between maximum and minimum vadose* water level only in places where that level is near the surface and oxygen can gain free access.

*Vadose water is seepage water occurring below the surface but above the water table, contrasted with phreatic water which refers to ground waters below the water table.

Under certain unknown conditions laterization from its earlier stages takes a concretionary form. Spherical masses of mixed colloidal ferric and aluminum hydrates form at approximately equal distances apart in a porous argillaceous medium; they grow outward by additions of the same hydrates in varying ratios until they meet one another; then the inner space only partly fills, passages always remaining open. The pisolites usually vary between 3 and 10 mm. in diameter (page 172).

1. Laterites exist as surface layers only, occurring either bare or covered by, at most, a few feet in thickness of soil. 2. Laterites occur on flat or gently sloping ground. 3. Laterite beds are very limited in thickness, rarely exceeding 30 feet. 4. They never occur superimposed one vertically above another with unlaterized ground or rock between, nor do they form under water (page 94).

Campbell (22) differentiates in the tropics the processes of *alteration* and *weathering* in the decomposition of rock. True weathering takes place in the presence of oxygen only within the zone of intermittent saturation of vadose water, and it is here that laterites form. Alteration takes place within the zone of permanent saturation of vadose water, where reduction reactions appear, and consists of the elimination of iron and the conversion of alkaline silicates into hydrous silicates of alumina. It is on these products of alteration that weathering proceeds later to form laterite. In this case, it is, therefore, a product of changes peculiar to the tropics acting on material which has previously been changed by the processes identical with those usually operating in temperate and cool climates.

Although it is well known that laterites are principally soils of the humid tropics and subtropics, still the exact nature of the climatic conditions for ideal laterite formation is not yet thoroughly understood.**

The climate of the tropics may be divided, according to Köppen (54) into two types, tropical rain-forest climate and savanna climate. The former is distinguished by an average temperature not lower than 18°C. and by a high humidity during any month of the year. Within this climatic zone, a subzone of monsoon forest climate may be isolated in which, in spite of the dry season, primeval forests exist. The savanna climate is distinguished by a definite dry season.

Glinka (Ch. 2, 26) maintains that in the tropics, the influence of an evergreen vegetation, on the one hand, and of savannas, on the other, must be considered in discussing the laterite formation. He is of the opinion that laterites may form under the climatic conditions both of forest and of savannas, except that in the latter the process is somewhat slower. His views differ from those of Richthofen (82) who believed that "the laterites in

---

**Whenever laterites are encountered in the climatic regions adjacent to the humid tropics or subtropics, they should be carefully scrutinized, as they might be remnants of ancient laterites from an earlier period during which tropical climatic conditions prevailed.

India, when formed, were under forests even though now they are covered merely with scrub trees and grasses."

Lang (Ch. 5, 59), in his investigations of the soils in Java and Sumatra, found no laterites in regions of extremely high rainfall and temperatures of 26-27°C. According to him, humus-rich and brown soils of the humid tropics are not the exception but the rule, and that in the rain-forests regions, kaolinization rather than laterization predominates. Lang considers the lateritic type of soil formation as transitional between the humid and arid regions, having a rain-factor between 60 and 40, below which the arid type of soil formation begins.

Harrassowitz states (40, p. 422):

A check-up on the distribution of laterites shows that they are a purely tropical soil formation. At one time, it was maintained that similar formations were found in the "Hessian Vogelsberg," as earlier products of weathering. *Laterite is one of the most characteristic weathered soil formations peculiar to the tropical climate.*

An examination of true laterites shows that they belong to the savanna climate where the dry and wet seasons alternate. During the rainy seasons of the year, the silicates undergo an intensive hydrolysis, because of the high moisture and temperature combination. Under such conditions, the movement of the soil solution is downward. With the approach of the dry season the reverse phenomenon occurs, to wit, a rise to the surface of substances in solution and their precipitation, and hence an enrichment at the surface.

Mohr (69) challenged the views of Harrassowitz who limited the laterites to the savanna climate. He repudiated (p. 152) the hypothesis of Harrassowitz on the formation of the crust in laterite as a result of ascending waters. Mohr believed that laterite crust was the result of eluviation followed by erosion. Mohr had a clear understanding of the factors operating in the weathering and soil forming processes in the tropics. As a matter of fact, Mohr had a pedologic approach of his own, inasmuch as he based his work on the principle of zonality of soil formation and discovered the vertical zonality of climatic soil types in 1913, without knowing, as pointed out by Senstius, that Dokuchaev had established the principle of vertical zonality in 1898. Mohr drew a distinction between regions of high, more or less continuous rainfall, and regions of intermittent rainfall. Laterite forms more slowly under intermittent rainfall than under continuously preponderating precipitation. This condition gives rise to yellow or brown lixivium, this term, in the nomenclature of Mohr, meaning *what has been leached out.* According to Senstius (91), the Mohr interpretation is that "in time this lixivium may naturally become dehydrated, and the soil become a red lixivium. On the other hand, if the temperature is high, rainy season alternating with more or less dry season, the result is a red lixivium. One condition, however, must persist in both cases. The soil must be pervious, otherwise other types, such as gray and black tropical soils, are formed."

Mohr has contributed a wealth of information, observations, and theoretical postulates on the soils of the tropics. He has noted, for instance (p. 45), that the temperature of the greatest part of the soils of the Netherlands Indies generally remains between 25 and 30°C. and varies little in the course of the year, seldom more than 1.5°C. These facts have an important bearing on the processes of humification and mineralization, with the latter keeping close on the heels of the former and thereby preventing an accumulation of organic matter. Mohr also has attributed to chemical oxidation (pp. 103-105) a share of the decomposition of organic matter.

On the basis of precipitation and other climatic data, Mohr has established a series of climatic groups which affect the soil. It is questionable whether the closely related groups on the scale of the two extremes, humid to arid, cause a difference in the broad features of the profiles or a radical departure from the fundamental process of laterization. Mohr did not consider the climatic groups from this point of view.

Mohr (p. 146) analyzed the formation of laterite from the point of view of the simultaneous reactions of weathering and soil formation. He did not differentiate between weathering and soil formation in this analysis, although in his discussion on soil formation he did. According to Mohr, the process of laterite formation takes place in 5 stages, and each one represents a soil type (actually it is a stage in the development of the profile characteristics: J.). Stage 1-he calls *fresh ash soils*; stage 2-so-called *tarapan* (a juvenile soil); stage 3-*brownish yellow lixivium,* brown earth; stage 4-*red lixivium;* and stage 5-*laterite.* Mohr, however, does not elaborate on the pedogenetic aspect of the stages. As a matter of fact, Mohr does not deal with the mechanism of the specificity of the process of laterization.

Senstius (92) expresses the view presented earlier by Campbell that laterites "are residual products of any kind of rock which has been subjected long enough to weathering in a hot climate with a short wet and long dry seasons, such as prevails in many parts of the tropics today, notably on the Indian peninsula. A hot climate with more than 25°C. average annual temperature is essential to prevent the permanent accumulation of humus."

Harrison (41), who studied the laterites in British Guiana, made the same distinction as Mohr that in regions of intermittent rainfall, under conditions of poor drainage, laterites may be resilicated by a capillary rise of ground waters containing silica or silicates in solution, or by a change in the ground water level.

Holmes (44), in his studies on the laterites in Portuguese East Africa, upholds the view that in order to form laterites, the climatic conditions of the region must at some time be conducive to the upward movement of the soil constituents by the capillary rise of water.

Bonnet (19), reporting on laterites in Puerto Rico, finds no sharp distinction between horizons and concludes that "laterization is largely a geologic process rather than a pedologic." It was not essential to invoke this concept for the orogenic condition of the profile discussed. Geologic erosion, which is intensive in the tropics, blocks the formation of mature profiles.

Hardy and Rodrigues (38) describe a profile in Grenada, British West Indies, on andesite-augite parent material. They point out that laterization of acid rocks liberates Al and SiO_2 which combine again to form kaolinitic minerals or even sericite mica, with very little free alumina left behind.

Basic igneous rocks liberate much lesser amounts of active silica in proportion to alumina and consequently the excess of free alumina is crystallyzing as gibbsite. Presumably, the formation and accumulation of gibbsite would be enhanced by free drainage, because this favors the rapid removal of silica in solution. Harrison repeatedly stresses the importance of free drainage in primary laterization, and it is generally agreed that kaolinization proceeds best under poor drainage conditions.

Hardy and Rodrigues discuss the vexing problem of resilication of minerals in laterites and the associated phenomenon of formation of indurated layers. They agree with Mohr that the theory on the upward movement of salts during the dry season, which might explain the condition of induration, is in most cases untenable. The cemented material in laterite and lateritic soils, slag-like and cellular in structure, is an illuviation layer and has the markings of such. A number of this type of B horizons has been examined by the author in Panama in various stages of development, from slag-like concretions and buck-shot to massive indurations of pisolitic structure and tube-like formations, so vividly described by Oldham (73). Surface deposits of this kind of formation have been observed in the savannas of Panama. tube-like ironstone formations of the Colts Neck soil in New Jersey are very similar to those observed in Panama. For this and other reasons (49), it has been concluded that this soil series is a relic of a tropical climate that had preceded the present climate. The ironstone formations resemble much the bog-iron formation which is considered as an illuviation horizon with occasional contact with ground waters. It is, therefore, possible that, in the case of the induration layers in laterites, some form of water movement had contributed to their formation. In this connection, the presence or absence of chalybeate water has to be considered. Pendelton and Sharasuvana (p. 435) describe cases where seepage waters have contributed to this type of induration. The novel theory of Hardy and Rodrigues (p. 374) (some inkling of this theory may be found in the work of Mohr) on the formation of resilicated minerals is given here:

We may first assume that the laterite layer is impregnated from below with a concentrated alkaline solution of colloidal silica throughout the wet season, and that excess of solution is continually draining away over the decomposing rock surface. We may further assume that the level of saturation falls rapidly in the intervals between rainy spells, and during these spells the upper part of the solution is subjected to dilution by descending acidic water. Under these circumstances, silica will be precipitated around the gibbsitic nuclei occurring in the upper part of the laterite layer. The marked change in reaction conditions in this part of the profile will favor the mutual adsorption of alumina and silica, for, according to the isoelectric theory as postulated by Mattson (Ch. 4, 48), the alumina particles will acquire electropositive charges when the reaction becomes more acidic than the isoelectric point of alumina (stated variously to range from pH 6.5 to 8.1), whereas the silica particles will be electronegatively charged, having an isoelectric point very low on the pH scale. By slow degrees, the coprecipitate will become stabilized through irreversible dehydration, favored especially by the onset of the dry season when the water table sinks to the level of the parent rock. It will slowly "age," passing through stages such as allophane, until it eventually crystallizes as a kaolinitic mineral, probably halloysite.

It seems likely, therefore, that both primary laterization and resilication occur across narrow boundary zones, and that reaction conditions, as well as degree of wetness and solute concentration, may fluctuate constantly between wide limits, setting up reversible gradients alternately favoring the one process and then the other.

A temporary shift in charge, from negative to positive, has been reported in the literature for the soils in the tropics and even for the B horizon of podzols where an accumulation of R_2O_3 takes place. Under these circumstances, one can see how the mutual coagulation of the silicate and of the Al ions may cause the formation of clay minerals. The intensity of the reactions, as advanced by Hardy and Rodrigues, will of course depend on the quantitative factors of the elements and radicals involved, their ionization, the effect of the products of the reactions formed, and the electrolyte content.

Vageler's (101) outline of the soils in the tropics and subtropics is primarily a methodical discussion of the known facts on geologic weathering of rocks and minerals in that climatic zone. His absurd conclusions that the views of Dokuchaev, Sibirtzev, and other orthodox Russian pedologists coincide with those of Richthoffen, the well known geologist-geographer, are due to his neglect of pedologic principles. Vageler's deductions on the soils of the tropics are on the order of Harrassowitz's, with some elements of Mohr's ideas. Harrassowitz, in turn, leans on Vageler's work. Vageler calls attention to the opinion of earlier observers on the large quantities of HNO_3 contributed to the soils in the tropics by rains. He quotes figures from Indochina, showing 30 to 35 kilograms of HNO_3 per hectare coming through precipitation. He also attributes enhanced oxidation of rocks and minerals to H_2O_2 and ozone, formed naturally under the climatic conditions of the tropics. How much these reagents contribute to the reactions in the process of laterization is not brought out by Vageler. He elaborates on the activities of termites in the decomposition of organic matter in the tropics. More pertinent are Vageler's observations on some morphological characteristics of the soils in the tropics and especially in the subtropics and his interpretations of the possible chemical reactions that might explain certain phenomena. It is to be noted that Vageler presents practically no analytical data. Instead, he brings in interesting elements of scholasticism which serve no reliable substitute for chemical data.

PROCESS OF LATERIZATION

In the process of laterization, the alumino-iron-silicate and other rocks and minerals decompose, the silica is removed, and the sesquioxides are left behind. It is generally accepted that the high temperature and moisture conditions in the tropics and subtropics are, in a large measure, responsible for this particular hydrolysis of the silicates, but the exact nature of the mechanism of the reactions involved has not as yet been very well established.

Theories on Laterization.—Wiegner (104) assumes that, under conditions of the tropical climate, the silicates hydrolyze in the presence of free OH ions which stablize the negatively charged hydrated silica, thereby facilitating its removal from the soil medium. Simultaneously, these OH ions react with the positively charged Al_2O_3 and Fe_2O_3, and coagulation takes place. In other words, the negatively charged OH ions replace the $HSiO_3$ ions, preventing the new formation of kaolin. The iron and aluminum oxides, or hydrated oxides, gel, age, become irreversible, and even form crystalline substances.

Gedroiz (31) considers the process of laterization similar to podzolization, since in both cases he found the soils unsaturated. Although this is generally true, it is well to remember that the base exchange capacity of the podzols is relatively high, whereas of laterites it is low, and the difference is undoubtedly due to the difference in hydrolytic cleavage. In the podzols, we have acid hydrolysis and hence a high $SiO_2:R_2O_3$ ratio which, in turn is the seat of the high base exchange capacity. In the laterites, we have a less acid or even an alkaline hydrolysis and a low $SiO_2:R_2O_3$ ratio. Gedroiz admits the decomposition of the silicates in the laterite region, but he does not indicate how it is accomplished. The small degree of unsaturation does not come in conflict with the process of alkaline hydrolysis. As a matter of fact, Gedroiz explains the precipitation of Fe and Al in the laterites by the presence of bases in circulation. Were it not for the low base exchange capacity of laterites, these bases would have entered the complex. As it is, they are only instrumental in increasing the OH-ion concentration whereby the silica is released and removed.

According to Mattson, the silicates are released in laterites because the Fe and Al are less basic than the silicates are acid. This phenomenon is associated with the reactions of hydrolysis in an alkaline medium, as discussed presently.

An important consideration in the elucidation of the process of laterization is the rapid decomposition and mineralization of organic matter. There are no more suitable conditions for microbial activities anywhere than in the humid tropics; temperature and moisture relationships are ideal. No intermediate products, such as organic acids and their acid salts, have a chance to react with the mineral fraction; they are utilized by the microbes as fast as they are formed. *The ash constituents of the mineralized organic matter quickly enter into circulation, and this gives the soil solution a less acid, if not a neutral or alkaline reaction. In other words, we get an alkaline hydrolysis instead of an acid hydrolysis.* In such a chemical system, the silica will go into solution more readily than will the sesquioxides, resulting in an accumulation of the latter in the surface horizon and a simultaneous loss of the former from it. In this connection, it is of interest to recall that the ground waters in the tropics contain high amounts of SiO_2. Polynov (Ch. 4, 62, p. 185) notes that the SiO_2 residue of river waters is, on the average, 12 per cent of the total solids, with special cases of tropical waters reaching 50 per cent SiO_2 or more.

Alkaline hydrolysis, as pointed out by Mattson, will bring about an increase in the ionization of the acid radical and a suppression in the ionization of the basic radical. With an increase in pH, the amount of silica combining with the sesquioxides is decreased, and, because of the lower isoelectric pH of iron hydroxide—pH 7.1 against pH 8.1 for aluminum hydroxide—the iron silicate will hydrolyze more readily at any particular pH than will the aluminum silicate, as shown by Mattson (Ch, 4, 48) in his highly instructive theories on isoelectric weathering. This reaction leads one to seek the process and degree of laterization in the factors active in the stabilization of the isoelectric precipitates of iron, aluminum, manganese, titanium, and other constituents. Undoubtedly, the rapid decomposition of the organic matter brings into the system the active humate ion and the PO_4 ion from the mineralized organic phosphorus compounds. The formation of complexes with these ions might help to explain why even at a low pH, the same alkaline hydrolysis will take place. These anions shift the pH of isoelectric precipitation downward. It is, therefore, natural to expect that with a decrease in alkaline hydrolysis the process of laterization will subside; that is what apparently happens in the red soils of the humid subtropics and still more so in the yellow soils. More and more does the soil solution become acid, and we finally approach the region of acid hydrolysis, the zone of podzolization.

THE CHEMICAL AND MINERALOGICAL CONSTITUENTS OF LATERITES

Mature laterites are made up primarily of iron, aluminum, silica, titanium, and water. The sesquioxides figure prominently in laterites as the hydrated oxides and somewhat as the kaolin-like minerals. It is with these compounds that the H_2O is tied up. As a rule, laterites are poor in alkalies and alkaline-earth metals. As compiled by Harrassowitz, the composition of typical laterites approximates the following:

H_2O.—With large quantities of alumina, the combined water in laterite varies from 25 to 30 per cent. Cases are recorded with 38 per cent of combined water.

Al_2O_3.—In general, this is the most abundant constituent in laterite, varying from 50 to 60 per cent. With an enrichment of iron, the alumina content is lowered. An increase in quartz may also reduce the percentage of alumina. Of the Al minerals, the mono and trihydrates are found.

Fe_2O_3.—The content of Fe_2O_3 may vary considerably. There are laterites with only 1 to 2 per cent of Fe_2O_3; on the other hand, there are laterites with an extremely high Fe_2O_3 content. Where the alumina is high, the Fe_2O_3 is low and vice versa. In determining the iron in laterite, it is important to consider not only the Fe_2O_3, but the FeO. No clear-cut minerals of Fe are found in laterites. The hydrated forms predominate; in some cases magnetite and titanite are encountered.

SiO_2.—In a typical laterite, there should be very little silica. The ratio of SiO_2 to Al_2O_3 (the ki of Harrassowitz) is an important index of laterites. In determining this ratio, the quartz silica must be eliminated. Opal and chalcedony may be encountered as secondary products of the process of laterization.

TiO_2.—Generally, the TiO_2 content is high, about 2 per cent. In a laterite sample of Lower India, as much as 18 per cent was found. Sometimes, however, it is lacking altogether.

Mn.—Frequently, this element is lacking, but generally it is present in varying quantities with the iron crusts. In certain areas, one may encounter such minerals as pyrolusite, manganite, wad, and psilomelane, either as remnants of the weathering processes or as new formations. A high Mn content has been reported for some laterites in Hawaii.

P_2O_5.—Generally, P_2O_5 is present in appreciable quantities, although sometimes only traces are found.

Cr and V.—In some laterites, relatively large quantities of Cr and V are found, usually when the native rock, like peridotite, is rich in these elements. Cases are known from Cuba and Guinea where the Cr_2O_3 content is as high as 3.14 per cent and the V_2O_5 is as high as 0.55 per cent. Bennett and Allison (16, p. 72) report a sample of perdigon-ferruginous pebbles, found in the Nipe soils of Cuba, with 7.68 per cent Cr_2O_3.

Alkali and Alkaline Earths.—Extensive leaching is responsible for the meager quantities of alkali and alkaline earth bases which do not, as a rule, exceed 1 per cent. For this reason, carbonates are generally not to be encountered in typical laterites. However, there are laterites with very little alkaline earth and considerable alkali bases.

Distribution of Constituents in the Laterite Profile

As an introduction to data and discussion on the distribution of the individual constituents in laterites, it might be of interest to examine table 101, giving the analyses of a young laterite profile. The data represent a soil profile in the island Lang-Eiland, East Indian Archipelago, which was covered 50 years ago with volcanic dust and other eruptive materials, forming in places a layer of pumice more than 40 m. thick. The depth of this layer illustrates the rapidity of weathering of rocks in the humid tropics. Within the short period of 50 years, an appreciable loss of SiO_2 and a definite accumulation of Fe, Al, and Ti took place within the surface layer.

Table 101

Composition of a young laterite profile

(After van Baren)

Constituent	A*	B*	C*	D*
	per cent	per cent	per cent	per cent
SiO_2	67.55	65.87	61.13	63.77
TiO_2	0.70	0.83	0.93	0.96
Al_2O_3	15.19	16.31	17.24	15.67
Fe_2O_3	1.52	1.74	2.56	2.89
FeO	2.15	2.05	2.59	2.15
CaO	2.89	3.07	3.61	2.86
P_2O_5	0.04	0.22	0.22	0.17
Organic matter			0.45	

*A, composition of native rock; B, composition of middle layer; C, composition of soil material; D, composition of weathered rock fragments in the soil material.

The data given in tables 102-106 are typical for reports on laterites. The more recent report by Seelye, Grange, and Davis (90) on laterites of western Samoa add important data on the reaction of laterites.

Mg and Ca.—The data in table 102 show that the alkaline earths suffer the highest loss. Practically no magnesium appears through a depth of close to 6 meters, notwithstanding the almost 34 per cent MgO in the serpentine parent material. This is true also for the Mg in th Cuban profile (table 103). Evidently, Mg is being washed out completely.

Table 102

Laterite profile from India

(After Harrassowitz)

	Surface	0.6 m.	1.2 m.	2.7 m.	5.8 m.	8.8 m. serpentine rock
	per cent	*per cent*	*per cent*	*per cent*	*per cent*	*per cent*
SiO_2	2.58	2.38	1.42	2.44	3.66	39.80
Al_2O_3	15.71	20.81	14.23	6.91	6.51	1.39
Fe_2O_3	66.20	64.70	68.70	72.40	69.20	10.14
MgO	—	—	—	—	trace	33.69
H_2O	10.20	10.63	9.50	12.35	12.73	13.31
Fe	46.37	45.34	48.09	50.63	48.42	7.10
Cr	0.92	0.96	1.04	2.08	2.43	0.20
Ni and Co	0.38	0.33	0.36	1.21	1.34	0.97
P	0.016	0.022	0.019	0.005	0.005	0.001
S	0.12	0.12	0.16	0.16	0.06	0.06

It appears as though the suggestion that the surface horizons of laterites are enriched with certain constituents by capillary rise does not hold true for magnesium and calcium, but why not? In this connection, it is of interest to recall the translocation and movement of Mg in the podzol profile. A good share of the eluviated Mg is fixed in the horizon of illuviation, probably partly in the base exchange complex and partly as new formations.

What has been said about the Mg is also true of the Ca. Fully developed mature laterites are poor in Ca. Bennett and Allison cite the soils of the Matanzas family with 0.31 per cent CaO, notwithstanding the limestone parent material containing 50 per cent CaO. An examination of the data on the other mature laterites discloses the same situation.

P_2O_5.—Phosphorus occupies a unique position, inasmuch as it is one of the essential elements for plant growth and is, therefore, actively circulating through the profile. Plants gather the phosphorus through their roots from the entire, or a certain portion, of the soil body and redeposit it on the surface after their death. Because of the insolubility of most of its com-

Table 103

Laterite profile from Cuba

(After Bennett and Allison)

	0-26 inches	26-40 inches	40-156 inches	156-192 inches	192 + inches
	per cent	*per cent*	*per cent*	*per cent*	*per cent*
SiO_2	3.28	2.25	1.83	1.55	41.93
TiO_2	0.80	0.26	0.80	0.80	0.05
Fe_2O_3	63.04	69.56	71.12	68.10	7.84
Al_2O_3	18.46	11.13	12.36	14.66	2.00
MnO	0.42	0.28	0.38	0.47	0.12
CaO	0.12	trace	0.01	0.15	1.50
MgO	0.33	0.48	0.64	0.60	34.02
K_2O	0.06	0.08	0.02	0.05	0.08
Na_2O	0.49	0.30	0.48	0.39	0.36
P_2O_5	0.03	trace	trace	trace	trace
Ignition loss	12.74	12.38	12.33	12.74	11.75
Organic matter	1.02	—	0.37	—	—
Cr_2O_3	—	3.14	—	—	0.10

pounds, the mobility of the phosphorus is hindered and it accumulates, relatively speaking, in the surface horizon. In mature laterites, the P_2O_5 is concentrated in the iron crusts of the surface layer, as shown by Bennett and Allison in their report on the comparative analyses of perdigon (iron crust) and the surrounding soil material.

S.—The somewhat higher solubility of sulfur compounds in the soil, as compared with those of phosphorus, brings about a lesser accumulation of sulfur in the upper horizon, even though it is also active in circulation through the soil-plant system.

K and Na.—These two elements, as shown by the data on the Cuban profile, do not seem to have suffered much in the process of laterization. It appears as if both participated actively in the circulation of the soil plant system, although generally little attention is being paid to Na. On the other hand, the data collected by Harrassowitz (40, p. 412) show a complete loss of these elements. Unquestionably, the phenomenon observed in the Cuban profile must be explained by some other factor. It is to be noted that the parent material is also poor in K which is probably locked up in a combination not readily released. It is of interest, as shown by Bennett and Allison, that more potash is found in the soil than in the perdigon. Apparently, potash does not migrate from the soil to the concretions.

Fe_2O_3 and Al_2O_3.—The sesquioxides are the striking morphological index of laterites. Their accumulation in the surface horizon is an indisputable fact, as shown by chemical analyses. As to the mode of accumulation, there seems to be no general agreement. Some investigators claim that it is a residual product in the process of decomposition of the various minerals, as outlined in the discussion of the process of laterization. Marbut (62), in his discussion of the laterites, seems to uphold this view. Some, however, claim that the enrichment of the surface with sesquioxides is brought about by the capillary rise of the ground waters during the dry period in the laterite zone. This opinion is shared by Campbell, Harrassowitz, and others, but no definite proof of this phenomenon is given. Although an enrichment of the surface horizon with R_2O_3 by the upward movement is plausible, the fact that other constituents do not behave in a similar manner seems rather inconsistent. It is well known that the ground waters in the tropics are rich in SiO_2, but none of it seems to be brought to the surface. Neither is it clear why such elements as Cr and Ti should not accumulate at the surface in larger quantities than they do. No experimental evidence in this direction has been offered.

In mature laterites, sesquioxides accumulate in the form of crusts and concretions. In some cases, the sesquioxides make up a honeycombed slag-like layer. Some investigators designate such a formation *cellular laterite*. Infrequently, tubular crust formations are encountered. Within the pores of the red or dark red celllular crusts rich in sesquioxides, a white soft mass rich in SiO_2 and poor in free alumina is found. Reference to such iron crusts have been made by Richthofen (82). In the *red loams* which are frequently found alongside true laterites, the slag-like or cellular formation and crusts are generally absent. Concretions, however, are sometimes found. As pointed out earlier, the more plausible origin of the crusts or indurated stone-like formation are the remnant of an illuviation horizon, exposed by erosion.

The laterite crust is rich in iron. According to Kooman, as quoted by Harrassowitz (40, p. 405), basic rocks allow a higher accumulation of this element than do acidic rocks. These crusts, which infrequently reach a depth of 2.4 to 3.7 m., are also, in some regions, rich in alumina. Usually, it is the trihydrate of aluminum which is very similar in composition to hydrargillite. Some monohydrate, which in this case is very similar to the bauxite formation, is also found.

SiO_2.—In mature laterite, the silica content of the surface layer is at a minimum and is sometimes lacking entirely. This has been generally accepted, and the facts are so apparent that they need not be elaborated upon.

SiO_2 : R_2O_3 and SiO_2 : Al_2O_3 ratios.—The low SiO_2 : R_2O_3 ratio in laterites was noted by van Bemmelen (13, 14) who considered the silica-free alumina as the end-product of lateritic weathering. In this connection, van Bemmelen made the important observation that the lateritic clays have practically no plasticity. Maxwell (66) investigated a series of Hawaiian soils, most of which were low in SiO_2 and high in Fe and Al, the average molar ratios of SiO_2 to sesquioxides being about 0.9. Hardy (35), in studying the significance of the shrinkage coefficient of a number of clays and soils, ascribed their specific physical characteristics to the lateritic nature, namely, the low SiO_2 : R_2O_3 ratio, and especially to the high alumina content.

Bennett (15) presents data on 24 samples of "friable tropical soils," with an average SiO_2 : R_2O_3 ratio of 1.25 with 0.15 as a minimum and 1.96 as a maximum. The peculiar properties of tropical clays, to wit, low plasticity, permeability to water, and high porosity, may be correlated with low SiO_2:R_2O_3 ratios. Bennett takes the SiO_2:R_2O_3 ratio up to 2.0 as a dividing limit in the grouping of some tropical soils.

Anderson and Byers (4) report the SiO_2:R_2O_3 ratios on the colloids of a ferruginous laterite (Nipe family from Cuba) as follows: in the surface horizon- 0 to 12 inches-, 0.31; in the next horizon- 40 to 60 inches-, 0.17; and in the third horizon- 100 to 144 inches-, 0.42. Ratios on a Davidson profile (from North Carolina), designated as lateritic, are about the same throughout the profiles: A_1-1.46, B_1-1.49, B_2-1.42, and C-1.40.

The low SiO_2:R_2O_3 ratio in laterites is readily explained by the work of Mattson (Ch. 4, 48) on isoelectric precipitation. Because of the alkaline hydrolysis, the iron and aluminum with their high isoelectric pH will not bind silicic acid to any appreciable extent, less so when other anions outside of the OH ion, like PO_4 and humate, are present to displace the $HSiO_3$.

Harrassowitz (39) uses the ratio of SiO_2 to Al_2O_3 instead of to R_2O_3. One of the reasons for eliminating the Fe from the calculation is that it exists also as FeO, in the form of Fe_3O_4, and in combination with other constituents besides the silicates. This ratio of SiO_2 to Al_2O_3 is known as the *ki* of Harrassowitz. It has been used by Joseph (51) in his studies on the properties of clays as soil colloids. Martin and Doyne (64) adhere to the view of Bauer (12) that the characteristic mineral ol laterite is hydrargillite or gibbsite. This view is, however, open to question. The so-called "ferruginous laterites" are low in alumina, and the *ki* of Harrassowitz in them might be higher than that which the adherents of the SiO_2 : Al_2O_3 ratio would suggest for true laterite. Harrassowitz's viewpoint seems to be more logical; although he does not include the Fe in his ratio, he does not exclude it as a nonessential constituent.

Robinson and Holmes (84) suggest that "all the silica, iron, alumina, and water in the colloidal matter (the clay fraction) are not present in the proportion to form the commoner hydrated silicates of alumina and iron, such as kaolinite $(Al_2O_3.2SiO_2.2H_2O)$ and nontronite $(Fe_2O_3 .2SiO_2 .2H_2O)$* There may, however, be some or a considerable part of the above constituents present in compounds of the composition of such minerals as kaolinite, nontronite, halloysite, or pyrophyllite." Robinson (83) claims that primary residual products of the chemical weathering of silicates are a mixture of kalinite and nontronite, or hydrated silicates of Fe and Al having the same silica-sesquioxide ratio, namely, 2.0. Variations from this ratio, Robinson ascribes to the processes of soil formation leading, in humid temperate climates, to the production of a more siliceous A horizon and a less siliceous B horizon and, in humid tropical climates, to the formation of laterite.

At present, even though it is recognized that Fe is an integral part of most laterites, its inclusion in the ratio with respect to silica does not give so clear-cut a constant for the identification of laterites as does the SiO_2: Al_2O_3 ratio. Undoubtedly, over a wide range of climatic conditions, it is simple to show that the $SiO_2 :R_2O_3$ ratio narrows as we approach the humid tropics. The work of Anderson and Byers (4), Holmes and Edgington (45), Byers and Anderson (21), and the theoretical postulates of Mattson (Ch. 4, 48) on isoelectic weathering, based on experimental evidence, are clear enough to justify the use of the $SiO_2 :R_2O_3$ ratio, but when it comes to a detailed analysis of the laterites, the *ki* of Harrassowitz seems to fit better.

Harrassowitz and Martin and Doyne show that the *ki* value is a reliable index of the extent of disruption of the feldspars. If silica is lost and a residue in alumina is left behind, it is a clear indication of laterization. A *ki* value (molar) below that of kaolinite (2.0) may be said to indicate the

---

*This mineral is now classified with the montmorillonitic group of clay minerals and the ratio of SiO_2 to Fe_2O_3 and the quantity of water are not definite.

presence of free alumina and can therefore be considered a safe index of the presence of uncombined alumina, except for a number of special cases where the naturally occurring alumino-silicates have a ki value below 2.0, such as the minerals *kollrite* and *scabrotite,* as pointed out by the Imperial Bureau of Soil Science (48).

From the ki values in table 104a, one can readily judge how far the process of laterization has progressed in the various formations. The lower the value, the more lateritic the soil is. And yet, we might very well encounter cases with a ki value above 2.0 and still have free alumina. For instance, a parent rock high in SiO_2, upon weathering, may accumulate free Al_2O_3 and yet not lower the ki value to 2.0. In such a case, HCl extract might help to show the free Al_2O_3 and thus surmount the difficulty presented by total analysis data.

Table 104a

ki values for some laterite profiles

(After Harrassowitz)

Constituents	Zone of enrichment			Zersatz				Red Loam	
	1	2	3	4	5	6	7	8	9
SiO_2	—	0.78	2.26	6.98	13.50	35.40	43.90	29.06	21.19
Al_2O_3	4.80	26.03	45.58	42.37	31.93	40.08	38.80	24.41	32.27
ki	—	0.058	0.084	0.28	0.719	1.46	1.94	2.02	1.13

No. 1—Allitic iron crust from peridotite: Guinea
No. 2—Hydrargillitic allit from pegmatite: Madagascar
No. 3—Alumina gel allit: Madagascar
No. 4—Hydrargillitic allit from amphobolite: Madagascar
No. 5—Alumina gel siallit from gneiss or granite: Madagascar
No. 6—Alumina gel siallit from nephelin-syenite: Madagascar
No. 7—Kaolinitic siallit from pegmatite: Madagascar
No. 8—Clay siallit from basalt: Madagascar
No. 9—Clay allitic siallit: Madagascar

In determining the $SiO_2 : R_2O_3$ or $SiO_2 : Al_2O_3$ ratios, the presence of quartz silica is to be considered. It has to be excluded from any silica ratio calculations. The Hardy and Follett-Smith (37), tri-acid digestion method —H_2SO_4, HCl, and HNO_3—seems to meet the difficulty. All the silicates, except the quartz silica, are dissolved out by the caustic soda after the acid digestion.

Table 104

Comparison of various ratios derived from chemical data for different profiles in British Guiana, South America

(After Hardy and Follett-Smith)

Source of parent material and type of ratio	Zone of alteration			Zone of secondary changes	Zone of leaching
	Parent rock	Commencing	Completed	Transition	Topsoil
Basic rocks					
(A) Hornblende schist					
I Ratio $\dfrac{\text{Combined } SiO_2}{\text{Total } R_2O_3}$	2.05	—	0.12	0.54	0.46	0.45
II Ratio $\dfrac{\text{Combined } SiO_2}{\text{Total } Al_2O_3}$	3.73	—	0.21	1.15	1.07	1.16
III Ratio $\dfrac{\text{Total } SiO_2}{\text{Quartz}}$	11.6	—	2.48	1.88	1.55	1.33
IV Ratio $\dfrac{\text{Combined } SiO_2}{\text{Combined } H_2O}$	113.7	—	0.35	2.20	1.93	1.71
(B) Dolerite					
I Ratio $\dfrac{\text{Combined } SiO_2}{\text{Total } R_2O_3}$	1.96	0.63	0.63	0.61	0.65	0.56
II Ratio $\dfrac{\text{Combined } SiO_2}{\text{Total } Al_2O_3}$	3.25	1.21	1.13	1.15	1.22	1.09
III Ratio $\dfrac{\text{Total } SiO_2}{\text{Quartz}}$	5.12	2.60	3.98	4.69	3.54	1.43
IV Ratio $\dfrac{\text{Combined } SiO_2}{\text{Combined } H_2O}$	127.7	3.25	2.69	2.10	2.18	1.34

Table 104 (*continued*)

| Source of parent material and type of ratio | Zone of alteration | | | Zone of secondary changes | | Zone of leaching |
	Parent rock	Com-mencing	Com-pleted	Transition		topsoil
Intermediate rock						
(C) Quartz diorite						
I Ratio $\dfrac{\text{Combined } SiO_2}{\text{Total } R_2O_3}$	0.79	0.54	0.43	0.80	0.86	1.04
II Ratio $\dfrac{\text{Combined } SiO_2}{\text{Total } Al_2O_3}$	1.18	1.25	0.62	1.30	1.31	5.12
III Ratio $\dfrac{\text{Total } SiO_2}{\text{Quartz}}$	1.48	1.24	1.25	1.29	1.23	1.12
IV Ratio $\dfrac{\text{Combined } SiO_2}{\text{Combined } H_2O}$ *Acidic rock*	32.2	1.56	1.21	2.13	2.14	1.55
(D) Granite						
I Ratio $\dfrac{\text{Total } SiO_2}{\text{Total } R_2O_3}$	2.51	1.88	1.37	1.24	1.18	1.20
II Ratio $\dfrac{\text{Combined } SiO_2}{\text{Total } Al_2O_3}$	2.84	2.16	1.52	1.34	1.24	1.28
III Ratio $\dfrac{\text{Total } SiO_2}{\text{Quartz}}$	2.30	1.79	1.68	1.87	2.06	1.77
IV Ratio $\dfrac{\text{Combined } SiO_2}{\text{Combined } H_2O}$	58.7	19.2	5.48	4.21	3.05	6.34

In order to establish the ratios, a quantitative analysis of the sesquioxides is imperative. Schmelev (87) introduced a method, based on the property of free sesquioxides to absorb alizarin red, whereby this is accomplished without recourse to detailed chemical analyses. Hardy (36) somewhat modified the method. Two portions of the material to be investigated are taken. One is ignited to dull redness (800°C) for 6 minutes, the other is not ignited. The quantity of adsorbed alizarin in the ignited sample gives the free alumina, for only after ignition does the alumina absorb the alizarin. On the other hand, the iron oxide adsorbs the alizarin only in the fresh unignited state.

Other Ratios.—A number of other ratios, besides those discussed, have been used. Harrassowitz suggested the molar ratio of SiO_2 to the total bases, alkali and alkaline earth. He designated this ratio by *ba*. Data of this nature, compiled by Hardy and Follett-Smith (37), are presented in table 104; they also show the differences in the composition of laterite as affected by the parent material.

The ratios shown in the table bring out the point that in laterites there is a loss of combined silica, with concomitant accumulation of sesquioxides and possibly secondary quartz. The change is more apparent in the basic than in the acidic rock, especially in the zone of secondary changes. There is, however, a similarity in composition of the soils formed from both basic and acidic rocks.

Hydrogen-Ion Concentration.—As a result of the alkaline hydrolysis in the zone of laterites, the OH ions prevail, and they in turn replace the silicate ions. With the iron and aluminum remaining behind, the tendency is toward the formation of their stable isoelectric state which, under ideal conditions, is pH 7.1 for the Fe and 8.1 for the Al. In the presence of other anions, phosphates, sulfates, and humates, the pH of the isoelectric complexes, formed with the Fe and Al hydroxides, shifts towards the acid side. The acid residue, however, is weak, and the tendency is toward a high pH rather than a lower.

Data on the pH of laterites are conflicting. Bennett's results on the soils of Cuba show the majority to be close to neutrality. Martin and Doyne (64) report that the laterites they have studied were acid. Seelye, Grange, and Davis (90) present pH data on laterites of Western Samoa. Harrassowitz (39, p. 433) states: "The proof that an acid reaction occurs in the laterite is easily forthcoming." He bases his argument on the total low base content in the material. This, however, cannot serve as a criterion, since the Fe and Al isoelectric complexes, in the absence of SiO_2 and in the presence of the soluble bases in the circulation through the mineralization of the organic matter, will tend to lower acidity.

Cation Exchange Capacity.—From the researches of Mattson (65) on the amphoteric behavior of colloids, it has been established that the exchange capacity of soil colloids depends primarily on the acidoid : basoid ratio. All other conditions being equal—pH, electrolyte content, etc.—, a high ratio means a high cation and a low anion exchange; a low ratio, a low cation and a relatively higher anion exchange. The laterites and lateritic soils represent a system with a low silica (acidoid) and a high sesquioxide (basoid) content. One should therefore expect the laterites to be low in cation exchange capacity and relatively higher in anion exchange capacity. Experimentally, this has been proved by Mattson on the adsorption (cation and anion exchange capacity) of ions by the Nipe colloids (from Cuba), as shown in table 105.

It is clear that in the Nipe, with its low acidoid :basoid ratio, there is a relatively high anion exchange and a low cation exchange capacity. It is well to remember that only a fraction of the acidoid is active in the exchange reactions. It is for this reason that the total exchange is low. In the phos-

Table 105

Adsorption of NH₄, Cl, SO₄, and PO₄ ions by the Nipe soil colloid (3 gm. in 100cc.
solution)

(After Mattson)

m. e. added		m. e. per gram adsorbed		Cataphoresis	pH
NH_4	Cl	NH_4	Cl	μ/sec./v./cm.	
2.242	2.00	0.039	0.00	— 1.30	7.25
2.121	2.00	0.021	0.003	— 0.030	6.7
2.00	2.00	0.014	0.011	+ 0.47	6.1
2.00	2.10	0.012	0.024	+ 0.82	5.8
2.00	2.20	0.006	0.038	+ 1.51	5.3
2.00	2.40	0.007	0.059	+ 1.78	4.05
	SO_4		SO_4		
2.242	2.00	0.042	0.00	— 1.44	7.2
2.121	2.00	0.032	0.007	— 1.32	6.9
2.00	2.00	0.017	0.029	— 1.08	6.65
2.00	2.10	0.017	0.046	— 0.87	6.25
2.00	2.20	0.012	0.066	— 0.61	5.9
2.00	2.40	0.011	0.105	+ 0.00	5.0
	PO_4		PO_4		
2.00	3.00	0.109	0.297	— 2.02	7.5
2.00	4.20	0.093	0.408	— 1.78	6.75
2.00	5.40	0.077	0.465	— 1.68	6.1
2.00	6.60	0.055	0.561	— 1.51	5.5
2.00	7.80	0.028	0.750	— 1.00	4.6
2.00	9.00	0.017	0.921	— slight	3.8

phated colloid, the acidoid activity increases, the complex becomes more negative and dissociates more of its anionic parts in the outside solution of the colloidal micelle, increasing thereby by anionic exchange capacity within certain limits. It is undoubtedly because of this behavior that the laterites "fix" P_2O_5.

Data on the base exchange capacity of laterites are scant, but the few there are, such as on the laterites in Cuba, as reported by Bennett and Allison, show that it is low.

Organic Matter.—Generally, it has been accepted that in the humid tropics and subtropics conditions are not favorable for the accumulation of organic matter. The high temperature and the abundant rainfall are conducive to microbiological activities. Indeed, the rapid disappearance of the luxuriant vegetation in the tropics is phenomenal and, in the light of our knowledge of microbial activities, is readily explained. One should therefore not expect an accumulation of organic matter in the regions of the humid tropics, except under special conditions, like swamping.

Bennett and Allison described the peat accumulation in the Zapata Peninsula of Cuba, a swamp covering an area of 1800 square miles. The extensive peat accumulations in the famous Florida Everglades which cover an area of about 10,000 square miles, are also typical subtropical swamps. Schürman (88) describes the peat deposits in eastern Sumatra which spread over an area of about 350 km. long and 125 km. wide on an average. Some soils in that region are covered with a layer of raw humus a meter deep. A review of peat and humus-rich soils in the tropics is given by Giesecke (33).

But besides the peat deposits in the genuine swamps, humus accumulations have been reported in some soils of the primeval forests. It is not clear, however, under what moisture conditions these accumulations take place. There are all kinds of gradations in the moisture regime between a well-drained soil and a waterlogged swamp. A temporary surface swamping or a periodic high water table may introduce partial anaerobic conditions and thus induce organic matter accumulation. We must therefore accept with reservations the claim made by Lang (Ch. 5, 59), Vageler (101), Bennett and Allison (16), and others about the high organic matter content of tropical soils.

Lang maintains that the humus-rich soils and brown soils are not the exception but the rule in the extremely humid tropics. Vageler points out that with respect to the humus content of tropical soils "the conclusions drawn from casual observations give a wrong impression. The humus content of the soils in the tropical climate, especially where rainfall is abundant, is by no means small." He calls attention to the existence of a raw humus layer in the soils of the primeval forests in Palembang (eastern Sumatra), southern Mozambique, and Guinea. Under the raw humus, a bleached horizon, a meter or more deep, is found. This is underlain by a well-developed ortstein.

In discussing the Matanzas soils of Cuba, Bennett and Allison (16, p. 74) state: "The supply of organic matter is higher than has generally been supposed for well-drained tropical soils, not in the least coinciding with the views of numerous writers who have assumed that with good porosity and consequent free aeration the organic matter of tropical soils is rapidly dissipated by oxidation. These red Cuban soils in particular have been picked out and emphasized as having lost their humus. Not only is this not true of the Matanzas soils of Cuba, but the same condition was found to apply to a number of similar soils found in Central America."

Table 106, compiled from the work of Bennett and Allison, shows the partial composition of two Cuban soils. It is to be noted that the Nipe is low in organic matter whereas the Matanzas is high. A closer examination of the two soils reveals that both have definite lateritic attributes, to wit, an accumulation of R_2O_3 in the surface layer and a loss of alkaline earth bases. As to the SiO_2 content, the Nipe, true to form, shows a loss whereas the Matanzas shows a tremendous gain. Apparently, the SiO_2 in the parent material of the Matanzas is quartz and it therefore accumulates. All of the aforementioned attributes, however, offer no clue to the variations in the organic matter content of the two soils. When we examine the chemical constituents of the Matanzas, we note that it is derived from calcareous parent material. From the genetic point of view,

Table 106

Organic matter and other constituents in laterite soils
(After Bennett and Allison)

Soil	Depth	SiO$_2$	CaO	MgO	Fe$_2$O$_3$	Al$_2$O$_3$	Organic matter
	inches	*per cent*	*per cent*	*per cent*	*per cent*	*per cent*	*per cent*
Nipe clay	0-26	3.28	0.12	0.33	63.04	18.46	1.02
Nipe parent material	192+	41.93	1.50	34.02	7.84	2.00	
Matanzas	0-3	46.23	0.93	0.19	8.66	23.77	6.33
Matanzas	156-168	6.13	48.80	0.66	1.26	3.31	
Young laterite soil (VanBaren)	0-35	61.13	3.61	0.76	2.56	17.24	0.45

one may consider the Matanzas as the equivalent of rendzina in the humid temperate regions. This would account for the high organic matter content in the Matanzas. As a matter of fact, rendzina-like soils with a high amount of organic matter have been reported among the so-called "terra rossa" that forms on limestone parent material. More detailed studies of the soils in the humid tropics, from the genetic point of view, will clarify the subject.

In the summary on the laterites and lateritic soils made by the Imperial Bureau of Soil Science (48), it is stated: "Organic matter does not occur within characteristic limits. It appears to fluctuate between 0.1 and 17 per cent; in the West African soils, it varies from less than 1 per cent to about 3 per cent."

Nothing definite may be concluded from the organic matter figures on the "young lateritic soil" from East India, reported by van Baren (10), and yet it is significant that the organic matter content is low. Idenburg (47) presents data on the organic matter content and other chemical and physical propetries of the soils of South Sumatra.

Any attempt to fix certain attributes in any soil type must relate them to the perfect type which possess recognized standard chemical and physico-chemical values. In the case of the laterites, the low $ba, SiO_2:Fe_2O_3$ and ki ratios, loss of bases, and low cation exchange capacity seem to be well definied physico-chemical indices. To evaluate the organic matter attribute in laterites, one must take the perfect type. To measure the organic matter content of any tropical soil and, from results obtained, to generalize for most of the laterites may lead to erroneous conclusions. Of course, the question comes up whether the recognized standard is the predominating type, or to be more accurate, the normal type.*

Carbon-Nitrogen Ratio.—In the humid tropics and subtropics, the C:N ratio, according to Vageler (p. 151), varies from 8 to 12 in the surface soil. The ratio drops sometimes to 4 in the subsoil of very acid soils, in which case the ratio of the surface soil rises to 15-16. In general, however, the average ratio is 10 ."In arid tropics and subtropics the average seems to be higher. For example, in Egypt and Sudan the ratio is 12 to 12.5."

Podzolized Soils in the Tropics

The Imperial Bureau of Soil Science (48) points out that,

. . . according to Hardy, the growth of primary laterite is dependent on the chances of resilication occurring. If the laterite goes on accumulating, a thin fertile topsoil

---

*That the normal type is not necessarily the predominating one is exemplified by the gray desert and semidesert soil type. In certain areas of this climatogenic soil type, the hydrogenic saline types predominate.

may be formed. Given very wet conditions and free drainage, this profile may show a slight or even very profound podzolization under vegetation whereby gibbsite and iron oxides are slowly lost. Under conditions of poor drainage, resilication may give rise to a kaolinite red earth which also may be podzolized into a quartzose, bleached surface soil coming under a category different from laterite soil. Red earths derived from true surface laterite by resilication may be markedly podzolized in tropical humid countries, e.g., British Guiana.

Hardy and Follett-Smith, in discussing the data, point out that, with respect to the zone of leaching, the silica sesquioxide ratios

. . . for the topsoil in the case of basic rock types are numerically about the same as those for the zones of secondary changes. In the case of the intermediate and the acidic rock types, however, the ratio values tend to rise indicating loss of sesquioxides through leaching (podzolization). Combined SiO_2: quartz ratios, in every case, show a steady decrease between the zones of alteration and the surface soils, indicating accumulation of resistant quartz, and implying that the chief process affecting the topsoil is a mechanical washing action by water whereby finely divided kaolin is transported to the lower layers. Combined SiO_2:H_2O ratios show continued marked decreases, indicating further hydration of siliceous minerals in the surface material.

A number of podzolic and podzol soils have been reported in the tropics. Marbut and Manifold (63) refer to the soils in the Amazon Valley as podzolic. Thorp and Smith (98) report genuine podzols in Puerto Rico on sands and on heavy parent material in the midst of typical ferruginous laterites. Giesecke (33), reviewing the subject on the existence of such soils in the tropics, also cites the formation of bleached soils.

Harrassowitz records Vageler's opinion that podzols are present in the tropics. Mohr (p. 147) takes exception to that, and his opinion has weight. Very few students of soil science have had as much experience with soils of the tropics as Mohr. Pendleton, in a footnote to Mohr's monograph (p. 148) which he translated, states: "I have found ground water podzols developed in the sands of the ridges formed as barrier beaches along the coast near Pattani, southern Thailand." On the other hand, Pendleton and Sharasuvana (75, 76) object strenuously to the term podzolization for tropical soils showing a bleached horizon. They show that these tropical bleached soils have no true podzol profile which has "a characteristic coffee-colored iron-organic matter illuvial horizon." Actually, this type of horizon is restricted to profiles of impeded drainage and resemble the indurated layer of laterites. What we *do* find in podzols is a compacted B horizon resulting from the accumulation of clay and R_2O_3. If such a layer could be demonstrated below the bleached layer in laterites, there would be valid cause for claiming podzols in laterites. In examining a great many profiles in Panama, no illuvial layer similar to that of podzols or podzolized soils has been noted.

Hardon (34) describes two podzol profiles on quartz sandy island plains in S. E. Borneo, near the equator. The parent material offers little in the way of silt, clay, or essential minerals that would contribute to the accumulation of the R_2O_3 noted and to the formation of hardpan in one of the profiles. It looks as if we are dealing with a topographic feature dominating the accumulation of iron and aluminum in the low lying plains. The surrounding slopes give "brownish colored streamlets," and one of the profiles is described as being inundated during heavy rains. The surface layers, 0-20 cm. and 0-10 cm. in the two respective profiles, consist of brownish black to black cover of half decomposed organic matter. The high pH of A_2, 6.1, against 2.8 and 2.7 of A_0 and 5.4 and 3.9 of B_1, makes it difficult to recognize the bleached layer as typical of a podzol soil. From the description and the data given, the two so-called podzol profiles do not belong to the normal eluvial series; they belong to the hydromorphic orogenic series. Somewhat similar soils are described by Mohr who, as pointed out, disclaimed the presence of podzols in the tropics.

Rodrigues and Hardy (85) record podzolization on some sedimentary clays in Trinidad. It is questionable whether an analysis of the facts and data would warrant to designate the case as podzolization which, among other reactions, involves the movement and translocation of R_2O_3. The authors state that there has been little leaching or segregation of Fe anywhere in the profile. At some point in the profile, the authors report the presence of gypsum. This fact would indicate perhaps a semidesert type of soil formation of an earlier climatic cycle. If that were the case, the possibility of solonetzic properties could be postulated. With a change to a more humid climate, solodi might have formed, and the bleached layer could be a remnant of the desalinization (see Index). The bleached layer might also mean a condition whereby the silica has been inactive in precipitating iron from solution. Another rather strange phenomenon is the 5 foot layer of soil affected by podzolization, a depth thus far not reported for the A_2 horizon of any podzol.

With all that has been said, it is perhaps possible to think of some podzolization, if the parent material has no or very little calcium.

General Remarks on Laterites

A review of the condensed presentation on laterites brings out forcibly the paucity of information on the profile characteristics of these soils, specifically the horizon differentiation. Except for the descriptions and analyses of the indurated material which bears the earmarks of pedologic nomenclature (it is considered as the horizon of illuviation, or B horizon), the data and discussions revolve around the process of weathering in the tropics and subtropics.

We are confronted with the problem discussed in chapters IV and V on the relation of the process of weathering to soil formation. These two segments in the cycle of geochemical and biogeochemical reactions are not marked off by a strict line of demarcation under the climatic conditions of these geographic regions. Both the agents of weathering and factors of soil formation are favored by the climate of the humid tropics and sub-tropics, and the process of weathering and soil formation seem to run parallel. It is difficult to differentiate where one starts and the other termi-nates. One definite result is obvious and striking: the bulk of the mass is represented, by and large, by end-products which can not be weathered much farther. These end-products are oxides of iron, aluminum, titanium, zirconium, manganese, and a number of accessory minerals. In this climatic belt, there seems to be no effective protection of parent material by the process of soil formation, as it seems to appear in other climatic belts, against the ravages of weathering. One may find a geologic profile, which might also represent in full or in part the soil profile, on basalt extending to depths of 100 and 150 feet deep.

There is no clear understanding of the reciprocal relations between the positively charged sesquioxides and negatively charged residual essential and secondary minerals. In some areas, the coatings of R_2O_3 seem to protect these minerals from further weathering. In the case of clay minerals, these coatings reduce the plasticity of the mass. On the other hand, in many more areas these R_2O_3 are of no avail against the disintegration and decomposition of most minerals, with very few exceptions, such as zircon and titanium-iron minerals, to the final end-products of weathering, R_2O_3 and, in some cases, quartz silica. Some sandy laterites retain their oxides of iron (as indicated by color) very rigidly, and the red color can be re-moved with difficulty upon continuous extractions with weak acids. Other sandy laterites give up the red color upon two or three extractions with distilled water.

Thus far, the pedologist has not succeeded in separating morpho-logically, mechanically, and chemically the specific features in the deposit of laterite material which would serve as criteria for soil profile character-istics. What Marbut stated in 1932 (62) is still true: "It is apparent that the existing literature contains no record of a normally developed wholly undisturbed soil profile examined, described, and interpreted by a student well trained in pedologic methods and equipped with the pedologic point of view. Some of the profiles described in the rather abundant geo-logical literature concerned with laterites may be such profiles, but the descriptions do not make it absolutely clear that such is the case." The indurated layer which has been conceded to be an element of pedologic sig-nificance need to be scrutinized more thoroughly by well-trained pedolo-gists. *The B horizon should be the starting point for pedologic investiga-*

tions. It would be well, first of all, to determine how widespread is the phenomenon of induration in the laterite and lateritic material of the tropics and subtropics.

Data and records in the literature on laterites, personal observations, even though limited, in Panama, Jamaica, Algeria, Palestine, and the southern states in the United States, and interviews with colleagues working in the tropics seem to show that indurated layers find their highest expression in the equatorial regions. These layers are not, as far as our investigations go, always present even in the laterites of the equatorial regions and become less frequent and pronounced in the humid subtropics. They are seldom encountered in the semiarid and arid tropics and subtropics. Their occasional presence in these geographic regions is to be looked upon as relics of an earlier humid climate. From the scant data available on the constitution and composition of profiles formed on freshly deposited volcanic ash and other lava flows of recent (historic) origin (see Van Baren's data in table 101), it is not clear whether there is evidence of induration in these young deposits.

Systematic studies are wanted on the morphology, physical, chemical, physico-chemical, and mineralogical properties of soils representing varying degrees of laterization (on the order of degrees of podzolization) along isohyetals in the tropics and subtropics. These studies should be especially fruitful on the indurated layers. A search for pedolites (minerals of soil formation origin) in these layers and all through the so-called laterite deposit would be helpful in tracing the soil forming process in the tropics and subtropics.

LATERITIC SOILS

The process of laterization extends over a large area in the humid tropics and subtropics, the degree of laterization varying within these extensive geographic regions. In a way, perhaps, this process may be compared with the process of podzolization, the degree of which determines the subgroups in the podzol zone.

That there should be some line of demarkation between true laterites, the highest expression of the process of laterization, and lateritic soils that exhibit various degrees of laterization has been recognized by Fermor (24), Lacroix (55), Marbut (62), and others. As a basis for the separation of lateritic soils from true laterites, Martin and Doyne (64) have suggested the ratio of SiO_2 to Al_2O_3 (the *ki* of Harrassowitz) in the clay fraction. Soils with a $SiO_2:Al_2O_3$ molar ratio of less than 1.33 should be designated as laterite, and those with a ratio of over 1.33 and less than 2.0 as lateritic. It is to be remembered that Harrassowitz (39, p. 403) had the *ki* value of the whole soil as the distinguishing chemical characteristic of red loam. "This ratio, if below 2.0, shows the presence of free alumina. And yet, it may be shown that even with a ratio higher than 2.0, the presence of free alumina is possible. The occurrence of quartz might increase this ratio." According to Harrassowitz, a ratio below 1.0 indicates that the red loam has lost its clay properties, turning into allit.

Bennett (15) does not draw the line between laterite and lateritic. He divides the soils of the tropics into friable and non-friable or plastic. Taking the molar ratio of $SiO_2 : R_2O_3$ at 2.0 as a dividing limit in the grouping of some tropical soils, Bennett found that this grouping is approximately identical with that based on friability and plasticity.

Whether the ratio suggested by Martin and Doyne for the lateritic soils will hold true for the several groups of red soils remains unknown because of the paucity of data on the colloid constituents, especially free alumina and oxides of iron, in the surface horizons of these soils. In table 107, data from Robinson and Holmes (84) are presented on the colloids of a series of soils from the southeastern part of the United States, a region with a climatic close to subtropical. It will be noted that the *ki* value is in very few cases below 2.0. This would exclude these soils from the lateritic, if we adhere to the suggestion of Martin and Doyne. And yet the *ki* value of these soils is not very much more than 2.0 . These soils belong to the so-called "red and yellow earths" which may be looked upon as transitional between the podzols and the laterites. Chemically, these soils possess a number of podzol attributes and should therefore be classified with the podzolic soils. On the other hand, the red soils do have definite markings of laterization, especially color.

In the regions adjoining the subtropics and in the subtropics proper, a soil type is encountered, the outstanding morphological characteristic of which is color. It is predominantly red, but this color is not so pronounced as in laterites; it is of a lighter shade and in a great many areas, especially in the more humid regions, the yellow color is interspersed. Within the boundaries of the zone of red soils, other types are found. Typical podzols, like the St. John and Leon series in Florida, brown forest soils among the red soils along the Mediterranean in France, and podzolic soils among the red soil districts of Batum along the Black Sea, are examples of types the character of which has to be elucidated. It seems to the author that in the more humid subtropics we are dealing with the superimposition of the process of podzolization on the process of laterization, and vice versa. *It is also very probable that we are dealing with laterites of an earlier tropical climate which serve now as parent material.*

Because of the predominating red color of the soils, there has been a tendency to identify a definite zone of red soils or red and yellow soils, as in the case of the soils in the southeastern United States. Because of their color and geographic position, they have been associated frequently with the process of laterization. And yet, the geographic distribution of these soils the world over, as may be judged from the available soil maps and

Table 107

Composition of colloids of some southeastern soils in the United States and their ki value

(After Robinson and Holmes)

Soil	$ki = \dfrac{SiO_2}{Al_2O_3}$	SiO_2	Fe_2O_3	Al_2O_3	CaO	Organic matter
	ratio	per cent	per cent	per cent	per cent	per cent
Norfolk fine sandy loam, North Carolina	2.08	38.25	11.25	31.21	0.54	4.69
Cecil clay loam, Georgia	1.60	33.95	11.02	36.06	0.31	2.25
Cecil clay loam, Georgia	2.15	36.20	16.67	28.59	0.51	4.63
Susquehanna clay, Mississippi	1.71	36.97	10.44	36.91	0.20	2.55
Chester loam, Virginia	2.12	34.82	15.93	27.88	0.17	5.54
Manor loam, Maryland	2.13	38.86	10.33	31.11	0.64	3.69
Chester loam, Maryland	2.22	39.00	11.27	29.98	0.93	4.11
Orangeburg fine sandy loam, Mississippi	2.21	40.35	10.11	31.04	0.51	4.26
Hagerstown loam, Maryland	2.34	39.93	9.45	29.02	1.25	6.97
Crowley silt loam, Louisiana	2.92	46.95	8.77	27.35	0.99	2.72

*The value for *ki* was calculated by Jenny, from whose paper this column was prepared.

scattered reports in the literature, brings them in contact with a number of soil types the zonal character of which is well known and from which we might attempt to ascertain their genetic relationships. Thus, we find red soils merging into the podzolic brown (Braunerde) and other forest soils in France and Italy. In Greece and Bulgaria, they adjoin the chestnut brown soils; in Palestine, the brown and semidesert gray soils; and in the United States, the brown forest soils and the southern prairie. From the nature of this geographic distribution, one might surmise that the soil forming processes would not be exactly the same throughout all the regions of red soils. Although no clear-cut distinction has been made from this point of view, the generally accepted two divisions of red soils, namely, the *terra rossa* and the *red loams,* are suggestive.

Terra Rossa

The red earths, known as *terra rossa,* are associated with the Mediterranean climate which is distinguished by a rainy winter season and a dry summer. The region of the red earths begins in the southwestern part of Europe. They occupy the southern part of Portugal, the middle of Spain, extending to the Bay of Biscay in the north and close to Cartagena in the south. In the eastern part of Spain, in the neighborhood of Valencia, a narrow strip of red earths is found along the Mediterranean coast. It continues beyond Barcelona up to Marseilles. Along the River Rona, this soil type cuts in into continental France. Red earths appear beyond Livorno, through the southern part of Italy, and they cover the islands of Corsica and Sicily. In the eastern part of Italy, the red earths extend to the north as far as Pomendung. They are widespread on the Balkan peninsula: in Greece, Bulgaria, Rumania, Montenegro, Dalmatia, Croatia, and Istria. They are also found on the north coast of Africa.

Reference to the climatic conditions of this group of soils and to their properties was made as early as 1875 by Fuchs (29). Blanck (17) points out that the Lower Istria red soils have been designated as such as early as 1848.

Origin of Terra Rossa.—A number of hypotheses have been advanced concerning the origin of the terra rosa, but all of them may be grouped into two main viewpoint trends. One is that the properties of the materials from which the terra rossa has formed are responsible for its formation. As to the source of the materials, the proponents of this view differ in their opinion. Some are inclined to look for an outside source, aeolian, marine, and volcanic dust and ash origin. Others stress the calcareous nature of the Mediterranean red soils. By applying the theory of solutions, it was brought out that in th case of the limestone material or any calcareous or base-rich material the divalent bases are leached as the bicarbonates, leaving behind a residue rich in iron. The other trend of the many hypotheses is that the properties of terra rossa are a result of the specific process of weathering under conditions of the Mediterranean climate.

In 1880, Taramelli (97) advanced the idea of the volcanic origin of terra rossa. He was supported in his hypothesis by Walther (103) and Schierl (86). The latter postulated that terra rossa attained its properties as a result of the metamorphosis of volcanic ash. Schierl indicated no definite geologic period of volcanic activity with which such widespread distribution of red earths might be identified. He simply pointed out the abundance of ash which volcanoes might supply, referring specifically to Vesuvius. He also claimed that the rounded and slag-like formations found in terra rossa are an indication of volcanic products.

Investigating the red earths of Istria, Stache (94) found areas with reddish clay shales, which led him to suggest the possibility of the marine origin of terra rossa.

Regny (80) suggests a unique theory on the formation of terra rossa, to wit, the precipitation from solutions rich in iron. He pointed out that iron precipitates not only from alkaline solution, but also in contact with finely divided limestone, dolomite, and clay. Because of this precipitation, cracks in limestone are enriched with iron. A small amount of iron would, under such conditions, impart to the finely divided particles a red color.

The concept of the aeolian origin of the material for the formation of terra rossa was developed by Galdieri (30). From studies on the red earths of southern Italy, he concluded that they were not related genetically to limestone. He made analyses on limestone and red earth residues and compared them mineralogically. He found that red earth residues contained minerals similar to those of dust; hence his conclusion that the red material was analogous to loess. Comel (23), in his studies of the terra rossa in Tripoli, upheld the theory of the aeolian origin of some terra rossa.

Zippe (106) was the first to point out the relation of red earth formation to limestone. He looked upon the terra rossa as a residual product of the chemical weathering of limestone. Lorenz (59) differentiated the formation of soils on limestone, sandstone, and gray shales of Croatia. Red earths were invariably associated with limestone, and light brown loams with other materials. Neumayr (71) also emphasized the limestone origin of terra rossa. He cited examples of such soils in Istria and Dalmatia, formed on the Karst limestone in Pilermi, on the marble formations in Pentelikon, and in the Jura and Alps regions wherever limestone prevails. He went as far as to say that there was no case where terra rossa would be associated with any other formation but limestone. The red soils on the sandstones in Dalmatia were considered by him as secondary formations transported from the Karst limestones. To prove the residual origin of terra rossa from limestone, Neumayr extracted the native limestone with acetic acid and obtained a residue equal to 0.044 per cent containing 20 per cent Fe_2O_3. Geologically, Neumayr associated the formation of terra rossa with Mesozoic limestone. Fuchs (29), a contemporary of Neumayr, cited examples of terra rossa formed on limestone of ages other than Mesozoic. An important point brought out by this investigator was that terra rossa formed only in semiarid or arid climatic regions where the vegetation was scant and hence the organic matter content was low.

Kerner-Marilaum (53) analyzed mathematically the average temperature and precipitation at various points in the Mediterranean region and deduced formulae which were supposed to indicate the intensity of the red earth formation at any particular point. The most suitable formulae obtained were the following:

$$\frac{\sqrt{Rw}.Ts}{Tw\sqrt{Rs}} \text{ and } \sqrt[3]{Rw}.Ts$$

where T = average temperature, R = precipitation, s = summer precipitation, w = winter precipitation. Whenever the formula $\sqrt[3]{Rw}.Ts$ indicated a value greater than 4.1, there was an agreement between the climatic conditions and the presence of red earth. Generally, however, the values did not agree with the actual facts, and for this reason the author did not recognize the red earths as a climatic soil.

A study on the origin and nature of terra rossa formation was made by Blanck (17) and Blanck and Alten (18). Blanck upheld the theory of the limestone origin of terra rossa. His concept is in some respects similar to that of Regny, but he broadened out the theory of the solubility effects of iron in solution in a limestone environment and explained the reactions involved and the anomaly of the diffusion of iron in an alkaline medium. The findings of Blanck and of Blanck and Alten may be summarized as follows: Iron solutions, primarily from sources other than the limestone, and in a small measure also from the limestone or dolomite, penetrate into the cracks, joints, and grooves of the limestone where the Fe precipitates upon coming in contact with the limestone. With a continuous supply of such solutions and in the presence of fresh supplies of water, the iron has the power, as shown by Liesegang's researches on diffusion, to penetrate the iron accumulations on the limestone. A metasomatic replacement takes place, thereby extending the depth of penetration of the iron into the limestone from the points of the cracks, joints, clefts, grooves, etc. Simultaneously, the action of CO_2 on the limestone or dolomite brings into solution the Ca and Mg as bicarbonates which are leached away. The residual silica and other constituents, together with the precipitated iron, form the terra rossa. An important consideration in the movement of Fe in the regions of terra rosa formation is the role of humus as a protective colloid. It imparts to the iron micelle a negative charge and makes it mobile. Only during the dry period does the humus oxidize, preventing further movement of the iron.

Blanck characterized the terra rossa as "a more or less deep red loam which differs from other soils by an enrichment with iron and aluminum oxides, release of some silica, impoverishment of alkali and alkaline earth bases, and generally poor in organic matter. The colloidal nature of the Fe and Al is markedly developed, and they are present in the form of hydrated gels. They always appear on limestone or other parent material rich in lime and frequently contain concretions of lime and iron."

Reifenberg (81) described terra rossa soils as follows:

They form on limestone under conditions of the typical Mediterranean climate. Their composition, when compared with the parent rock, limestone, shows an accumulation of sesquioxides and silica. When compared with the soil types of the humid regions, they show a higher content of alkali and alkaline earth bases. The high iron content and the low organic matter content impart to the Mediterranean red earths their usual bright red color. These soils are mostly alkaline in reaction, of a loamy texture, and are endowed with Ca and Fe concretions.

Reifenberg made an attempt to show that, under the climatic conditions of the Mediterranean, the silicic acid sol may serve as the peptizing agent for the Al and Fe sols in the presence of $CaCO_3$.

The relatively high salt content in the soils of Palestine coagulates the humates and they become fixed as Ca-humates. The soluble organic matter can, therefore, exert no protective effect on the movement of the R_2O_3 constituents.* In such a chemical system, the hydrolyzed colloidal silicic acid protects the Fe and Al sols. The silicic acid sol, in a medium with latent alkali and yet slightly acid, may exert this peptizing effect. The alkali tied up in the silicic acid micelle may be replaced by a metal oxide. This process increases the alkalinity of the soil solution. A change in the charge of the Fe and Al sols takes place even in the presence of electrolytes, because of the charge on the silicic acid sol. Under the prevailing conditions of weathering in the Mediterranean region, an upward movement of the soil solution takes place during the summer. In contrast to the easily flocculated unprotected Fe sols, those that are protected by the silicic acid sols are more stable and coagulate only at a higher electrolyte concentration encountered in their upward movement. In general, the Fe_2O_3 coagulates completely and is split off from the bulk of silicic acid which is more stable. Under such circumstances, the appearance of free alumina, as well as iron hydroxide, is possible. The flocculated silicic acid may, under certain conditions, in the course of time undergo some physical and chemical transformations and even form stoichiometric, and sometimes crystalline, well-defined compounds.

Reifenberg considers the terra rossa as a preliminary stage to laterite formation. No evidence is presented in support of this opinion.

According to Ramann (Ch. 3, 53, p. 29), "the calcareous soils of the Northern Mediterranean districts form a continuation of the calcareous soils of Central Europe." Two types of terra rossa are recognized by Ramann:

One is dominant on the table-lands of the Karst and of the limestone formation as far as Croatia, and probably extends farther to the south in the Balkan peninsula. The soil is dun, yellow-brown to red-brown, the subsoil brownish-red to dark red. The second type of terra rossa consists of reef formations which are found as red and reddish-brown crusts on the calcareous rocks and accumulate in cracks and depressions, forming brown-red masses. The slopes and crags of the mountains owe their remarkable colors to the separation of large quantities of ferric hydroxide on the limestone rock.

---

*One may take issue with this statement, inasmuch as the formation and movement of the humates takes place in Palestine during the rainy winter season. Besides, at the time of formation, Ca-humates are soluble, becoming insoluble only upon desiccation, as expounded in chapter on chernozem.

The reef red earths acquire their characteristic properties through the high temperatures of the soil and the intense desiccation during the dry season. The formation of organic matter is not significant on slopes which are deficient in water during the summer, while the mild winters bring about a rapid decay of the organic residues. Hence the soils have a low organic matter content and display the brilliant colors characteristic of soils poor in organic matter.

In another place, Ramann (p. 105) stated: "The position of the red earths in the soil classification is uncertain. The author has seen red earths in Spain with horizons of calcareous concretions, occurrences of which denote arid or semiarid conditions. On the other hand, many of their properties indicate a semihumid origin."

Leiningen (57), summarizing his numerous investigations on terra rossa, states that these soils are to be associated with limestone or dolomitic parent material under conditions of a somewhat arid climate. He cites evidence of terra rossa formation on the ruins of marble structures of Roman times and even of the Middle Ages. Geologically, he places the terra rossa formation in the early Tertiary age. This opinion is also shared by Glinka (Ch. 2, 26) who considers the terra rossa as soils of the lateritic

Table 108

Chemical composition of a number of samples of terra rossa
(Compiled from Blanck's data collected in his monograph)

No.	Source of sample	SiO_2	Fe_2O_3	Al_2O_3	CaO	MgO
		per cent	*per cent*	*per cent*	*per cent*	*per cent*
1	Jerusalem: surface soil	55.13	8.78	12.37	3.83	1.61
2	Jerusalem: at junction with limestone	40.30	21.40	6.72	4.88	1.74
3	Nablus, Palestine: surface soil	48.08	7.81	14.94	6.35	1.38
4	Nablus, Palestine: subsoil	50.39	9.19	16.50	3.39	0.75
5	Mt. Borron at Nice	57.26	11.60	15.05	2.50	3.08
6	St. Marguerithe at Cannes	54.12	14.50	15.55	1.80	3.43
7	Northern Italy: average of 5 soils	64.50	6.58	10.86	5.49	1.88
8	Istria and Dalmatia: average of 10 soils	48.46	11.40	20.97	1.20*	1.25*
9	Croatia, coast land: average of 7 soils	36.85	12.90	28.10	†	Trace
10	Montenegro and Rumania: average of 5 soils	50.80	9.53	16.55	1.57	0.97

* Among the 10 samples there is one which shows only a trace of Ca and Mg.
† The CaO content varies from a trace in Zlobin to 14.44 per cent at Zupanyak.

type. Vageler (101) associates the terra rossa with allit, a hydrated Al_2O_3 with an admixture of SiO_2, Fe_2O_3, and TiO_2, which is technically a bauxite-like rock.

A search through the voluminous literature for data on the profile constitution of the terra rossa is of no avail. With a few exceptions, all the investigations report analyses on surface soil at arbitrary depths, and besides, a great many analyses had been made on acid extracts (10 per cent HCl). Although these cannot be fully interpreted pedologically, they do furnish indirect evidence of the genetic relationships of the soils. Thus, an extract of soils from the tropics brings into solution appreciable quantities of SiO_2 and Al_2O_3, but practically none from the soil material of the podzols.

Table 108 gives analyses of terra rossa from several localities of the Mediterranean region. Unfortunately, analyses on both surface soil and subsoil are available for one soil only, namely, the Palestine terra rossa. Nothing can therefore be inferred about the translocation of the constituents in the profile, something which would throw some light on the processes involved. These terra rossa soils appear to be what Harrassowitz designates as siallitic-allitic material, i.e., kaolinite-like material enriched with a hydrated Al_2O_3 complex which contains admixtures of SiO_2 Fe_2O_3, and TiO_2. Most significant, however, is the relatively high alkaline earth base content in most of the terra rossa on which data are available. In this respect, the terra rossa differs from the laterites which are low in base content, even though the turnover of bases, due to the luxuriant vegetation, is high.

In connection with the general understanding of terra rossa formation on limestone or materials rich in lime, the data of Reifenberg presented in table 109 are interesting, even though they represent just surface soil. Both the limestone and basalt give rise to a soil almost identical in composition, and yet the color of the limestone soil is red and that of the basalt is chocolate-brown. Both soils, however, show definite lateritic features, as indicated by the solubility of the Al_2O_3 and Fe_2O_3 in a HCl extract; almost 90 per cent of the total Al_2O_3 has been extracted. On the other hand, it is obvious that while the R_2O_3 are easily split off, the SiO_2 does not move. This circumstance speaks not for laterization. It is probable that we are dealing here with some reaction still not interpreted. Profile data are wanted.

The danger of basing the genetic relationship of a soil on color only has been brought out by Filosofov (25). Upon analyzing samples of soil and parent material from the terra rossa region, 15 miles southeast of

Rome,* he pointed out that in color these are not typically terra rossa. Chemically, however, they do show distinct evidence of the lateritic process: a loss of SiO_2, an accumulation of R_2O_3, and the presence of free alumina. In concluding his discussion on the theories of terra rosa formation, Filosofov states: "The disagreement between the theories of limestone residue

Table 109

Composition of two soils and their parent material under the same climatic conditions
(After Reifenberg)

Chemical constituent	Red earth profile			Basalt profile		
	Limestone rock, nearby	Red earth		Basalt rock	Soil	
		Total analyses	Hcl extract		Total analyses	HCl extract
	per cent	per cent	per cent	per cent	per cent	per cent
SiO_2	0.19	49.93	0.17	43.85	49.16	0.79
Al_2O_3	0.07	16.67	15.08	11.91	13.40	11.24
Fe_2O_3	0.24	10.35	⎰ 10.11	6.43	11.34	⎰ 7.69
FeO	—	1.05	⎱	7.44	3.41	⎱
Mn_3O_4	—	Trace	Trace	1.32	0.75	0.51
CaO	57.35	4.00	2.38	10.31	2.07	1.95
MgO	0.40	1.13	0.24	8.86	1.17	1.35
K_2O	Trace	0.78	0.32	1.76	0.98	0.08
Na_2O	Trace	0.68	0.18	4.41	1.67	0.07
P_2O_5	Trace	0.06	0.06	0.54	0.02	0.02
SO_3	—	0.12	0.12	Trace	0.09	0.09
CO_2	40.98	0.57	—	0.60	2.66	—
N	—	0.06	—	—	0.09	—

and that of climatic origin of terra rossa arises from a difference in understanding of the classification concept. The 'limestone theory' designates as 'terra rossa' the residual product of limestone only. The 'climatic theory' applies the term 'red earths' to all of the soils of the Mediterranean

*These samples were taken by Glinka while at the International Soil Conference in Italy in 1924.

region as long as they are enriched with iron and aluminum, even though their color is not as bright as on the limestone soils."

From what has been said, it seems logical to place the Mediterranean red earths, the so-called "terra rossa," in the group of soils affected by the process of laterization. The possibility of laterite as parent material should not be overlooked in this connection. *From extensive observations and examinations of the soils in Palestine and Algiers, the author is inclined to believe that many areas of red soils in the Mediterranean region are a relict of an earlier geologic age when a humid tropical climate prevailed.* This suggestion does not exclude the possibility of some degrees of laterization under conditions of Mediterranean climate. Löwengart (60), in his studies on the geology of the Coastal Plain in Palestine, refers to the red earths as a formation of an earlier climate. We must remember that with the change from the humid to the present-day Mediterranean climate a hydromorphic element has been supplementing the elements of eluviation. During the dry season, salts move upwards and the bases and their associated anionic groups counteract the eluviation reactions. The pH of these soils is much higher than that of laterites. Under such conditions, the bulk of the R_2O_3 that is released becomes fixed and not much of the SiO_2 has a chance to move as the silicate ion. Since the upward movement of salts is not a uniform phenomenon (the water table, the texture and composition of the material and the distribution of rainfall affect this movement), one may encounter more advanced and less advanced stages of laterization. It seems that hard limestone is conducive to laterization effects more than other parent materials. Still, other parent materials may be placed locally in situations favorable to laterization and thus give rise to terra rossa. There is, however, evidence that other soil types may form under the conditions of the Mediterranean climate.

Nevros and Zvorykin (72) corroborate the findings of Liatsikas (58) on the formation of rendzina on soft lime marl in Crete and Greece. They also present data on the formation of red soils on hard limestone, in the Karst region of Crete. In table 110, data are presented on the composition of the two soil divisions.

In the case of the rendzina, the description is typical of this soil—a dark colored granular A horizon, gray colored nutty structure B horizon, and a sharp line of demarcation at the white to gray-white calcareous parent material. The data in the table indicate an accumulation of R_2O_3 and SiO_2, and a high cation exchange capacity. In the case of the red soils, the data seem to indicate a relative increase of Fe in A. The high SiO_2 content is attributed to the presence of quartz grains in the limestone. Analyses of

Table 110

Composed of several profiles in the region of terra rosa in Crete

(After Nevros and Zvorykin)

I Rendzina on marls

Horizon	Depth	H₂O lost at 105°C	Loss on ignition	CO₂	SiO₂	Al₂O₃	Fe₂O₃	CaO	MgO	SiO₂ / Al₂O₃	SiO₂ / R₂O₃*	Exchange capacity
	cm	per cent	per cent	per cent	per cent	per cent	per cent	per cent	per cent			m.e.
A₁	0-30	7.37	12.23	0.35	52.73	20.54	4.66	4.66	3.48	4.3	3.8	39.26
B	30-45	6.65	9.46	3.88	48.23	19.41	4.54	10.31	3.20	4.2	3.6	46.3
C	45-60	4.00	6.04	23.91	22.91	8.94	2.48	33.81	1.92	3.9	3.5	
					II Red earths on hard limestone							
I (A₁)	0- 7	4.40	7.48	0.04	70.30	12.36	6.88	1.56	0.72	9.6	7.2	26.54
II	7-41	5.55	6.43	Trace	65.48	19.76	4.71	0.95	0.92	5.6	4.9	27.21
III	41-81	6.39	7.31		62.83	21.61	5.13	0.92	1.12	4.9	4.2	28.31

*These ratios are based on organic matter free mineral constituents.

the $< 2\,\mu$ fraction (see original paper) give a $\dfrac{SiO_2}{R_2O_3}$ ratio of 1.8, 2.0, and 1.9 in the respective horizons. These ratios substantiate the lateritic nature of the soils. There seem to be not much differentiation in the profile; the cation exchange data indicate this trend.

Nevros and Zvorykin agree with Agafonoff (3) that terra sorra is a product of the weathering of limestone." They mention the fact that the marble columns of the temple of Jupiter in Athens show red coloration. They conclude, however, that on the soft lime marls rendzina is formed. Evidence of rendzina formation has been observed in southern France on the limestone of the ruins of a water-mill built by the Romans. Some semblance of rendzina has been reported on some kunkar (consolidated line marls) in Algeria. While on tour with the delegates of the International Pedologic Conference held in France and Algeria in the summer of 1947 (50a), these soils were examined; their rendzina character is doubtful. Prasolov and Petrov (77a) also question the possibility of rendzina in the Mediterranean region.

The "residue theory" on the formation of terra rossa from limestone has been reviewed by Hollstein (43). He presents data on the composition of limestone, showing that there is sufficient iron to account for the accumulation of the oxides that give the distinctive color to terra rossa.

Red Loams

According to Harrassowitz (39, p. 372),

the red loam is found in the regions of the monsoon forests, the savanna, and even in the steppe. Very frequently, the color of red loam is lighter at the surface, the loamy character is suppressed, and the color appears again only in the illuvial horizon. Whereas in the Mediterranean region, on limestone parent material, the red color is always apparent, in the tropics it varies. In Cuba, one may find all sorts of color shades. This is also true for the soils in the East-Indian archipelago, as shown by the work of Van Baren. In many of the red loams, the horizons in the profile are well expressed, but in the neighborhood of the laterites these are not apparent. It has been reported that in the Matanzas soils the profile remains the same to a depth of 30 meters.

From Harrassowitz's presentation, it is apparent that he is inclined to include in the red loams the red soils of the tropics, those of the Mediterranean region, and even those of central Europe. He does distinguish certain variations in the group of red loams, namely, the allitic (red laterite) which is enriched with alumina, and siallitic (real red loam) which contains more of the kaolinite-like material. In differentiating the two red loams, Harrassowitz (p. 386) points out that in the red laterite the P_2O_5 content is high, whereas in the real red loam it is low. The reverse of this quantitative relationship for the two soils is true for the nitrogen content.

In contrast to the somewhat hazy differentiation by Harrassowitz, Marbut (62) assigns to the red loams a more definite type of soil formation. According to Marbut,

the term (red loams) is applied to a group of red soils similar in color to laterites but differing from them in the presence of a high percentage of aluminum silicate as a constituent rather than of aluminum hydroxide. The accepted definition of the term does not exclude the presence of aluminum hydroxide, but the amount present, relatively to that of the silicate, is small. They are usually free from accumulations of iron oxide crusts or other forms of segregation. They have a low percentage of organic matter, have developed under timber cover, and in warm to hot climate with high rainfall.

In the red loam region of the United States, south of Chesapeake Bay, and in the region of the Russian "Krasnozem" (red soils) in the Caucasus, on the Black Sea coast, the climate is more humid than in the region of the Mediterranean terra rossa. In addition, the distribution of the rainfall and the humidity are different. In the red loam region, the rainfall is more or less uniformly distributed throughout the year, with the summer rainfall almost always the highest of any season, and the humidity is high. In the terra rossa region, the summers are dry and the winters are wet. In some sections, like Palestine, central Asia Minor, southern Italy, and central Greece, the summers are practically rainless and the humidity is low. Naturally, the biosphere element is different. Although forests are common in the terra rossa region, in some sections, the stand is not as solid as in the red loam region of the United States.

In the southeastern portion of the United States, the color of the Coastal Plain sandy soils tends to be yellow rather than red. Soils lying immediately along the bluffs of the streams in the Costal Plain are red in color. The deep red soils in the Georgia section of the Coastal Plain are, according to Marbut (62), a result of erosion that has exposed the B horizon and of the calcareous parent material. Those of the southern Piedmont are predominantly red, with some yellow soils interspersed. The yellow color of the Coastal Plain sandy soils, of which the Norfolk series is representative, is explained by Marbut as a result of poor drainage.

Tables 111-115 present data on the red and yellow soils of this region, as reported by the Bureau of Soils. In all of these soils, except the Cecil, the podzolization is very evident. One could almost reconstruct the horizon differentiation in the profile of the Tifton sandy loam. The 0-4 inch depth is the A_1 horizon; the 5-11-inch depth, the A_2 horizon; and the other two depths are probably the B_1 and B_2 horizons. The accumulation of SiO_2 in the A_2 horizon, the low R_2O_3 content in the A horizon, the low P_2O_5 content in the A_2 and the high P_2O_5 content in the B horizons, the similar distribution of N in the A_2 and B_1 horizons, and finally the marked accumulation of R_2O_3 in the B horizon are definite indisputable attributes of the process of podzolization.

The data on the Georgeville silty clay loam and on the Norfolk sandy loam are not so striking, in part perhaps, because the samples, taken at arbitrary depths, distort the horizon differentiations in the profile. Thus, the second depth in the Georgeville soil undoubtedly includes the A_2 and B_1 horizons; the first depth of the Norfolk soil includes a portion of the A_2 horizon. And yet, one cannot fail to recognize the attributes of the podzolization process, such as the distinct accumulation of R_2O_3 in the B horizon, the relative decrease of SiO_2 in the same horizon, and the typical distribution of Ca. The same deductions may be made from the data on the Brazillian soil.

In this connection, it will be of interest to examine the data in table 116 on the composition of exchangeable cations in a red loam from the

Table III

Chemical composition of Tifton sandy loam, $1\frac{1}{2}$ miles N. E. of Meigs, Georgia
(After U. S. Bureau of Soils)

Constituents	Depth in inches			
	0-4	5-11	19-33	34-39
	per cent	*per cent*	*per cent*	*per cent*
SiO_2	91.81	94.01	77.26	76.94
TiO_2	0.38	0.38	0.72	0.66
Fe_2O_3	1.12	1.43	4.50	5.77
Al_2O_3	1.98	2.80	12.27	11.64
MnO	0.016	0.006	0.005	0.003
CaO	0.34	0.30	0.34	0.36
MgO	0.16	0.08	0.18	0.11
K_2O	0.15	0.16	0.20	0.19
Na_2O	0.19	0.10	0.30	0.24
P_2O_5	0.03	0.02	0.07	0.08
Loss on ignition	4.47	1.62	5.60	5.18
N	0.10	0.02	0.034	0.02

Caucasus. We note a high exchange capacity of which 65 per cent is
hydrogen, i.e., a high unsaturation, which is an attribute of the podzolization
process. Such a chemical makeup is, as a rule, not to be expected in the
soils of the terra rossa region.

The data in table 115 are on the Cecil soils which have been recognized as lateritic in nature. Again, it should be remembered that the analyses do not represent the true profile features. The second depth, from
6 to 40 inches, undoubtedly includes the A_2 and B horizons. One may,
however, infer certain tendencies in the translocation of the soil constituents which will help to determine the zonal type. Thus, the almost total
loss of Ca and Mg is an attribute of the process of laterization. The retention of large quantities of Al_2O_3 and the accumulation of P_2O_5 in the A_1
horizon are also evidence, if not fully in favor of the process of laterization,
certainly not in favor of the process of podzolization. The SiO_2 content

Table 112

*Chemical composition of Georgeville silty clay loam, 2 miles S. W. of Henrico,
North Carolina*

(After U. S. Bureau of Soils)

Constituents	Depth in inches			
	2-6	6-34	34-48	48-60
	per cent	per cent	per cent	per cent
SiO_2	69.46	54.03	58.96	62.31
TiO_2	0.81	0.66	0.44	0.97
Fe_2O_3	5.10	8.30	7.52	6.11
Al_2O_3	15.09	25.97	22.44	20.26
MnO	0.02	0.013	0.013	0.004
CaO	0.04	0.30	0.14	0.22
MgO	0.21	0.23	0.21	0.38
K_2O	1.23	1.56	1.73	4.35
Na_2O	0.19	0.26	0.28	0.30
P_2O_5	0.08	0.13	0.14	0.13
Loss on ignition	7.40	8.86	7.53	4.67
N	0.05	0.014	0.008	0.003

at the various depths indicates podzolization, and yet one would like to see data on the SiO_2 and Al_2O_3 of an acid extract. A high soluble Al_2O_3 content would indicate the lateritic process, the reverse—the podzolization process.

It has been pointed out elsewhere (50) that in laterites and lateritic soils TiO_2 accumulates in the A horizon, whereas in podzols and other zonal soil types TiO_2 accumulates in the B horizon. An examination of the analytical data (table 117) on the colloids of the various soils in the United States, as reported by Robinson and Holmes (84), prove the aforesaid. However, instances may be cited, like the Tifton sandy loam, where the TiO_2 accumulates in the B horizon.

From the foregoing discussion, it is evident that in the red loam, as typified by the yellow and red soils in the southeastern portion of the United States, there is a struggle between the processes of podzolization and of laterization, with the former in the lead. We find an analogous struggle in the transition zone of the forest steppe, where the chernozem type of soil formation is invaded by the podzol type of soil formation as a result of the advance of forests, and *vice versa*. Just as the degraded chernozem in the forest steppe is podzolic in nature and transitional between the chernozem and the podzols, so is the red loam, in contact with the laterite, podzolic in nature and transitional between the true podzol type of soil formation and the true laterites. The contact of the red loams with the prairie soils is another transition to be considered.

The Yellow Soils

An entirely different, one might say original, concept of the soils of the humid southern latitudes is offered by Afanasiev (2). His contention is that "the zonal soil of the humid subtropics and tropics is invariably the 'zheltozem' type—the yellow." In his map of the soils of the world, the forest regions of the southern latitudes are marked as the zone of yellow soils. He says:

The red soils and the laterites resulting from a parent material rich in iron are, in our opinion, intrazonal soils, just as amidst the chernozem and podzol soils the humus-carbonate or rendzina soils, resulting from parent material rich in carbonates, are intrazonal soils. In some cases, soils attain the red color after having been disturbed by tillage and erosion. Numerous facts oblige us to recognize that in typical zonal soils of the humid regions in the southern latitudes, the R_2O_3 are removed from the A horizon as in the podzol soils of the northern latitudes. Under such conditions, the eluvial A horizon of the soils in the southern latitudes takes on a yellow tone, and for this reason we assign the name 'yellow soils' to this type. We do not, however, deny the widespread distribution of red soils in the humid southern regions where the R_2O_3 accumulate at the surface. These soils are designated as 'Krasnozem,' red soils, a separate group of lithogenic-intrazonal formations. The phenomena of laterite formation we are inclined to relate chiefly to the processes of geologic weathering in the southern humid regions. The presence of parent rocks rich in iron, especially in the ferrous state, is, however, imperative for the formation of the red belt of weathering. The zonal type of soil formation in these regions manifests itself by the removal of bases and R_2O_3 from the A horizon. This process, therefore. runs in the opposite direction of laterite formation.

Although there is much to be said for the views of Afanasiev, it must be admitted that his theoretical postulates are not supported with sufficient

Table 113

Chemical composition of Norfolk sandy loam, 3 miles North of Raiford, Georgia
(After U. S. Bureau of Soils)

Constituents	Depth in inches				
	0-7	8-12	13-18	19-30	31-70
	per cent	*per cent*	*per cent*	*per cent*	*per cent*
SiO_2	93.07	89.44	83.28	80.08	79.85
TiO_2	0.34	0.44	0.53	0.65	0.71
Fe_2O_3	1.10	2.07	3.20	4.00	3.20
Al_2O_3	2.27	4.97	8.35	11.35	10.42
MnO	0.05	0.03	0.01	0.005	0.005
CaO	0.60	0.30	0.60	0.36	0.30
MgO	0.14	0.06	0.08	0.08	0.12
K_2O	0.16	0.23	0.16	0.20	0.25
Na_2O	0.24	0.30	0.31	0.31	0.39
P_2O_5	0.09	0.05	0.06	0.05	0.07
Loss on ignition	2.07	2.46	3.80	4.22	4.54
N	0.03	0.02	0.02	0.02	0.01

evidence. As was stated earlier, there are not enough data, morphological, chemical, and physical on the profile basis of these soils.

Besides the analytical data on the total constituents of these soils, there is need for information on the acid- and alkali-soluble Al_2O_3 and SiO_2. A knowledge of the Harrassowitz *ki* and *ba* values, of the SiO_2: R_2O_3 ratios of the soils, and of the colloid fraction would help to differentiate the two soil groups. Leachings from lysimeters installed on the horizon basis would give definite information on the constituents translocated and thereby clarify the soil-forming processes involved in these two groups of red soils. Information on the exchange capacity, exchange neutrality, type of exchangeable cations, ultimate pH, and the other physico-chemical concepts now in vogue in soil studies would add still more to our knowledge of these soils.

Table 114

Chemical composition of soil from Sao Francisco, Furus River, Brazil, South America
(After U. S. Bureau of Soils)

Constituents	Depth in inches				
	0-15	15-30	30-60	72-180	180-300
	per cent	per cent	per cent	per cent	per cent
SiO_2	87.40	85.29	59.34	62.88	80.12
TiO_2	1.19	1.62	1.46	1.34	0.75
Fe_2O_3	1.02	2.75	11.33	7.45	2.02
Al_2O_3	5.54	6.68	19.40	18.73	11.96
MnO	0.012	0.012	0.006	0.008	0.008
CaO	0.28	0.36	0.24	0.18	0.28
MgO	0.28	0.28	0.41	0.41	0.24
K_2O	0.36	0.41	1.37	1.58	1.06
Na_2O	0.25	0.25	0.38	0.38	0.28
P_2O_5	0.06	0.05	0.04	0.03	0.02
Loss on ignition	3.36	2.98	6.75	6.47	3.81
N	0.07	0.03	0.03	0.03	0.03

Tyurin (100), in his review on the soils of North America, doubts the zonality character of the red soils. Treitz (99), Stremme (96), and Marbut (62) hold the view that the color of the red soils is to be ascribed to the R_2O_3 of an exposed B horizon as a result of erosion. *It is not unlikely that some of the red soils of the Coastal Plain in the United States are relics of laterite formed during an earlier humid tropical climate.* Some of these soils have been covered and uncovered by one or another erosion cycle during the Post-Glacial (Wisconsin) time in the course of the climatic sequences, from those days to our present-day climate. Pedologic evidence in support of the ideas expressed has been presented elsewhere (49).

A discussion on the podzolic features of the yellow soils is to be found in chapter XI.

Table 115

Chemical composition of Cecil Clay Loam, ½ mile N. W. of Green Hill, North Carolina

(After U. S. Bureau of Soils)

Constituents	Depth in inches			
	1-6	6-40	40-84	84-
	per cent	*per cent*	*per cent*	*per cent*
SiO_2	58.33	49.95	44.68	51.39
TiO_2	1.47	1.43	2.11	1.23
Fe_2O_3	6.38	9.31	11.36	5.56
Al_2O_3	20.06	26.54	27.68	24.72
MnO	0.056	0.040	0.095	0.123
CaO	Trace	Trace	Trace	1.03
MgO	0.58	0.45	1.30	1.43
K_2O	2.20	1.43	1.88	5.84
Na_2O	0.45	0.40	0.32	1.90
P_2O_5	0.10	0.04	0.18	0.64
Loss on ignition	10.70	10.63	10.59	5.63
N	0.081	0.026	0.006	0.00

DARK COLORED SOILS IN TROPICS AND SUBTROPICS

Dark colored soils have been observed, analyzed, and described in some parts of the tropics and subtropics. Notable among these are the black cotton soils of India known as *regur,* and the black soils of Morocco known locally as *tirs,* ethnologically a Berberian name meaning "black humus earth." In Algeria, tirs is associated with a heavy clay soil.

At one time, the black soils of the tropics were considered a type of chernozem. Kossovich (Ch. 2, 40, p. 244) looked upon regur being "closely related to chernozem, covering an area of about 200,000 square miles." Dokuchaev who examined laboratory samples of regur expressed his doubts on regur being related to chernozem. Glinka (Ch. 2, 26, p. 357) seemed skeptical about the chernozem nature of regur. He said: "We are not at all sure about the similarity between Indian regur and our European-Asiatic chernozem, for we are not informed sufficiently on the morphology of the former." According to Hilgard (Ch. 2, 30, p. 414), the regur soils "in their physical character, chemical composition, and cultural characteristics are very similar to the 'prairie soils' of the cotton states and especially to the black adobe of California." Marbut (62) refers to the occurrence of

Table 116

Composition of exchangeable cations in a red loam from Chakva, the Caucasus

(After Gedroiz)

Horizon	Depth	Composition of exchangeable cations			Total exchange capacity	Composition of exchangeable cations		
		H	Ca	Mg		H	Ca	Mg
	cm.	m. e.	m. e.	m. e.	m. e.	per cent	per cent	per cent
A	0-14	11.4	2.0	4.2	17.6	65	11.4	23.6
A$_2$-B	14-45	8.5	0.9	1.1	10.5	81	8.6	10.4
B-C	40-80	9.3	0.8	2.6	12.7	74	6.3	19.7
C$_1$	95-193	9.6	0.6	2.3	12.5	77	5.0	18.0
C$_2$	135-175	8.2	0.5	2.2	10.9	75	5.0	20.0

Table 117

TiO₂ in colloid fraction of various soils in the United States

(After Robinson and Holmes)

Soil type and location	Depth	TiO₂
	inches	*per cent*
Cecil clay loam, Ga.	0- 9 9-18	0.62 0.52
Norfolk fine sandy loam, N. C.	0- 8 12-36	0.79 0.71
Orangeburg fine sandy loam, Miss.	0-10 10-36	0.54 0.44
Clarksville silt loam, Ky.	0-10 10-36	0.81 0.63
Sassafras silt loam, Md.	0- 8 8-22	0.63 0.70
Huntington loam, Md.	0- 8 8-30	0.40 0.47
Chester loam, Md. .:....................	0- 8 8-32	0.58 0.70
Ontario loam, N. Y.	0-12 12-22	0.38 0.56
Carrington loam, Ia.	0-12 15-36	0.47 0.65
Marshall silt loam, Nebr.	0-14 14-36	0.48 0.50
Miami silty loam, Ind.	0-10 10-30	0.70 0.79
Wabash silt loam, Nebr.	0-15 15-36	0.49 0.56

black soils in Africa outside of Morocco. He considered these soils similar to chernozem. In later years (personal communication), Marbut realized that the black soils of Africa were not chernozems.

Giesecke (33) gives a comprehensive summary of the investigations on the black soils of the tropics up to 1929. He seems to be in agreement with Richthoffen and the others who looked upon regur as a member of the chenozem soils.

Annett (5) is of the opinion that the black color of the regur is due not so much to the organic matter as to the presence of titaniferous magnetite in the parent material. From the analyses compiled by him, presented in table 118, it is difficult to interpret the type of soil with which we are dealing, since the samples represent surface soils only, and the data therefore offer no criteria as to the movement and translocation of the constituents. The low N percentage is evidence enough of the low organic matter content. Annett quotes Leather (56) that "the analyses of Tween, as quoted by Kossovich, must have been carried out by igniting the soil and hence the organic matter found includes combined water." Annett also

Table 118

Analyses of some regur soils of India

(After Annett)

Constituents	Nagpur farm	Akola	Average of 18 soils (After Leather)
	per cent	*per cent*	*per cent*
Insoluble silicates	68.71	56.11	68.41
Fe₂O₃	11.25	9.83	7.13
Al₂O₃	9.39	10.68	10.14
MnO	0.26		0.17
CaO	1.82	6.59	2.90
MgO	1.79	2.51	2.27
K₂O	} 0.45	0.37	} 0.41
Na₂O		0.23	
P₂O₅	0.06	0.08	0.06
Organic matter and combined H₂O	5.83	9.42	6.58
Total N	0.05	0.03	0.03

quotes Clouston who mentions that "it is a well known fact that black cotton soils are deficient in humus." In his own analyses, Annett shows that the carbon in regur does not run much higher than 1 per cent.

Harrison and Ramaswami Sivan (42) agree with Annett about the origin of the dark color of the regur. They describe these soils from their own observations and those of Oldham (73):

Regur in its most characteristic form varies greatly in color, consistence, and fertility, but possesses the constant character of being highly argillaceous and somewhat calcareous, of becoming highly adhesive when wetted, and of expanding and contracting to an unusual extent under the respective influences of moisture and dryness. Hence, in the dry season the surface is seamed with broad and deep cracks, often 5 to 6 inches across and several feet deep. When dry, it usually breaks up into small fragments. Regur consists to a very large extent of aggregate or compound particles, and it differs from ordinary clayey soils in that it is amenable to agricultural operations within a comparatively short time after it has been wetted by rain.

This latter property reminds one of the lateritic clays in Cuba described by Bennett and Allison (16). Harrison and Ramaswami Sivan also mention the fact that the black soils are interspersed with red soils: "The red soils are distinctly seen to be produced by the weathering of gneiss wherever the latter appears as a hillock or mound, as at Ottapidaram, and generally they slightly overlap adjacent black soils. The latter in turn are found overlapping low level laterite."

Fischer (26) gives a comprehensive account of the tirs soils in Morocco, where they lie side by side with the widespread *Hamri* soils which are red in color, probably the Mediterranean terra rossa. Tirs is dark brown and dark gray when dry and chocolate brown and practically black when wet. The chief belt of black soils in Morocco begins at the Tensift, the main river of southwestern Morocco, and terminates in the north along the river Bu-Regreg which empties into the sea at Rabat. It covers an area 300 km. long and 50 to 60 km. (in some places 80 km.) wide. Fischer considers these soils as steppe soils. Along the Mediterranean coast, the black soils are found in island-like fashion among the red earths, but in the interior the steppe soils predominate. Tirs is generally not a deep soil; it usually extends down from 0.5 to 1.0 m., although in some places it reaches depths of 2 and even 6 m. During the dry summer, the soil cracks, and during the winter rains, the openings fill up with surface material. Its parent material varies from soft calcareous tuffs to sandstone, shales, clays, and other materials. Fischer associates the origin of the black earth belt in Morocco with loess formation. According to him, the loess was blown in from the dry steppe in the hinterland, caught by the vegetation, and fixed there by the heavy dews which fall in that region during the dry summer.

A good deal of Fischer's evidence is based on the numerous investigations of the French geologists. Of these, the work of Gentil (32) is of interest. He compares the tirs with the Russian chernozem, more definitely with the humus-carbonate soil originating from calcareous parent material. Analyses of a number of black earth samples, as presented by Schwantke (89), are reproduced in table 119.

Hosking (46) made a comparative study of Indian regur which are tropical in their geographic position, and Australian black earths which extend from subtropical to tropical latitudes.

The Australian black earths find their best-known development on the Darling Downs, to the west of the Great Divide as a practically continuous formation, except where replaced by red to chocolate soils of the red loam type. Extensive black earth plains are also developed over basalt or basaltic alluvium on the Peak and Meteor Downs to the north. . . . Where soils are formed over alluvium from both basaltic and sandy carboniferous formations, gray to gray-brown soils, intermediate in character between the typical black earths and weakly podzolized soils. are to be found. . . . Although the soils are typically black in the surface horizon, the subsoil color is modified not only by the presence of calcium carbonate but also by the nature of the parent material and varies generally from grey through grey-brown to brown. . . . During the dry season of the year these soils crack considerably, fissures up to 4 inches or even 8 inches wide and over 3 feet deep become common, and the soils develop a distinctly columnar structure which persists throughout the year in the deeper layers. The surface when dry has a distinctly granular structure. The soils become markedly cloddy in the subsurface with a distinct nut structure which passes down into the characteristic columnar formation.

Table 119

Composition of tirs in Morocco

(After Fischer and Schwantke)

Constituents from a HCl extract	Sample from Abda	Sample from Schauia	Sample furnished by Fischer
	per cent	*per cent*	*per cent*
N	0.110	0.023	0.089
P_2O_4	0.128	0.090	0.052
Ca	1.070	2.640	2.819
K	0.324	0.452	0.432
Mg	0.727	1.368	1.359
SO_3	0.172	—	
Fe_2O_3	2.511 ⎫		
Al_2O_3	5.399 ⎬	14.14	
H_2O	5.876 ⎭	—	3.131
Organic matter	6.367 ⎫		0.812*
Volatile substances	— ⎬	17.94	
Total	22.684	36.653	
Residue	77.316	63.347	
Residue from HCl extract: R_2O_3, Mn, and Na			10.378
R_2O_3: soluble in H_2SO_4			10.400
Alkaline earths and alkali: soluble in H_2SO_4			2.281
CO_2			1.085
Sand			67.162
		Total	100.000

*Designated as humus.

In discussing the data on the composition of the regur and the black soils of India, Hosking points out that the figures for the organic matter content of regur reported by the earlier investigators are extremely exaggerated. His analyses seldom show much more than 1 per cent organic matter in regur, whereas the Australian black soils have an organic matter content ranging from 2 to 5 per cent, with many as low as 1 per cent and some as high as 10 per cent. It is suggested that the difference in the organic matter content of the soils in the two regions is due to the higher temperature in India and the cultivation of the regur over a period of centuries.

In table 120, data substantiating the views of Hosking are presented on the composition of regur and the black earths of Australia, compiled from the analyses of Hosking.

Outside the difference in organic matter content, the black soils of India and Australia are very similar in composition. Neither of the soils reported on by Hosking show definite horizon differentiation. There is indication of a profile development in some of the Australian soils. The high C:N ratio is an indication of anaerobic conditions some time in the history of these soils. It is very probable that slow chemical oxidation accompanied frequently by reduction took place when these soils were waterlogged. These soils also show salinization and desalinization effects (see Index), with Na in the exchange complex generally present, or evidence of its having been there. The columnar structure is generally the result of Na in the complex. Cracking of the soil into fissures is also an index of the presence of Na or the effects of a former Na influx. The podzolization attributes noted by Hosking are probably solodi effects (see Index).

Table 120
Composition of regur and Australian black earths
(After Hosking)

Locality	Horizon	Depth	Re-action	CaCO₃	P₂O₅	K₂O	Mn₃O₄
		cm.	*pH*	*per cent*	*per cent*	*per cent*	*per cent*
Northern	A	0-10	8.0	10.09	.196	.568	.057
Queensland,	B	10-24	8.6	21.53	.126	.446	.029
Australia	BC	24-35	9.4	27.32	.086	.286	.037
	C	35-42	9.5	16.6	.048	.292	—
Central	A	0-9	7.8	0.05	.055	.122	.162
Highlands,	AB	9-18	8.5	0.64	.052	.121	.153
Australia	BC	18-27	8.8	5.79	.080	.122	.122
	A	0-6	6.5	—	.328	.459	.228
Gough, N.S.W.	B	6-20	6.7	—	.408	.340	.211
Australia	BC	20-27	6.6	0.01	.401	.292	.235
Bombay,	A	0-6	8.1	0.09	.105	.649	.155
India, Broach	AB	6-12	8.4	0.05	.102	.656	.159
district	B	12-24	8.4	0.11	.095	.635	.159
Central Prov-	A	0-8	8.0	1.55	.093	.612	.218
inces, India ;	B	24-48	8.0	2.22	.073	.673	.173
Nagpur	BC	48-	8.2	11.6	.083	.656	.155
	A	0-6	8.8	0.05	.035	.458	.050
Bombay Presi-	AB	11-17	8.9	0.06	.033	.456	.053
dency ; Dhaz-	B	26-32	9.2	0.82	.027	.457	.051
wah district	BC	32-44	9.2	1.25	.030	.473	.051

(Continued on page 514)

Table 120 — (Continued)

N	Organic matter	Carbon Nitrogen	Exchangeable bases, milliequivalents per 100 gms. of soil				
			Ca	Mg	K	Na	Mn
per cent	per cent	ratio					
.441	10.3	13.5	27.3	19.8	3.35	3.6	.01
.184	5.3	16.7	16.3	24.0	2.65	2.2	Tr.
.087	2.6	17.3	7.4	15.3	1.36	5.5	Tr.
.082	2.2	15.8	—	—	—	—	
.074	2.1	16.8	49.5	22.4	.32	.38	.05
.070	2.1	17.5	49.0	22.4	.24	.48	.05
.069	2.1	17.6	45.6	21.6	.23	.60	.06
.186	4.6	14.3	30.4	21.5	1.12	.40	.20
.118	3.0	14.5	33.0	22.2	0.73	.61	.08
.110	3.0	15.6	30.0	21.2	0.63	.91	.09
.035	0.7	11.8	40.0	12.2	1.21	.48	Tr.
.030	0.6	12.3	39.1	12.1	1.09	.58	Tr.
.030	0.6	12.3	38.7	12.9	0.65	1.30	Tr.
.054	1.4	15.0					
.045	1.4	17.5					
.027	0.5	11.2					
.028	1.0	21.3	41.5	19.4	0.91	1.19	
.028	1.0	21.5	40.0	22.2	0.86	2.14	
.028	0.9	20.1					
.027	0.9	19.6					

Prescott and Hosking (78) report red soils on basalt in Australia. They emphasize their observation that a high feldspar content (orthoclase, albite, and anorthite) in the parent material gives rise to a high clay content. These soils seem to be closely related in composition, as shown by the N, P, K, and exchange capacity, to the black earths described by Hosking. They are, however, more on the acid side, generally not below pH 6.0 and not above 7.1. These soils have appreciable quantities of free R_2O_3, an indication of a high degree of laterization. It is very possible that these red soils, which resemble very much the terra rossa of the Mediterranean region, have been formed on the higher elevations within the areas of the black soils and at the edges of these.

Miege (68), in studies on the soils of Morocco, describes tirs and hamri, the latter a red soil, and gives comparative data on the SiO_2, Al_2O_3, and Fe_2O_3 of these soils. The tirs are less weathered than the hamri soils and contain less colloids. The hamri soils contain more KOH-soluble Al_2O_3 and SiO_2, indicating a higher degree of laterization, and more Mg in the exchange complex. Miege expresses the idea that the red clay had formed under a climate different from the present. He considers the hamri as a formation in the cycle of weathering preceding the tirs.

Bal (9) reports analyses of regur on different parent materials in the Central Provinces of India, showing that the lime content varies inversely with the rainfall. Some Ca and SiO_2 is leached out from the surface of these soils and most of them are low in organic matter. In the more humid areas, 48 inches of precipitation, the pH is 6.5-6.8; in the less humid areas, the pH is about 8.0.

Raychaudhuri and associates (74) made a comparative study of red and black soils lying side by side. The surface 0-2 feet layer of the black soils was black in color, clayey texture, pH 8.0; the 2-4 feet layer contained some white calcareous nodular concretions, gravelly texture, pH 7.9. The 0-1.75 feet layer of the red soil was a red loam, pH 7.4; the 1.75-2.75 feet layer was dark red, gravelly texture, pH 7.1; the 2.75-4 feet layer was also dark red, gravelly texture. The $SiO_2:Al_2O_3$ ratio of the clay fraction of both red and black soils increases with depth. The $SiO_2:Al_2O_3$ and $SiO_2:R_2O_3$ ratios are higher in the black clay fraction. The percentages of free SiO_2 increases with depth and are higher in the black soil. The Al_2O_3 content is higher in the black and the Fe_2O_3 in the red soils. At corresponding depths, the black soil contained more clay. There was not much difference in the N content of the two soils at about the same depths, 0.05 and 0.042 per cent for the black, and 0.04 and 0.051 for the red. The C content was higher in the black soil, as indicated by the C: N ratio, 14.7-11.79 for the black against 10.11, 10.25, and 7.0 for the red.

Kanitkar (52), in his monograph on dry farming in India, describes regur varying little in mechanical and chemical composition to depths of 6 and more feet. The N content is very low, from 0.018 per cent in the first foot and 0.013 per cent in the sixth foot of soil. Without giving comparative analyses or attributes, Kanitkar classifies regur as chernozem. Of some interest are the data on the black soils at the Rohtak Research Station, in the Punjab. These soils show some profile differentiation. However, the alluvial nature of the parent material makes it doubtful whether the apparent profile development is the product of soil forming processes or of geologic deposition.

In his excellent monograph on the soils of South Africa, Merwe (67) gives detailed descriptions and copious data on the mechanical and chemical composition of "subtropical black clay soils." In an attempt to classify them, Merwe repudiates their chernozem character. After obtaining some vague ideas from European colleagues, to whom he presented some soil samples and data, he comes to what appears to be the only conclusion that these soils are similar to the black soils of the tropics and subtropics, such as regur, tirs, or the black soils in Australia, described by Hosking.

While on a trip with the International Pedologic Conference in Algeria (50a) in May of 1947, observations and examinations were made on the dark brown to black soils in the Mitidja plain. Similar soils were noted in the plains on the railroad line from Algiers to Relizane, with red islands interdispersed through the large areas of the dark colored soils, with brown and red soils edging off the plains on the mountain slopes. Most of the parent material of these soils is of alluvial, deluvial, and coluvial origin, varying in depth. In many places, like the one near El-Alia, the water table was 6 to 8 feet below the surface. All of these soils are undoubtedly similar in origin to that of the tirs in Morocco. Similar soils have been observed and examined in the Valley of Jezreel and other depressions in Palestine. Most of these soils are dark brown to black in color, varying in depth from 2 to 6 feet and deeper, with little differentiation of the profile constitution, distorted in some areas by the influx of sodium causing dispersion. These soils have a low organic matter content, 1 to 1.5 per cent.

Origin of Dark Colored Soils—Various theories have been proposed on the formation of dark colored soils in the tropics and subtropics, primarily in reports on regur in India. At one time, the origin of regur had been associated with basalt as the parent material. This theory became untenable when regur was found on metamorphic and other rocks. It was then proposed that parent materials giving rise to heavy textured soils are a prerequisite for regur formation. When regur and other black soils of light and medium texture have been reported in India and other tropical and subtropical countries, another explanation had to be offered. As pointed out earlier, Annett associated the dark color of regur with titaniferous magnetite. Others explained the origin of these soils as a result of the presence of calcium in the medium. Shokal'skaya (93), in the review of the literature on regur, quotes investigators who considered regur a fluviogenic "formation of fresh water basins and lagoons." While she was careful not to commit herself to this theory, she was inclined to share this view. Polynov (77), commenting on Shokal'skaya's paper, identified regur with chernozem.

Mohr (69) was puzzled over the black soils in Netherland East Indies. He had an inkling of the hydrogenic nature of these soils and advanced the possibility of such origin; at the same time he argued against it. Wohltmann (105, pp. 174-175) also postulated the possibility of regur having originated under conditions of temporary waterlogging. He did not, however, follow through his own idea and actually opposed the hydrogenic nature of regur.

Raychaudhuri and associates (79) quote the view of Basu on the specific nature of the red and black soils and the view of Sen who claimed that "the black soil is the transported red soil from elevated places subsequently converted black in situ after its deposition in the valley bottoms and that iron in the soil plays the main role in this color change." Raychaudhuri and associates have treated regur with H_2O_2, but did not succeed in removing the black color. They concluded that the color was not due to the presence of organic matter, but they did not analyze the residue for organic substances after H_2O_2 treatment. They have corroborated the findings of Nagelschmidt, Desai, and Muir (70), on the mineral composition of the red and black soils. The main contrast between the two is that the red clay contains predominantly kaolinite or halloysite, whereas the black clay contains mainly beidellite.

To del Villar (102) goes the credit for proving beyond a doubt the hydrogenic origin of the dark colored soils of the tropics and subtropics. Reporting on 200 profiles of tirs in Morocco, del Villar describes a number of varities of tirs, such as glei tirs, dess (gray tirs), crust tirs, and chestnut tirs. The variations are associated with the state of waterlogging of these soils in the course of their formation, elevation, and rainfall. Thus, the dess is usually found at the edge of depressions, where black tirs, as well as glei tirs are found. In some of the latter, lime crusts are found at various depths. The chestnut tirs is to be found in regions of less rainfall, but always in depressions. del Villar points out that many of the tirs areas "become waterlogged under the heavy winter rains and occasional floods. In many cases, this condition is of such long duration each year that the land becomes a more or less permanent marsh. . . . The low flat plains of the tirs are depression areas similar to the areas of saline patches throughout the world. In both cases, the depression is not the cause of the hydro-hypogenic process, but the effect." del Villar presents proof on the upward movement of salts from the depression areas of tirs. In many areas, he demonstrates the presence of chlorides and sulfates. He also assumes that most of the tirs areas have been in forest at one time or another.

Stebut (95) revised his ideas on the nature of the black soils of Serbia, known locally as *smonitsy*. Originally, these soils were classified as chernozem; now they have been identified as tirs.

Reason for Dark Color.—In the discussion on the dark colored soils of the tropics and subtropics, the source of the black color has been a kind of an enigma. At first, the color was attributed to the organic matter, but when the facts demonstrated a low organic matter content of these soils, another explanation had to be provided. del Villar is of the opinion that magnetite (Fe_3O_4) is responsible, in a large measure, for the dark color. Raychaudhuri and associates are of the opinion that the dark color is not due to the organic matter. Samples of dark colored soil collected by the author in the Blida section of Algeria and in the Valley of Jezreel of Palestine remained dark after H_2O_2 treatment, but lost their color and turned red upon ignition at 400-500°C.

It might be that the dark colored substances that persist after H_2O_2 treatment *consist of humins and perhaps some type of bitumens. These high carbon organic constituents may form under the conditions of the high temperatures and periods of lowering of water table, when the dark colored soils are subjected to a change from anaerobic to aerobic state.* According to Sedlestskii (Ch. 4, 81), organic pedolites, which are embrionically a coal-like formation, would make their appearance in such a system. These coal-like substances may cause a darkening of the soil when present in small quantities. *These high carbon content compounds undoubtedly are responsible for the high C:N ratio of the dark colored soils of the tropics and subtropics.*

References

1. Adams, F. Dawson 1929 The geology of Ceylon. *Canad. J. Res.* 1: 425-465.
2. Afanasiev, Ya. N. 1931 Fundamental features of the earth's soil surface. (In Russian and German.) Belorus. Akad. Nauk, Minsk.
3. Agafonoff, V. 1936 Le sols de France au point de vue pedologique. Paris.
4. Anderson, M. S. and Byers, H. G. 1931 Character of the colloidal materials in the profiles of major soil groups. U. S. Dept. of Agr. Tech. Bul. 228.
5. Annett, H. E. 1910 The nature of the color of black cotton soil. *Memoirs Dept. Agr. India* (Chem. Ser.) 1: 185-203.
6. Arsandaux, H. 1909 Contribution to the study of laterite. *Comp. Rend. Acad. Sci.,* 149: 682-685; 1082-1084.
7. Arsandaux, H. 1913 Contribution to the study of the alteration of alumina silicate rock in tropical regions. *Bul. Soc. Francais de Mineral.* 36: 70-110.
8. Baeyens, J. and collaborators (8 in number) 1938 Les Sol de l'Afrique Centrale, specialement du Congo belge. *Publ. de l'Inst. Nat. pour l'etude Agron. du Congo belge.* Bruxelles. Tom I: de Bas Congo. pp. 375.
9. Bal, D. V. 1935 Some aspects of the black cotton soils of central provinces, India. *Emp. Jour. Exptl. Agr.* 3: 261-268.

10. Baren, J. van 1931 Properties and constitution of a volcanic soil, built in 50 years in the East Indian Archipelago. *Geolog. Inst. of the Agr. University,* Wageningen (Holland), no. 17, pp. 1-29.

11. Bauer, M. 1898 Beitrag zur Geologie der Seychellen, insbesonder zur Kenntinis des Laterits. *Neues Jahrb. f. Min. Geol. u. Pal. 2*: 163-219.

12. Bauer, M. 1907 Beitrag zur Kenntnis des Laterits, insbesondere dessen von Madagaskar. *Neues Jahrb, f. Min. Geol. u. Pal.* Festband zum Feier des 100 Jahrigen Bestehens, 56: pp. 38-90.

13. Bemmelen, J. M. van 1904 Beitrage zur Kenntnis der Verwitterungsprodukte der Silikate in Ton-Vulkanischen und Laterit-Boden. *Zutsch. Anorgan. u. Allg. Chemie* 42: 265-314.

14. Bemmelen, J. M. van. 1910 The various kinds of weathering of the silicate rocks of the earth's crust. *Ztsch. Anorgan. u. Allg. Chemie* 56: 322-357.

15. Bennett, H. H. 1926 Some comparisons of the properties of humid-tropical and humid-temperate American soils, with special reference to indicated relations between chemical composition and physical properties. *Soil Sci.* 21: 349-374.

16. Bennett, H. H., and Allison, R. V. 1928 The soils of Cuba. Tropical Plant Research Foundation, Washington, D. C.

17. Blanck, E. 1930 Die Mediterran-Roterde (terra rossa). Blanck's Handbuch der Bodenlehre 3: 194-257. (This is a summary of Blanck's many investigations).

18. Blanck, E. and Alten, F. 1924 Experimentaler Beitrag zur Entstehung der Mediterranean Roterde. *Landw. Ver. Sta.* 103: 73-90.

19. Bonnet, J. A. 1939 The nature of laterization as revealed by chemical, physical, and minerlogical studies of a lateritic soil profile from Puerto Rico. *Soil Sci.* 48: 25-40.

20. Buchanan, Hamilton F. 1807 Journey from Madras, Canara, and Malabar. London, 3 volumes. Reference to v. 2, p. 440.

21. Byers, H. G. and Anderson, M. S. 1932 The composition of soil colloids in relation to soil classification. *Jour. Phys. Chem.* 36: 348-366.

22. Campbell, J. M. 1917 Laterite: its origin, structure, and minerals. *The Mining Magazine* 17: 67-77; 120-128; 171-179; 220-229.

23. Comel, Alvise. 1933 Le terra rosse degli altipiani della Tripolitania. Soil Res. (Inter. Soc. Sci.), 3: 126-132.

24. Fermor, L. L., 1911 What is laterite? *Geol. Magaz.* n. s. 8: 454-462; 507-516; 559-566.

25. Filosofov, B. 1928 On the characteristics of terra rossa in the neighborhood of Rome. (Russian). Pamyati Glinki; Leningrad Selsko-Khos. Inst., 191-207.

26. Fishcer, Th. 1910 Schwarzerde und Kalkkruste in Marokko. *Ztsch. für praktische Geologie* 18: 105-114.

27. Fox, C. S. 1923 Bauxite and aluminous laterite occurrences in India. *Mem. Geol. Surv. India,* v. 49, pt. 1, p. 221.

28. Fox, C. S. 1936 Buchanan's laterite of Malabar and Kanara. *Records Geol. Survey Ind.* 69: 389-422.

29. Fuchs, Th. 1875 Zur Bildung der terra rossa. *Verh. d. K. K. Geolog. Reichsanst.* (Wien), p. 194.

30. Galdieri, A. 1913 L'origine della terra rossa. *Boll. Soc. Naturalisti;* Ann. R. Scuola d'Agric. Portici. Quoted from Blanck.

31. Gedroiz, K. K. 1925 The soil absorbing complex and the absorbed cations as a basis for the genetic classification of soils. (Russian). Nossov. Sel'skokhoz. Opuit. Stantz. Bul. 38.

32. Gentil. L. 1909 Rapport sur une mission scientifique au Maroc en 1908 *Nouv. Arch. des Missions Scient.* 18: 47-50.

33. Giesecke, F. 1930 Tropische und subtropische Humus-und Bleicherdebildungen. Blanck's Handbuch der Bodenlehre, 4: 184-224.

34. Hardon, H. J. 1938 Podzols in the tropical lowlands (in English). *Pedology* (U.S.S.R.) No. 3: 325-331.

35. Hardy, F. 1923 The physical significance of the shrinkage coefficient of clays and soils. *J. Agr. Sci.* 13: 243-264.

36. Hardy, F. 1931 Studies in tropical soils. I. Identification and approximate estimation of sesquioxide compounds by adsorption of alizarin. *J. Agr. Sci.* 21 : 150-166.

37. Hardy, F. and Follett-Smith, R. R. 1931 Studies in tropical soils. II. *J. Agr. Sci.* 21 : 739-761.

38. Hardy, F. and Rodrigues, G. 1939 Soil genesis from andesite in Grenada, British West Indies. *Soil Sci.* 48: 361-384; see also pp. 483-495.

39. Harrassowitz, H. 1926 Laterit. *Forschritte der Geologie und Palaentologie* 4: 253-566.

40. Harrassowitz, H. 1930 Boden der tropischen Regionen. Blanck's *Handbuch der Bodenlehre* 3: 362-436.

41. Harrison, J. B. 1910 The residual earths of British Guiana commonly termed "laterite". *Geol. Mag.* n. s. 7: 439-488; 8(1911) : 120-353.

42. Harrison, W. H. and Ramaswami Sivan, M. R. 1911-1912 A contribution to the knowledge of the black cotton soils of India. *Memoirs of the Dept. Agr. India* (Chemical Series), 2: 261-280.

43. Hollstein, W. 1938 Beitrage zur Bodenkunde des Mittelmeergebietes. *Soil Res.* (Inter. Soil Sci. Soc.) v. 6, No. 2: 91-121.

44. Holmes, A. 1914 Investigation of laterites in Portuguese East Africa. *Geol. Mag.* n. s., VI, No. 1: 529-537.

45. Holmes, R. S. and Edgington, G. 1930 Variations of the colloidal material extracted from the soils of Miami, Chester, and Cecil series. U. S. Dept. of Agr. Tech. Bul. 229.

46. Hosking, J. S. 1935 A comparative study of the black earths of Australia and the regur of India. *Trans. and Proc. Roy. Soc. South Australia,* v. 59: 168-200.

47. Idenburg, A. G. A. 1937 Systematische Grondkaarteering van Zuid—Sumatra (English summary), pp. 1-165. G. W. Van der Wiel & Co. Arnhem.

48. Imperial Bureau of Soil Sci. 1932 Laterite and laterite soils. Tech. Common. No. 24: 1-30.

49. Joffe, J. S. 1941 Climatic sequences of the Post-Wisconsin glacial age as revealed in the soil profile. *Proc. Soil. Sci. Soc. Amer.;* v. 6: 368-372.

50. Joffe, J. S. and Pugh, A. J. 1934 Soil profile studies VI: Distribution of Ti in soils with special reference to podzols. *Soil Sci.* 38: 245-257.

50a. Joffe, J. S. 1948 Notes on the International Conference of Pedology in the Mediterranean region. *Soil Sci.* 65: 417-424.

51. Joseph, A. F. 1925 Clays as soil colloids. *Soil Sci.* 20: 89-94.

52. Kanitkar, N. V. 1944 Dry farming in India. *Ind. Imper. Coun. Agr. Res.,* Sci. Monograph No. 15, pp. 66-108.

53. Kerner-Marilaun, F. 1923 Sitzungsber. Akad. der Wiss. in Wien, *Mathem.-Naturwiss.* Klasse, 1, 132: 119-142.

54. Köppen, W. 1918 Klassifikation der Klimate nach Temperatur, Niederschlag und Jahreslaug. *Pet. Mitt.* 64: 200.

55. Lacroix, A. 1913 Les laterites des les Guinee et les produits d'alteration qui leur sont associes. *Nouv. Arch. de Museum du Hist. Nat.,* ser. 5, v. 5: 255-358; see also *Compt. Rend. Acad. Sci.* (1914), 158: 335-338.

56. Leather, J. W. 1898 Composition of Indian soils. *Agr. Ledger* (Agr. Ser. No. 24), No. 2, p. 83.

57. Leningen, W. Graf. 1917 Entstehung und Eigenschaften der Roterde. *Int. Mitt. f. Bodenkunde* 7: 39-65, 177.

58. Liatsikas, N. 1935 Die Verbreitung der Bodentypen in Griechenland. *Soil Res.* (Inter. Soil Sci. Soc.) v. 4: 413-441.

59. Lorenz, J. R. 1860 Bericht uber die Bedingungen der Aufforstung und Kultivierung des kroatischen Karstgebirges. *Mitt. K. K. geogr. Ges. Wien* 4: 115. Quoted from Blanck.

60. Lowengart, S. 1928 Zur geologie der Küstenebene Palästinas. *Centralblatt f. Min., etc.* Abt. B, No. 9, 498-518.

61. Marbut, C. F. 1923 The soils of Africa. *Amer. Geogr. Soc. Res. Series* No. 13: 115-221.

62. Marbut, C. F. 1932 Morphology of laterites. *Proceed. and Papers Second Inter. Cong. Soil Sci.* 5: 72-80.

63. Marbut, C. F. and Manifold, C. B. 1926 The soils of the Amazon basin in relation to agricultural possibilities. *Geogr. Review* 16: 414-442.

64. Martin, F. J. and Doyne, M. A. 1927 Laterite and lateritic soils in Sierra Leone. *J. Agr. Sci.* 17: 530-547; 20(1930): 135-143.

65. Mattson, S. 1931 The laws of soil colloidal behavior: VI. Amphoteric behavior. *Soil Sci.* 32: 343-365.

66. Maxwell, W. 1905 Lavas and soils of Hawaiian Islands. Hawaii Sugar Planters' Assoc. Spec. Bul. A.

67. Merwe van der, C. R. 1940 Soil Groups and Subgroups of South Africa. Dept. of Agr. and Forestry, Union of S. Africa, *Science Bulletin 231*, Chem. Ser. No. 165, pp. 316.

68. Miege, E. 1931 Contribution a l'etude des soils du Maroc. *Soil Res.* (Inter. Soil Sci. Soc.) v. 5: 239-284.

69. Mohr, E. C. J. 1944 The Soils of Equatorial Regions. Edward Bros. Ann Arbor, Michigan.

70. Nagelschmidt, G., Desai, A. D., and Muir, A. 1940. The minerals in the clay fractions of a black cotton soil and a red earth from Hyderabad, Deccan State, India. *Jour. Agr. Sci.* 10: 639-653.

71. Neumayr, M. 1875 Zur Bildung der Terra Rossa. *Verh. K. K. Geol., Reichsanst.* Wien 50, 51. Quoted from Blanck.

72. Nevros, K. and Zvorykin, I. 1939 Zur Kenntnis der Boden der Insel Kreta. *Soil Res.* (Inter. Soc. Soil Sci.) v. 6, No. 4-5: 242-307.

73. Oldham, R. D. 1893 A manual of the geology of India, Calcutta.

74. Pendelton, R. L. 1941 Laterite and its structural uses in Thailand and Combodia. *Geogr. Rev.* 31: 172-202.

75. Pendelton, R. L. and Sharasuvana, S. 1942 Analyses and profile notes of some laterite soils and soils with iron concretions of Thailand. *Soil Sci.* 54: 1-26.

76. Pendelton, R. L. and Sharasuvana, S. 1946 Analyses of some Siamese laterites. *Soil Sci.* 62: 423-440.

77. Polynov, B. B. 1932 From the subcommission for the compilation of the soil map of Asia, International Society of Soil Science. *Contrib. to the Knowledge of the Soils of Asia* (in English), No. 2, Dokuchaev Inst. of Soil Sci., Acad. of Sci. (U.S.S.R.), 3-8.

77a. Prasolov, L. I. and Petrov, B. F. 1944 The soils of Western Europe from the point of view of the Russian school of pedology. *Pedology* (U.S.S.R.) No. 9: 393-409.

78. Prescott, J. A. and Hosking, J. S. 1936 Some red basaltic soils from eastern Australia. *Trans. and Proc. Roy. Soc. of S. Australia,* v. 60: 35-45.

79. Raychaudhuri, S. P., Sulaiman, M., and Bhuiyan, A. B. 1943 Physicochemical and mineralogical studies of black and red soil profiles near Coimbatore. *Ind. Jour. Agr. Sci.* 13: 264-272.

80. Regny, Vinasse de. 1904 Sull's origine della terra rossa. *Boll, Soc. Geol. Ital.,* Roma 23: 158. Quoted from Blanck.

81. Reifenberg, A. 1929 Die Entstenhung der Mediterran-Roterde (Terra rossa). *Kolloidchem. Beihefte* 28: 56-147.

82. Richthofen, F. von 1860 Bemerkungen über Ceylon. *Ztsch. der deutsch. geolog. Gesel.* 12: 531-33; 533-545.

83. Robinson, G. W. 1928 The nature of clay and its significance in the weathering cycle. *Nature* 121: 903-904.

84. Robinson, W. O. and Holmes, R. S. 1924 The chemical composition of soil colloids. U. S. Department of Agr. Bul. 1311.

85. Rodrigues, G. and Hardy, F. 1947 Soil genesis from a sedimentary clay in Trinidad. *Soil Sci.* 64: 127-142.

86. Schierl, A. 1906 Über die rote Erde des Karstes. 23 Jber. dtsch. Landes-Obberrealschule in Mahr. Ostrau. 6. Quoted from Blanck.

87. Schmelev, L. A. 1928 A method of determining free aluminum oxide in silicate mixtures and its application to the study of clays. (Russian) *Trans. Ceram. Res. Inst.* (Moscow) 14, pp. 1-24.

88. Schurman, H. M. E. 1924 Uber die neogene Geosynklinale von Südsumatra und das Entstehen der Braunkohle. *Geol. Rdsch.* 14: 327.

89. Schwantke, A. 1910 Untersuchung der Schwarzerde von Marokko. *Ztschr. für praktische Geologie* 18: 114-119.

90. Seelye, F. T., Grange, L. I., and Davis, L. H. 1938 The laterites of Western Samoa. *Soil Sci.* 46: 23-31.

91. Senstius, M. W. 1930 Studies on weathering and soil formation in tropical high altitudes. *Proc. Amer. Philosoph. Soc.* 69: 45-97.

92. Senstius, M. W. 1931 Laterites and polar migration. *Gerlands Beitrage zur Geophysik* 32 (Koppen Band I): 134-140.

93. Shokalskaya, Z. Yu. 1932 The natural conditions of soil formation in India. *Contrib. to the Knowledge of the Soils of Asia* (in English) No. 2, Dokuchaev Inst. of Soil Sci., Acad. of Science (U.S.S.R.), 53-152.

94. Stache, G. 1872 Geologische Reisenotizen aus Istria. Vhre. K. K. Geol. Reichsanst., Wien. p. 217.

95. Stebut, A. I. 1946 Smonitsy of Serbia and the black soils of the southern regions. *Pedology* (U.S.S.R.) No. 3: 135-154.

96. Stremme, H. 1915 Laterit und Terra Rossa als illuviale Horizonte humoser Waldboden. *Geol. Rundschau* 5: 480-499.

97. Taramelli, E. T. 1880 Dell' origine della terra rosa eguli affiori amenti di suolo calcare. *R. Inst. Lombardo, Rendic* (2) XIII, 261. Quoted from Blanck.

98. Thorp, J. and Smith, L. R. 1933 Concerning the origin of the white quartz sands of Northern Puerto Rico. *Jour. Dept. of Agr. of Puerto Rico,* 17: 157-170.

99. Treitz, P. 1914 Bericht über die agrogeologischen Aufnahmen des Jahres. 1913. *Jahresber, Kgl. Ungar Geol. Reichsanst.* fur 1913, Budapest, II: 482-486.

100. Tyurin, I. V. 1928 About the soils of North America. (Russian). *Uchennuie Zapiski Kazan Gosudarst.* Univ. 58: 27-48.

101. Vageler, P. 1938 Grundriss der tropischen u. subtropischen Bodenkunde. Ferlagsgesellsch. für Ackerbau M. B. H., Berlin.

102. Villar del, E. H. 1944 The tirs of Morocco. *Soil Sci.* 57: 313-339.

103. Walther, J. 1916 Das geologische Alter und die Bildung des Laterits. *Pet. Mitt.* v. 62, H. 1 and 2, pp. 1-7, 46-53; see also *Ztsch. deut. geolog. Gesellsch.* 57 (1915).

104. Wiegner, G. 1924 Boden u. Bodenbildung in kolloidchemischer Betrachtung.

105. Wohltmann, F. 1892 Tropische Agrikultur: I.

106. Zippe, F. V. M. 1853 Über die Grotten und Hohlen von Adelsberg, Lueg, Planina und Laas. p. 214. Wien, Quoted from Blanck.

Part III

Soil Systematics
Climatogentically Subdued
Soil Types

PART III

CLIMATOGENICALLY SUBDUED SOIL TYPES

In the evolution of soils, patterned by the climate and biosphere as the major active factors of soil formation, other minor factors come into play, independent of the others. As a result, besides the climatogenic zonal soil types, modified forms of these, and what might be designated as new ones, may appear. The principal types thus far recognized because of the independent factors are the following:

1. Soil types formed as a result of the upward and downward movement of salts due to fluctuations of the water table. These types of soils are classified as *hydrogenic*.

2. Marsh and bog type of soil formation where eluviation effects are subdued and hydromorphic factors prevail. With it are associated alluvial formations of recent origin. These soils are classified as the *hydromorphic* and *fluviogenic* soil types.

3. Soil types where the parent material asserts itself and masks the effects of the major active factors of soil formation are classified as *lithogenic*.

4. Soil types of the eluviation series that are affected in their eluviation by topographic features. These soils are classified as *orogenic*. In their highest expression, the orogenic soils are identified with the elements of vertical zonality. Strictly speaking, mountain soils are not true climatogenic soils inasmuch as the latter are associated in their soil forming processes with *horizontal zonality of the latitudinal climate*. Mountain soils are therefore a transitional type, between climatogenic and climatogenically subdued. Actually, mountain soils carry the specific effects of the specificity of the mountain climate.

The 4 soil types enumerated have been named *climatogenically subdued,* to distinguish them from the zonal climatogenic soils. They are also referred to as intrazonal, a name not appropriate for these soils, since some of them are limited to one or two zones only. Besides, each of these types is nothing more than a dynamic equilibrium point in the cycle of soil genesis, or a stage in the development of the normal zonal soil hindered momentarily in its evolution by another factor.

CHAPTER XIV

SALINE SOILS

Introduction.—Hydrogenic soils, reflecting the characteristics and properties brought about by the reactions of the circulation of soluble salts in the profile, are grouped under the type-name *saline soils.* Vilenskii (155) designates these soils as *hydro-halogenic,* probably because of the prominence of NaCl, the term *halogenic* signifying "producers of sea salt."

In the evolution of saline soils, 3 stages have been recognized, and each one represents a well defined soil forming process resulting into a soil type.

The first stage represents a process of salinization, i. e., the accumulation of soluble salts at the surface or at some point below the surface of the soil profile. Such a soil type is known as *solonchak.*

The second stage represents a process of desalinization, whereby the soluble salts are removed from the surface or pushed down to the bottom of the B or into the C horizon, and the exchange complex is subjected to a considerable saturation with the Na-ion and sometime Mg-ion. Such a soil type is known as *solonetz.*

The third stage represents a more thorough leaching of the profile, whereby the soluble salts are completely removed from the profile and, as a result of hydrolytic reactions, the silicates are split and SiO_2 is released. The soil attains a bleached appearance and resembles a podzol. At this stage, the soil type is known as *solodi.*

Geographic Distribution.—Harris (55), Sigmond (130), and Vilenskii (154) devote some space to the distribution of saline soils. According to Vilenskii,

These soils are distributed among the normal (zonal) soils of the arid regions on the earth's surface. They are found in wide belts or more frequently as encroaching spots, primarily in relation with certain elements of topography. Thus, according to Glinka and Hilgard, these soils are distributed in Europe in the Iberian Peninsula, southern France, Rumania, southern and southeastern Russia up to the northern limits of the chernozem, in the eastern part of Northern Caucasia, and the eastern part of Transcaucasia. In Asia, they appear in western Siberia and in a part of eastern Siberia up to the Zabaikal and Yakutsk provinces, in the desert and semi-desert steppes of Mongolia and Manchuria, the Kirgiz steppe region, Russian and Chinese Turkestan, Khiva, Bukhara, Persia, Asia Minor, Arabian Peninsula, and in India, where they occupy the stretches along the coast of the Arabian Sea and in the interior up to Afghanistan.

In North America, these soils may be found in many western states of the United States, in some of the western provinces of Canada, and in many of the states of Mexico. In South America, they are widespread in Chile, Peru, in western Brazil, and in Argentine east of the Andies. These soils are also encountered in many of the other states in South and Central America. In Africa, they are encountered all through the northern part, also in the east central portion of the continent and in many sections of the Union of South Africa. Large areas of saline soils are found in Australia. It has been estimated that 39 per cent of the world's dry land area is covered by these soils.

The saline soils are not restricted to the arid and semiarid temperate, subtropical, and tropical climates. Neustruev (Ch. 2, 50) cites the presence of salinized soils in the podzolized region of Western Siberia. Vilenskii (154) reviews the investigations of Dolenko (33), Dranitsyn (36), Abolin (1), and others on the saline soils in the Zabaikal region, between the meridians 80° and 90° extending as far north as the 62° latitude where in places a layer of perpetually frozen ground is located 3 to 4 feet below the surface.

Historical.—The literature on saline soils is very extensive. Vilenskii (154) cites 445 Russian references, some dating back to the 18th Century. In his monograph on Hungarian alkali soils, Sigmond speaks of "Samuel Thessedik, a Protestant vicar of Szarvas in the 18th Century, who secured a parish garden from his patron in 1769. This garden consisted of unproductive alkali (szik) lands which the vicar cultivated with great preseverance and wisdom." Sigmond and Arany (134) compiled a bibliography of 757 titles on saline soils.

Considerable confusion has prevailed among students of soils (and a great many are still confused) on the process of formation of saline soils until 1912, when Gedroiz (41) clarified experimentally and theoretically the genetic relationship between the processes of salinization and desalinization in soils. Before that time, different types of saline soils, their morphological, chemical, and physical characteristics and properties have been recognized and described, but no one elucidated the mechanism of the reactions responsible for the features of these soils.

In the United States, Hilgard tops the list of a number of investigators. His researches of the so-called alkali soils date back to 1888, as hinted in his publication (59) of 1892, and a summary of his work may be found in his famous book, "Soils." His theories were acclaimed and accepted throughout the world. According to Hilgard (Ch. 2, 30, p. 422):

The existence of alkali soils is in the majority of cases definitely traceable to climatic conditions alone. They are the natural result of a light rainfall, insufficient to leach out of the land the salts that always form in it by progressive weathering of the rock powder of which all soils largely consist . . . In extremely arid climates, the entire mass of the salts remains in the soils; and, being largely soluble in water, evaporation during the dry season brings them to the surface, where they may accumulate to such an extent as to render ordinary useful vegetation impossible, as is seen in 'alkali' spots and sometimes in extensive tracts of 'alkali desert'. Three compounds, viz., the sulfate, chloride, and carbonate of sodium usually form the main mass of these saline efflorescences. Magnesium sulfate (Epsom salt) is in many cases a very abundant ingredient; some calcium sulfate is nearly always present, and calcium chloride is not infrequently found.

Hilgard (Ch. 2, 30, p. 441) divided the alkali soils into two types: white alkali and black alkali. In the former, the white colored chlorides and sulfates of sodium and sometimes of magnesium prevail; in the latter, the carbonates of sodium prevail. These alkali salts dissolve some organic matter which imparts the black color to the soil.

The term *alkali* does not represent the true conditions of the white and black alkali soils. These soils also contain alkaline earth salts, $CaCl_2$, $MgCl_2$, $CaSO_4$. $2H_2O$, and $MgSO_4$. It is, however, noteworthy that Hilgard's white alkali soils correspond fully to solonchak, whereas the black alkali do not necessarily correspond to solonetz. As shown presently, there may be solonchak (white alkali) containing Na_2CO_3, and the soil may or may not be black.

Neither Hilgard nor his contemporaries and followers, Whitney and Means (158), Traphagen (148), Cameron (24, 25), Dorsey (34), Headden (56-58), Stewart and Peterson (139), Harris (55), and others have appreciated the genetic relationship of the different types of saline soils. The numerous early investigations at the California Experiment Station by Kelley and associates prior to their studies on base exchange, as well as those at other western experiment stations, were primarily concerned with the agro-chemical and agronomic rather than the pedogenic features of the saline soils.

Among the earliest comprehensive contributions to our knowledge of saline soils are those made by the Hungarian students of soil science. Treitz, who translated Hilgard's work, fully accepted the theories of Hilgard on the origin of alkali soils, distinguishing two types: white and black alkali. Sigmond (130), in his monograph on alkali soils (*szik*), reviews the early investigations of Szabo (145) and others and discusses the influence of Hilgard's views on the trend of studies on alkali soils made in Hungary. In his early reports, Sigmond divided the alkali soils into two types: *heavy clay szik* and *szik soda soils,* following the nomenclature of Szabo. The origin of these soils was explained on the basis of climate, topographic features, and the drainage conditions of an impervious subsoil layer. The formation of soda was attributed to the interaction of the carbonates with the sodium chloride present in these soils. In his later work, Sigmond, after becoming acquainted with the theories of Gedroiz, applied base exchange reactions in elucidating the origin and development of various types of saline soils. This was summarized by him in his report to the First International Congress of Soil Science in 1927 (131) and in the "Transactions of the Alkali Subcommission of the International Society of Soil Science" (132). Sigmond applied the name "solonetz" and "solodi" to his "clay szik" soils and "solonchak" to the "soda szik." In his book "The Principes of Soil Science," Sigmond (133) goes out of his way to minimize the contributions of Gedroiz and to show that his early work on soda soils antedate Gedroiz's work. As a matter of fact, the sections on saline soils in his book are far from being clear. In an attempt to introduce his own terminology in place of the universally accepted Russian terminology of solonchak, solonetz, and solodi, Sigmond confuses the meaning of the terms. He places the genetically related three types of soil formation of the hydrogenic series into a soil order under the name "Sodium Soils." This order is subdivided into the following types: 1. "Saline Soils" which correspond to the solonchak; 2. "Salty Alkali soils," a kind of mixture of solonchak and solonetz; 3. "Leached Alkali soils," the true solonetz; 4. "Degraded Alkali Soils," the solodi.

In Russia, modern studies of saline soils date back to the time when Hilgard had already worked out his classical separation of white and black alkali. According to Kovda (81), the first comprehensive description of these soils was made by Zemyatchenskii in 1894. It is noteworthy that whereas Hilgard studied the two successive stages in saline soils, even though he did not appreciate their true genetic relationship, Zemyatchenskii was confronted exclusively with solonetz, the second stage. As a matter of record, Dokuchaev recognized saline soils in his classification system and, as stated by Kovda, he supervised the early work of Zemyatchenskii, Glinka, and others who have contributed to the study of saline soils. Sibirtzev (128) published a treatise on the soils of Russia in 1897 in which he designated the saline soils as intrazonal soils.

It may be stated that the influence of Hilgard's systematic contributions on the alkali soils (to use Hilgard's nomenclature) of California on Russian investigations of similar soils have not been fully appreciated. It was through the work of Tulaikov (151) that the Russians got an idea of the classical contributions of Hilgard.

In 1912, Gedroiz presented his classical researches on the colloidal properties of soils in relation to exchangeable cations and the implication of these reactions in the processes of soil formation, with special emphasis on the genesis of the saline soils. Gedroiz utilized the information, morphological, chemical, and physical, accumulated by his Russian predecessors on the specificity of the two principal types, the structureless solonchak and structured solonetz. The contributions of Dimo and Keller (Ch. 2, 11),

Dimo (30, 31), Glinka (Ch. 2, 27), and Neustruev (Ch. 2, 50) are good examples of the ground work from pedologic point of view.

The work of Gedroiz served as a stimulus to a series of researches the world over on cation exchange and to the application of its reactions in the study of saline soils. Among the first to apply the theories of Gedroiz in the United States to the study of saline soils were Joffe and McLean (65). These studies appeared in a series of papers. In the summary of the second paper they stated: "The theory of exchange is the four cornerstones of the research on the origin of alkali soils." And in the fourth paper they stated: "This series of papers reporting the work with alkali soils should be looked upon as an attempt to bring before the investigators in this important field of research a clear picture of the problem as revealed by the most recent theories on the subject, especially that of Gedroiz." Kelley and Brown (75) and Cummins and Kelley (27) followed with investigations on the alkali soils of California. Similar investigations have been conducted at the Arizona Agricultural Experiment Station by McGeorge and associates (92), Breazeale and McGeorge (17), Burgess and McGeorge (21), and Burgess (20). However, not until the theories of Gedroiz were applied by students of pedology was it possible to work out clearly the sequence of the three stages in the evolution of saline soils and understand fully the formation of solonchak, solonetz, and solodi and varieties of these.

A series of studies on alkali (saline) soils have been made at Utah, Colorado, Wyoming, Idaho, and Oregon. All of their investigations, up to 1930, have not been of a pedologic nature. However, these studies have contributed a great deal to our knowledge on the amelioration of these soils.

Plant Cover.—Plant indicators for recognition of the type of soils have been used extensively by ecologists, geobotanists, and pedologists. They are very useful in distinguishing the distribution of saline soils among the normal soils, since certain plants in the arid regions are seldom found except where the soil contains some soluble salts. According to Davy (29), "there are at least 197 species native of California which are restricted to alkali soils." The plant associations serve the farmers in the alkali districts as indicators for determining the suitability of the land for reclamation. Hilgard (p. 536) points out that "the plants which may serve best as such indicators in California are the following: Tussoc-grass (*Sporobolus airoides* (Torr.); Bush Samphire (*Allenrolfea occidentalis* (Wats.) Ktze); Dwarf Samphire (*Salicornia subterminalis* Parish); Saltwort (*Suaeda torreyana* Wats., and *suffrutescens* Wats.); Greasewood (*Sarcobatus vermiculatus* (Hook) Torr.); Alkali-heath (*Frankenia grandifolia campestris* Gray); (*Cressa truxillensis* Choisy); and Salt-grass (*Distichlis spicata*)." A detailed report of the distribution and adaptation of the plants mentioned to

Table 121

Plant cover on saline soils in the chernozem zone
(After Vilenskii)

Solonchak	Solonetz	Degraded Solonetz	
		Depressions	Crusts
Carbonates	*Festuca sulcata v. glauca*	**First belt**	**1. Solonetzic steppe**
Artemisia laciniata	*Gilaus Besseri*	Close to water	
Atriplex littorale	*Artemisia maritima*		*Festuca sulcata*
Cirsium esculentum	*Statice Gmelini*	Meadow bog	*Agropyrum repens*
Glaux maritima	*Atropis convoluta*		*Arenaria graminifolia*
Hordeum pratense	*Bassia sedoides*	*Helcocharis palustris*	*Aster Linosyris*
Melilotus dentata	*Plantago maxima*	*Butomus umbellatus*	*Silaus Besseri*
Plantago maxima		*Gratiola officinalis*	*Galium verum*
Plantago Cornuti		*Juncus atratus*	*Peucedanum alsaticum*
Triglochin maritimum			
Suaeda maritima		**Second belt**	**2. Solonetz steppe**
Aster Tripolium		Flooded meadow	
Halicornia herbacea			*Festuca sulcata*
Carex diluta		*Alopecurus pratensis*	*Artemisia maritima*
Cirsium carum		*Agropyrum repens*	*Statice Gmelini*
Astragalus sulcatus		*Nasturtium brachy carpum*	*Atropis convoluta*
Glycyrhiza uralensis			
Atropis festucaeformis		**Third belt**	**3. Solonetz meadow**
Statice Gmelini		Meadow	
			Agropyrum repens
Meadow		*Festuca sulcata*	*Beckmannia eruciformis*
		Alopecurus pratensis	*Statice Gmelini*
Agropyrum repens		*Statice Gmelini*	*Peucedanum latifolium*
Alepecurus ventricosus		*Iris güldenstediana*	*Artemisia maritima*
		Thalictrum minus	*Polygonum arenarium*

Table 121—*Continued*

Statice Gmelini *Silaus Besseri* *Geranium collinum* *Beckmannia eruciformis* *Koeleria Delavignei* *Carex dilusa* *Juncus Gerardi* *Juncus cetratus* *Astragalus sulcatus* *Plantago maritima* *Plantago Cornuti* *Gypsophila trichotoma* *Iris Güldenstedt* *Melilotus dentatus* *Ononis hircina v.* *spinescens* *Pedicularis laeta* *Melilotus dentata* *Cirsium esculentum* *Centaurea glastifolia*	*Trifolium montanum* and others **Fourth belt** **Meadow steppe** *Festuca sulcata* *Agropyrum cristatum* *Medicago falcata* *Galium verum* *Phlomis pungens* *Arenaria longifolia* *Stipa capillata* *Goniolimon Besserianum* and others In more salinized areas *Statice Gmelini* *Plantago tenuiflora* *Galatella punctata*	**4. Willow type** *Salix cinera* *Poa pratensis* *Carex nutans* *Calamagrostis Epigeios* *Trifolium pratense* *Lotus corniculatus* *Silaus Besseri* and others **5. Poplar type** *Populus tremnla* *Poa serotina* *Carex vulpina* *Phalaris arundinacca* and others **6. Birch type** *Betula verrucosa* *Acer tataricum* and others **7. Oak type** *Quercus pedunculata* *Acer platanoides* *Tillia parvifolia*

the various types of saline soils in the western states is to be found in the work of Hilgard. Harris (55) gives a classified list and description of plants found on the saline soils in the United States. Vilenskii (154) presents his findings on the succession of plant associations with respect to the metamorphosis of solonchak to solonetz and finally to solodi in the arid steppe and chernozem soils. The data are presented in tables 121-122.

SOLONCHAK

Introduction.—Solonchak is the most prevalent of the three types of saline soils. It is most abundant in the gray-red semidesert and arid brown zonal soils, but is also found in the chernozem zone and may be encountered in almost any other soil zone. According to Vilenskii (154), the term *solonchak* was first used by Glinka to designate saline soils having a non-structural profile constitution.

Salinization.—The sources of the salts in solonchak, or the course of salinization, are associated with the hydrologic conditions of the surface deposits and especially the level of the ground waters. A number of hypotheses has been suggested as to how and wherefrom the salts in solonchak originate. One of these hypotheses attributes the accumulation of salts to ancient salt deposits or residues of former seas. Another hypothesis postulates the formation of salinized areas by the reduction of huge inland lakes by evaporation into salt lakes and salt accumulations within the borders of the original area of the inland lake. Geomorphologically, therefore, the conditions for salt accumulation occur generally in areas of basin shaped topography, usually in the lowest parts of a given drainage basin. Good examples of huge inland lakes, now reduced to small lakes whereby salts have accumulated in the ancient shoreline areas, are the ancient Lake Bonneville, represented by the Great Salt Lake in Utah, and the Caspian Sea of the Caspian Basin. The Jordan Valley associated with the Dead Sea is a special case, since it was at one time connected with the ocean.* Hilgard recognized seacoast and continental types of salinization. Other geomorphologic conditions conducive to salinization are lagoons, river deltas, flood plains, first river and lake terraces, and a variety of inclosed topographic depressions with impeded drainage.

Gerasimov and Ivanova (47) question the universality of the theory on the relation of salinization of ground waters and soils to sea borne salt deposition. They claim that under arid conditions water basins receiving

---

*The problem of the origin of salts in the oceans is discussed by Clarke (26), Linck (88), Treitz (149), Kossovich (79), and others. Linck calculated that the oceans contain 45 billion metric tons of salt, of which 34 to 35 billions are NaCl, 3 billions—$MgCl_2$, 2 billions—$CaSO_4$, and 1 billion—KCl.

Table 122
(*Continued on page* 534)
Plant cover on saline soils in the arid steppe
(After Vilenskii)

Solonchak			Transitions between solonchak and solonetz
Wet	Mellow	Meadow	
First belt (originates in water)			
Salicornia herbacca L.	*Halocnemum strobilaceum*	*Atropis distans*	*Atriplex canum*
Second belt	*Ofaiston monandrum*	*Agropyrum repens*	*Suaeda physophora*
Suaeda maritima		*Artemisia salina*	*Brachylepis salsa*
Suaeda linifolia			
Suaeda artissima	*Capsella procumdens*	*Statice Gmelini*	*Artemisia pauciflora*
Third belt	*Frankenia pulverulenta*	*Aeluropus littoralis*	*Agropyrum ramosum*
Atropis distans		*Centaurea glastifolia*	
Statice caspia	*Senecio coronopifolius*		*Sterigma tomentosum*
Atriplex pedunculatum		*Atriplex laciniatum*	
			Cachrys odontalgica
Fourth belt	*Kalidium foliatum*	*Petrosimonia crassifolia*	
Artemisia salina			
Statice Gmelini			
Fifth belt			
Statice suffruticosa			
Atriplex verruciferum			
Petrosimonia crassifolia			

surface water become salinized primarily with carbonates and sulfates of Ca and Mg that originate in the process of weathering. Water basins receiving ground and spring waters become salinized primarily with chloride-sulfate salts. These salts in part originate in the process of ion exchange.

The sources of origin of salts, outside of direct sea or ocean origin, have been ascribed to sedimentary rocks, to ancient ocean bottom deposits, and to the salts brought in by precipitation. On the latter point, Clarke (26) points out that the annual supply of Cl per acre at Rothamsted is

Table 122—*Continued*

Normal solonetz			Degraded solonetz on depressions
Prismatic	Columnar	Deep columnar	
			First belt (originates in water)
Artemisia pauciflora	*Artemisia pauciflora* *Camphorosma monspeliacum*	*Kochia prostrata* *Camphorosma monspeliacum*	*Heleocharis palustris* *Butomus umbellatus* *Nasturtium brachycarpum* *Carex nutans* *Cirsium incanum*
Brachylepis salsa			
Salsola brachiata	*Kochia prostrata*	*Pyrethrum achilleifolium*	
	Aster glabratus		**Second belt**
Salsola laricina *Bassia sedoides*	*Agropyrum desertorum*	*Artemisia maritima L. v. incana Keller*	*Agropyrum repens* *Alopecurus pratensis* *Beckmannia eruciformis* *Polygomnu arenarium* *Statice Gmelini* *Nasturtium brachycarpum*
		Agropyrum desertorum	
		Artemisia pauciflora	**Third belt**
			Agropyrum cristatum *Festuca sulcata* *Artemisia maritima* *Koeleria gracilis* *Serratula nitida* *Stipa capillata* *Statice Gmelini*
			Fourth belt
			Artemisia maritima v. incana *Pyrethrum achilleifolium* *Agropyrum ramosum* *Poa bulbosa v. vivipara*

14.4 pounds; Ceylon—180.7 pounds; British Guinea—129.2 pounds; Calcutta—32.8 pounds; Odessa—17 pounds. Harris (55), summarizing the views of American workers, adheres to the hypothesis of salts being leached from sedimentary rocks of ocean bottom origin. In describing the saline soils of Western Australia, Burvill (22) points out that the salts originate from the decomposition of rocks and from the deposition of cyclic salt brought by rain from the sea.

Sokolovskii (137) holds the view that salts of saline soils, salt lakes, and of saline surface water have one and the same source of supply—from ancient seas, lagoons, and bays which have been buried by one of the many geologic revolutions. Essentially, this view is a version of the "continental salt accumulation" hypothesis.

The biological origin of salts in depressions is one of the hypotheses proposed. Kovda (p. 25) illustrates the basis of this hypothesis: "Salts distributed in the rock are selectively absorbed by specific species of the *Artemesia* and *Salicornia* type. These salts concentrate in the surface horizons of the soil, to be removed later by runoff waters or blown into the depressions together with the plant residues. There the salts accumulate to form solonchak." Kovda doubts the formation of solonchak by biological mobilization of salts. He cites Hilgard's data on the composition of the ash of plants grown in saline soils of the United States, and gives Keller's (67) analyses of a list of plants growing in the saline soils on the shores of lake Elton, including a light chestnut brown soil and a saline marsh. Plants, such as *Suaeda, Halocnemum,* and *Salicornia,* bring to the surface primarily chlorides; other plants, such as *Petrosomonia,* accumulate chlorides and sulfates. The huge quantities of salts in these plants are reflected in the ash content, *Salicornia herbacea* having 50.67 per cent and Suaeda (annual)—49.95 per cent. It is noteworthy that the Ca content of plants increases with the evolution of saline soils, from solonchak, through solonetz, and to normal steppe soil. This phenomenon emphasizes the role of Ca in the biosphere and in the process of soil formation.

In a more recent paper, Kovda (83) returns to the problem on the role of the biosphere in the mobilization of salts for the process of salinization and comes to the conclusion that plants do contribute considerably to this process.

Types of Solonchak.—If the salinization of solonchak is associated with soils that have not been subjected to any of the zonal types of the eluviation series, it is known as a *primary solonchak.* Its characteristic features are no horizon differentiation and a low organic matter content; it has no well defined structural profile constitution. This type of solonchak is prevalent in the semidesert. In this climatic belt, the salts of the solonchak are seldom subjected to percolation because of the paucity of rainfall and this type is sometime known as *dry solonchak.* The salt content is highest on the surface, diminishing with depth, consisting primarily of the chlorides of Na and Ca.

If the salts appear in any of the zonal soils, there may be: arid brown solonchak, chestnut solonchak, and chernozem solonchak. These soils maintain to a considerable degree their constitutional profile and are sufficiently modified in their morphological, chemical, and physical properties to be distinguished as solonchak. If the salinization has not advanced far enough, the term *solonchakic* is used. If the process of salinization does not cause the salts to rise to the surface of the soil, but keeps them at some point in the profile (where capillary tension ceases to act), the soil is known as an *internal, disguised,* or *hidden solonchak.*

If a solonchak undergoes desalinization, as shown presently in the cases of solonetz or solodi formation, and salts appear again in the profile, the soil is known as a *secondary regraded solonchak.*

Besides classifying solonchak according to the mode of salinization with reference to the zonal types, there is a classification of solonchak types according to the kind or kinds of salts prevailing in the soil. For the continental type of salinization, Kovda (81, p. 76) presents the following scheme of solonchak types, based on the kind of prevailing salts and their source of origin:

1. Chloride-nitrate solonchak, sometime with borates, associated with river deltas, lower flood plains, and delta sinks, such as the Salton sink of the ancient Colorado river delta.

2. Sulfate-chloride solonchak, associated with first river and lake terraces.

3. Mixed chloride-sulfate-soda solonchak, associated with inland continental water basins having no outlet.

4. Chloride-sulfate solonchak, associated with inland partially drained basins, lake shores, and poorly drained first river terraces.

5. Sulfate-gypsum solonchak, associated with the relatively well drained first and second lake and river terraces.

6. Sulfate-soda solonchak, associated with hemmed in secondary depressions on well drained ancient and third river terraces, watersheds, and shores of periodically open lakes of these regions.

7. Soda-solonchak, associated with geomorphological features similar to those in 6, wtih a lower erosion base level.

8. Coastal sulfate-chloride solonchak, associated with sea and delta terraces.

9. Lagoon chloride-sulfate-gypsum solonchak, associated with lagoon bottoms, bays cut off from the ocean.

10. Bottom sulfate-chloride-calcium carbonate salinization, associated with littoral deposits.

The first 7 types thus far recognized are of the *continental* group of salinization. Of these, the first three are in the stage of progressive salinization and desalinization. Types 6 and 7 are in the stage of progressive desalinization. Types 8, 9, and 10 are of the *sea* group of salinization where progressive salinization is going on.

Ivanova and Rozanov (63) present a scheme for two subtypes of solonchak: *meadow solonchak,* forming by the rise of salts from the ground waters; *steppe solonchak,* becoming salinized by the movement of the salts from the salt-bearing parent material, with or without the limited participation of the ground waters. Subdivisions of these two subtypes are separated on the basis of the quality of salts.

The meadow solonchak which is dominant in the forest-steppe soils may have subdivisions of surface salinization or of deep salinization, the former having an accumulation of salts on the surface with a decreased content of these with depth, and the latter, a heavy accumulation of salts through some depth of the profile. Evaporation, percolation, and mineral composition of ground waters determine the subdivisions. Within these subdivisions, there are stages, such as progressive salinization (Kovda speaks of this stage as primary solonchak), whereby the relative accumulation of $NO_3 \geqq CI > SO_4 > HCO_3$ represent the status of the type of salts; the stage of desalinization or alternating salinization and desalinzation is characterized by the accumulation of salts in the following qualitative order: $HCO_3 \geqq SO_4 > Cl > NO_3$. A number of varieties within the subdivisions are separated on the basis of molar ratios of $HCO_3 : Cl + SO_4$, $HCO_3 : Cl$, and $HCO_3 : SO_4$. It is well to remember that there are nitrate solonchaks, examplified by the niter spots in Utah, Colorado, and other parts of the world. The origin of the nitrates has been discussed extensively by Sackett (122), Headden (56, 57), Stewart (138), and Kostychev (80). Selyakov (125) returns to the problem and comes to the conclusion that nitrates accumulate as the result of the process of nitrification in organogenic rocks, of nitrification in soils (chemical and biological), and nitrates brought in by rains. Occasionally, soluble phosphates are found in the salts of solonchak.

Insoluble carbonates and soluble bicarbonates of Ca and infrequently similar salts of Mg are associated with solonchak. In the solonchak of chernozem, chestnut, brown, and gray zonal soils, the Ca and Mg carbonates are not only the result of illuviation but also of the process of salinization. These compounds are, therefore, distributed all through the profile instead of at some points.

Gedroiz (43) differentiated solonchaks according to the cations prevailing in them. He thus recognized Na, Ca, Mg, and mixed cation solonchaks, depending on the cation or cations dominating the salts. According to Vilenskii (154), $MgCl_2$ seems to react somewhat like Na_2CO_3, imparting a dark color to the solonchak. Zakharov (Ch. 2, 91, p. 366) ascribes the dark brown color of solonchak to Na_2CO_3 and $MgCl_2$, both of which are hygroscopic. Apparently, it is the water of crystallization and hygroscopic water that bring into solution some organic substances.

Ivanova and Rozanov (63) present a series of cation ratios associated with different types or subdivisions of solonchak, both in the meadow and steppe solonchak. The following types are recognized:

A ratio of $\dfrac{Na + K}{Ca + Mg} > 4$ represents a Na-solonchak

A ratio of $\dfrac{Na + K}{Ca + Mg} = 1$ to 4 and of $\dfrac{Ca}{Mg} < 1$ represent a Na, Mg-solonchak

A ratio of $\dfrac{Na + K}{Ca + Mg} = 1$ to 4 and of $\dfrac{Ca}{Mg} > 1$ represent a Na, Ca-solonchak

A ratio of $\dfrac{Na + K}{Ca + Mg} < 1$ and of $\dfrac{Ca}{Mg} > 1$ represent a Ca-solonchak

A ratio of $\dfrac{Na + K}{Ca + Mg} < 1$ and of $\dfrac{Ca}{Mg} < 1$ represent a Mg-solonchak

Table 123, compiled by Hilgard (p. 422), gives the salt content of a series of saline soils in Europe, Asia, Africa and America. In spite of the fact that the analyses are on surface soils only, and no line is drawn between solonchak and solonetz, the data bring out sufficiently clear the variations in solonchaks. For data on profile basis, the analyses of saline soils by Sigmond (133) and Kovda (81) are to be consulted.

An excellent index of the stage of salinization is the pH value. Whenever the pH is not above 8.2—8.4, the solonchak has, as a rule, no Na_2CO_3, and the soil is probably in the stage of progressive salinization. Only with the appearance of Na_2CO_3 does the pH go up, and such soils are in the stage of desalinization.

Mamaeva (90) discusses the formation of salt concretions in saline soils. She points out that by analyzing the concretions one may tell their origin and evolution and the type of saline soils they come from.

Rost and Chang (114) report on solonchak in the prairie soils. It looks like one of the regraded solonchak-solonetzic varieties of the Ca and Mg type, with sulfate and bicarbonate as the chief anions. The high pH value and kind of salts indicate that profile 1 is a soda-solonchak. The huge quantities of gypsum present will cause a natural amelioration of this soil with no solonetz development.

Capillary Movement of Salts in Solonchak.—Briggs and Lapham (18), in their capillarity studies, used soils from James Island, North Carolina, and salts which approximated the composition of those in alkali soils, namely, NaCl, Na_2SO_4, and Na_2CO_3. In the summary, they state that "dissolved

(After Hilgard)

Table 1

Type of salt	EUROPE — Hungarian Plain "Szekso"		ASIA — Aralo-Caspian Plain Saline Crusts		ASIA — Aden		ASIA — India "Reh"			AFRICA — Egypt			
	De-brec-zin	Ka-locsa	(1)	(2)	"Hurka"	"Kara"	Gursikar Aligarh, 6 feet	Jellalabad, Panjah, 1.5 feet	Bayamati (Regur), Deccan, 2 feet	Trona (Commercial) (1)	Trona (Commercial) (2)	L. Abukir Alkali	Fezzan Trona (Com'l)
K₂SO₄	.2	1.6										6.49	0.6
Na₂SO₄	48.1	92.5	18.2	10.4	15.5		15.5	58.5	2.3	38.3	23.6	.82	
Na₂CO₃	51.7	4.4	12.1	14.7	69.0	67.2	56.9	22.9		47.7	28.2	1.13	98.7
NaCl		1.5	69.7	74.6	15.5	32.8	27.6	18.6	97.7	14.0	48.2	89.74	.7
Na₃PO₄													
CaCl₂													
MgCl₂				.3								1.82	
Total	100.0	100.0	100.0	100.0	100.0	100.0	100.0	100.0	100.0	100.0	100.0	100.0	100.0

Table 2

Type of salt	California									Washington			
	Merced Falls	Overhiser, San Joaquin Co.	Visalia	Expt. Station, Tulare	Kern Island	Mojave Plateau	San Bernardino, near Hunts	Santa Ana, near Westminster	Imperial	Yakima Co. on Atahnam Creek	Kittitas Valley	Whitman Co. Lake Creek	Spokane Co. Cottonwood Springs
KCl			20.23	3.95	10.13	0.92	5.31	20.62	1.15	3.90	0.16	4.53	6.27
K₂SO₄	4.67												
K₂CO₃	12.98	13.00			88.42	43.34	66.08	6.59		18.44	15.17	15.90	
Na₂SO₄	75.95	52.22	65.72	25.28	0.42	15.38	15.85	62.22	8.21	75.61	80.36	77.10	87.14
NaNO₃				19.78		39.34							
Na₂CO₃	1.46	33.00	3.98	32.58	0.51				.58	0.52	1.76	1.34	4.03
NaCl	4.94	1.78	8.42	14.75	0.52	1.02	11.47	10.57	31.82	1.53	2.55	1.13	2.56
HNa₂PO₄													
MgSO₄			1.65	2.25			0.59						
CaCl₂				1.41					58.42				
MgCl₂									2.81				
(NH₄)₂CO₃													
Total	100.00	100.00	100.00	100.00	100.00	100.00	100.00	100.00	100.00	100.00	100.00	100.00	100.00

(Continued on page 540)

Table 123—Continued

	Montana – Upper Missouri Valley				Nevada				Wyoming – Sweet Water Valley		Wyoming – Laramie Farm	
	Upper Missouri, Valley, near Centerville	Prickly Pear Plain, Helena	Ford on Sun River	Fort Benton	Robert's Creek, Musselshell Valley	Near Reno	Near Reno	Churchill County	Rock Lake Independence	Saint Mary's Station	Alkali	Waste Irrigation Water
K_2SO_4	2.37	3.07	1.77	8.59	3.07			0.55				
Na_2SO_4	56.54	43.38	83.35	47.10	76.79	80.30	52.15		73.17	88.93	59.29	41.19
$NaNO_3$	9.39											
Na_2CO_3				.71				96.78				
$NaCl$	27.47	14.60	0.91	.18	13.99	15.24	45.37	2.67	22.08	11.63	17.01	2.18
$MgSO_4$	4.23	38.94	13.97	43.42	6.15	4.46	2.48		3.85		23.70	43.82
KCl												12.81
	100.00	100.00	100.00	100.00	100.00	100.00	100.00	100.00	100.00	100.00	100.00	100.00

	Colorado				New Mexico – Pecos Valley – Roswell Region			New Mexico – Carlsbad Region	
	Near Denver	Grand Junction	Rocky Ford	Rocky Ford	Bremond	Michelet	Roswell	Carlsbad	Delaware River
K_2SO_4			0.10	13.74					
Na_2SO_4	93.40	56.05	62.54	17.36	54.61	2.62	67.46	35.16	37.11
Na_2CO_3		18.97	2.08	5.53					
$NaCl$	6.60	24.98	3.86	11.53	51.60	65.16	10.00	26.88	34.31
$MgSO_4$			31.42	44.43	13.79	32.22	22.54	38.06	28.58
$MgCl_2$				5.76					
$Mg_3(PO_4)_2$				1.65					
	100.00	100.00	100.00	100.00	100.00	100.00	100.00	100.00	100.00

salts in general do not increase the capillary rise of soil waters; neutral salts in dilute solution have no influence on the extent of capilary action; concentrated or saturated solutions of all salts materially diminish capillary activity." The increased density in concentrated solutions appears to be responsible for the slowing up of capillary action, even though the increased surface tends the other way. "Sodium carbonate differs from neutral salts, the capillary rise being considerably greater than for neutral solutions of equal concentration. This may be due in part to the saponification of traces of fatty substances on the surface of soil grains."

Kossovich (78) reported just the reverse of what Briggs and Lapham found: neutral salts increased the capillary rise and Na_2CO_3 decreased it. Dimo (30), in his researches on the origin and formation of saline soils, pointed out that a strongly salinized dry solonchak barely permits any capillary rise. Over a period of 30 days the capillary rise was 5 cm. only. Dimo also reported, that "the alkaline earth carbonates possess the greatest capillary mobility, followed by the sulfates, with the NaCl being the slowest." Tulaikov (150) noted that the capillary rise in sand and sandy loams of the salinized type of soil was higher than in the fine-textured soil. One would therefore expect a greater salinization in the coarse-textured soils than in the fine. Gorkova (50) presents a review and theoretical analysis on the capillary rise of salts.

Polynov and Bystrov (104) conducted a series of experiments on the differential behavior of the Cl and SO_4 ions with respect to the amount which diffuses through the soil. They found that Cl rises higher in a column of soil or sand than does SO_4 and the quantity fixed at various heights in the columns is also greater than that of SO_4. Gardner (40) made a study on permeability and capillary movement of moisture as affected by salinity. It deals primarily with the effect of gypsum on physical properties of saline soils.

Summary Statement.—Soluble salts are an inherent feature of the structural or non-structural profile constitution of solonchak. Whatever the mode of formation of any of the subtypes and subdivisions of solonchak (whether in the stage of progressive salinization, salinized, desalinization, or regradation), certain equilibrium conditions must prevail. Percolation and leaching can not remove the salts that have accumulated or are in the process of accumulation. Any factor that might contribute to a shift in equilibrium in the direction of removing the salts will start off a new set of reactions that will usher in the next stage in the evolution of saline soils, the desalinization. These factors may be: 1, a lowering in the level of the ground waters, cutting off the supply of salts; 2, a change in the mineral composition of the ground waters; 3, the establishment of better drainage;

4, increase in precipitation, which involves a change in climate; 5, the effort of men to rid the soil of salts by irrigation.

Taykr Formation and Solonchak

In the region of solonchak formation, especially in the desert and semi-desert, a peculiar saline soil type known as takyr has been described. Walter (Ch. 8, 50) identified takyr with the African *sebcha* which represent lake bottoms with salts crystallizing out. Takyr resembles the playa of the plains and deserts of Texas, New Mexico, and Arizona. Russell (119a) described salt and mud playa of Lake Lahowtan, Nevada, in 1885. They are so hard and caked when dry "as scarcely to receive an impression from a horse's hoof and so sun cracked as to resemble tessellated pavements of cream colored marble." He described the surface of playa having a coating of salt giving the appearance of drifting snow. "The dry surface material is something blown about by the wind or caught by whirlwinds and carried to a great height, forming hollow columns of dust. These columns, often two or three thousand feet high, rising from the plains like pillars of smoke, form a characteristic feature of the desert."

According to Vilenskii, from whose paper the photographs in plate 33 were reproduced, takyr soils "have a smooth, almost polished surface, broken by small cracks into a mosaic-like pattern with light-milky yellowish-colored edges, sometimes showing a raspberry color tinge. Typical takyrs are free from vegetation. A crust 3 to 5 cm. deep covers the surface below which a horizon of loose material, laminated at the bottom, is found. At a depth of 8 to 10 cm. it extends into a cloddy horizon. The latter varies in depth, with an average of 10 to 15 cm." The low soluble salt content in the upper layer and other properties of the takyrs prompted Vilenskii to place them in the solonetz or solonetzic type of soil formation. Located in depressions, the taykrs receive a lot of fine material from the surrounding elevated areas. During the rainy season, water accumulates and, because of the imperviousness of fine material, leaching is not effective enough to produce a typical solonetz, but at the same time it keeps the salts below the surface layer. Thus, the takyr is a transition type between the true solonchak and the solonetz.

Gerasimov (46) investigated the nature of takyrs and, from the data obtained, concluded that they represent a solonchak formation with a solonetzic or even solonetz surface horizon. He pointed out that the rainwater, as it reaches the depressions, is alkaline and, while it washes out some of the salts from the surface, it also saturates it with Na. With the

Fig. 1. *The takyr-like saline soil on the coast of Sivash*
Phot. by Vilenskii

Fig. 2. *The surface of the takyr*
Phot. by Skvortzov

PLATE 33

Surface appearance of takyr-like soils
(After Vilenskii)

advent of the dry period, the salts rise and salinize the solonetz-like surface horizon, imparting to it the properties of the so called regraded solonchak.

Sushko (144) contributed a number of analyses on the composition of takyrs which he placed in the solonchak-solonetz type of saline soils. According to him, takyrs are of recent origin and are usually associated with the chloride, chloride-sulfate solonchak.

Uspanov (153) points out that in the language of the natives of Central Asia and Kazakhstan takyr means a naked, hard, and smooth surface. In everyday language, the term is used for a number of concepts, thus *takyr-bas* means a baldheaded; *takyr-kedei*—a pauper.

In appearance, takyr is a naked, hard, smooth, irregular system of polygons, with superficial cracks. Travelers claim that no horseshoe or iron rim of wheels leave an impression on takyr surface. In the spring, after thawing and melting of snow or after rain, water stands on the surface for weeks. In some of the water holes used by the Kirgiz tribes, it has been observed that 2-3 inches below the bottom of the water the soil is dry. The natives call these holes *rainwater lakes.*"

Bolyshev and Evodkimova (15) made a study of the crusts in takyr. When dry, the crusts are from 0.2 to 0.8 cm. thick, and some investigators give the thickness as much as 2-3 cm. When broken, the edges show a rough surface on which thin hairs are noted, resembling dry rootlets. Upon wetting, the crusts swell to 1-2 cm. thick, become highly elastic, and take on a specific plush-like sheen. Upon drying, the edges roll up giving the appearance of tubules. After rains, the surface of takyrs becomes very slippery and the soil mass very sticky.

A microscopic examination of the crusts, when wet, disclosed that the thread-like rootlets were nothing more than webs of blue-green algae of the species *Phormidium* and *Lyngbiya,* family *Oscillatoriaceae.* Analyses of these crusts show that it has 2.47 per cent organic matter, 2.4 per cent N, and pH 7.4. Some of the N is in the form of nitrates.

It is obvious that the case described by Bolyshev and Evodkimova is a takyr solonchak. Chemical data on a water extract of this takyr show from 18.6 to 60.8 milliequivalents of Cl and 62.6 and 36.5 milliequivalents SO_4 per 100 grams of salt. Analyses of other takyrs presented by these investigators and others show the presence of soluble carbonates, an indication of desalinization. It is thus clear that takyrs may exist in all the stages of salinization and desalinization.

PLATE 34
Columnar solonetz
(After Kassatkin and Krasyuk)

SOLONETZ

Exchange of Cations in Solonchak.—The pattern of exchangeable cations in the soil profile is shaped in the course of salinization and solonchak formation. The replacement of bases in the exchange complex takes place concurrently with the salinization of the profile. If the solonchak is of the Na-chloride type, the exchange complex gradually gives up the Ca, K, and Mg and becomes predominantly saturated with Na, even in the presence of $CaCO_3$. The Ca, Mg, and K in solution together with the Na salts rise to the surface and accumulate there. As the salts move downward, a mixed solonetz would form, with Na leading. In the presence of sulfates, the slightly soluble $CaSO_4.2H_2O$ (gypsum) may accumulate. However, the gypsum would provide a source of Ca to prevent the formation of a solonetz with a high Na content. Seldom is there a 100 per cent Na saturated solonchak, unless there is no other salt than NaCl.

Whenever the salts in solonchak consist of K, Na, Ca, and Mg chlorides, bicarbonates, and sulfates, a series of complications arise. Chances are that the divalent ions may compete successfully with the monovalent Na and K ions for positions in the exchange complex. In case of an abundance of Mg salts, the exchange complex may be saturated predominantly with Mg. One can surmise a series of salt combinations whereby the exchange capacity of the respective solonchak types may be satisfied with a number of bases in varying proportions. An important element in these possibilities is the preferential absorption by different mineral and organic complexes capable of exchange for specific cations, as shown by Schachtschabel (124). For a discussion of this interesting problem, the reader is referred to the paper by Joffe and Zimmerman (66).

Hissink (60) made use of base exchange reactions in elucidating the nature of saline soils. His researches corroborate the findings of Gedroiz.

Solonetz Formation.—When the removal of soluble salts (desalinization) from the solonchak begins, the cations that prevailed at the time in the exchange complex suffer no change. After the complete removal of the soluble salts, hydrolysis sets in, and in combination with the acids produced in the process of humification a replacement of some bases with hydrogen ions begins. Before reaching this point, the soil is technically speaking a *solonetz,* with the bases in the complex intact. Since Na salts are usually present in solonchak, and the complex therefore contains some absorbed Na ions, solonetz has been associated with a sodium saturated soil which, when freed of soluble salts, at least from the A horizon, attains specific morphological, chemical, and physical features and properties. A Ca saturated solonchak, even after the complete removal of the soluble salts, will not show the properties of a solonetz. It has been reported that a Mg saturated soil does attain properties similar to a Na solonchak freed of its soluble salts. Theoretically we can, therefore, speak of a Mg solonetz. According to Prasolov and Antipov-Karataev (106-107), Ivanova (62), and Pankov and Shavrygin (102), the Mg content in some solonetz is as high as 40 to 67 per cent of the exchange capacity. Antipov-Karatev, in his many learned discussions on the colloidal properties of soils, discusses the Mg problem in relation to solonetz. He concludes that, in combination with Na in the exchange complex, Mg acts additively towards solonetzization. In one of his latest papers, Antipov-Karataev, in collaboration with Sedletskii (7), does not attribute much solonetzic effect to the Mg ion. There is room for clarification of this problem. By itself, the Mg ion does not bring about solonetzic properties, according to Sushko (144). In the work of Joffe and Zimmerman (66), the complementary activity of Mg in the presence of Na is brought out.

With the complex saturated with sodium, a series of reactions takes place soon after the excess of soluble salt has been washed down deep into the profile or into the C horizon. If the alkaline earth carbonates are present, as is usually the case, an exchange takes place between the weakly ionized $CaCO_3$ and the Na-saturated complex, according to the following equation:

$$2 \text{ Na-sat. complex} + CaCo_3 = \text{Ca-sat. complex} + Na_2CO_3.$$

In the presence of $Ca(HCO_3)_2$, the $NaHCO_3$ forms. This type of reaction is possible only after the excess of soluble Na salts has been washed out; otherwise, the preponderance of a large number of Na ions in solution prevents the entrance of the Ca ions into the complex. After a certain concentration of Na_2CO_3 has been reached, no further exchange will take place, since there will be an exchange between the Na from the Na_2CO_3 and the Na in the complex. Only upon the removal of the reaction product—Na_2CO_3—will there again be an exchange.

The classical explanation of Hilgard on the formation of black alkali soils was that the alkali salts reacted with the $CaCo_3$; $2NaCl + CaCO_3 = CaCl_2 + Na_2CO_3$. In the light of the theories of Gedroiz, it is the Na from the exchange complex that reacts with water giving rise to NaOH. It, in turn, reacts with the CO_2 of the soil air and forms Na_2CO_3. In the absence of free $CaCO_3$, a rather unusual case in saline soils, the exchangeable Ca may form $CaCO_3$.

$$\text{Ca-complex} + Na_2CO_3 \rightarrow \text{Na-complex} + CaCO_3$$

To prove his theories (proclaimed in 1912), Gedroiz conducted a series of ingenious experiments that are classical in the literature of soil chemistry. Only a few of these may be cited here.

Gedroiz (44) treated 10 gm. portions of a chernozem soil with 80 cc. of Na_2CO_3 solution of various concentrations. The data in table 124 show that the Na has rapidly been fixed by the soil, i.e., it has entered the exchange complex. In the interpretation of Gedroiz, "not until the soil has been saturated with Na and not until all the Ca in the complex has been replaced will the soda (which can form by the interaction of Na as it is released from the exchange complex) interact to form $CaCO_3$. After the

Table 124

Absorption of sodium by a chernozem soil
(After Gedroiz)

Concentration of Na_2CO_3 added	Concentration of Na_2CO_3 found after mixing with soil	Na absorbed by soil:	
		In terms of per cent of weight of soil	In terms of per cent of Na_2CO_3 absorbed
normality	*normality*	*per cent*	*per cent*
0.10	0.056	0.82	44
0.08	0.040	0.66	50
0.06	0.029	0.57	52
0.04	0.020	0.37	50
0.02	0.009	0.20	55
0.01	0.004	0.11	60

soil has been saturated with Na, a natural exchange takes place between the Ca of the $CaCO_3$ and the sorbed Na, and not between the sorbed Na and the Na of the Na-salts. In the former case, one of the reaction products is a combination of very difficulty soluble compounds—the absorbing complex containing absorbed Na. In the latter case, both reaction products are soluble compounds."

In further support of his theory on the formation of Na_2CO_3 in saline soils, Gedroiz presented direct proof by comparing the effects of water on a non-salinized and salinized soil.

In the chernozem soil, water decomposes the aluminum silicate and humate complexes. A decrease in the quantity of water per unit weight of soil (chernozem) increases the concentration of substances extracted, but the total quantity extracted from one and the same quantity of soil decreases. Neither the increase per gram of soil nor the total quantity extracted is proportional to the change in quantity of water used, as may be judged from the data in table 125. These results show that the action of the water on the soil consists in decomposing the soil constituents and, if any other reactions take place, like solubility of soluble and insoluble salts, their effects, in comparison with the decomposition power of water, are secondary in scope.

In the case of the saline soil rich in soluble salts, the effect of solubility is greater than decomposition. With a decrease in the quantity of water taken per unit of soil, the concentration of the extract is inversely proportional to the quantity of water. The quantity of substances extracted per unit weight of soil (for 100 gm.) remains almost unchanged.

Table 125
Effect of various quantities of H_2O on soils
(After Gedroiz)

| Soil water ratio | Unsalinized chernozem soil | | Sodium-calcium solonchak | |
| | Total mineral substances extracted from soil by water, in gm. | | Total quantity of water— soluble mineral salts extracted from soil, in g.... | |
	per 100 cc. of extract	per 100 gm. of soil	per 100 cc. of extract	per 100 gm. of soil
1 :20	0.0020	0.0400	0.185	3.699
1 :10	0.0037	0.0370	0.370	3.697
1 :8	0.0043	0.0344	0.463	3.700
1 :6	0.0049	0.0294	0.613	3.679
1 :5	0.0056	0.0280	0.737	3.685
1 :4	0.0067	0.0268	0.918	3.670
1 :3	0.0080	0.0240	1.234	3.702
1 :2	0.0106	0.0204	1.846	3.692
1 :1	0.0189	0.0189	3.701	3.701

If the solubility of the difficultly soluble salts is the prevailing reaction, the results obtained by extracting such a soil with water are as given in Section A of table 126. The data show that this soil behaves in a manner opposite to that of the soil containing a high concentration of soluble salts. The concentration of substances in the extract remains constant at the various ratios of soil to water, but the quantity of substances extracted per unit weight of soil is directly proportional to the quantity of water taken.

Now let us examine how the alkalinity changes in a water extract of solonetz with the change in the soil-water ratio. The soil used was a carbonate solonetz free from soluble sulfates and chlorides. The results are presented in Section B of table 126. The data show that the effect of water on solonetz differs from its effect on soils containing either soluble or insoluble salts. It approaches the decomposition effect on non-saline soils. The quantities of Na extracted from the soil, such as soda and Na-humates (H_2O extract), increase with the increase of the water ratio per unit of soil, but the concentration of these compounds in water decreases and neither the quantitive nor the concentration factor is directly proportional to the quantity of water.

Thus, the studies on the effect of water on solonetz show that in the absence of the chlorides and sulfates such soils have no available supply of soda. It is being formed in the process of the interaction of water and soil as a result of the exchange between the cations of Ca and H found in the soil solution. If the soda in a solonetzic soil containing chlorides and sulfates of Na had formed by the interaction of the bases with the $CaCO_3$, then the highest concentration of the soda should be found in the first water extract and diminish with every succeeding extract. But this is not the case. Thus, all the accumulated evidence opposes the theory of the formation of soda in solonetz soils by the interaction of $CaCO_3$ and the soluble salts of Na.

Table 126

Effect of various quantities of water

(After Gedroiz)

	A On a soil containing difficultly soluble salts (9.8 per cent $CaSO_4$)		B On solonetz	
Soil water ratio	Total quantity of water soluble mineral constituents extracted with water, in gm.		Alkalinity from carbonates and humates of Na expressed in gm. of Na_2CO_3	
	per 100 cc of extract	per 100 gm. of soil	per 100 cc. of extract	per 100 gms. of soil
I : 20	0.193	3.804	0.039	0.780
I : 10	0.193	1.931	0.049	0.490
I : 8	0.188	1.504	0.054	0.432
I : 6	0.193	1.159	0.061	0.366
I : 5	0.191	0.955	0.065	0.325
I : 4	0.189	0.756	0.070	0.280
I : 3	0.190	0.570	0.077	0.231
I : 2	0.193	0.386	0.083	0.166
I : 1	0.191	0.192	0.099	0.099

To summarize, the reaction involved in the formation of soda in saline soils containing $CaCO_3$ is between the Na ion of the complex and the residual carbonate from the slightly ionized $CaCO_3$ and from the more highly ionized $Ca(HCO_3)_2$ (the presence of the latter depends on the CO_2 content in the soil air), in the absence of the soluble alkali salts.

Because of the saturation of the complex with Na and the presence of free Na_2CO_3, the solonetz becomes highly dispersed, and the fine particles move to the B horizon to be cemented, forming the typical columnar features.

In saline soils without the carbonates of Ca and Mg, the formation of soda takes place by the interchange of the H ions, dissociated from H_2O, with the Na in the complex. Under such conditions, the Na_2CO_3 content is low, the complex is somewhat unsaturated, and yet a soil water extract indicates a high alkalinity.

An interesting contribution on the effects of ameliorative irrigation measures on salinized soils has been made by Rozov (118, 119). He shows that by irrigation practices it is possible to produce all the morphological features of a solonetz profile without having the complex fully saturated with Na. There is even the possibility of a typical solonetzic B horizon (morphologically), with Ca or Mg in the exchange complex and without any Na. Such a condition may come about through a secondary salinization of the B horizon which might or might not have been partially saturated with Na. If the solution, in the process of secondary salinization, contained Ca or Mg, it is easy to comprehend how the B horizon would rid itself of the Na and take in the Ca or Mg.

From studies made on California alkali soils at the New Jersey laboratories by Joffe and McLean (65), it appears that at least some of them are not purely Na-soils. Apparently, some of the solonetz has developed either from Ca or Mg solonchak or a secondary salinization process was effective.

An interesting sidelight on the properties of saline soils has been presented by Rozmakhov (117). He claims that with the change of salt content, in the course of salinization and desalinization, a change takes place in the microrelief, drainage, and volume of the soil. It is very probable that the phenomenon noted by Rozmakhov is associated with the vesicular structure of the surface horizon in this type of soil. This structure is due to the interstices produced by the crystallization of the salts. The shape and size of the crystal systems prevailing in the soils is not always the same. Besides, the soluble salts vary in quantity from season to season. These circumstances will bring about a change in volume. In this connection, the observation of Nikiforoff (Ch. 8, 18, p. 39) on the gray soils in California may be of interest.

Morphology of Solonetz.—Four groups of normal solonetz have been recognized by Vilenskii (154): (a) chloride-sulfate lumpy-prismatic and prismatic solonetz, associated with the brown zone; (b) chloride-sulfate columnar, associated with the chestnut zone; (c) soda columnar, in the chernozem zone; and (d) nutty, in the forest steppe transition zone. All of these succeed one another with a definite regularity as the climatic conditions change from arid steppe to the forest steppe. All four groups have, as described by Vilenskii,

clear cut horizon differentiation. The depth of the A horizon varies from 0 to 30 cm. and more. Usually it is stratified, with a laminated structure, very porous, even alveolar. The individual platelets are darker on the lower than on the upper surface. In the prismatic solonetz, the predominating color of A is gray or yellowish gray. In the columnar solonetz, the A horizon has been divided into three subhorizons: A_1, A_2, and A_3. The last two are always light grayish or light color, compacted, and when crushed give floury powder which resembles the coating on the material of the B horizon in a podzol. The color of A is gray or dark gray in this group and black in the soda columnar group. •

As for the B horizon, it is uniform throughout in the prismatic solonetz, the material breaking into prisms, 10-15 cm. high and 3-6 cm. wide, with flat surfaces. These prisms are compact and sharply separated from the overlying A and underlying C horizons, the latter usually being cemented with $CaCO_3$ and at some point containing soluble salts.

In the chloride-sulfate columnar solonetz, the B horizon is subdivided into B_1 and B_2. In B_1, the columnar units have flat surfaces at the bottom and rounded at the top. They are from 8 to 13 cm. high and 4 to 5 cm. in thickness, brown or chestnut brown in color, with shiny lacquer-like coated surfaces. The columns are separated by vertical cracks, usually filled with powdery material from A_2, and the transition between A and B is very sharp. When crushed, the material from B, especially B_2, breaks into grain or nut-like units, with the lacquer coating on the outside and a dull lighter color inside. B_2 merges with C gradually, the latter not differing much from that of the prismatic solonetz.

In the soda columnar solonetz, the B horizon is subdivided into B_1, B_2, and B_3 subhorizons. B_1 consists of columns 10-15 cm. in height and width, black in color with shiny surfaces, flat on bottom and rounded on top. B_2, 10 to 15 cm. deep, falls apart when crushed into nut-like units, black in color. B_3 is transitional with respect to C, spotted brown in color, the lumpy angular structure units being permeated with veins of $CaCO_3$ which is more expressed in the C horizon in the form of spots and concretions.

In the nut-like group of solonetz, the A horizon is dark in color, with a more or less clearly expressed grayish tinge. B_1 is 20-25 cm. deep, of crumbly nutty structure, black in color, with shiny surfaces of a dark grayish tinge. In the lower part of this horizon, the material when crushed falls apart into small nuts, yellowish brown in color.

In table 127, the depths of the horizons of the four respective groups of the normal solonetz are clearly brought out.

Table 127

Horizon depths (cm.) in various types of solonetz
(After Vilenskii)

Type of solonetz	A	B_1	B_2	B_3	B_4	A + B	B
Prismatic	5	15				20	15
Columnar chloride-sulfate	10	13	13			36	26
Columnar soda	7	15	18	25		65	58
Nutty	32	9	10	37	42	130	98

Kelley and Brown (73-76) investigated the base exchange properties of a number of alkali soils and discovered that some of these soils contain considerable amounts of replaceable Ca. They state, "A considerable portion of the alkali areas of California is probably of this nature." This study, as well as others that followed, considered primarily the relation of the saturation of alkali soils with various cations to their effect on plant growth. A number of interesting points, from the standpoint of amelioration and crop production, have been established.

From the data presented by Kelley and Arany (72), tables 128, 129, even though reported on soils sampled at arbitrary one-foot depths, one might get some idea of the nature of the saline soils in the Fresno region, California.

The figures in table 128 show that the Fresno soils are highly saturated with Na, the saturation decreasing with depth. The K content is generally small, but it follows the tendencies of the Na. The reverse is true for the position of the divalent Ca and Mg; their content increases with depth. Such a condition indicates that the soil has been salinized, with tendencies to desalinization, i.e., towards solonetz formation. The figures in table 129 on the soluble salt content of these soils substantiate the deductions made on the basis of the base saturation data. It is to be noted that, notwithstanding the irrigation to which these soils have been subjected, the salt content in the first foot is fairly high.

On the other hand, the high CO_2 content indicates solonetz formation. Whether the shift in salt content and base saturation is a result of irrigation or of natural conditions cannot be inferred from the data on hand. At any rate, the soils under consideration are to be looked upon as solonchak-solonetz which are undergoing the process of desalinization. The relatively high Ca content in the base-exchange complex and the decreased Na content in the lower horizons may serve as evidence of this. It also indicates that these soils, in their solonchak stage, probably contained some soluble Ca salts.

In a series of publications from the Arizona station, the problem of saline soils has been treated from the agronomic point of view, with special reference to the chemical composition of the soils and methods of study. No particular attention has been given to the relation of the soil-forming processes of saline soils and their composition. The base-exchange complex (so-called "zeolites") was investigated and a number of important facts established. Most of the soils studied belong to the so-called "black alkali." Reviewing some of the Arizona studies, Gedroiz (44) designates these soils as solonetz-solonchak.

An interesting point on the part played by Mg in saline soils was brought out by Breazeale (16), who shows that $MgCO_3$ does enter rapidly into base replacement reactions. This would indicate that in the presence

Table 128

Exchangeable bases (m.e. per 100 gm.) in saline soils of Fresno, California
(After Kelley and Arany).

Plot No.	Depth in inches	K	Na	Ca + Mg	Na, per cent of total	Plot No.	K	Na	Ca + Mg	Na, per cent of total
4	0 - 12	0	3.70	1.10	75	10	0.28	2.69	2.60	48
	12 - 24	0	3.42	1.52	69		0.12	3.07	2.40	55
	24 - 36	0	2.39	2.53	49		0.04	2.81	3.20	46
	36 - 48	0	2.01	3.22	38		0.07	2.50	3.38	42
11	0 - 12	0.49	3.44	1.12	68	17	0.46	3.14	1.38	63
	12 - 24	0.05	3.24	2.10	60		0.21	2.64	2.35	51
	24 - 36	0	1.71	4.38	28		0.10	2.12	2.99	41
	36 - 48	0	1.18	5.18	19		0	2.29	2.81	45
19	0 - 12	0.36	3.31	2.07	58	45	0.30	3.09	2.54	52
	12 - 24	0.09	2.85	2.93	49		0.12	2.84	3.10	47
	24 - 36	0.08	2.72	3.39	44		0.0	2.05	4.65	31
	36 - 48	0.10	2.82	3.78	42		0.03	2.16	4.34	33

Solonetz from Ergeni plateau (U.S.S.R.)

Horizon	Depth in cm	Ca	Mg	Na	K	Na, per cent of total
A₁	0 - 5	8.46	5.40	1.93	0.77	11.6
B₁	7 - 15	2.06	20.1	6.77	0.70	22.6

Compiled by Renezev: Solonetz, N. Caucasia (U.S.S.R.)

Horizon	Depth in cm	Ca	Mg	Na		Na, per cent of total
A₁	12 - 16	7.5	4.2	3.3		22
B₁	16 - 23	14.4	16.3	7.3		19

Solonetz on chernozem (After Remezev).

Horizon	Depth in cm	Ca	Mg	Na	Na, per cent of total
A₁	0 - 5	27.0	20.27	3.79	7.4
A₂	5 - 10	22.75	16.72	4.33	9.9
B₁	10 - 24	10.55	32.03	12.51	22.7
B₂	24 - 27	13.85	39.82	15.54	22.5

Chernozem Solonetz in Canada (After Riecken)

Horizon	Depth in inches	Ca	Mg	Na + K	Ratio of exch. Ca:Mg
A₁	1 - 4	22.2	8.9	3.4	2.5
A₂	5 - 8	7.8	5.4	1.5	1.4
B₁	11 - 16	15.2	23.4	1.8	0.2

Table 129

Water-soluble constituents (m.e. per 100 gm.) in saline soils of Fresno, California
(After Kelley and Arany)

Depth in inches	Plot 4					Plot 10				
	Ca	Mg	K	Na	CO₂	Ca	Mg	K	Na	CO₂
0 - 12	tr	tr	0	3.01	1.04	tr	tr	0.02	5.24	1.14
12 - 24	tr	tr	0	2.61	0.71	tr	tr	0	3.30	0.54
24 - 36	tr	tr	0	2.10	0.66	0	0	0	2.72	0.66
36 - 48	tr	tr	0	1.77	0.56	0	0	0	2.26	0.60

Depth in inches	Plot 11					Plot 17				
	Ca	Mg	K	Na	CO₂	Ca	Mg	K	Na	CO₂
0 - 12	tr	tr	0.05	3.90	1.19	tr	tr	0	4.49	1.38
12 - 24	tr	tr	0	3.14	0.89	0	0	0	2.29	0.50
24 - 36	tr	tr	0	2.67	0.71	0	0	0	1.80	0.30
36 - 48	tr	tr	0	1.92	0.40	0	0	0	1.27	0.11

Depth in inches	Plot 19					Plot 45				
	Ca	Mg	K	Na	CO₂	Ca	Mg	K	Na	CO₂
0 - 12	tr	tr	0.07	4.73	1.15	tr	tr	0.03	3.70	0.58
12 - 24	tr	tr	0.03	2.53	0.50	tr	tr	0	2.03	0.29
24 - 36	tr	tr	0	2.04	0.23	tr	tr	0	1.44	0.10
36 - 48	tr	tr	0	2.19	0.03	tr	tr	0	1.35	0.03

of this carbonate, the problem of replacing the Na in solonetz is somewhat different from that when $CaCO_3$ is present. The latter does not react so prominently in the exchange reactions.

The work of Nikiforoff (94) on the saline soils of the Red River Valley in Minnesota are of interest. His studies bring out clearly the climatogenically subdued character of the saline soils in the United States, and, as pointed out in the discussion on "Prairie Soils," they throw some light on the zonal characteristics of the prairie soils.

The normal soils within the region of the Red River Valley in Minnesota are represented by two soil series, the Fargo and the Bearden, which have a number of morphological and chemical characteristics of the chernozem type of soil formation. The solonchak within the zonal soils is developed in the depressions where the effects on the rising water table make themselves evident in the form of salt accumulation in the A horizon. It is primarily encountered in the Bearden series. In the Fargo series, Nikiforoff found typical solonetz. The following description is given by Nikiforoff:

The typical mature solonetz has been observed at several points in the Red River Valley, chiefly in Wilkin County. This soil does not cover any considerable area but is scattered in small spots throughout the body of alkaline or even normal Fargo. The A horizon of our solonetz is divided into two sub-horizons: A, from 2 to 6 inches thick, light gray to ashy or even almost white in color, finely laminated (foliated) with a typical difference in color of the upper light and lower dark faces of its plates. There is a very sharp change from it to the B horizon.

The B horizon, from 5 to 15 inches thick, black, extremely compact, sticky when wet and hard after drying, has a well developed columnar structure. The columns vary from less than an inch to more than two inches in their horizontal diameter and on the average are from 3 to 5 inches in height. They always occupy the upper portions of the horizon, the lower part of which is broken into more irregular lumps. The columns, as a rule, have sharp edges, often being more or less prismatic in form and have markedly polished faces. Two forms of their tops have been observed, flat (so-called prismatic solonetz) and well rounded (the columnar solonetz).

All three horizons, A_1, A_2, and B, are typically free from any incrustations of salts and do not show even the slightest effervescence, but beneath the B horizon both concretions of carbonates and aggregates (nests) of sulfate crystals are very common, and the proportion of these salts is often very high.

A description of a solonetz in the zonal semidesert and desert type (gray and red) of soil formation in southern Arizona, the Tubac series, is given by Lapham (87):

0-5″—Dark dull reddish brown to light reddish-brown sandy loam of somewhat coarse gritty texture, containing some fine gravel, friable, slightly granular. Barren areas between desert shrubs and other plants are frequently covered with well developed desert pavement of water-worn pebbles with some larger stones. The pebbles are covered on sides and upper surfaces with a characteristic desert varnish of bluish-black vitreous highly burnished appearance. This horizon is leached of lime and is mildly acid.

5-12″—Dark dull red to deep red or maroon colored heavy tight plastic clay of typical solonetz structure. Columnar, the columns 1 to 3.5 inches in diameter, breaking straight across, rounded on top. The columnar fragments are much coated with dark colored colloidal staining and there is a light sprinkling of leached gray siliceous material in cracks and on surfaces of the soil aggregates. This horizon underlies the surface soil very abruptly, and is noncalcareous.

12-20″—Rich brown to light brown clay or heavy clay loam, columns are less well developed than in horizon above; colloidal glazing is less pronounced and the material is less tight and impervious and is mildly calcareous and slightly mottled with lime in the lower part.

20-36″—Light grayish-brown loam or light clay loam, slightly columnar, columns irregular, fragile and breaking into rather soft clods, much mottled with accumulated lime.

36-44″—Similar to horizon above, but of higher lime accumulation, compact and softly cemented, vesicular structure.

44-72″—Light gray, gravelly loam, highly calcareous and with lenses and layers of gravelly material firmly cemented by lime carbonate.

Lapham raises the question of the origin of this solonetz. This soil "occupies the most elevated, steepest and most rapidly drained slopes of desert valleys," and because of this it is difficult to reconcile the fact that this soil has even been subjected to imperfect drainage as demanded by the theory of the origin of solonetz from solonchak. Lapham is therefore inclined to believe that the Tubac solonetz has perhaps developed "by long continued processes of weathering without intervention of the high water table or of excessive moisture." Lapham, however, is not justified in looking upon the steepness of slope as a negative factor in the process of rising of salts by capillary action. We know, from studies of orogenic soils, that on the slopes they receive much drainage from the higher elevations, and the dissolved salts do rise by capillary action to the surface horizon. On this basis only, the phenomenon of a high zone of lime accumulation at comparatively shallow depth in mountain chernozem has been explained.

An interesting characteristic of the Tubac solonetz is its low pH (6.85) in the upper layer, with a constant rise in pH with depth. Lapham justly remarks that the scant desert vegetation does not bring into circulation enough bases to counterbalance the loss by eluviation, small as it is.

In describing solonetz-like soils in Southern California, Nikiforoff (95) notes that the principal physical character of solonetz is its B horizon, varying in thickness from 5 inches to 2 feet. It has an exceedingly dense (compact) consistency, impervious, sticky when wet, and almost stonelike (in laymen's nomenclature) when dry. The color is always darker than of any horizon, varying from black to brown, drab-gray, or olive gray. It is usually of heavier texture, of coarse angular and firm clods which, in the top section, appear as rough angular prisms whose vertical axis is 2 to 4 times that of the horizontal. Usually, the top is rounded biscuit-like. Frequently this structure is obscured, or disappears for a while, to appear again.

Chemical Properties of Solonetz.—Vilenskii points out:

. . . in horizons A and B₁ there are no appreciable quantities of soluble salts. At any rate, they do not exceed double the quantity of salts found in the neighboring non-salinized soils. More than half of the soluble salts is not mineral but organic in nature. An appreciable salt content is usually noted in B_2, increasing with depth. And what is more significant, the variations in the chemical composition of the salts are determined by the physico-geographic position of the respective soils.

In the prismatic type of solonetz, the accumulation of salts begins in C where $CaCO_3$, $MgCO_3$, $CaSO_4$, $MgSO_4$, K_2SO_4, Na_2SO_4, and NaCl are found. In the chloride-sulfate columnar type of solonetz, the accumulation of salts begins in B_2, and they are of the same character as those in the prismatic group, but occur in somewhat smaller quantities. In the soda columnar solonetz, B_2 contains Na_2CO_3 and $NaHCO_3$; B_3 contains Na_2CO_3, $NaHCO_3$, $CaCO_3$, and $MgCO_3$; and C contains $CaCO_3$, $MgCO_3$, $CaSO_4$, Na_2SO_4, and K_2SO_4. In the nutty group, B_1 contains organic salts of the alkali and deeper down, also Na_2CO_3, $NaHCO_3$, and appreciable quantities of $CaCO_3$ and $MgCO_3$.

The relative proportions of the various H_2O-soluble salts in the fundamental types of the normal series of solonetz are presented in table 130.

Table 130

The composition of water extracts in the various types of normal solonetz
(After Vilenskii)

Type of solonetz		Mineral sub-stances	Total alka-linity	Na_2CO_3	Cl	SO_3	CaO
		per cent	*per cent*	*per cent*	*per cent*	*per cent*	*per cent*
Prismatic	A	0.0625	0.0250	None	0.0024	0.0054	?
	B	0.0599	0.0505	None	0.0023	0.0060	?
	C	1.4268	0.0368	None	0.0736	0.6946	?
Columnar chloride sulfate	A	0.026	0.018	None	Traces	None	None
	B_1	0.064	0.053	None	Traces	None	None
	B_2	0.216	0.123	0.030	0.054	0.042	0.012
	C	0.472	0.041	Traces	0.045	0.226	0.049
Columnar soda	A	0.026	?	None	None	None	Traces
	B_1	0.090	?	None	None	None	Traces
	B_2	0.111	?	0.060	None	None	0.005
	B_3	0.120	?	0.096	None	None	0.005
	C	0.100	?	0.081	None	None	0.005
Nutty	A	0.046	0.014	None	None	Traces	Traces
	B_1	0.064	0.005	None	None	Traces	Traces
	B_2	0.035	0.003	None	None	Traces	Traces
	B_3	0.043	0.006	None	None	Traces	Traces
	C	0.100	0.063	None	None	Traces	Traces

Odynsky (96) reports gypsum in the lower C of a solonetz in Alberta, Canada. The pH of A varies from mildly alkaline in the brown soil zone to mildly acid in the black soil (chernozem) zone (the latter is probably in some state of solodization: J.). With depth, alkalinity (pH) increases (again pointing to solodization: J.). B_1 - 7.6, B_2 - 8.0, and C - 8.2.

Antipov-Karataev and Sedletskii (7) ascribe the compaction of the B horizon in solonetz first to peptization—breakdown of soil aggregated to the state of primary particles; this is followed by partial dispersion—

fractionation of primary particles; and in the most advanced stages of solonetz development, the solution stage enters as a factor. Dispersion is impeded by electrolytes which cause a low osmotic pressure in the collodial mycelles, as shown by Mattson (91).

Antipov-Karataev (6) gives the mineralogic composition of a number of solonetz profiles and discusses the formation of hardpan and claypan in solonetz profiles. In table 14, Sedletskii enumerates the minerals associatel with saline soils.

Kovda (81, p. 90) reports Li in the ground waters, soils, and ash of plants associated with solonchak and solonetz of the Caspian basin. Of course, Li will cause a greater dispersion than any of the monovalent cations. The work of Sharov (126) is of interest in this connection. He shows that Li-bentonite takes up 1175.6 per cent H_2O; Na - 1054.2; K - 223.4; Mg - 111.9; Ca - 99.4; and H - 113.6.

Aleksandrova (3) reports that 59-64 per cent of the total organic matter in solonchak is humin. In the surface layer of solonchak, there is 15-16 per cent humic acid and 16-21 per cent fulvic acid. The lower part of the solonchak profile contains very little organic matter. As the solonchak is desalinized, the solonetz begins to lose organic matter. In a columnar solonetz, there was 13.2 per cent of humic acid with an increase in fulvic acid. The C:N ratio in the humic acid of solonetz varied from 12 to 17. Its exchange capacity (calculated on ash free humic acid) at pH 8.0 varied from 441 to 524 milliequivalent per 100 grams.

As to the quantity of Na encountered in solonetz, the data by Arany and Kelley (table 128) show a minimum of 19 and a maximum of 75 per cent of the exchangeable cations, depending on the position in the profile. The data compiled by Remezov (109), as given in table 128, show no such high percentages of Na. In the extensive data presented by Kovda (81), the fully developed solonetz has a maximum of 30 per cent Na.

Ivanov (62), Prasolov and Antipov-Karataev (107), and Pankov and Shavrygin (102) show that solonetz properties begin at 5-10 per cent Na in the exchange complex. At 15-20 per cent we have typical solonetz.

Antipov-Karataev and Sedletskii (7) differentiate four degrees of solonetzicity based on the Na content in the exchange complex: 1, with less than 5 per cent of the exchange capacity the soil is not of the solonetz type; 2, from 5 to 10 per cent of the exchange capacity the soil is weakly solonetzic; 3, from 10 to 20 per cent—solonetzic; 4, more than 20 per cent—solonetz. With the same quantity of replaceable Na, *the solonetz properties are more pronounced in the less arid regions than in the more arid regions.* The desiccation effects in the arid regions mitigate considerably the dispersion of the colloids.

A number of interesting papers on solonetz soils of Canada and the United States, in different stages of desalinization and in some cases secondary salinization, have been presented by Ellis and Caldwell (39), Mitchell and Riecken (93a), Mitchell (93), MacGregor and Wyatt (89), Rost (113), Kelley (69-71), Shaw and Kelley (127), and Bentley and Rost (10).

Bentley and Rost (10) have tried to explain the high Mg content in the horizon by the precipitation of this element made mobile by the process of solodization. An analysis of their data seems to show that the high water soluble Mg is perhaps an indication of a secondary salinization. Riecken (110) reviews the literature (mostly English) on the source and origin of Mg in solonetz and does not arrive at any definite conclusion.

Solonetzic Subtype.—Besides the normal type of solonetz, there are some solonetzic subtypes. Their characteristic features are given by Vilenskii (p. 13) as follows:

> They differ markedly from the neighboring normal soils by the compactness of the B horizon. It is usually dissected by vertical cracks, giving rise to columnar-like and cloddy units not well formed, but sharply differentiated from the A horizon. The latter is lighter in color especially in the lower part, in contact with B, where a powdery coating is found. In these soils, the horizon of effervescence and of accumulation of soluble salts in the profile is closer to the surface than in the surrounding soils. Usually, they accompany the solonetz soils found in the depressions, edging them off or distributing themselves among them on the more elevated areas. They might be looked upon as transitional between the solonetz and the phytogenic soils.

The solonetz-like soils of Southern California, described by Nikiforoff (95), are of the solonetzic subtype.

For a clear exposition of the different subtypes of solonetz, the work of Kovda illustrated with extensive data, graphs, and discussions should be consulted. The monograph on the saline soils of Siberia by Orlovskii (98) is a valuable addition to the subject. Together with Vilenskii's (154) monograph on saline soils, these treatises are the standard reference handbooks on the subject.

Summary Statement.—The specific properties of solonetz and solonetzic soils make their appearance with the desalinization of solonchak. In the order of their removal from the profile, the chlorides and nitrates come first, followed by the sulfates and carbonates (as bicarbonates). In one and the same area, one may find the different stages of solonetzicity of the profile, depending on the physiography of the landscape and the source of supply of salts, related to level of the ground waters and their composition.

As the electrolytes are removed, the soil colloids become peptized, the degree of peptization depending on the type of cations and their quantitative relationship in the exchange complex. In general, the cation effect on dispersion, which is an expression of peptization and can be measured quantitatively, decreases in descending order following the Hofmeister series; Li, Na, K, Mg, Ca, Ba.

As the electrolytes are being pushed downward, and the carbonate effects of Na become more prominent, the distinctive features of solonetz appear.

A well defined index of solonetzicity of the soil, as mentioned earlier, is the pH value. When above 8.0-8.2, chances are that the solonetz has a high Na content in the exchange complex with some soluble carbonates.

As the degree of alkalinity increases, the silicate complexes become highly dispersed, hydrolyzed in part, and silica gels may appear. Some Na-silicates may form, and these, together with the soluble humates, serve as cementing agents, giving occasionally a hardpan or a hardpan-like layer in the B horizon. This version of reaction is given by Kovda. Antipov-Karataev is not in full accord with this view.

At this stage in the evolution of solonetz, most of the soluble salts are pushed to the bottom of the profile, and the breakdown of the silicates, designated as degradation, begins.

The high Mg content in the exchange complex of solonetz, especially in the B horizon, is undoubtedly associated with the usual abundance of Mg salts in solonchak. These and the other salts are retained in the profile during the course of desalinization, increasing in quantity with depth. Until these salts are removed from the profile, they tend to move upward, even though slowly because of the dispersion of the B horizon, and saturate the B horizon with the cations in solution. Since sulfates are usually present, the relatively insoluble gypsum formed reduces the entrance of Ca into the complex, and therefore favors the Mg. With the onset of degradation, the release of silicate ions favors the formation of the Mg-silicate rather than Ca-silicates because of the lower solubility of the former.

SOLODI

The third stage in the evolution of saline soils is the degradation of the exchange complex, causing some distinct changes in the profile characteristics and properties. The soil formed as a result of the reactions accompanying the degradation is known as *solodi* and the process involved as *solodization*.

Morphology.—The A_1 horizon is dark in color, with a low organic matter content. When dry, the surface shows a granular structure which is very unstable, the granules turning into mud when in contact with water. Rusty spots are occasionally found in A_1, but more frequently in B_1.

The A_2 horizon is light gray to ash gray in color and platy in structure. Because of its color, it resembles the bleached A_2 of podzols.

The B horizon is compact and, whereas the rounded tops of the columnar structure disappear with solodization, the columns are generally retained, with cloddy units making their appearance. Ortstein grains and even veins are a common occurrence.

As a rule, solodi is associated with areas of solonetz and solonetzic-solonchak types. In examining the saline soil complex (by this is understood an area where two of the three stages in the evolution of solonetz or the different subtypes are located side by side), the normal climatogenic type should be looked for, in comparative morphologic studies.

Process of Formation.—The evolution of the stages in the saline process of soil formation is associated with the hydrologic conditions of the landscape. As more water becomes available for leaching and percolation because of a change in climate, or when the same precipitation becomes more effective because of a change in the upward movement of salt or improved drainage, the last stage in the saline process of soil formation is related to the exchange of Na by H.

As in the processes of podzolization and laterization, if not more so, hydrolytic reactions—hydrolysis and solutions—are in a large measure responsible for the change from solonetz to solodi. The specificity of the hydrolysis in the medium of solonetz deprived of its soluble salts is: first, high alkalinity resulting from the replacement of Na by the H; and secondly, the increased reactivity of the constituents due to the increase in active surface as a result of the dispersion of the colloids.

As a consequence of the dispersion, a change in the phases of the colloid system takes place when the impeded percolation results in a waterlogged state whereby the solid phase becomes the dispersed phase and the water becomes the disperse medium, whereas ordinarily the reverse is the case. Under these circumstances, relatively large quantities of organic and mineral constituents go into solution. Whereas in podzols, laterities, chernozems, and other normal zonal soil types, the water soluble constituents do not exceed the 0.01 - 0.09 per cent mark (for chernozem it is about 0.05 per cent), the degraded solonetz may give 0.8 per cent water soluble constituents. Gedroiz (43, p. 8) points out that the solubility of organic matter from a solonetz may be 35 times as high as from a chernozem.

In the stages of desalinization, the biosphere factor of soil formation (the plant cover) is not participating to any extent. With no vegetation, there is no source of alkaline earth and other bases to enter in circulation. This specific moment is typical in the formation of solodi. With no outside supply (through the humification and mineralization of generations of plants) of the bases mentioned, the A horizon becomes acid.

During the wet season, reduction reactions are conducive to the movement of iron in the ferrous state. The dispersed condition causes a movement of fine particles into the B horizon. It has been shown by Ponomarev and Sedletskii (105) that in solonetz, particles on the order of 0.002-0.000.2 mm. and smaller in size are removed from the A horizon and accumulate in the B horizon. Such a movement is more strongly pronounced with the onset of solodization. In chernozem soil with its stable structure, the 0.002 mm. particles are evenly distributed in the profile, with a slight maximum in the upper part of the A horizon, a slight drop at the lower part, and a rise again in the B horizon.

In table 131, taken from Gedroiz (44), data are presented on the mobility of the clay fraction and the change in particle size of normal chernozem and the same chernozem converted artificially into a solonetz by washing it with NaCl. Twenty-gram samples of these two soils were placed in 200 cc. graduated cylinders, water added to the mark, and the contents shaken and allowed to stand for 6 months. The original chernozem occupied a volume of 29 cc., the soil column was 3.5 cm., and the moisture content 70 per cent. The Na-saturated chernozem occupied a

Table 131

Mechanical composition of the clay fraction of a chernozem converted into a solonetz
(After Gedroiz)

Treatment	Clay	Percentage composition of various particles					
		$1.0-$ 0.54μ	$0.54-$ 0.40μ	$0.40-$ 0.28μ	$0.28-$ 0.22μ	Less than 0.22μ	Total
1. *Original chernozem (saturated with Ca)*							
Per cent of total soil	39.9	10.6	20.8	4.0	1.2	1.3	37.9
Per cent of total clay	—	26.6	51.9	10.0	3.0	3.3	
2. *Chernozem saturated with Na*							
Per cent of total soil	59.9	2.6	4.3	3.2	1.8	45.3	57.2
Per cent of total clay	—	4.5	7.3	5.6	3.1	79.2	

volume of 185 cc., the soil column was 21.5 cm., and the moisture content was 897 per cent.

With the complete breakdown of the structure and slaking of the colloids to their ultra-mechanical composition, some of the silicates become hydrolyzed to the point where amorphous silica separates. According to Gedroiz, this silica may be extracted with a hot 5 per cent KOH solution. It is this silica that gives the A$_2$ horizon of solodi its bleached appearance, similar to that of a podzol. Chemically, the solodi also resembles the podzols. The A horizon is poor in divalent bases. However, in the case of the solodi, the loss of these bases is the result of Na replacing them, whereas in the podzols the bases are replaced by H.

When the Na ions are out of the exchange complex and the pH of the A horizon drops to 6.0 or even lower, the reaction of the B horizon also becomes less alkaline. By that time, the A horizon is a suitable medium for plant growth and the native flora makes its appearance. Roots penetrate deeper and deeper into the soil profile, and after a number of years the biosphere factor brings into circulation the bases. The soil becomes normal, taking on gradually the features of the climatogenic type.

Gedroiz's Views on Solodization

Gedroiz (42) differentiates two types of solodization:

1. *On solonetz practically free from carbonates,* i.e., no effervescence from the surface, with little or no CaCO$_3$.

2. *On solonetz containing carbonates,* i.e., effervescence is apparent from the surface and CaCO$_3$ is abundant in the profile.

Solodization of Carbonate-Free Solonetz.—An outstanding feature of this type of solodization is the rapid loss of organic matter from the surface horizon. This is attributed by Gedroiz to the ease of hydrolytic cleavage of the highly dispersed humates and the consequent utilization of the water-soluble organic constituents by the microorganisms. He says:

> As a result of the complete desolonetzization (solodization), the entire fraction of the organic matter of a carbonate-free solonetz saturated with Na disappears. Apparently, the more strongly the soolonetz properties are developed, i.e., the more absorbed Na the soil contains, the more strongly will the solodi be expressed with respect to its organic matter content, as compared with the original solonetz, and the earlier will the degradatin features of the solonetz become apparent to the eye.
>
> If a solonetz or a solonetzic soil is not completely solodized, then the solodi must possess some solonetzic features, i.e., it must contain in its base exchange complex residues of absorbed sodium. If any podzol-like soil, encountered under climatic conditions incongruent with the podzolization process, should upon investigation prove to contain absorbed Na, it would be fair to designate it as a solodized solonetz. However, if solodi represents the final stage of solonetz degradation, i.e., complete removal of the absorbed sodium, then in order to establish the nature of such a soil, other chemical attributes are pertinent. Such specific attributes in solodi on carbonate-free solonetz are to be sought in the organic and mineral fraction of the soil.

Organic Matter in Solodi.—In the solodization process, as we have seen, there is a very rapid removal of the organic absorption complex, i.e., the organic sols, from the soil. In the process of degradation of the non-solonetzic chernozem, there is simultaneous leaching and decomposition of organic matter, with the transition of the base exchange complex from the saturated to the unsaturated state. The loss of organic matter is, however, very gradual. With the loss of the soluble (sols) humus, a reverse process ensues in both cases. More of the organic base exchange complex is being formed from the dead organic residues and from the inactive† fraction of the organic matter. The solonetzic character of the soil is not likely to speed up these "new formations." For that matter one might expect a more rapid increase of the ratio of inactive organic matter to one capable of base exchange in the process of solodization than in the process of chernozem degradation or the process of podzolization in general. We therefore believe that the inactive organic matter* should prevail in the solodized rather than in the podzol soils. It is probable that the organic matter of the two soils differs not only in the quantitative relationships of the components, but also qualitatively. Furthermore, it is probable that the degree of oxidation of the organic matter, i.e., the relation between the organic matter determined as carbon and by the permanganate method, is different in the two soils. There should also be a difference in the nitrogenous organic substances in the solodi and in podzolized soils. In the solodi, the nitrogenous substances should show less mobility. The percentage of nitrogen in the organic matter of these two soils should also differ. In this direction there are great possibilities for research which might throw some light not only on the genesis of the southern podzol soils but also on the origin and properties of organic matter.

Alumino-Silicate Absorption Complex in Solodi.—In the mineral portion of the absorption complex, the reactions are altogether different. We have seen that in the process of solodization, in contrast to the process of podzolization, an intensive decomposition of the alumino-silicate nucleus of the absorption complex takes place. The soil solution of the solodizing soils should be very rich, in comparison with the podzolized soils, in colloidally soluble silicic acid and sesquioxides. Because of their comparatively high concentration, these compounds should be in less stable condition than in the soil solution of podzolized soils. Their instability in solodized soils is further accentuated because of the presence of some soluble Na salts in the solonetz at the time when this process begins, and because of the high content of soda in the soil solution in the later stages of solodization. Electrolytes are more evident in the solodized than in the podzolized soils. In the latter the process only begins when the soil has been deprived of soluble salts.

An analysis of the data in table 132 shows that in the normal chernozem from Poltava and the profile from Orenburg, very little amorphous silica is present, as indicated by the extraction with a 5 per cent KOH solution. Whatever silica has been extracted can be attributed to the decomposition of some clay. In the gray semidesert soil that shows morphologically solonetzic features, there is some amorphous silica.

The extractions of morphologically distinct solodi show an excess of SiO_2. Gedroiz points out that "the absence of clearly expressed morphological attributes of solodization does not mean that the solonetz has not been affected by this process. In my opinion, the presence of a less solonetzic horizon above the columnar horizon is a definite indication of a partial solodization of the solonetz." The data on the solonchak-solonetz

---

*By the "inactive organic matter fraction" Gedroiz apparently means that Sokolovskii (136) termed the "fraction of organic matter which is not endowed with the property of base exchange."

Table 132

Extraction of chernozems, and a gray solonetzic soil, and typical solodi with a 5 per cent KOH solution

(After Gedroiz)

Soil type	Depth in profile	SiO_2	Al_2O_3	$Al_2O_3.2SiO_2$	Excess over $Al_2O_3.2SiO_2$	
					SiO_2	Al_2O_3
	cm.	per cent	per cent	per cent	gm.	gm.
Chernozem	0-20	0.534	0.320	0.698	0.156	—
from Pol-	45-70	0.440	0.344	0.751	0.033	—
tava	120-150	0.424	0.376	0.783	—	0.017
Chernozem	0-5	0.720	0.330	0.720	0.330	—
from	10-15	0.760	0.400	0.873	0.287	—
Orenburg	20-25	0.660	0.590	1.218	—	0.032
	40-45	0.490	0.552	0.905	—	0.137
	60-65	0.459	0.480	0.831	—	0.099
	100-105	0.430	0.420	0.894	—	0.056
Solonetzic	1-6	0.554	0.200	0.434	0.320	—
gray soil,	6-20	0.480	0.180	0.393	0.267	—
Semirechie	35-45	0.430	0.250	0.545	0.135	—
	70-100	0.504	0.330	0.720	0.144	—
Solodi	A	2.680	0.206	0.449	2.437	—
from	B	0.968	0.310	0.676	0.602	—
Tambov	C	1.000	0.670	1.462	0.208	—
Solodi .	A	5.808	0.156	0.340	5.624	—
from Orenburg	B	1.176	0.428	0.934	0.670	—
in a depres-						
sion						
Solodi	1-5	4.526	0.102	0.223	4.405	—
from	15-20	1.928	0.244	0.532	1.640	—
Voronezh	30-35	0.840	0.420	0.916	0.346	—
(a "podzol" in	60-65	0.940	0.680	1.484	0.136	—
a depression.)	85-90	0.746	0.520	1.135	0.131	—
Solodized	0-5	6.752	0.170	0.371	6.551	—
solonetz	5-10	6.374	0.114	0.249	6.239	—
from Western	10-24	1.432	0.564	1.231	0.765	—
Siberia	20-27	1.304	0.534	1.165	0.673	—
	40-45	1.362	0.558	1.218	0.702	—
	100-105	1.174	0.392	0.855	0.711	—
Solonchak-	0-5	0.868	0.176	0.384	0.660	—
solonetz from	7-22	0.904	0.244	0.532	0.616	—
Chelyabinsk	40-45	0.766	0.312	0.681	0.397	—
(Siberia)						

soil from Chelyabinsk illustrate how the presence of a soluble salts prevents the process of solodization (the solonchak-solonetz designation means that just below the surface some soluble salts are still present and during dry periods they may even rise to the surface). There is very little excess of amorphous silica.

In table 133, data are presented on the extraction of soils from the podzol zone, i.e., soils in which the alumino-silicate nucleus containing no

Table 133

Extraction of soils of the podzol type with a 5 per cent KOH solution
(After Gedroiz)

| Depth in profile | SiO_2 | Al_2O_3 | $Al_2O_3.2SiO_2$ | Excess over $Al_2O_3.2SiO_2$ | |
| | | | | SiO_2 | Al_2O_3 |
cm.	per cent	per cent	per cent	gm.	gm.
Podzol soil from Leningrad					
5-10	1.220	1.450	2.252	—	0.418
15-20	0.986	1.260	1.820	—	0.426
35-40	0.880	1.560	1.624	—	0.816
45-50	0.956	0.984	1.865	—	0.175
95-100	0.750	0.490	1.069	0.171	—
Podzol soil from Moscow					
0-10	0.910	0.550	1.200	0.260	—
20-25	0.776	0.680	1.432	—	0.024
25-40	0.690	0.842	1.265	—	0.267
50-60	0.864	1.164	1.595	—	0.438
60-80	0.920	0.658	—	0.142	—
100-120	0.914	0.768	1.687	—	0.013
Flooded meadow soil along the Volkhov River (podzol zone)					
0-10	3.97	0.59	1.39	3.27	—
11-20	2.20	0.68	1.48	1.40	—
20-30	1.53	0.61	1.33	0.81	—
30-40	1.07	0.43	0.94	0.56	—
40-50	0.84	0.42	0.92	0.34	—
80-90	0.54	0.37	0.81	0.10	—
120-130	0.41	0.26	0.57	0.10	—
152-160	0.50	0.26	0.57	0.19	—
200-205	0.47	0.22	0.48	0.21	—

Na in its exchange complex is being disrupted. The data for the various samples, except for the meadow soil, demonstrate that under conditions of podzolization no amorphous silica accumulates. On the contrary, more Al_2O_3 is being extracted, which shows that in the process of podzolization either free alumina is formed or the base exchange complex becomes enriched with Al_2O_3.

In the meadow soil, there is an excess of SiO_2 and even though it is in the podzol zone, the data point to some solodization. Gedroiz makes the assumption that this soil, being a secondary soil, had in its primary stage some Na in the exchange complex, and the amorphous silica is thus a relic of the primary stage.

The second type of solodization is described by Gedroiz as follows:

Solodization of Carbonate Solonetz.—It has been shown that by extracting with water a natural carbonate solonetz or an artificially prepared Na-saturated soil in the presence of lime, no disruption of the alumino-silicate nucleus takes place. The quantity of silica and sequioxides extracted with water from such soils does not exceed that from non-solonetzic soils. It is clear that in such cases there is no chance for the accumulation of appreciable quantities of amorphous silica in the process of desolonetzization. The attribute which served to differentiate solodi from podzolic soils or from the carbonate-free soils does not apply to the solodi which originate on carbonate solonetz. The absence of amorphous silica does not, therefore, mean that the particular soil was not solonetzic at some earlier time.

What appears to be a solodi has been described by Storie (140) in his studies of the solonetz soils in California. Of the four profiles reported, none has any replaceable sodium in the A horizon; the reaction of the soil in this horizon is acid, with an increase of alkalinity in B_1 and B_2. This indicates solodization. In table 134, the Antioch fine sandy loam soil is described; it is also more or less typical of the other three profiles. It will be noted that no data are available on the presence or absence of amorphous SiO_2 or on either the base exchange capacity or the distribution of R_2O_3. The only evidence of solodization is the low pH of the A horizon, the increase in B, and the low clay content of the A horizon.

A typical solodi is presented in plate 35, adopted from another publication by Storie (141). At the right in the picture, just below the A

Table 134

Profile characteristics of an Antioch fine sandy loam (California)
(After Storie)

Horizon	Depth in inches	Moisture equivalent	Total clay	Colloidal clay	pH
		per cent	*per cent*	*per cent*	
A_1	0-18	18.64	27.84	10.21	5.63
A_2	18-20	18.30	—	—	5.90
B_1	20-34	26.82	46.90	35.85	6.80
B_2	34-48	22.84	31.38	24.32	7.80
C_1	48-72	21.92	24.50	14.50	7.60

horizon, there is the sandy clay A_2 horizon, not designated by Storie as such. At the left in the picture, remnants of the columnar structure of the solonetz are still apparent. The surface A horizon is somewhat acid, and the colloid content is low. No mention is made by Storie of this soil's being a solodi, but the trained pedologist will easily recognize it as such.

PLATE 35

A profile of Olivechain loamy fine sand in California resembling a typical solodi
(After Storie)

An extensive series of investigations on the solodi process has been made by Ivanova (62). She presents voluminous data and illustrations on the morphological and chemical characteristics of solonetz and solodi soils in western Siberia. The transition from a solonetz to a solodi is presented in plate 36. It represents an extensive profile cut, over 80 feet long, in which the elements of topography are instrumental in converting the solonetz into a solodi.

In solodi formation, Mg is released from the surface horizon and accumulated in the lower horizons. This is especially striking with respect to the replaceable Mg in the profile. In the A horizon, the base exchange capacity decreases because of the breakdown of the so-called zeolitic substances and the release of organic matter.

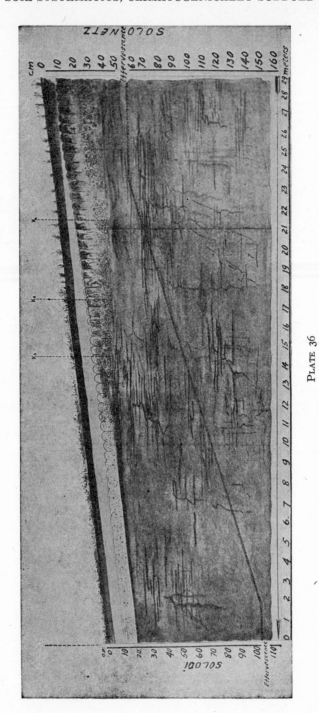

PLATE 36

A soil complex in western Siberia illustrating solonetz and solodi formations

(After Ivanova)

Prasolov and Antipov-Karataev (10) determined the amorphous SiO_2 and Al_2O_3 in a number of normal soils and in soil complexes of the brown and chestnut brown zones. The data in table 135 show that in the normal brown soil the A_1 horizon has an appreciable excess of SiO_2 over Al_2O_3 even for the ratio of $Al_2O_3 : 6 SiO_2$. It means a disruption of the exchange complex, which indicates solodization. In this horizon, the exchange capacity is relatively low (see table 136). The light chestnut soil

Table 135

SiO$_2$ and Al$_2$O$_3$ extracted with a 5 percent KOH solution from a number of soils
(After Prasolov and Antipov-Karataev)

Horizon	Depth	Per cent of dry weight		Excess over $A_2O_3 : 2SiO_2$		Excess over $Al_2O_3 : 6SiO_2$	
		SiO_2	Al_2O_3	SiO_2	Al_2O_3	SiO_2	Al_2O_3
	cm.			*gm.*	*gm.*	*gm.*	*gm.*
Solonetz							
A_1	0-5	1.9016	0.3196	1.5229	—	0.7268	—
B_1	7-15	1.6169	0.5269	0.9926	—	—	0.0720
B_2	20-30	1.0098	0.1895	0.7871	—	0.3379	—
Light chestnut solonetzic soil							
A_1	0-9	2.5468	0.3057	2.1854	—	1.4624	—
A_2	12-20	1.4031	0.3435	0.9979	—	0.1843	—
B_1	22-32	1.1516	0.4318	0.6405	—	—	0.0011
B_2	35-45	1.0027	0.3287	0.6136	—	—	0.0458
C	55-65	0.8240	0.2657	0.5088	—	—	0.0330
Brown solonetzic soil							
A_1	0-10	2.7753	0.2369	2.4955	—	1.9706	—
B_1	15-25	1.2556	0.5580	0.5891	—	—	0.2045
B_1	30-40	0.4356	0.2702	0.1191	—	—	0.1476
Brown soil (normal)							
A_1	0-10	2.2079	0.1389	2.0424	—	1.7157	—
B_1	16-28	1.3029	0.2656	0.9875	—	0.3610	—
B_2	45-52	1.1582	0.0708	1.0749	—	0.9062	—

Table 136

Total analyses of two brown soils, per cent of dry soil

(After Prasolov and Antipov-Karataev)

Horizon	Depth cm	Organic matter	CO$_2$	SiO$_2$	Fe$_2$O$_3$	Al$_2$O$_3$	Mn$_3$O$_4$	CaO	MgO	K$_2$O	Na$_2$O	P$_2$O$_5$	SO$_3$
Brown solonetzic soil													
A$_1$	0–10	2.54	—	75.73	4.39	9.59	Not Deter.	0.46	0.24	0.44	2.1	0.07	0.21
A$_2$	15–25	1.78	—	72.92	3.98	10.21		0.71	0.25	—	—	0.15	0.14
A$_3$	30–40	1.12	—	71.93	4.25	10.42		0.93	0.46	0.25	0.48	0.10	0.15
B$_1$	45–55	1.27	9.06	62.92	4.82	12.42		5.32	0.86	0.62	0.87	0.10	0.14
B$_2$	75–85	1.03	7.07	61.45	7.03	13.25		5.07	0.83	0.43	1.11	0.09	0.18
C	125–130	1.03	5.34	68.09	7.34	10.00		5.26	0.75	0.21	0.54	0.10	0.27
Normal brown soil													
A$_1$	0–10	4.33	—	73.45	3.78	10.27	—	0.09	1.37	Not Deter.	Not Deter.	0.06	0.48
A$_2$	16–28	2.07	—	68.45	5.63	15.40	0.17	0.11	1.86			0.02	—
B$_1$	42–52	1.18	1.78	64.83	5.59	16.23	0.43	3.71	2.32			0.14	0.07
B$_2$	87–92	0.29	5.54	61.76	4.84	12.78	0.32	7.12	2.66			0.12	0.16

shows a similar disruption of the complex in A_1 and A_2, with a high excess of amporphous SiO_2. In the brown solonetzic soil, the solodization is also pronounced in the upper horizon. This holds true also for the solonetz and points to the conclusion that, with the solonetz process, solodization sets in.

Bentley and Rost (10) report on solodi as a part of a solonetzic soil complex. From the data presented, it would appear that even the calcareous zonal profile is solonetzic, as judged by the percentage of exchangeable Na and pH in the profile at depths from 12 to 48 inches. It looks as if we are dealing with soils hindered in solodization by a secondary salinization with $MgSO_4$ as the principal salt.

Rozanov (116) points out that $CaCO_3$ and $MgCO_3$ do not prevent the deterioration of the exchange complex and the formation of solodi. Rybakov (121) ascribes the formation of solodi to the upward and downward movement of water and reagents in solution. Dranitsyn (36) cites alkaline water extracts of podzols which are probably a relic of solodi. Bazilevich (9) claims "that the soil complex in the transition belt of the forest-steppe soils adjoining the taiga is represented primarily by meadow solonchakic, bog, solodized, and podzolized soils. From the descriptions of Dranitsyn (35), Gorshenin (51), Il'in (61), Otryganev (99), and Gerasimov (no reference given to Gerasimov's paper), the podolized soils of the taiga zone of the Western Siberian lowland (the Vasyugan-Narymsk region) frequently effervesce and have two humus horizons." Basilevich presents extensive data on exchangeable cations, composition of water extracts, and pH of the different soil types. He points out that with the advance of solodization Ca is lost more rapidly than Mg from the A_2 horizon, whereas the Mg accumulates in the B horizon. He postulates the accumulation of SiO_2 in A_2 as a result of the upward movement of salts of diatom origin. The accumulation of amorphous SiO_2 in A_2 is not considered by Bazilevich as a trustworthy index of solodization, since the upward movement of alkali may cause the separation of SiO_2.

Kovda (82) points out that the SiO_2 of solodi in chernozem soils is the result of the movement of amorphous silicic acid and its hydrolysis. He leached cylinders containing gypsum with Na_2SiO_3 and obtained $CaSiO_3$, and upon passing CO_2 he obtained $Ca(HCO_3)_2$ and SiO_2, the latter coating the gypsum.

Rost and Maehl (115) present data, some of which is given in table 137, on 17 profiles assembled into three groups, which may be looked upon as three types that represent stages of solodization. Group I still contains soluble salts in the B horizon. Group II and III have no soluble salts in the profile, but group III shows more soluble SiO_2. The A_1 in group III

Table 137

Texture, reaction, exchangeable cations, and soluble SiO_2 and Al_2O_3 of three groups of solodized soils

(After Kost and Maehl)

Horizon	Thickness	Texture as moisture equivalent	Reaction	Total exchange capaciay	Exchangeable Cations, Percentage of Total					Soluble SiO_2	Soluble Al_2O_3	Excess SiO_2 over Al_2O_3 $2SiO_2$
					H	Ca	Mg	Na	K			
	inches		pH	m.e.						per cent	per cent	per cent
Group I												
A₁	6.5	31.3	5.9	33.8	20.7	51.0	25.5	1.4	1.3	6.05	0.129	5.90
A₂	4.5	19.2	6.0	16.6	22.0	41.1	32.4	3.5	1.1	4.48	0.164	4.29
B₁	4.0	36.0	7.1	36.9	6.8	24.3	64.0	3.5	1.4	2.37	0.405	1.90
B₂	4.8	34.9	7.6	38.2	2.7	31.0	63.9	2.7	0.7	1.94	0.296	1.59
BC	4.8	33.1	7.9	39.0	0.0	42.2	55.3	1.6	1.0	1.65*	0.201	1.42
C	8.7	31.8	8.0	35.0	0.0	59.1	38.6	0.5	1.8	2.24	0.137	2.08
Group II												
A₁	7.0	33.1	5.9	31.7	15.7	59.4	21.2	0.7	3.0	9.13	0.102	9.01
A₂	5.7	23.8	6.3	19.6	12.9	56.0	25.9	1.3	4.0	5.90	0.183	5.68
B₁	4.7	31.9	6.4	33.3	8.8	58.2	28.7	0.9	3.5	3.05	0.335	2.65
B₂	10.0	35.5	6.6	37.1	7.3	60.3	28.5	0.7	3.3	3.30	0.314	2.93
BC	5.6	35.1	7.2	35.3	4.5	63.2	28.5	0.7	3.2	4.34	0.208	4.09
C	5.8	35.3	7.5	34.3	2.7	65.2	28.2	0.9	3.0	4.44	0.140	4.28
Group III												
A₁	5.2	42.1	6.7	48.7	7.7	68.4	19.8	0.4	3.9	7.26	0.082	7.17
A₂	7.2	31.2	5.9	30.6	16.8	55.5	23.3	0.8	3.6	7.27	0.128	7.12
B₁	5.3	36.1	5.3	40.8	16.6	50.5	29.3	0.8	2.9	4.38	0.222	4.12
B₂	7.3	38.9	5.4	42.1	12.7	51.8	31.9	0.9	2.8	3.82	0.258	3.52
BC	4.0	38.2	6.3	39.5	6.0	55.7	34.6	0.9	2.8	3.62	0.232	3.35
C	7.3	36.7	7.7	34.6	0.9	59.9	35.8	0.9	2.6	3.43	0.168	3.23

is less acid, indicating the natural tendency of the soils to become ameliorated and turned into a normal steppe soil again. The Mg content in the respective groups may also serve as an index of the state of solodization, being highest in the early stages and diminishing towards the stage of true solodi. In its final evolution, solodi takes on the appearance of the climatogenic soil prevailing in the area.

Akimtsev (2) reports extensive data on solodi formation in the dark and light chestnut brown soils and gray semidesert. He expresses the thought that a gray saline soil, upon solodization, may become a chestnut brown, subsequently a chernozem, and finally even a forest soil. It seems logical to assume that, since solodization is made possible by increased precipitation, it is associated with a change in climate which in turn determines the type of soil. Irrigating gray or brown, etc., soils (the human entering as a factor of soil formation), one may anticipate a change in soil type, if the soils are solodi. The question arises whether it would not be feasible to expedite solodization and thus change the soil to the desired type.

While on a visit at the Versailles Agricultural Institute in 1938, Dr. Demolon called the attention of the author to a strange profile in the neighboring forest. This profile at first sight gave the impression of a mature podzol. Upon closer examination, it was discovered that the B horizon had a columnar-prismatic structure resembling a degraded solonetz. According to Dr. Demolon, the bleached A_2 horizon was neutral or slightly alkaline. This fact precludes the podzol nature of this soil. Apparently, we are dealing with a case of an ancient solodi preserved by some set of circumstances. The particular location represents a 'saucer shaped basin surrounded by hills of limestone formation. It is possible that the seepage waters kept up the alkalinity of the soil in the area and preserved the aboriginal solodi. A similar case has been reported to the author by a former student from an area in Ontario, Canada.

Summary Statement.—Solodi is the third stage in the evolution of saline soils. Next comes the normal climatogenic soil.

Solodi forms from solonetz, and the higher the Na content in the exchange complex, the more pronounced is the process of solodization.

Solodi develops as a result of intensified leaching and percolation. In the zone of chernozem, where more precipitation prevails—in comparison with the other soil types of the grass country—solodi is more frequently encountered. This does not exclude solodi from other zonal soil types. Generally, solodi is more frequent in depressions.

In mature solodi, the biosphere enters once more as an active factor of soil formation, and the result is the gradual development of the normal climatogenic soil of the area.

MICROBIOLOGICAL CHARACTERISTICS OF SALINE SOILS

Whereas investigations on the relations of plants to saline soils are abundant, studies of the microbiological characteristics of these soils are surprisingly meager. Very few reports dealing with this problem can be cited. Those of Barnes and Ali (8), Joffe and McLean (65), and Greaves (52-54) are concerned primarily with surface soils. They show that the salinity of the soil decreases the numbers of microorganisms and impedes some of their activities, but the N-fixing organisms are not affected adversely (this has a bearing on the problem of niter spots). None of the investigations mentioned looked into the problem of the distribution and functions of microorganisms in the profile.

Prikhodko and Belikova (108) studied the microbiological activities in artificial saline soils produced by Vilenskii in the course of his investigations on the salinization process in a slightly degraded chernozem. In all, 84 samples were taken during the summer and fall seasons at depths of 0-2, 5-10, 15-20, and 45-50 cm. Determinations and studies were made on the numbers of microorganisms, the processes of nitrification, nitrogen fixation by *Azotobacter* and *Clostridium Pasterianum,* and cellulose decomposition under aerobic and anaerobic conditions. They showed that Clostridium is stimulated by the saline condition. Sodium chloride was found to be more injurious to the microbial flora than Na_2SO_4, especially with respect to numbers. As a matter of fact, Na_2SO_4 stimulated microbial activities, and the numbers relatively increased when compared with the controls. Contrary to expectations, the number did not decrease, except in a few cases, with depth; in most cases, the number increased with depth. Aerobic cellulose decomposition was somewhat affected by NaCl, but in general it was active and decreased only at the depth of 45-50 cm. Anaerobic cellulose decomposition was erratic throughout the various depths, and consequently no definite conclusions were drawn. No change in nitrification was noted, except at the lowest point—45 to 50 cm. —, where it decreased. Similarly, the process of N fixation was not affected much with depth. Both Azotobacter and Clostridium were stimulated by the NaCl and Na_2SO_4. In general, the results of Prikhodko and Belikova are at variance with those of Rokitzkaya (111, 112) and of Keller and Karel'skaya (68).

Samsonov, Samsonova, and Chernova (123) studied the distribution and activities of the microflora in a solonchak soil in Central Asia and their conclusions are, in general, similar to those of Prikhodko and Belikova. Nitrifiers were found to prevail in the upper horizon, and ammonifiers down to a depth of 25-35 cm. No regularity was observed in the distribution of fungi and actinomycetes. The NaCl salines inhibited the activities of microorganisms more than did the Na_2SO_4. Denitrifiers were somewhat depressed in the highly salinzed soils. More humus accumulated under a NaCl environment, probably because of the inhibition of the microbes instrumental in the decomposition of the scant vegetation prevailing on solonchak soils. With a decrease in salinity, the cellulose decomposition increased.

Brodskii and Yankovskaya (19), who studied the protozoa in saline soils, found that the flora increased in numbers down to a depth of 20-30 cm. and then decreased. Infrequently, another increase was found at a depth of 60-80 cm. In general, however, the numbers were low—500 per gram of soil.

Germanov (48) reviewed most of the investigations dealing with the biodynamics of saline soils. Among the most interesting points noted were the behavior of microbes in the three types of saline soils. Ammonification, nitrification, and especially N-fixation went on unabated in solonchak and solonetz, but not in solodi. He ascribed this behavior to the generally disturbed conditions in the base-exchange complex of the solodi. Orlovskii (97) studied the nitrification process in the profile of solonetzic soils.

Genkel and Danini (45) sum up their study on the microbial activity in solonetz as follows: 1, there is no distinct difference in the ammonifying power of the horizons; 2, nitrification is limited to the A horizon; 3, with cultivation, nitrification extends to the B horizon; 4, there is a seasonal fluctuation of nitrification, especially in the B horizon where it comes to a standstill because of the accumulation of soluble sulfates; 5, acid phosphate and gypsum applications depress nitrification; 6, denitrification may occur in the lower horizons; 7, it is substantiated that Azotobacter are in abundance; 8, cellulose is rapidly decomposed in the A horizon; 9, there is an intensive microbial activity in these soils; 10, the ideas of Sigmond, Zuker, and other Hungarian investigators of a low microbiological activity in solonetz stem from the fact that they have been working with soils of a high salt content.

Sushkina (142) reports on the distribution of Azotobacter in a number of soil types of the saline series.

VILENSKII'S VIEWS ON THE EVOLUTION OF
SALINE SOILS

In tracing the evolution of the three stages—solonchak, solonetz, and solodi—in the processes of saline soil formation, Vilenskii associates it with the geological history and the climatic conditions prevailing in the region. A few points of his scholarly deductions deserve the attention of pedologists and are therefore reproduced in the following pages:

On the basis of the voluminous paleontological, soil, and general geographical evidence, one may consider it as established beyond any doubt that the climate during that epoch (Post-Glacial) was much more arid and apparently warmer than it is now. Because of this, the arid zones the world over have been extended and have reached out towards the north.

In the contributions of Berg (11-14), evidence may be found showing that, contrary to the opinion of a number of geologists who recognize the aridity factor only, the bulk of evidence also favors the factor of a higher temperature during that epoch. Botanical data testify to this fact, and on their basis Drude (27) named this the "xerothermic epoch." Andersson (4) calculated that the summer temperature in Scandinavia was 2 to 25°C. higher than it is now, and all geographical data point in that direction, as pointed out by Berg.

The latest findings proving the more arid conditions of the climate in the steppe and desert regions in Post-Glacial times are those of Ryabinin (120). He excavated remnants of lions—*Felis lei var. spelac*—in districts north of Perm. According to Ryabinin, the distribution of lions during the Quaternary period reached in eastern Russia the 59° northern latitude, and there is evidence showing that they disappeared only in historic times.

Not much light has been shed on the question of the physico-geographical conditions of the Post-Glacial epoch, namely, the hydrologic regime of the surface deposits and especially the level of the waters in the open basins and the depth of the water table. And yet, almost all investigators who have expressed their views on this problem recognized that the level of the waters in all the basins was, at least in the early part of the Post-Glacial epoch, considerably higher than it is now. For that reason and because of the poor drainage of the Post-Glacial valleys, the level of the ground waters was also higher, as pointed out by Glinka (Ch. 2, 27), Dubyanskii (38), and Izmailskii (64).

Having advanced the evidence which geology and geography offer on the problem of Post-Tertiary deposits and on the physico-geographical conditions of that epoch (it was then that the soil cover began to form on these deposits), we may undertake a more detailed analysis of the conditions of soil formation in the Post-Glacial epoch and follow up the transformations which the Post-Glacial soils had to undergo with the advent of our present epoch.

At this point, we must note that the proposed theory of the origin of salines demands the unconditional recognition of the postulate that no catastrophical changes had occurred in the surface features of the land all over the area of the glacial depositions. A normal cycle in the development of the topography, coupled with the erosion processes, took place. To harmonize the evidence on the origin of salines with the eolian theory on loess formation, one must accede to the proposition that the process of shifting the moraine deposits took place during one of the interglacial ages, whereas during another age (Würm) the loess deposits had been under waters supplied by the Scandinavian ice sheet. On the other hand, if we accept the earlier view of Professor Tutkovskii (152), Sokolov (135), and others that loess is a Post-Glacial formation, i.e., it originated only after the final retreat of the ice sheet, it is clear that the existence of salines on loess-like parent materials is in definite conflict with the eolian hypothesis of loess formation. Its existence testifies that during this epoch deluvial pro-

cesses played no significant part in the valleys. The probable conditions of soil formation during that epoch have been skillfully described by Dokuchaev (32) :

"Judging by the condition of loess formation in southern Russia and the marine
Post-Tertiary deposits in the adjoining regions, our steppes in the early days of their
development must have been an endless valley with irregularly shaped hollows, enclosed
saucer-shaped depressions, etc. The majority of the present-day rivers and gullies
were not in existence. There must have been, however, many temporary swamps and
lakes. In short, the steppes represented the typical landscape features of a primary
valley in its youthful stage. As it emerged from under water, such a valley could not
have been differentiated vertically except in minor local depressions which were not
distributed with any regularity in the region. These depressions served as moisture
accumulators, and lakes and limans were scattered throughout the valley; here and
there, along the depressions streams began to find their course. It is self-evident that
in such a poorly drained valley, the water table was not deep. Under the conditions
of Post-Glacial time when the level of the streams has risen, as evidenced by the river
terraces, the water table has risen too. There can be no doubt, therefore, about the
bounty of water and of a high water table in those times."

The hydrologic conditions described destined the formation of a soil cover with
the characteristics of a "soil complex," and the predominance of the hydrogenic types.
Later on, this complex was differentiated into a number of types in accordance with
the climatic conditions which prevailed in the Post-Glacial valley. Mention has been
made that the climate in the Post-Glacial epoch was in general warm and dry, which
apparently caused the melting of the glaciers. There is, however, no basis for the
belief that the climate was homogenous throughout the latitude of Eurasia. On the
contrary, all evidence points to the prevalence of climatic zones similar to those of
the present day. The zones alternated from the equator to the poles; the dry belts
were extended and the humid ones locally displaced. On the basis of soil data, we
may definitely state that the northern limits of the Post-Glacial steppe in European
Russia extended to the 51° northern latitude in the western part, to the 55° in the
central part, and to the 57° in the eastern part. In Siberia it extended further north:
59° at Naruim and 63° in the Yakutsk region. Towards the south of the steppe, the
semidesert and desert zones were located; the exact northern limits of these zones
are not known. They could easily be established with accuracy by the soil method of
investigation. As in present-day climate, the forest zone must have been then north
of the steppe, and it probably extended further north than it does now and occupied a
portion of our present day tundra. In some sections of Europe immediately adjoining
the Scandinavian ice sheet which covered northwestern Russia and northern Germany,
the regularity of the zonal distribution was disturbed, especially soon after the retreat
of the ice and the invasion of the forest zone by the tundra. Under such conditions, it
was possible for the steppe to come in direct contact with the tundra, a phenomenon
which may now be observed in the mountain regions of the semidesert where the
subalpine belt joins directly with the steppe or even the semidesert.

It is perfectly clear that if the climatic zones of the Post-Glacial epoch were essentially the same as those of the present day, then the soil-forming processes and
the soil types formed must have been the same as those of today. In particular, in
the desert steppe zones where the evaporation exceeded the precipitation, the hydrogenic process of soil formation should have led exclusively to the formation of *solonchak* enriched more or less with soluble salts. This was the *solonchak period* in the
history of the formation of the soil cover on the Post-Tertiary deposits. The energetic
formation of solonchak during that period was undoubtedly favored considerably, not
only by the climatic and hydrological conditions, but by the chemical composition of
the parent material and ground waters. One must not forget, as pointed out by Dokuchaev (32), that the glacier, "having moved a distance of more than 1,000 kilometers
from northwest to southeast, to its most southerly and southeasterly steppe limits,
broke up, crushed, mellowed, and partly sorted out, with the aid of glacial streams,
hundreds of kinds of rocks encountered in its way and moved them to a more southern
latitude. Because of this process, which probably lasted thousands of years, and because of the simultaneous chemical and physical weathering of these rocks, there
must have been all kinds of products of glacial activity. Among them, there must have

been substances dissolved in the glacial waters, such as the carbonate, sulfates, chlorides, and other salts." A considerable portion of these salts was carried away into the sea, but a portion, not less than that carried away, remained in the ground waters. The salts were then distributed throughout the depth of the soil, enriching the lower layers as the ground waters penetrated deeper into the soil. This process added to the zonality feature of the mechanical composition of the soil, a zonality of chemical composition and water-soluble salt content. Where the topographical conditions were favorable for the evaporation of the ground waters, the salts came to the surface and remained in the surface horizons.

After the final retreat of the ice and the complete cessation of glacial phenomena, fundamental changes took place in the moisture regime of the primary valley described above. These were caused by the sharp decline in the quantity of water entering the hydrographic network of the valley. With the decrease in the quantity of water, a lowering in the level of internal land seas must have occurred, with the consequent general lowering of the base-level of erosion in the valley. The former lake-like basins had been converted first into the irregularly outlined wide streams which, upon cutting their channels into the deep beds of glacial deposits and upon the establishment of an equilibrium between the inflow and outflow of water, became narrower and deeper and attained the features of our contemporaneous rivers.

With the development of the hydrographic network and the branching out of its system and with the formation of gullies, the natural drainage of the Post-Glacial valley began. First of all, the surface dried up, and a lowering of the water table took place. The valley entered the second stage of its erosion cycle which has appropriately been named by Davis (28) "the stage of maturity." Naturally, such a gradual drying up of the land surface, under the climatic conditions of the desert-steppe zones, must have been accompanied by an energetic salinization of the upper horizons and the consequent formation of solonchak, especially in areas with favorable topographic features. Later on, when the ground waters sank deeper and lost contact with the surface horizons, the solonchak entered into a new phase of its development; it had undergone a metamorphosis under the influence of leaching and percolation by precipitation. As a consequence, the solonchak soils had been transformed into various groups of *solonetz* which were distributed with a strict geographical regularity within the borders of the various zones, in accordance with the climatic conditions.

In this manner, the second period in the history of the development of salinized soils on Post-Tertiary deposits made its appearance. This may be called *the solonetz period*. This period, in all probability, lasted to the end of the Post-Glacial epoch, and was accompanied by a further lowering of the base-level of erosion in connection with the lowering of the level of the internal seas to the present-day stage and perhaps lower, as shown by Berg (13). With every such lowering (probably also connected with the epirogenetic processes), the river terraces, after they emerged from under water, must have gone through a cycle of development similar to that of the primary valley, i.e., at first they were enriched with solonchak and later on with a soil complex permeated with solonetz.

With the advent of the present-day geologic epoch, which differed from the previous one by a more humid climate, a shifting of the climatic zones from north to south and the consequent migration of the flora took place. This migration was more marked in the region north of the chernozem zone, where the forests advanced on the steppe and thus gave rise to a new zone, the forest-steppe. This phenomenon, however, also prevailed in other zones. Simultaneously, an intensified metamorphosis of the solonetz took place in the southern zones. In the northern zones, the depressions occupied by the solonetz became filled with water, forming a countless number of temporary and permanent lakes. The standing waters in the temporary lakes facilitated a forced tempo of leaching, and in places the solonetz had been subjected to the effects of degradation. These temporary lakes with the standing waters were ideal for the development of forest vegetation, and they served as the advanced posts in the invasion of the steppe by the forest. With the waters standing in the depressions, their penetration into the deeper layers became imperative. This was intensified after the process of degradation had destroyed the structural horizon. Consequently, a process of swamping ensued in the areas where the depressions and solonetz have developed considerably. In the beginning, a surface water table formed, but gradually the swamping extended and the surface water table established contact with the deeper lying ground waters. Thus, with the change in climate, a reversion to the conditions of the poorly drained primary valley took place.

This process of gradual swamping of surface soils and subsoils is still going on in Siberia, where the topographic features and the close proximity of the impervious Tertiary deposits markedly favor the accumulation of ground waters. Therefore, perhaps, the advance of the forest on the steppe in Siberia has been going on with a rapid tempo; birch groves penetrated almost immediately into the dry steppe zone. In European Russia, where the surface drainage is in general satisfactory, the swamping process has not made much headway, and the larger portion of chernozem zone has remained intact.

In connection with this type of swamping, coupled with the accompanying degradation process, a tendency was noted towards the reversion of the solonetz to its original type—a *regradation of the solonchak*. This process of regradation has been especially intensified ever since human efforts began to interfere with natural forces. Cutting of forests, especially the destruction of swamp forests, stimulated this process. At the same time, the swamping in Siberia induced the formation of secondary salinized soils —solonchakic chernozem and carbonate solonchak—by the rising of salts from the deep illuvial horizons.

On the basis of the combination of enumerated phenomena, the last period in the history of the evolution of salinized soils may be designated as *the period of solonetz degradation*.

Thus, we see that the theory presented is fully capable of explaining all the peculiarities of salinized soils; their constitution, composition, and distribution. From the point of view of this theory, the steppes, with the solonetz in the Zabaikal and Yakutsk regions, are the most northerly islands of the Post-Glacial steppes which were preserved because of the continentality of the climate. In these steppes and even farther south, we witness in our epoch the formation of the horizon of eternal freezing, which offers the opportunity to observe in a single profile cut the odd interplay of attributes of the dry steppe semidesert and tundra, illustrated by gypsum layers lying side by side with the layer of eternal freezing. *It seems that such a phenomenon serves as proof that the climate of today is cooler than the climate of preceding epochs.*

In the same manner, the stretches of the swamps of Baraba and of the largest area of the steppe in western Siberia are islands that constantly accumulate salts above the surface of the ground waters because of topographic features, proximity of impervious Tertiary formations, and abundance of residual solonetz from the Post-Glacial epoch. This resulted in a widespread development of the process of solonchak regradation, accompanied by a secondary swamping and salinization of the phytogenic soils. The phenomenon indicated, as well as the submerging of the solonetz depressions, something which is widespread even in the dry steppe zone, *may serve as proof that the change in the climate of today is in the direction of a more humid condition.*

And finally, the entire zone of the semidesert is to be considered as an island preserved from the Post-Glacial epoch without much change, because of the scant rainfall, not sufficient to percolate the solonchak soils and thus convert them into solonetz.

Although the point of view presented has been applied for the first time to soils in such a rounded out form, its inception could be traced in the work of several others, especially botanists-geographers. Thus, Professor Beketov, as early as 1874, in his notes to the translation of Griezebach's "Plants of the World" stated: "The origin of the treeless steppe may be pictured in the following manner: As the land emerged from under the waters of the Pliocene sea, salt lakes, and solonchak remained. These were inhabited by the saliniferous grasses. As long as they predominated, tree growth was impossible. With the leaching of the soil and the washing out of the excess salt, other grass species began to appear." Speaking of the vegetation of southern Russia during the Glacial period, Beketov points out that "the coniferous forests were then widespread in central Russia; they would have reached the shores of the Pliocene sea if it were not for the solonchak, which in those times had already controlled the treeless condition." Somewhat later, Krause (86) presented the view that steppes and deserts had originated after the drying out of the saline water basins. Similar ideas were expressed in recent years by Pachoskii (100, 101).

It has been pointed out that the regularities noted in the properties and distribution of salinized soils, and the phenomena associated therewith become tangible, if we agree that the present-day climate, as compared with that of the immediate Post-Glacial period, has become more humid and colder.* Whatever the causes of this change might have been—cosmic in nature or, as some investigators believe, associated with the changes in the underground moisture resources controlled by the plant cover —*the soil data indicate beyond doubt that the change did take place.* The existence of solonetz on the Post-Tertiary deposits in the chernozem, forest steppe and forest zones, in the light of the interpretation presented, serves as a very sound argument in favor of the widespread distribution of the dry zones in the Post-Glacial epoch and their shift father north. And it is similarly true that the existence of a geographic regularity in the distribution of these soil groups throughout the various zones and of the strongly developed process of degradation testifies to the reversal of the zones now going on. Nature has preserved in solonetz that record from the Post-Glacial epoch, the absence of which in the south (of Russia) Professor Tanfiliev deplored. There is then much less basis for the other hypothesis which claims that the climate has not changed during the entire Post-Glacial period, as postulated by Tanfiliev (146, 147). Still less probable and contradictory to all soil, botanico-geographical, and general geographical evidence is the third hypothesis, supported by Kropotkin (85), Penck (103), and others, which claims that the change in the present-day climate is towards aridity and expansion of the dry zones. With reference to soils, this hypothesis is being strongly supported by Professor Bushinskii (23) who points out "that the desert is advancing on the steppe and forests and in its forward movement strives to engulf and conquer from humanity the cultivated unstable dry regions which at present are the granary of the State." Unfortunately, Bushinskii offers no valid proof in support of his contention. One cannot accept as proof "those threatening warnings of the periodically recurring droughts which may become a real fact and wipe out the cultivated soil of the human." What has been said above and a series of other data definitely oppose this point of view.

Thus, all the evidence set forth and a number of other well-founded propositions, firmly established in pedology, speak not for a progressive salinization but for a gradual sweetening of the Quaternary valley. What Dimo, 15 years ago, thought of "as an enticing, beautiful dream, and nothing more than a dream," is now becoming a reality. With all the branches of geography converging to the same conclusion, arrived at by various methods of approach, practical agronomy may rest assured of the possibility and fruitfulness of agricultural efforts in the dry regions. For it is not a battle against the elements of the desert, but against the ignorance and plundering of "homo-sapiens" who by his unsound management is apt to convert the most blooming region into a desolate waste.

The widespread distribution of saline soils in the steppe latitude, in connection with the theories advanced on their origin, is of outstanding theoretical interest. Since the solonetz is a relic of the Post-Glacial epoch and since it represents a record of the Post-Glacial water basins, marshes, and all places in which the ground waters were close to the surface, then it should be possible through them to reconstruct the picture of the distribution of the steppes, deserts, and water basins. And because solonetz

---

*The views held by Vilenskii are in harmony with the findings in the United States on the Pleistocene history of the Great Basin. Thus Antevs (5) states: "In short, the end of expansion and the retreat of the ice-sheets were connected with an increase in temperature and decrease in precipitation in the glacial areas. The rise in temperature probably increased evaporation which must have been considerable, since a strong windiness still persisted during the ice retreat." The problem of the climate in the prehistoric Post-Glacial period has a bearing on the origin of our prairies, which is discussed in the section on "Prairie Soils."

soils are not so easily destroyed, and because they reflect so vividly the effects of the environmental conditions, geographical science which searches to unravel the history of the Post-Glacial surface features of the earth may find in them an auxiliary method of investigation—the solonetz method. In our opinion, this method may be very useful in the study of the problem of the steppes as well as of the "latest page" in geology in general. We have seen the importance of the solonetz problem to pedology generally and how intimately it is related to the most fundamental problems of geology. We believe that the solonetz problem also has an important bearing on the problems of botanical geography, to which it is related in historical perspective in the same degree as to pedology. In short, for botanical geography it offers the possibility of:

1. Approaching the old perplexing problem of the treelessness of the steppe from a new angle. It seems that both views were apparently correct: that which, on the basis of historical evidence, old legends, etc., contended that forests existed in early times in the steppe, and that which claimed that the steppe soils bear no evidence of a former deforestation. A more detailed study of steppe depressions seems to offer the key to this problem.

2. Finding an explanation for the origin of the plant associations in relation to the microrelief.

3. Explaining the phenomenon of steppe swamping noted by almost all investigators.

4. Explaining the origin of the birch-aspen groves as the advanced posts in the invasion of the steppe by the forest.

5. Establishing with certainty the limits of the extension of the Post-Glacial steppes and deserts, and thereby simplifying the solution of a series of botanico-geogrpahical problems, such as plant successions, advance of pines, etc.

And for general geography, all that has been said about solonetz serves as new proof for the occurrence of a shift of physico-geographical zones towards the north after Post-Glacial times, during the period of the drying up of the surface from the glacial waters and of a reversal of this shift in later times; it offers the means to establish the border line of the physico-geographical zones during the Post-Glacial, epoch; and it helps to find an explanation for the origin of a number of peculiarities in present-day landscape of the valleys.

References

1. Abolin, R. I. 1913 In the taiga of the Lena-Vilyui valley. Report on the investigations of the soils in Asiatic Russia during 1912. (Russian). St. Petersburg. (After Vilenskii).

2. Akimtsev, V. V. 1937 Solodization of soils in Hinter-Caucasia. *Pedology* (U.S.S.R.) No. 1:33-64 (Extensive English summary).

3. Aleksandrova, L. N. 1944 On the composition of the humus of the soils of the solonetz complex. *Pedology* (U.S.S.R.) No. 10:471-481.

4. Andersson, G. 1900 Swedish climate in the late-Quarternary period. Die Veränderungen des Klimas seit dem Maximum der letzten Eiszeit. Stokholm.

5. Antevs, E. 1925 On the Pleistocene history of the Great Basin. *Carnegie Institution of Washington,* Publ. No. 352:51-114.

6. Antipov-Karataev, I. N. 1939 On the question of the genesis of the illuvial horizons in solonetz. *Pedology* (U.S.S.R.) No. 7:81-91.

7. Antipov-Karataev, I. N. and Sedletskii, I. D. 1937 Physicochemical processes of solonetz formation. *Pedology* (U.S.S.R.) No. 6: 883-907.

8. Barnes, J. H. and Ali, Barkat. 1917 Alkali soils; some biochemical factors in their reclamation. *Agr. Jour. India.* 12:368-389.

9. Bazilevich, N. I. 1947 On the problem of the genesis of solodi. *Pedology* (U.S.S.R.) No. 4:227-239.

10. Bentley, C. F. and Rost, C. O. 1947 A study of some solonetzic soil complexes in Saskatchewan. *Sci. Agr.* 27: 293-313.

11. Berg, L. S. 1908 The Aral Sea. *Izv. Otd. Russk. Geogr. Obshch.* v. 5, St. Petersburg.

12. Berg, L. S. 1911 On the climatic changes in our epoch. *Zemlevedenie.* Book III.

13. Berg, L. S. 1913 On the problem of the dislocation of climatic zones in the post-Glacial time. (Russian and French). *Pochvovedevie* (Pedology) 15, No. 4: 1-26.

14. Berg, L. S. 1922 Climate and Life (Russian). Moscow.

15. Bolyshev, N. N. and Evdokimova, T. I. 1944 On the nature of takyr crusts. *Pedology* (U.S.S.R.) No. 7-8: 345-352.

16. Breazeale, J. F. 1929 Magnesium and calcium in zeolitic soils. Arizona Agr. Expt. Sta. Tech. Bul. 26: 37-65.

17. Breazeale, J. F. and McGeorge, W. T. 1926 Sodium hydroxide rather than sodium carbonate the source of alkalinity in black alkali soils. Arizona Agr. Expt. Sta. Tech. Bul. 13: 307-335.

18. Briggs, L. J. and Lapham, M. H. 1902 Capillary studies and filtration of clay from soil solutions. U. S. Dept. of Agr., Bureau of Soils, Bul. 19.

19. Brodskii, A., and Yankovskaya, A. 1930 Contribution of the knowledge of the soil flora in the soils of Central Asia. *Pedology* (U.S. S.R.) No. 1-2: 32-70.

20. Burgess, P. S. 1928 Alkali soil: studies and methods of reclamation. Arizona Agr. Expt. Sta. Bul. 123: 157-181.

21. Burgess, P. S. and McGeorge, W. T. 1927 Zeolite formation and base exchange reactions in soils. Arizona Agr. Expt. Sta. Tech. Bul. 15: 359-399.

22. Burvill, G. H. 1947 Soil salinity in the agricultural area in Western Australia. *Jour. Aust. Inst. Agr. Sci.* 13: 9-19.

23. Bushinskii, V. P. 1923 The evolution of agriculture in southeastern Russia. *Sel. i Les. Khoz.* No. 8 (After Vilenskii).

24. Cameron, F. K. 1902 Formation of sodium carbonate, or black alkali by plants. U.S.D.A. Rpt. No. 71, pp. 61-70.

25. Cameron, F. K. 1911 The soil solution. pp. V + 136. Easton, Pa.

26. Clarke, F. W. 1924 The data of geochemistry. United States Geol. Survey Bul. 770.

27. Cummins, A. B., and Kelley, W. P. 1923 The formation of sodium carbonate in soils. Calif. Agr. Exp. Sta. Tech. Paper 3: 1-35.

28. Davis, W. M. 1898 Geographical cycles. *Geog. Jour.* 14: 481-504.

29. Davy, J. B. 1895-1897 Investigations on the native vegetation of alkali lands. *Cal. Sta. Rpt.* pp. 53-75.

30. Dimo, N. A. 1911 The effect of artificial irrigation and of the natural supply of moisture on the soil forming processes and on the translocation of salts in the Golodnaya steppe, Samarkand region (Russian). Saratov.

31. Dimo, N. A. 1913 The chief types of salinization of soils on the territory of Russia. Ezhegodnik Otdel. Zemled. Uluchsch. za 1913. Pt. I, St. Petersburg.

32. Dokuchaev, V. V. 1892 Our steppes, in the past and at present (Russian). St. Petersburg.

33. Dolenko, G. I. 1913 The Lena River valley near Yakutsk. Prelim. rept. on the investigations of the soils in Asiatic Russia during 1913. St. Petersburg; also report for 1914. (After Vilenskii).

34. Dorsey, C. W. 1906 Alkali soils of the United States. U.S.D.A. Bur. of Soils Bul. 35.

35. Drantisyn, L. N. 1915 Contributions to the pedology and geology of the Western portion of the Narymsk region (Russian). Trudy pochv. -botan. expeditsii po issled. kolon. raionov Aziat. Rossii, pt. I. Petrograd.

36. Dranitsyn, D. A. 1916 Northern Enisei river expedition. Prelim. rpt. on the investigations of the soils in Asiatic Russia during 1914 (Russian). Petrograd. (After Vilenskii).

37. Drude, O. N. 1910 Die Veränderung des Klimas seit dem Maxim, der letzten Eiszeit. Stokholm.

38. Dubyanskii, A. A. 1915 A hydrological sketch of Belui Kolodetz, Voronezh government, Valuisk county. *Izv. Dokuchaev. Pochv. Komit.* No. 1.

39. Ellis, J. H. and Caldwell, O. G. 1935 Magnesium clay solonetz. *Trans. Third Intern. Cong. Soil Sci.* 1:348-350.

40. Gardner, R. 1945 Some soil properties related to the sodium salt problem in irrigated soils. U. S. Dept. of Agr. Tech. Bul 902.

41. Gedroiz, K. K. 1912 Colloid chemistry in problems of pedology. *Zhur. Opyt. Agron.* (Russian) 13:363-420.

42. Gedroiz, K. K. 1926 The solodization of soil. Nosovsk. Sel'sko-Khoz. Opyt. Stantziya, Bul. 44.

43. Gedroiz, K. K. 1928 Solonetz, its origin, properties, and amelioration. Nosovsk. Sel'sko-Khoz. Opyt. Stantziya Bul. 46.

44 Gedroiz, K. K. 1929 On the absorbing properties of soils. (Russian). Novaya Derevnya. Moscow-Leningrad, 1-156. A German translation is available.

45. Genkel (Henkel), P. A. and Danini, E. M. 1935 The microbial characteristics of solonetz. *Trudy Biol. nauch. Issled. Inst. Perm Gosud. Univ.* v. 7, No .1-2: 95-118.

46. Gerasimov, I. P. 1921 About takyrs and the process of their formation. *Pedology* (U.S.S.R.) No. 4: 5-13.

47. Gerasimov, I. P. and Ivanova, E. N. 1936 On the geographic types of the salt balance and the forms of salt exchange in the crust of weathering. *Problemy Fiziches. Geographii,* Bul. III, Acad. Sci., 31-52.

48. Germanov, F. N. 1932 Methods of counting bacteria in soils (German). *Proceed. and Papers. Second Inter Soil Sci. Congress,* 3: 239-247.

49. Germanov, F. N. 1933 The biology and biodynamics of solonchak, solonetz, and solodi. *Pedology* (U.S.S.R.) No. 3: 203-208.

50. Gor'kova. I. 1937 Some obscure problems of the contemporary theory on saline soils. *Pedology* (U.S.S.R) No. 1: 93-98.

51. Gorshenin, K. P. 1927 The soils of the chernozem belt of western Siberia. Omsk.

52. Greaves, J. D. 1929 The microflora of leached alkali soils: I. Synthetic alkali soil. *Soil Sci.* 28: 341-346; II. A leached NaCl soil. *Soil Sci.* 29:79-83.

53. Greaves, J. E. 1927 The microflora and productivity of leached and non-leached alkali soil. *Soil Sci.* 23:271-302.

54. Greaves, J. E. and Greaves, J. D. 1930 The microflora of leached soil. *Bot. Gaz.* 90: 224-230.

55. Harris, F. S. 1920 Soil Alkali. John Wiley and Sons, New York.

56. Headden, W. P. 1914 The excessive quantities of nitrates in certain Colorado soils. *Jour. Ind. Engin. Chem.* 6:586-590.

57. Headden, W. P. 1918 Alkalies in Colorado. Colo. St. Bul. 186.

58. Headaden, W. P. 1922 Fixation of K in Colorado soils. Col. Agr. Expt. Sta. Bul. 277, pp. 48.

59. Hilgard, E. W. 1892 A report on the relation of soil to climate. Bul. No. 3, Weather Bureau, U. S. Dept. of Agriculture, 1-59.

60. Hissink, D. J. 1922 Beitrag zur Kenntnis der Adsorptions Vorgänge im Boden. *Inter. Mitt. Bodenk.* 12: 81-172.

61. Il'in, P. S. 1930 Nature studies in the Narymsk region (Russian) Tomsk.

62. Ivanova, E. N. 1930 Contribution to the study of the solodi process in the soils of Western Siberia. *Trudy Pochven. Inst. Imeni Dokuchaeva,* No. 3-4: 207-284.

63. Ivanova, E. N. and Rozanov, A. N. 1939 Classification of salinized soils. *Pedology* (U.S.S.R.) No. 7: 44-52.

64. Izmailskii, A. S. 1894 Soil moisture and the water table in relation to the topography and cultural conditions of the surface of the soil (Russian). Poltava.

65. Joffe, J. S. and McLean, H. C. 1924 Alkali soil investigations. I: A consideration of some colloidal phenomena. *Soil Sci.* 17: 395-409. II: Origin of alkali soils; physical effects of treatments. *Soil Sci.* 18: 13-30. III: Chemical effect of treatments. *Soil Sci.* 18: 133-149. IV: Chemical and biological effects of treatments. *Soil Sci.* 18: 237-251.

66. Joffe, J. S. and Zimmerman, Miryam. 1944. Sodium, calcium and magnesium ratios in the exchange complex. *Proc. Soil Sci. Soc. Amer.* 9: 51-55.

67. Keller, B. A. 1929 The accumulation of salts in plants and saline soils (Russian). *Trudy Botan. Opyt. Stan. Imeni Kellera,* No. 1. Voronezh (Quoted from Kovda).

68. Keller, B. A. and Karel'skaya, A. F. 1926 Investigations in the realm of the geography and ecology of soil microbes. (Russian). *Piroda i. sel.-khoz. zasushl obl. U.S.S.R.* No. 1-2 (After Prikhodko and Belikova).

69. Kelley, W. P. 1934 The so-called solonetz soils of California and their relation to alkali soils. *Amer. Soil Survey Assn. Bul.* 5: 45-52.

70. Kelley, W. P. 1934 The formation, evolution, reclamation, and the absorbed bases of alkali soils. *Jour. Agr. Sci.* 24: 72-92.

71. Kelley, W. P. 1937 The reclamation of alkali soils. Calif. Agr. Expt. Sta. Bul. 617.

72. Kelley, W. P. and Arany, A. 1928 The chemical effect of gypsum, sulfur, iron sulfate, and alum on alkali soil. *Hilgardia* 3: 393-420.

73. Kelley, W. P. and Brown, S. M. 1921 The solubility of anions in alkali soils. *Soil Sci.* 12: 261-285.

74. Kelley, W. P. and Brown, S. M. 1923 The removal of sodium carbonate from soils. Calif. Agr. Exp. Sta. Tech. Paper No. 1: 1-24.

75. Kelley, W. P. and Brown, S. M. 1924 Replaceable bases in soils. Calif. Agr. Exp. Sta. Tech. Paper 15: 1-39.

76. Kelley, W. P. and Brown, S. M. 1925 Base exchange in relation to alkali soils. *Soil Sci.* 20: 477-495.

77. Kelley, W. P. and Thomas, E. E. 1928 Reclamation of the Fresno type of black-alkali soil. Calif. Agr. Exp. Sta. Bul. 455.

78. Kossovich, P. S. 1903 Solonetz, the relation of plants to this type of soil and the methods of determining the degree of solonetzosity. *Zhur. Opyt. Agron.* 4: 1-42.

79. Kossovich, P. S. O krugovorote sery i khlora na zemnom share (On the cycle of sulfur and chlorine on earth). Bureau of Agr. and Soils, St. Petersburg. Reprint from the *"Zhurnal Opytnoi Agronomii,"* 14, 18.

80. Kostychev, S. P. 1930 The mobilization of soil nitrogen and nitrification in the Bukhara nitrate deposits (Russian). *Trudy Inst. Sel.-Khoz. Mikrobiol.* v. 4 (Quoted from Bolyshev and Evdokimova).

81. Kovda, V. A. 1937 Solonchaki i solontzy (Solonchak and solonetz). Acad. of Sci. (U.S.S.R.), Dokuchaev Soil Inst. Leningrad-Moscow, pp. 243.

82. Kovda, V. A. 1940 The movement and accumulation of silica in salinized soils. *Trans. Dokuchaev Soil Inst.* v. 22, No. 1: 3-30.

83. Kovda, V. A. 1944 Biological cycles in the movement and accumulation of salts. *Pedology* (U.S.S.R.) No. 4-5: 144-158.

84. Kovda, V. A. 1946 Proiskhozhdenie i rezhim zasolennykh pochv (Origin and regime of saline soils). v I Academy of Sci. Moscow.

85. Kropotkin, P. 1904 The desiccation of Eurasia. *Geog. Jour.* 23 (From Vilenskii).

86. Krause, E. H. L. 1893 Die salzigen Gefilde. Ein Versuch die zoologischen Ergebnisse der europäischen Quartarforschung mit den botanischen in Einklang zu bringen. *Engler's Bot. Jahrb.* Bd. 17, H. 1-2 (Beibl. 40, pp. 21-31).

87. Lapham, M. H. 1932 Genesis and morphology of desert soils. *Amer. Soil Survey Assoc. Bul.* 13: 34-52.

88. Linck, G. 1912 Kreislaufvorgänge in der Erdgeschichte; also: Kreislauf der Stoffe in der anorganischer Natur. Handwörterbuch der Naturwissenschaften (1934), Band 5.

89. MacGregor, J. M. and Wyatt, F. A. 1945 Studies on solonetz soils of Alberta. *Soil Sci.* 59: 419-435.

90. Mamaeva, L. Ya. 1940 The composition of salt concretions of the Transvolga region. *Trans. Dokuchaev Soil Inst.* (U.S.S.R.) 22, No. 1: 91-104.

91. Mattson, S. 1927 The influence of exchangeable bases on the colloidal behavior of soil materials. *Proc. and Papers of the First Inter. Congr. Soil Sci.* 2: 185-198.

92. McGeorge, W. T., Breazeale, J. F. and Burgess, P. S. 1926 Aluminum hydroxide in alkali soils and its effect upon permeability. Arizona Agr. Expt. Sta. Tech. Bul. 12: 257-305.

93. Michtell, J. 1937 Alkali soils in Saskatchewan. *Sci. Agr.* (Canada) 18: 120-125.

93a. Mitchell, J. and Riecken, F. F. 1937 The chemical nature of some typical soil profiles of Saskatchewan. *Sci. Agr.* (Canada) 18: 109-119.

94. Nikiforoff, C. C. 1930 Solonetz and solonchak soils of the Red River. *Amer. Soil Survey Assoc. Bul.* 11: 141-150.

95. Nikiforoff, C. C. 1937 Solonetz-like soils in Southern California. *Jour. Amer. Soc. Agron.* 29: 781-797.

96. Odynsky, W. 1945 Solonetz soils in Alberta. *Sci. Agr.* (Canada) 25: 780-790.

97. Orlovskii, N. V. 1930 The natural fertility factors of a solonetzic chestnut soil. Zapadno-Kazakhstan. Sel'sko-Khoz. Opyt, Stantz. Bul. 4.

98. Orlovskii, N. V. 1941 Salinization of soils in western Siberia (Russian). Gosurdarstv. izdatel., Novosibirsk.

99. Otryganiev, A. V. 1910 A short description of the western portion of the Narymsk region. Mater. po izuchen. kolon, raion. Aziat. Rossii. St. Petersburg.

100. Pachoskii, I. 1908 Steppes of the Black Sea region. Zap. Obshch. Sel. Khoz. Yuzh. Rossii.

101. Pachoskii, I. 1912 Marsh solonetz on the lower Dnieper. *Trudy Bot. Sada Yur'ev. Univ.* v. 13.

102. Pankov, A. M. and Shavrygin, P. I. 1934 On the composition of the absorption complex of the soils in the Primanych area. *Trudy Pochv. Inst. Acad. Nauk* (U.S.S.R.) 9: 205-235.

103. Penck, A. 1913 Die Formen der Landoberfläche und Verschiebungen der Klimagürtel. *Sitzungsber. Preuss. Akad. Wiss.* 77-97. Berlin.

104. Polynov, B. and Bystrov, S. 1932 Soluble salt changes in its circulation through the soil. *Pedology* (U.S.S.R.) 27: 298-303.

105. Ponomarev, G. M. and Sedletskii, I. D. 1940 The genesis of chernozem and solonetz soils in the Chernigov forest steppe. *Trans. Dokuchaev Soil Inst., Acad Sci.* (U.S.S.R.) 24: 243-307.

106. Prasolov, L. I. and Antipov-Karataev, I. N. 1929 On the solonetzic character of chestnut brown soils of Ergeni and methods of determining it. *Trudy Pochven, Inst. imeni Dokuchaeva.* No. 3-4: 161-206.

107. Prasolov, L. I., and Antipov-Karataev, I. N. 1939 The chestnut brown soils. *Soils of the U.S.S.R.* No. 1, Moscow-Leningrad.

108. Prikhodko, M., and Belikova, M. 1929 On the biodynamics of salinized soils. *Pedology* (U.S.S.R.) No. 3-4: 145-167.

109. Remezov, N. P. 1938 Exchange capacity and composition of exchangeable cations in the chief soil types. *Pedology* (U.S.S.R.) No. 5: 639-694 (A list of 265 Russian references is given).

110. Riecken, F. F. 1943 Some considerations in the magnesium cycle of weathering of solonetz. *Proc. Soil Sci. Soc. Amer.* 8: 391-395.

111. Rokitskaya, A. I. 1928 The microflora of the soils in the Golodnaya steppe of the Samarkand province in Turkestan. *Izv. Nauch. Melioratz. Inst. Bul.* No. 17: 105-184.

112. Rokitzkaya, A. I. 1931 The microflora in the soils of the Zolotaya Orda, Turkestan. *Pedology* (U.S.S.R.) No. 1: 35-79.

113. Rost, C. O. 1936 Characteristics of some morphological solonetz soils of Minnesota. *Jour. Amer. Soc. Agron.* 28: 92-105.

114. Rost ,C. O. and Chang, P. C. 1941 Exchangeable bases of solonchak of the Red River Valley. *Proc. Soil Sci. Soc. Amer.* 6: 354-359.

115. Rost, C. O. and Maehl, K. A. 1943 Some solodized soils of the Red River Valley. *Soil Sci.* 55: 301-312.

116. Rozanov, A. N. 1939 Soda-solonetz and solodized soils of the valley of the river Chu. *Problemy Sovet. Pochvoved.* No. 9: 3-6.

117. Rozmakhov, I. G. 1940 Origin and development of solonetz complexes. *Trudy Pochv. Inst. imeni. Dokuchaev.* 22, No. 1: 31-87 (English summary).

118. Rozov, L. P. 1932 The solonetzic process and amelioration. Trans. *6th Commission Inter. Soc. Soil Sci.* (Russian Section). Vol. A: 30-69 (in English).

119. Rozov, L. P. 1932 The solonetz process in relation to amelioration. *Pedology* (U.S.S.R.) No. 4: 304-341.

120. Ryabinin, A. N. 1909 Excavating lions in the Urals and Hinter-Volga region. *Trudy Geolog. Komit. Nov. Ser.,* Vypusk 168.

121. Rybakov, M. M. 1939 The solodization of soils in the chernozem zone. *Problemy Sovet. Pochvoved.* No. 9.

122. Sackett, W. G. 1914 The nitrifying capacity of Colorado soils. Col. Agr. Expt. Sta. Bul. 193.

123. Samsonov, P. F., Samsonova, F. M., and Chernova, T. A. 1930 Microbiological characteristics of soil in Central Asia. *Pedology* (U.S.S.R.) No. 1-2: 71-99: No. 3: 74-103. See also *Pedology* (U.S.S.R.) (1929) 3-4: 5-33.

124. Schachtschabel, P. 1941 Untersuchungen über die Sorption der Tonmineralien und organische Bodenkolloide. *Bodenk. u. Pflanzenernäh.* 23: 1-17. See also Ref. 79, Ch. 4.

125. Selyakov, S. N. 1941 Nitrate chloride solonchaks and the salpeter deposits of Middle Asia. *Trans. Dokuchaev Soil Inst.* (U.S.S.R.) 22, No. 2: 1-81 (English summary 82-84).

126. Sharov, V. S. 1936 Method of determining the swelling capacity of clays and soils. *Pedology* (U.S.S.R.) No. 2: 299-301.

127. Shaw, Ch. F. and Kelley, W. P. 1935 The meaning of the term solonetz. *Proc. Third Inter. Congr. Soil Sci.* v. 1: 330.

128. Sibirtzev, N. 1897 Etude des Sols de la Russie. Congress International 7-eme Sessions, Russie, p. 118.

129. Sigmond, A. A. J. de 1926 Contribution to the theory of the origin of alkali soils. *Soils Sci.* 21: 455-479.

130. Sigmond, A. A. J. de 1927 Hungarian alkali soils and methods of their reclamation. University of California. (Translation from Hungarian).

131. Sigmond, A. A. J. de 1928 The classification of alkali and salty soils. *Proc. and Papers First Inter. Congr. of Soil Sci.,* v. 1: 330-344.

132. Signond, A. A. J. de 1929 Report on the genetics of alkali soils. Trans. of the Alkali Subcommission of the *Inter. Soc. of Soil Sci.* v.A: 5-8.

133. Sigmond, A. A. J. de 1938 The Principles of Soil Science. Thomas Murby and Co. London.

134. Sigmond, A. A. J. de, and Arany, A. 1929 A bibliography relating to alkali (saline) soils. Trans. of the Alkali Subcommis. of the *Inter. Soc. of Soil Science.*, v.A: 41-80.

135. Sokolov, N. A. 1909 On the history of the steppes adjoining the Black Sea from the late Tertiary period on (Russian). (After Vilenskii).

136. Sokolovskii, A. N. 1921 (1919) From the realm of phenomena related to the colloidal fraction of the soil. *Izvestia Petrovskoi Sel'-sko-Khoz. Akademii* (Moscow). No. 1-4: 85-225.

137. Sokolovskii, A. N. 1941 Salinized soils as one of the manifestations of salt phenomena on the surface of the earth. *Pedology* (U.S.-S.R.) No. 7-8: 3-29.

138. Stewart, R. 1913 The intensity of nitrification in arid soil. *Centrbl. Bakt.* II, 36: 477-490.

139. Stewart, R. and Peterson, W. 1927 Origin of alkali. *Jour. Agr. Res.* 10: 331-353.

140. Storie, R. E. 1933 Profile studies of the solonetz soils of California. *Amer. Soil Sur. Assoc. Bul.* 14: 43-46.

141. Storie, R. E. 1933 The classification and evaluation of the soils of Western San Diego County. Univ. of Cal., College of Agr. Expt. Sta. Bul. 552.

142. Sushkina, N. N. 1935 On the occurrence of Azotobacter in soils of the southern steppe region of the U.S.S.R. (In English). *Studies in Genesis and Geography of Soils, Acad. Sci., Dokuchaev Soil Inst.* Bul. 1: 159-169.

143. Sushko, E. S. 1934 Soil crusts in cotton fields. *Trudy Leningr. lab. VIYA.* No. 34: 17-26.

144. Sushko, S. Ya. 1932 Genesis of takyrs and methods of amelioration. *Pedology* (U.S.S.R.) 27: 452-461.

145. Szabo, J. 1861 A treatise on the geology and soils of the counties of Bekes and Csamad. Pest. (After Sigmond).

146. Tanfiliev, G. I. 1912 Is there evidence showing that the climate in southern Russia fluctuated during the Post-Glacial epoch? *Pochvovedenie* (Pedology) No. 2: 31-47.

147. Tanfiliev, G. I. 1928 On the origin of chernozem and the South Russian steppe (German). *Pedology* (U.S.S.R.) No. 1-2: 5-23.

148. Traphagen, F. W. 1904 The alkali soils of Montana. Mont. Sta. Bul. 54.

149. Treitz, P. 1928 Preliminary report on the alkali land investigations of the Hungarian great plain for 1926. *Proc. and Papers First Inter. Cong. Soil Sci.* 4: 589-600.

150. Tulaikov, N. M. 1907 Some laboratory experiments on the capillarity of soils. *Zhurnal Opyt. Agron.* 8: 629-666.

151. Tulaikov, N. M. 1922 Solonetz, its improvement and utilization. (Russian). Narodny Kommissariat Zemledeliya, opytnoameliorativnaya chast', Bul. 16: 1-233.

152. Tutkovskii, P. A. 1899 On the problem of loess formation Zemlevedenie. (After Vilenskii).

153 Uspanov, U. U. 1940 The genesis and reclamation of takyrs (Russian). *Trans. Dokuchaev Inst.* 19. No. 1: 3-116.

154. Vilenskii, D. G. 1924 Salinized Soils, their Origin, Composition, and Methods of Amelioration. (Russian). Novaya Derevnya, Moscow.

155. Vilenskii, D. G. 1927 Alkali soils of Ukraine. Contribution to the study of Ukraine; Report to the First Inter. Cong. Soil Sci., No. 6. pp. 107-128 (In English).

156. Vilenskii, D. G. 1930 Saline and alkali soils of the U.S.S.R. *Pedology* (U.S.S.R.) No. 4: 32-86.

157. Vilenskii, D. G. 1938 Investigations on the salinization of the soils in the Bugaz Valley and the composition of the waters of the Sumgait-Chai river in Azerbaidzhan U. S. S. R. *Trudy Nauch. Issledovat. Inst. Pochvoved.* Moscov.-Gosudar. Univ. No. 18 (Pochvovedenie): 111-159.

158. Whitney, M., and Means, T. H. 1898 The alkali soils of the Yellowstone Valley. U.S.D.A. Bur. of Soils Bul. 14.

CHAPTER XV

HYDROMORPHIC AND FLUVIOGENIC SOILS
Bog and Marsh Soils

The inclusion of all kinds of peats, mucks, and "organic soils" in general in the bog and marsh type of soil formation is not justified. We must draw the line between the peats as a geologic formation and peat-bog soils exhibiting some characteristics of a soil profile as defined in this treatise. But few pedologic investigations have been made on representative specimens of bog and marsh soils. With our present store of knowledge of these soils, therefore, no sharp line of division can be made between a peat soil and a peat geologic deposit, although the extremes of these may easily be differentiated.

We also need to differentiate the concepts bog and marsh. According to Dachnowski (7):

> *Marsh (fen), bog, heath,* and *swamp* are terms used largely on account of the well marked physiognomy of vegetation which they represent and because they are common names in many languages. The plant remains of each group accumulating as peat are among the most distinctive of peat materials, and the field conditions of each have a more or less differentiating character. The deposits are quite variable in origin and structure, but their structure is primarily dependent on the form of the land surface on which they are found and upon the height of the water table while they are formed.
>
> The words "marsh" and "swamp" on the one hand, and "bog" and "heath" on the other, correspond, in a very general way, with the terms "Flachmoor" and "Hochmoor" used by most European writers. The line of distinction and the transition between them is, of course, nothing like as sharp as the terms would seem to indicate except in regions having climatic conditions where they reach their best development. "Hochmoor" is applied, as a rule, to a class of peat land which rises from the edges toward the middle and thus shows a convex upper surface. "Hochmoor," or "raised bog," develops typically in regions of high humidity or rainfall, partly on account of the habit of growth of the sphagnum mosses which form the main component of the surface vegetation cover. "Flachmoor" represents a class of peat land with a flat or even a slightly concave surface. Often a distinction is made on the basis of chemical differences, especially the absence or presence of lime or of acid reaction, but this distinction is not exact.

From the standpoint of the process of soil formation, both the bog and marsh have a number of similar features. Both are restricted in their eluviation reactions, both undergo changes due to anaerobic conditions. They differ, however, in the character of the biosphere, the marshes harboring, according to Dachnowski, primarily "sedges, reeds, cat-tails, rushes and grasses," the bogs, at first localized plant associations of the marsh stage and later heath, mosses, and sedges which "inhibit the natural growth of plants other than the bog xerophytes." In bogs and marshes, certain true

596

species—deciduous and coniferous—establish themselves and naturally aid in supplying the reactive agents for the soil-forming processes. Besides the two types mentioned, there are a number of other sub-divisions, such as fresh and salt water marsh.

Since no divisional pedological investigations have been made on the bog and marsh soils, both types of soil formation will be discussed as one, the term moor being applied to both.

MOORS

An examination of the map of the northern hemisphere shows that the northern portions of America, Europe, and Asia abound in lakes and are honeycombed with streams. In conjunction with this network of water basins, vast stretches of marshes and bogs dot the landscape. A great many marshes are also found in the southern temperate, subtropical, and tropical regions, as pointed out elsewhere in this treatise.

Most estimates of bog and marsh land have been made in connection with surveys on peat deposits. For the United States, the area has not been determined with any degree of accuracy: it has been variously estimated to be from 65 to 102 millions of acres. Dachnowski (8, 9), the authority in the United States on this subject, cites the estimate made by Elliott; the data are reproduced in table 138. This area is exclusive of the coast lands which are overflowed by tidewater.

The distribution and nature of moor soils in western Europe has been studied by a number of investigators. The widespread distribution of fresh water and salt marshes and bogs along the North and Baltic seas stimulated studies by German, Dutch, Swiss, Scandinavian, and other workers. Of these, one might mention the early investigations of Stelzner (32), Senft (31), Müller (Ch. 5, 70), Virchow (40), Thoms (37), Van Bemmelen (2), and others, who contributed fundamental knowledge about marshes and bogs and the resulting peat formations. At the beginning of the century, the interest in these formations was greatly stimulated, and we had a series of investigations covering a great many angles of the problem under consideration, even though the pedogenic point of view was neglected. There was the work of Westermann (42) on the moor soils in Denmark; Früh and Schroter (16) on the moors of Switzerland; of Weber (41), Tacke (34), Schreiber (28), Minssen (25), Schucht (29), and a great many others,* on the moor soils, peat deposits, and related formations in

---

*An extensive discussion on marshes, bogs, peat formations, and peat soils is given by Tacke in Blanck's "Handbuch der Bodenlehre," v. 4 (1930). An extensive bibliography on the subject is given in the "Internationale Mitteilungen für Boden-kunde," v.10 (1920), pp. 153-168 and 233-248, and in the "Literatursammlung aus dem Gesamtgebiet der Agrikulturchemie," Band I, Bodenkunde (1931), by Niklas, Czi-bulka, and Hock.

Table 138

Classification of unreclaimed swamp and overflowedd land

(After Elliott, from Senate Document 443, 6th Congress, 1st Section, 1908)

States	Permanent swamp	Wet grazing land	Periodically overflowed	Periodically swampy	Total
	acres	*acres*	*acres*	*acres*	*acres*
Alabama	900,000	59,200	520,000	——	1,479,200
Arkansas	5,200,000	50,000	531,000	131,300	5,912,300
California	1,000,000	1,000,000	1,420,000	——	3,420,000
Connecticut	——	10,000	20,000	——	30,000
Delaware	50,000	50,000	27,000	200	127,200
Florida	18,000,000	——	1,000,000	800,000	19,800,000
Georgia	1,000,000	——	1,000,000	700,000	2,700,000
Illinois	25,000	500,000	400,000	——	925,000
Indiana	15,000	100,000	500,000	10,000	625,000
Iowa	300,000	200,000	350,000	80,500	930,500
Kansas	——	59,380	300,000	——	359,380
Kentucky	——	100,000	300,000	44,600	444,600
Louisiana	9,000,000	——	1,196,605	——	10,196,605
Maryland	100,000	——	92,000	——	192,000
Maine	156,520	——	——	——	156,520
Massachusetts	20,000	——	39,500	——	59,500
Michigan	2,000,000	947,439	——	——	2,947,439
Minnesota	3,048,000	2,000,000	——	784,308	5,832,208
Mississippi	3,000,000	——	2,760,200	——	5,760,200
Missouri	1,000,000	——	1,439,600	——	2,439,600
Nebraska	——	100,000	412,100	——	512,100
New Hampshire	5,000	——	7,700	——	12,700
New Jersey	326,400	——	——	——	326,400
New York	100,000	100,000	329,100	——	529,100
North Carolina	1,000,000	500,000	500,000	748,160	2,748,160
North Dakota	50,000	50,000	50,000	50,000	200,000
Ohio	——	——	100,000	55,047	155,047
Oklahoma	——	——	31,500	——	31,500
Oregon	254,000	——	——	——	254,000
Pennsylvania	——	——	50,000	——	50,000
Rhode Island	——	——	6,000	2,064	8,064
South Carolina	1,500,000	——	622,120	1,000,000	3,122,120
South Dakota	100,000	——	511,480	——	611,480
Tennessee	639,600	——	——	——	639,600
Texas	1,240,000	1,000,000	——	——	2,240,000
Vermont	15,000	——	8,000	——	23,000
Virginia	600,000	——	200,000	——	800,000
Washington	20,500	——	——	——	20,500
West Virginia	——	——	23,900	——	23,900
Wisconsin	2,000,000	——	——	360,000	2,360,000
Total	52,665,020	6,826,019	14,747,805	4,766,179	79,005,023

Germany; of Feilitzen (15) and others on similar formations in Sweden; and of Cajander (6) on the moors of Finland.

A number of contributions on the nature and distribution of marshes, bogs, and peats in Russia have appeared; some of them stand in a class by themselves, having given to the investigations a certain pedologic slant. Foremost among these contributions are those of Tanfiliev (35, 36) who for more than three decades pioneered in his researches on marshes and bogs; of Sukachev (33) who investigated the profile constitution of the tundra marshes and other hydromorphic formations in the temperate zone; of Dokturovskii (13) whose monograph covers the subject thoroughly; of Dranitsyn (14) who concerned himself primarily with the profile of the various types of marsh and bog soils; of Kirsanov (22a) who investigated the peat soils of White Russia; and of many others, reference to which has been made extensively by Dokturovskii.

The soils of the marsh and bog type of soil formation are also encountered in other regions. Thus, Zakharov (Ch. 2, 91) points out the existence of leached, gray, moist meadow soils in the hollows and depressions of the chernozem zone. At the foot of river terraces, marly and ferrugenous meadow-bottom or bench soils are a common occurrence. In the chestnut brown zone, we may observe, he says, "chernozem-like and dark colored soils in the depressions and limans, and similar dark and gray soils may be found in the flood plains. In the latter, rushes and reeds predominate. The soils are not highly leached, are alkaline, and frequently contain soluble salts," an indication of the solonchakic process. "In the gray soil zone, analogous meadow soils rich in organic matter are found in the depressions. Some of the mountain meadows soils belong to this group of hydrogenic soils."

Most of these, and many other contributions, have been summarized from the pedologic point of view by Glinka (Ch. 2, 27), Zakharov (Ch. 2, 91), Tyurin (Ch. 10, 63), and Kravkov (Ch. 6, 20) in their respective texts on pedology. A digest of what these authorities have to say follows:

Morphological and Chemical Properties of Moor Soils.—The morphological constitution of a moor profile in its general outlines is as follows:

A_0: Organic matter debris in various stages of decomposition, ranging in depth from a few centimeters to several decimeters; it is known as the peat horizon.

A_1: Dark colored layer, sometimes even black, varying in depth; it is a mixture of humus and mineral constituents.

A_2 Lighter in color than A_1, frequently showing podzol features.

B: Spotted, rusty or brown in color, ocherous-glei.

G: Bluish gray glei.

Depending on the degree of swamping, type of mineral constituents, drainage, vegetation, seasonal rainfall, temperature distribution, etc., the morphological features described vary. Under certain conditions, only three or even two horizons may be distinguished.

The primary feature of the moor type of soil formation is the excess of moisture which disturbs the natural course of events in the process of soil formation. It impedes eluviation because of the poor leaching capacity of the waterlogged G and infrequently B and even A horizons. There is also a definite effect on the process of illuviation, inasmuch as the waterlogged condition reduces the oxidation potential, increasing thereby the reduction potential, and allows a rise of substances from the ground waters to the horizon of illuviation. We are thus confronted with a new set of reactions running parallel with the normal reactions of eluviation and illuviation.

Because of the moisture conditions in the moor type of soil formation, anaerobic microbial activities set in, resulting in the formation of substances of a lower state of oxidation, such as methane, H_2S, etc. Incompletely oxidized organic substances and slightly carbonized plant residues accumulate on the surface and constitute the peat layer, the A_0 of this type of soil formation.

Nothwithstanding the poor leaching capacity of these soils, there is definite eluviation. Because of the prevailing condition of moisture saturation, the sesquioxides have no chance to age and they easily move downward to be precipitated in the horizon of illuviation, where the pH is higher, as ocherous spots and sometimes even as a continuous layer. In the formation of the latter, the composition of the ground waters is an important consideration. If the ground waters are rich in iron and aluminum, these constituents precipitate as they come in contact with the horizon of illuviation. Together with the R_2O_3 from above, the enrichment of iron at the horizon of illuviation may thus become of considerable moment. Some of the bog-iron deposits may be traced to the process described.

Under conditions of continuous saturation with water, some of the iron is reduced, especially in the presence of some organic substances. The color changes from rusty brown to bluish gray or greenish-bluish-gray, with the characteristic mottling effects. Rusty spots occur along the root paths where there is a chance for aeration at periods when the water table recedes. According to Glinka, vivianite ($Fe_3(PO_4)_2 8H_2O$) pyrite (FeS_2), marcasite (FeS_2), and crystalline and amorphous $FeCO_3$ (siderite) are found at this point in the profile. Hilgard (Ch. 2, 30, p. 44) also discusses the accumulation and formation of bog areas and their transformations with the change in moisture regime of the soil. This layer in the profile is known as the glei horizon and is designated by the letter G (see p. 418).

Among the moor soils more thoroughly investigated, morphologically and chemically, are those of the cool temperate regions. Glinka (Ch. 2, 27) divides them into two chief groups: fresh-water moor soils, and seaboard marsh soils.

Fresh-Water Moor

Fresh-water moor soils may be classified first of all on the basis of the character of the plant remains which take part in the formation of these soils. In this respect they may roughly be divided into peat-bog and silty bog related to each other through a number of transition forms. Besides the classification-earmark mentioned, there are others, namely; degree of swamping, mechanical composition, etc. The influence of the degree of swamping is most easily followed in places where the wet meadow or silty bog gradually changes in the neighborhood of a slope. Entering the lower third of the slope, there is a gradual change from a silty bog into a podzolic peat-bog and podzolic-glei soil, which in turn gradually change to a soil of the meadow or forest podzol type. The characteristic features of the moor type of soil formation gradually disappear, to be replaced by those of the podzol type.

The profile of a typical silty bog soil is as follows:

A: The surface horizon is dark, often black, and contains undecomposed plant remains. It is impregnated and spotted with brown streamers and spots of hydrated iron oxide. Occasionally, the lower part of the horizon is darker than the rest because of the presence of carbonized plant remains. Since the deeper lying soil horizons are less accessible to the air than the surface horizons, their organic matter decomposes more slowly than that in the surface horizons. The thickness of this horizon varies, but generally it is fairly deep.

G: The second horizon, which may be called the glei because it forms not only by the percolation effects but also by the rising ground waters, is characterized by bluish, light blue, and greenish tinges. These are due to the reduction processes which ensue because of the waterlogged conditions, primarily by the ferrous compounds of iron. Vivianite ($Fe_3(PO_4)_2.8H_2O$) is one of the Fe compounds encountered. In the unoxidized state it is white in color, but with the first traces of oxidation it takes on a bluish hue. Upon further oxidation, the ferro-phosphate compounds are converted into ferri compounds which give rise to a series of intermediate compounds. It is to be noted that frequently we find in the G horizon rusty splotches and streaks which have been formed in cracks and root cavities because of the more ready access of oxygen in such places.

The presence of vivianite in moor soils is, in all probability, due to the interaction of ammonium phosphate with the ferrous compounds in solution. It is conceivable that in the moor soils the ammonium compounds are more easily retained than in soils properly aerated; nitrification is impeded. This might explain the formation of ammonium phosphate. During the dry summer period, some bogs dry out enough to admit oxygen, and the ferrous compounds become oxidized. Pyrite and marcasite give rise to the formation of a series of sulfate compounds, and in some cases alumnium sulfate enters into circulation.

Seaboard Marsh Soils

Generally speaking, marsh soils are not associated with the seaboard only. They are prevalent also along low-lying lands over river flood-plains, estuaries, deltas, and lake outlets. The German word *Marsch* (Plattdeutch *Mar,* English *Marsh*) has, according to Stelzner (32), the same root as the Latin word *Mar.* Etymologically, therefore, marsh should include those soils whose parent material was built up by the sea. This, however, is not the case. Under the term marsh, a wide range of fresh and salt water formations is implied.

A characteristic feature of the marsh soils is their origin through the process of sediment deposition, either by the river currents or by wave action and tidewaters.

Glinka (Ch. 2, 27) describes the formation of marine marsh soils as follows:

The marine deposits on which marsh soils are formed consist not only of inorganic material but of the remains of plants and animals as well. There are algae, diatoms, and sometimes also the remains of other plants, occasionally coming from the land. The animal remains consist of shells of Rhizopods and other organisms. All these materials appear as fine mud which exhibits very few traces of organic structure, either animal or plant. The marine mud, rich in disintegrated or decomposed organic matter, is laid down by the sea durig the summer. In winter, on the other hand, most of the deposition of inorganic material takes place. The alternation of light colored and dark colored layers in all exposures of a good marsh section is explained in this way.

When the marsh is elevated above the reach of low tides, salt loving plants soon appear. As soon as it is raised enough to be above tidal influence. *Poa maritima* appears also. The meadow vegetation develops only after the elevation rises to some three or four feet above sea level and the surface becomes relatively dry. In northern Russia, the meadow region which is covered with sea water at high tide is called "laidy." It is covered with *Plantago maritima, Trigiochin maritimum, Pisum maritium, Alismo plantago*, etc. From this group of plants, it is evident that the young marshes contain considerable quantities of sea salt. Sometimes, the salt disappears by natural processes, and many times the disappearance is hastened by the use of dikes and drainage.

Strictly speaking, the formation of marsh soils cannot begin until the marine deposits become covered with vegetation. When an unbroken grass cover is formed, soil development proceeds with energy. The further development of marsh soils corresponds to the development of the meadow soil. The general characteristics of old marsh soils are essentially like those of the silty swamp or meadowland soils. The west European investigators look upon the whole deposit from top to bottom as soil, and often describe their profiles to great depths. In this way, however, they include in one description the soil and parent material which has never been influenced by soil forming processes.

In order to get a clear picture of the constitution or build of the marsh soils, their parent material, and subsoils, we shall give van Bemmelen's description of the marshes in the Netherlands. These deposits are argillaceous in the upper and sandy in the lower part. In the central part of the province of Gronigen, soils are found whose surface horizon is called Roodarn. In places, it has a reddish color, due to the presence of hydrated iron oxide, is rich in humus, and reacts faintly acid. Beneath the surface horizon lies *Knick*.* 0.2 to 0.4 meters thick, which comprises the parent material of the marsh soils. It contains concretions and spots of iron oxide. The upper horizon of the *Knick* corresponds to the second horizon B of the meadowland soils. The whole Knick layer consists mainly of mineral material, but contains some organic matter. Its organic matter content amounts to about 5.5 per cent. This has apparently not originated through the processes of soil formation, but has been laid down with the mineral matter as marine deposit. Occasionally, the Knick is thicker (1 to 3 meters), becomes richer in lime with depth, and passes into a special soil layer, the *Wühlerde*. In places, this clay is rich in gypsum and other sulfates. Whether the gypsum is a product of soil forming processes or is a product of geological processes which took place earlier is not entirely clear. Beneath the Knick lies the *Darg*, a material sometimes very rich in organic substances formed by marine action.

See (30) describes a number of G profiles of the marsh soils of Elba and Oste rivers. In practically all of the profiles examined, See found a brownish black humus layer which turns gray upon drying. It contains fine sand and clay material. In depth, it varies from 12 to 36 cm. Beneath it

---

*By *Knick*, a tough and sticky layer beneath the plowed layer is generally understood. It is usually more or less rich in clay.

lies a layer of clayey fine sand, Knick-like in structure, i.e., tough, tenacious, and sticky. It is free from iron spots, is light brownish yellow, light gray when dry, and is usually hard. Many of the pores are filled with root remains. In depth, it varies from 6 to 18 cm. This layer is followed by the genuine Knick which appears as a band of black humus-clay, with or without iron rust spots, and is very porous. In depth, it varies from 10 to 30 cm. Beneath it appears another layer of Knick or Knick-like material, usually lighter in color than the layer above, with veins of the genuine Knick, with rust spots or even iron concretions, and is very porous. It varies in depth from 10 to 50 cm. This layer is followed by another Knick-like layer with few rust spots, bluish gray in color, or mottled. In some profiles, it is even black in color, either throughout or in the form of spots. Beyond this layer, the several profiles vary. Some contain lime materials, with or without rust spots; some have sandy material. All of them, however, have a mottled layer, depending on the depth of the water table. These profiles represent marsh soils which have been drained. This, of course, modifies the general features of the profile. See designates the soils as glei-podzolic.

Of the many chemical properties of marsh soils, and this is true also for the bog and meadowland soils, the colloidal nature is outstanding. The exchange capacity is extremely high, especially in the layers rich in organic matter which is well-known for its exchange capacity. Weight for weight, the organic matter has an exchange capacity 6 to 10 times, or even more, that of the mineral constituents. In the process of eluviation, the lime is washed out from the surface layers of the marsh soils. If the parent material happens to contain lime, as is frequently the case in marine marshes, it is gradually washed downward. And yet, some calcium is retained by the complex in a replaceable state, and the less replacable Ca there is, the more acid is the marsh; in other words, it is more unsaturated. With the lowering of the water table and the establishment of aerobic conditions in the marsh soils, a decomposition of the organic matter ensues, provided the complex is not fully unsaturated. When this happens, the marsh soils sink to a lower level, a great deal of the organic matter disappears, and the podzol process of soil formation replaces the marsh process.

Meadow Bog Soil

Zakharov identifies the "silty bog" soils of Glinka as meadow bog or meadowland soil. These are usually covered with meadow grasses, sedges, and rushes. They are influenced by the substances brought in by the ground waters and consequently are rich in plant nutrients. The morphological characteristics of the meadowland are described by Zakharov as follows:

A: Black or grayish black, without any well-expressed structure, frequently impregnated with dark brown veins of iron oxide, somewhat compact, almost always wet, of variable depth, from 10 to 30 cm.

B (G):   Light, pale yellowish, spotted, and mottled, sometimes gray, structureless, with rusty spots along the cracks and root paths. It is designated as the podzolicocherous glei horizon of variable depth.

C: Parent material showing effects of waterlogging.

These soils sometimes effervesce at a certain depth and even at the surface. Lime accumulations in the form of coarse-grained sand-like veins are frequently found. An example of such lime accumulation may be found in the meadow bog soils of Bavaria and in the middle and central part of the European portion of the U.S.S.R. Vivianite, pyrite, marcasite, and siderite also accumulate. Sometimes, so much iron accumulates that it forms an unbroken ferruginous shield, and the soils have been named "wrought iron" soils.

Chemical analyses made on the various layers of meadow bog soils indicate the translocation of iron compounds which, under the anaerobic conditions and in the presence of organic substances, are converted into the ferrous state. The organic matter content of these soils is by far less than that in genuine peat soils into which the meadow bog is sometimes gradually transformed. Water extracts of these soils are usually weakly alkaline, and the humus fraction is higher than the mineral in the upper horizon. The reaction favors the breaking-up of the minerals and the accumulation

Table 139

Composition of meadow land soil of Seja Bureja in the Amur Region
(After Glinka)

Constituents	Horizon A: 0-15 cm.	Horizon A: 15-30 cm.	Horizon B: 30-45 cm.	Horizon B: 45-60 cm.	Horizon C: —
	per cent	*per cent*	*per cent*	*per cent*	*per cent*
H_2O at 100° C.	6.38	5.60	5.70	5.96	6.26
Humus	8.48	3.47	2.50	1.18	0.97
N	0.13	0.06	0.05	0.05	0.03
Loss on ignition	12.89	7.27	7.20	6.52	5.47
SiO_2	60.26	63.91	63.90	63.67	64.28
Al_2O_3	16.07	17.32	17.65	17.71	17.95
Fe_2O_3	3.68	4.99	4.91	5.83	6.39
Mn_3O_4	0.24	0.05	0.49	0.13	0.05
CaO	1.75	1.35	1.06	1 06	1.07
MgO	0.55	0.76	0.49	0.87	0.86
K_2O	2.50	2.50	2.25	2.20	2.23
Na_2O	1.67	1.59	1.50	1.51	1.66
P_2O_5	0.14	0.09	0.11	0.11	0.06

of argillaceous substances; in this respect, the process differs from that of the podzol type of soil formation.

In some localities, during the dry summer, a whitish effloresence of salts forms on the surface of meadowlands.

In table 139, adopted from Glinka (Ch. 2, 27), analyses are presented on a soil from the Amur region which approaches in its characteristics the silty bog soils.

Glinka points out "that the amount of SiO_2 and Al_2O_3 in the soil horizons and in the parent material is almost equal. The lime accumulation in the upper layer is associated with the accumulation of organic matter. The iron oxide has been partially removed from the upper horizons. These features are characteristic of soils formed under swamp conditions, even though no leaching of bases or accumulation of SiO_2 in the weathered horizons can be detected, as was thought to be the case by Stremme and Endell."

It is interesting to note that the N content is rather low in the upper layer for the large percentage of organic matter. For a similar quantity of organic matter in chernozem, the N content is higher. Another interesting point to be noted is the mobility of the Mg. Whereas the Ca shows distinct accumulation in the layer with the highest quantity of organic matter, nothing of the kind happens to the Mg. Generally, the two common alkaline earth bases—Ca and Mg—behave alike; frequently, however, the Mg exhibits properties of its own. The nature of the peculiar behavior of Mg is not known. From studies conducted by Joffe, Kardos and Mattson (20, 21), it seems that this behavior might be linked with the formation of certain types of Mg-silicate complexes.

In table 140, composition of the water extract of meadow land soil from the Seja Bureja watershed is presented.

Glinka points out that "the most characteristic feature of the water extract is its alkalinity and a marked predominance of soluble organic matter in the upper humus horizon. The alkaline character of the water extract of swamp soils explains the brown color of the streams originating in swamp areas. The waters of the northern swampy zones, as well as those of the tropics are chacterized by their brown color. The color disappears in calcareous regions only where the lime transforms the humic matter into the gel state or combines with it to form salts. In northern regions, as well as in the tropics, the soils react feebly alkaline; in the latter case, this is true of all soils, in the former, of swamp soils only."

Peat-Bog Soils

This type of soil is identified with what is generally known as *Hochmoor*. As has been pointed out, this term is applied to peat land which rises from the edges toward the middle and thus shows a convex upper surface. Zakharov states:

These soils form under a moss vegetation cover adapted to thrive in the depressions of the watersheds. They are characterized by a strongly developed peat horizon, under which, at certain depth, the glei horizon is found. Descending from the neighboring more elevated area occupied by podzols toward the center of the bog, one might follow the steps in its development. With the lowering of the region, the degree of saturation increases, the vegetation changes, a moss cover appears, and, parallel there-

Table 140

Water extract of meadow land soil from Seja Bureja Watershed, Amur Region
(After Glinka)

Constituents	Horizon A: 0-15 cm.	Horizon A: 15-25 cm.	Horizon B: 25-45 cm.	Horizon B: 45-65 cm.	Horizon C: —
	per cent	*per cent*	*per cent*	*per cent*	*per cent*
Total alkalinity	0.0062	0.0058	0.0034	0.0038	0.0034
Alkali bicarbonates	0.0050	0.0034	0.0026	0.0026	0.0026
Alkaline earth bicarbonates	0.0012	0.0024	0.0008	0.0012	0.0008
Residue on drying	0.066	0.0404	0.0252	0.0222	0.0264
Mineral matter	0.0178	0.0118	0.0096	0.0116	0.0096
Loss on ignition	0.0483	0.0286	0.0156	0.0108	0.0168
SiO_2	0.0016	0.0016	0.0026	0.0015	0.0010
$Al_2O_3 + Fe_2O_3$	0.0041	0.0019	0.0012	0.0010	0.0010
CaO	0.0048	0.0028	0.0020	0.0018	0.0030
MgO	trace	trace	—	0.0003	0.0004
K_2O	0.0011	0.0010	0.0011	0.0008	0.0007
Na_2O	0.0028	0.0021	0.0016	0.0008	0.0011
P_2O_5	0.0006	trace	trace	trace	trace
SO_3	0.0014	trace	trace	0.0008	0.0009
Cl	0.0012	0.0018	0.0006	0.0014	0.0007
Color	Very Faint yellowish	Almost colorless	Almost colorless	Colorless	Colorless

with, the soil features change; some horizons grow in thickness, while others are replaced and forced out. Thus, the forest floor of the podzolic soil, the A_0 layer, is gradually replaced by a peat horizon which increases more and more in depth. Simultaneously, the G horizon develops, while the characteristic A_2 horizon of the podzol is forced out; the illuvial B horizon at first grows in depth, but later it disappears to be replaced by G. Correspondingly, these changes produce a series of soils: podzolic, podzolic-glei, peat-podzolic-glei, peat-podzolic-ocherous-glei, peat-ocherous-glei, peat-glei, and peat.

The series of soils from the peat-podzolic-glei to the peat-ocherous-glei are sometimes called "semi-swamp soils," and the last two, "pure swamps" or "bogs." In the course of time, the deeper horizon of the bog soil becomes converted into a peat organogenic native deposit.

The peat-bog soils are very poor in plant food constituents. The root system of the plants loses contact with the mineral portion of the soil as the peat horizon develops in thickness.

The peat-bog soils differ from the meadowland soils, inasmuch as the latter have a silty horizon and the former a massive peaty horizon. The organic matter is not so thoroughly decomposed in the peat bogs as in the silty meadow soils.

Glinka cites the work of Bersch (4) and quotes his analyses on three types of peat: sphagnum peat, peat of the transition bog, and grass peat. The data are reproduced in table 141. It is to be noted that the sphagnum moss peat is poorest in N, K_2O, P_2O_5, and CaO. It is, therefore, more acid than the other two types, the peat of the transition bog and the grass peat, and one should expect a slower decomposition.

Bersch (4) points out the occurrence of *Dopplerite* segregations in peat. It fills cracks and covers the remains of roots. While fresh, it is a black, soft elastic mass with a fatty appearance, but on drying it becomes a rather hard, brittle obsidian-like body. Its composition in air-dry condition is as follows: H_2O, 18.08 per cent; C, 43.54; O, 31.09; H, 3.24; N, 0.79; and ash, 3.27. *Sapropelit,* an organic mass forming primarily from plankton, is frequently found under the peat.

Other Moor Soils

As stated earlier in the discussion of the marsh and bog soils, they are not limited to any particular climatic zone. The investigations of this type of soil formation are, however, mainly confined to regions in the cool temperate zone, but there are some studies on the marsh and bog soils in the tropics and subtropics. The tundra marsh soils, although usually distinguished as an independent zonal type, are closely related to the bog type of soil formation.

Vageler (39), in his discussion of tropical soils with reference to the organic matter content, points out the existence of a raw layer in the soils of the primeval forests. And Lang (23) maintains that the wet (marsh) soils in the tropics are not simply an accidental occurrence or an exceptional phenomenon; they are "typical formations of a definite tropical region confined indeed in the wet zones." An all-around discussion of moor soils in the tropics and subtropics is given by Keilhack (22). He points out the existence of Hochmoor in the tropics, something which was not recognized until later by Potonie (27), another prominent investigator of moor soils

Table 141

Composition of three types of peat.

(After Bersch)

Type of peat	C	H	O	N	K$_2$O	P$_2$O$_5$	CaO
	Average per cent and variations within limits						
Sphagnum peat	57.03 (61.13 to 50.98)	5.79 (7.40 to 4.63)	35.58 (40.88 to 31.03)	1.60 (2.54 to 0.87)	0.08 (0.01 to 0.11)	0.11 (0.04 to 0.22)	0.52 (0.22 to 1.01)
Peat of a transition bog	57.20 (60.94 to 54.45)	6.61 (7.55 to 5.21)	34.74 (37.86 to 30.82)	1.95 (2.91 to 1.41)	0.10 (0.02 to 0.13)	0.13 (0.07 to 0.22)	1.38 (0.55 to 3.21)
Grass peat	54.18 (61.10 to 44.78)	5.67 (7.87 to 3.85)	37.27 (47.62 to 28.48)	2.88 (4.28 to 1.80)	0.10 (0.03 to 0.25)	0.16 (0.06 to 0.47)	2.95 (0.49 to 6.68)

in the tropics. Bennett and Allison (3) describe extensive peat accumulations in the Zapata peninsula of Cuba, a swampy area of 1,800 square miles. The extensive peat accumulations in the famous Florida Everglades, covering an area of about 5,000 to 6,000 square miles and described by Allison and Dachnowskii-Stokes (1), are also typical subtropical moors. Mohr (Ch. 13, 69) describes marsh and bog soils in Java, Sumatra, and Borneo. He distinguishes a number of types which could be classified into the two chief groups of Glinka, fresh-water bog and meadowland, and marsh soils. In Deli and Serdang he found humus formations resembling those of the Alpine moors. Along the river deltas, estuaries, and bays, marshes and marsh soils prevail. No peat, as a rule, is found, as is the case in the northern latitudes. In the presence of lime, the vast quantities of plant remains decompose at the surface, leaving behind the most resistant constituents, the gums and resins. Glinka points out that the tree species in these regions are rich in gums and resins, and that the closer to the sea the region is, the higher is the content of gums and resins in the plant species.

In the areas of still waters, the insufficiency of oxygen prevents the decomposition of the greatest portion of organic matter, and much of it sinks and forms bogs. According to Mohr (Ch. 13, 69) these "occur only to a very small extent in Java." In most places, however, the mineral material is impregnated with humus and humus-rich muds. Mohr describes the marsh soils as having a shallow yellowish gray surface layer underlain with material of a bluish gray tint which extends to a depth of 0.7m. Mohr elaborates on the reduction processes that go on in the tropical moors, and Glinka remarks: "These reduction processes are the same in tropical as in other regions, but this does not mean that all other attributes are the same. It is very probable that the process of decomposition of the aluminum silicates is more energetic in the tropical moors than in the soils of the temperate regions. This might lead to the release of free alumina. The investigations of the dark colored soils of Madagascar by Müntz and Rousseau (26) show the presence of alumina."

A great many investigations on the distribution and properties of moor soils in the tropics could be cited, but most of them deal with the practical side of moor culture and give little information on the constitution of moor soils and their pedologic characteristics. An extensive review of this type of investigations is to be found in the paper by Giesecke (17).

ALLUVIAL OR FLUVIOGENIC SOILS

As the name implies, these soils are limited to the areas bordering stream channels, flood plains, river deltas, and bottom lands in general. These soils are a transition type, starting with the true hydromorphic stage, followed by an improvement in drainage conditions which gives rise to soil complexes, including areas of hydrogenic soils, and ending up with the normal soils when the rivers mature, deltas become stabilized, and geologic shifts establish river terraces.

In the history of mankind, alluvial soils have played an important role from the dawn of civilization. The wealth of Babylonia and of ancient Egypt, the expanse of China, and the population concentration of India and of other parts of the world have been associated with the alluvial soils. They support a larger proportion of the world's population than do any other great soil groups.

Alluvial soils referred to as such are generally young, composed of rather diversified parent materials, the origin of which lies in the geologic history of drainage basins of the rivers and lakes. In their extensive report on alluvial soils of the Mississippi drainage basin, Holmes and Hearn (19) make the following interesting observations on the relation of the source of material to the composition of the alluvial soils:

> The chemical composition of the colloids of all the soils of the lower Mississippi delta are essentially similar . . . The composition of the colloids from the various tributaries reflects the character of the soils drained by them and also the gelogic material. The phosphate deposits and phosphatic soils of Tennesee are reflected in the colloidal material deposited by the Tennessee and Duck Rivers which drain them. Likewise, the alluvial soil of the Clinch River shows the influence of the limestone area drained by that river. Again, the influence of the high percentage of potassium and magnesium in the Permian Red Beds of Texas and Oklahoma is very pronounced in the Red River alluvium . . . The chemical composition of the soils and colloids of the Mississippi lowlands shows definitely that the major portion of this matter is derived from the eastern slopes of the Rocky Mountains and of the Great Plains area.

Holmes and Hearn point out that the $SiO_2 : R_2O_3$ ratio of the alluvial material brought in by the tributaries from the Great Plains (arid, semiarid, and subhumid climate) is 3.08, and that of the material transported from the eastern tributaries (humid temperate climate) is 2.24. In other words, the parent material of alluvial soils is a composite of weathered rocks and eroded soil material of different climatic zones.

An interesting attribute of alluvial formations is that "the greater part of the coarser material is not carried long distances from its source. The texture of the alluvial material becomes more uniform and smaller in particle size, as the distance that it is transported increases. The alluvial soils of the lower Mississippi are composed almost wholly of varying quantities of silt and clay."

Liwerant (24) presents data on the alluvial soils of the Garonne Valley in France. He discusses some of the profiles, chiefly from the point of view of their composition in relation to crop production. A similar study has been made by Brioux and Jouis (5) on the old and recent alluvium of the Seine Valley.

Glazovskaya (18) presents analyses showing that bog soils of deltas of middle latitudes are characterized by the accumulation of $CaCO_3$ and ferrous iron as sulfides. As the delta develops and drainage improves, oxidation leads to formation of $Fe(OH)_3$, $CaSO_4$, and later even free H_2SO_4. Mangrove soils of the tropics are characterized by a high amorphous silica content.

No specific pedogenic characteristics may be assigned to young alluvial formations. A great many of these are constantly subject to floods, and the new sediments mask whatever embrionic profile characteristics might have developed between flood periods. These sediments produce a stratified effect, but no definite profile, as a rule, develops.

There are old alluvial formations, such as the terraces of river valleys made up of stratified clay, sand, silt, and gravel, usually unconsolidated. These alluvial deposits are the product of the meandering rivers in degrading valleys. There are also lake terraces and marine terraces. When uplifted, these deposits are not subject any more to the effects of floods and wave action. The result is that the soil forming processes begin their work and bring about horizon differentiation and creation of a soil profile. It is not, however, an easy task for the average field man not trained in pedology to note the intricate features of a profile on parent material of alluvial origin. The erosion to which alluvial soils are subjected to and their usual stratification add to the difficulties of following up the translocation, movement, and distribution of constituents in the profile. A series of soil complexes is forming on this type of parent material. Because of the complexity of alluvial formations, soil surveyors (in the nomenclature of the United States Soil Survey Division) are baffled when they come in contact with the constantly changing profile characteristics and properties of alluvial soils. The standard criteria and methods of mapping soils on profile basis as prescribed by the "official manuals", do not apply to alluvial soils. The result is that every change in profile characteristics serves as a basis for a new series. That is why the Coastal Plain soils of the United States are being so "diligently" surveyed and resurveyed. Any one familiar with the staggering rise in number of soil series isolated in the Coastal Plain will appreciate how a thorough pedologic approach would eliminate the difficulty.

Along the river courses in the arid regions, where xerophytic vegetation predominates, we find stretches of forests on flood plains, meadows, and alluvial swamps. These forest soils are modified in their profile characteristics not only by the specificity of the alluvial deposits but also by their displacement from the true forest climate environment.

In concluding the fragmentary discussion on alluvial soils, it may be pointed out that for a thorough understanding of alluvial soils one should be familiar with the geology and mineralogy of sedimentary deposits. The standard text of Twenhofel (38) is to be consulted.

References

1. Allison, R. V., and Dachnowski-Stokes. 1932 Physical and chemical studies upon important profiles of organic soils in the Florida Everglades. *Proc. and Papers, Second Inter. Cong. Soil Sci.* 6: 222-245.

2. Bemmelen, J. M. van 1900 Über das Vorkommen, die Zusammensetzung und die Bildung von Eisenanhaufungen in und unter den Mooren. *Z. anorg. u. allg. Chem.* 22: 313-379.

3. Bennett, H. H. and Allison, R. V. 1928 The soils of Cuba. Tropical Plant Research Foundation, Washington, D. C.

4. Bersch, W. 1907 Moore Oestrreich. Eine botanisch-chem. Studie. *Ztsch. für Moorkultur und Torfverwert.* 5: 65, 175, 195, 343. See also his "Handbuch der Moorkultur" (1909), Vienna.

5. Brioux, C. and Jouis, E. 1942 Les alluvions anciennes et modernes de la vallee de la Seine. *Ann. Agron.* (n.s.) 12: 1-18.

6. Cajander, A. K. 1913 Studien über die Moore Finnlands. Helsingfors.

7. Dachnowski, A. P. 1919 Quality and value of important types of peat material. U. S. Dept. of Agr. Bul. 802.

8. Dachnowski, A. P. 1920 Peat deposits in the U. S. and their classification. *Soil Sci.* 10: 453-465.

9. Dachnowski-Stokes, A. P. 1929 The botanical composition and morphological features of "high moor" peat profiles in Maine. *Soil Sci.* 27: 379-388.

10. Dachnowski-Stokes, A. P. 1930 Research in regional peat investigations. *Jour. Amer, Soc. Agron.* 22: 352-366.

11. Dachnowski-Stokes, A. P. 1932 Peat profiles of the delta land of California. *Proc. and Papers Second Inter. Cong. Soil Sci.* 6: 212-221.

12. Dachnowski-Stokes, A. P. 1935 Essentials of a general system of classifying organic soils. *Amer. Soil Survey Asso. Bul.* 16: 105-109. A summary may be found in: *Trans. Third Inter. Cong. Soil Sci.* 1:416-418.

13. Dokturovskii, V. S. 1922 Swamps and peats, their development and constitution (Russian). Moscow.

14. Dranitsyn, D. A. 1916 Northern Enisei River Expedition. Prelim. report on the investigations of the soil in Asiatic Russia during 1914 (Russian). Petrograd.

15. Feilitzen, H. 1905 Wieviel Pflanzennährungsstoff wird mit dem Drannierungswasser und den Ernten von Moorböden verschiedener Art bei deren verschiedener Kultur hinweggeführt. Svenska. Moss Kultur fur. Tidskrift. 193-210.

16. Früh, J. and Schroter, C. 1904 Über die Moore der Schweiz mit Berücksichtigung der gesamten Moorfrage. A. Franke, Bern.

17. Giesecke, F. 1930 Tropische und subtropische Humus-und-Bleicherdebildungen, Blanck's Handbuch der Bodenlehre 4: 148-224.

18. Glazovskaya, M. A. 1945 Soil formation in maritime deltas. Pedology (U.S.S.R.) No. 3-4: 209-215.

19. Holmes, R. S. and Hearn, W. E. 1942 Chemical and physical properties of some of the important alluvial soils of the Mississippi drainage basin. U. S. Dept. Agr. Tech. Bul. 833, pp. 82.

20. Joffe, J. S., Kardos, L. T., and Mattson, S. 1935 The laws of soil colloidal behavior: XVII Magnesium silicate—its base exchange properties. Soil Sci. 40: 255-268.

21. Kardos, L. T. and Joffe, J. S. 1938 The preparation, composition, and chemical behavior of the complex silicates of Mg, Ca, Sr, and Ba. Soil Sci. 45: 293-307.

22. Keilhack, K. 1917 Über tropische und subtopische Torfmoore auf der Insel Ceylon. Jb. Kgl. Preuss. Landesanstalt f.d. Jahr. 1915. 36, pt. II: 103-143.

22a. Kirsanov, A. I. 1918 Cultivation of Peat. Sistematich. Vvedenie v Izuch Voprosov Melioratsii i Kultury Bolot (Russian) Gorki.

23. Lang, R. 1915 Versuch einer exakten Klassifikation der Böden in Klimatischer und geologischer Hinsicht. Inter. Mitt. fur Bodenkunde, 5: 312-346.

24. Liwerant, J. 1941 Les sols d'alluvions de la valée de la Garonne. Ann. Agron. (n.s.) 11: 59-82.

25. Minssen, H. 1913 Beiträge zur Kenntnis typischer Torfarten. Landw. Jb. 44: 269-330; also later reports.

26. Müntz, A. and Rousseaux, E. 1900 A study of the agr. value of the soils of Madagascar. Bul. de Ministere d'Agr. 19: 910-1123.

27. Potonie, H. 1912 Die rezenten Kanstobiolithe, und ihre Lagerstatten. Abh. Kg. Preuss. Geol. Landesanst., N. F., 55. III.

28. Schreiber, H. 1927 Moorkunde nach dem gegenwärtigen Stand des Wissens auf Grund dreissigjähriger Erfahrung. P. Parley, Berlin (References are given to the author's early work).

29. Schucht, F. 1905 Die Bodenarten der Marschen. *Jour. für Landw.* 53: 309-328.

30. See, K. v. 1920 Über den Profilbau der Marschböden. *Intern. Mitt. für Bodenkunde.* 10: 169-185.

31. Senft, F. 1862 Die Humus-Marsch.-Torf-und Limonit-bildungen. W. Engelmann, Leipzig.

32. Stelzner 1827-1828 Die Marschgegenden im Königreich, Hanover. *Moglinsche Ann. d. Landw.* Bd. 20: 200-320. 409-499; 21: 227-342.

33. Sukachev, V. N. 1923 Bogs, their formation, development and properties (Russian). Ed. 2, Petrograd.

34. Tacke, Br. 1930 Die Humusböden der gemäsigten Breiten. Blanck's "Handbuch der Bodenlehre," 4: 124-184.

35. Tanfiliev, G. I. 1903 Bogs and Peats (Russian). Agr. Encyclopedia.

36. Tanfiliev, G. I. 1911 The limits of forests in the polar regions of Russia according to investigations in the Tundra region of the Timan Somoyeds (Russian). Odessa.

37. Thoms, G. 1876 Beiträge zur Kenntnis baltischer Torfsarten. *Land. Ver Sta.* 19: 423-35.

38. Twenhofel, W. H. 1926 Treatise on Sedimentation. Williams and Wilkins Co., Baltimore, Md.

39. Vageler, P. 1930 Grundriss der tropischen und subtropischen Bodenkunde. Berlin.

40. Virchow, C. 1883 Das Kehdinger Moor, eine chemisch-geologische Studie. *Landw. Jahrb.* Bd. 12: 83-128.

41. Weber, C. A. 1926 Die Entwirklungsgeschichte unserer Moore. S. A. des Vereins zur Forderung der Moorkultur in Deutschen Reich (References are given to the author's early work).

42. Westermann, T. 1902 Moorböden Dänemarks. Kopenhagen.

CHAPTER XVI

OROGENIC AND LITHOGENIC SOILS

These two soil types and their subdivisions, such as are known and described, are presented together for convenience of chapter arrangement and not because of any specific genetic relationship between them.

Orogenic or Mountain Soils

In orogenic soils, the factor of topography is instrumental in modifying the climatogenic characteristics and in imparting some specific characteristics to the profile. The factor of topography is frequently referred to as *relief*. In case of mountain soils, it is *macrorelief* that concerns the pedologist in distinction of *microrelief* which introduces the concept of soil complex, or its close relative, the *catena*.

Mountain Soils and Zonality Principle.—Dokuchaev, on investigating the mountain soils in Transcaucasia, promulgated the principle of soil zonality. According to this principle, the succession of zonal soil types on a horizontal plane over a wide geographic area on a relatively level topography repeats itself (as manifested in the broad features of the profile constitution or on a vertical plane over a small geographic area in mountainous country. Sibirtzev furthered the zonality principles, pointing out that "soils are distributed geographically on the surface of the earth in regional belts, each one having a definite set of soil formers of which the climate is the most important one." From an intensive study of the known soils in their geographic distribution and of the environmental factors, climatic and geobotanical, Sibirtzev, following the principles of soil zonality, constructed a soil map of the world.

Glinka, quoted by Afanasiev (Ch. 2, 2), describes the vertical distribution of soil types in the Caucasus from Erivan, the capital of Armenia, to the top of Ali Bek and other mountains.

The immediate vicinity of Erivan is a desert steppe, with gray desert soils derived in part from unconsolidated deposits and in part from basalt lava. Rising higher, we enter a zone of typical chernozem which begins to show signs of degradation in the vicinity of Darachichag; a little higher, the chernozem grades into typical gray forest loams covered mainly with oaks. These soils are replaced, as we go up the Ali Bek, by well developed podzol soils. Still further up, we find the dark-colored mountain-meadow soils, and above them the peat soils of mountain summits. In other words, from Erivan to the top of Ali Bek, a distance of 60 kilometers, we find all the soil belts encountered in traveling from Baku to North Cape on the Arctic Ocean. If we climb to the top of Zhkra-Zkaro from Mikhailovo to Borzhom and from there to Bakuryany,

we can see again the change from chernozem to gray forest soils and to possible podzolic soils. Still higher, we find the dark-colored wet meadow soils which are replaced
on the summit by brown-peat soils.

Neustruev (Ch. 2, 50) established the following alternation of soil
types in the mountain regions of Karatan and Altai in Siberia: gray soils,
chestnut, chernozem-like, sub-alpine, and alpine meadow soils. Prasolov
(22) distinguished the following vertical soil zones: 1, the light brown
loams of the semidesert; 2, chestnut-brown soils; 3, chernozem steppe soils;
4, chernozem-like mountain meadow under tall grass cover; 5, leached
mountain meadow under short grass cover; and 6, zone of snow and ice.

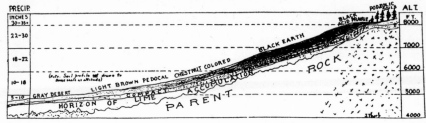

PLATE 37

Gradation of soil profile from desert to humid mountain top—
west slope of Big Horn

(After Thorp)

The forests are not of the closed stand type; they appear as sporadic islands
"on the slopes and in the glens. It is impossible to separate definite belts of
coniferous or deciduous forests." In the region of Dzhungar Altai, the chernozem is succeeded by mountain meadow. Prasolov also describes other
climatogenically subdued soil types among the orogenic soils, noting the
presence of solonchak in the mountain meadow soils.

Thorp (31) established the vertical soil zones in the northern Wyoming region of the Rocky Mountains, starting from the valley of the Big Horn
Basin. In plate 37, Thorp illustrates the gradation of soil profiles from desert to humid mountain climate. Studies of vertical zonation have been reported by Jenny (7) for Switzerland and by Senstius (Ch. 13, 91) for
tropical high altitudes. Mikhailovskaya (17) presents analyses, exchangeable bases, pH, and organic matter content, of the vertical series of soils in
the mountain regions of Mongolia, Crimea, and the Caucasus. The work
of Sabanin (24) and Vysotskii (34) dealing with the hydrologic conditions of mountain soils should not be overlooked. These authors present
interesting facts on the movement of water and its relation to temperature
in soils of vertical zonation.

Powers (21) presents the vertical zonation of soils in the mountain
regions of Oregon. As the elevation increases from 285 to 5070 feet and

the precipitation from 7.5 to over 38 inches, the soils change from gray semidesert to light brown, chestnut, chernozem, prairie-like, and podzolic.

Nikiforoff (20) shares the opinion of the Russian pedologists that the replacement of horizontal by vertical zonation does not follow the same pattern on all mountain ranges. Specific mountain types develop. He points out:

> The Cascades, standing as a barrier across the path of the prevailing westerly winds from the Pacific ocean, create on their western slopes and foothills an independent, exceedingly humid west-coast natural province, and casts a dry climatic shadow over the part of Washington and Oregon east of the mountains. The exceedingly high humidity of the humid province . . ., coupled with luxuriant forest vegetation composed mainly of evergreens, creates an environment that has caused the development of a group of soils fundamentally different from any of the definitely established great soil groups.

Martin and Fletcher (16) describe the soils of vertical zonation on Mt. Graham, Arizona, that rises from an elevation of 2900 feet to 10,500 feet. The rainfall rises from an average of about 10 inches at 3000-3600 feet to 24.4 inches at 8000 feet and higher. The succession of zonal soil types is: from the red desert soils, through reddish-brown of the grasslands, the brown forest, and the gray-brown podzols of the mull and mor types. The authors summarize in an interesting table "the zonal soil types distributed vertically in mountainous areas as reported by various investigators." They give data on elevation, rainfall, temperature, and vegetation of the areas in Utah, Wyoming, Oregon, and Washington.

Spilsbury and Tisdale (27) present morphological and chemical data of profiles of vertical zonation of soils in the Tranquille Range, southern interior of British Columbia. They make an interesting comparison on the position (altitude) of the vertical zonal soil types of the Tranquille Range in British Columbia (latitude 51°) and of similar soil types of Big Horn Mountain in Wyoming (latitude 44°):

Altitude of Big Horn	*Altitude of Tranquille Range*
Brown steppe: ......5000-5500 feet	1100-2300 feet
Dark brown: ....5500-6500 feet	2300-2800 feet
Chernozem: ....6500-7700 feet	2800-3200 feet

If it were possible to compare, the climate in the two mountain regions (at the points of the similar soil types) would very likely be similar, although not identical.

Klingebiel, Walker, and Stewart (9) correlate soil types of vertical zonation in Utah. They report sage-brush on semidesert gray soils at 5000-6500 feet; oak-brush—with chestnut brown soils at 6500-8000; aspen and fir—with chernozem at 8000-9000 feet; and spruce and fir with podzo-

lic soils above 9000 feet. They describe the chernozem under forest, a rather
unusual association.

Specificity of the Orogenic Type of Soil Formation

General Considerations.—While the analogous soils in the horizontal
and vertical planes are in their fundamental natural features one and the
same, those in the vertical plane have certain characteristics of their own.
Thus, the mountain meadow can not be identified with any analogous soil
in the horizontal plane; columnar solonetz in the vertical plane is not found
outside the brown zone. Neither is the succession of the zonal types always
alike in the two planes. The chernozem soils in the vertical plane are sometimes succeeded by meadow rather than forest soils. A number of instances
have been reported where meadows prevail all along the mountainside, from
the foot up to the snow line. Morphologically, these mountain meadow soils
are chernozem-like soils. Chemically, however, they are more like the
bog type of plains, having an acid reaction and no calcium carbonate accumulation, and yet they show no distinct marsh conditions. A succession of
this kind, chernozem followed by meadow, in the horizontal zones has not
been reported as yet.

The regularity in alternation in types of soils in the mountain regions
is conditioned by the change in climate with altitude. It is, however, well to
remember that the climates in the vertical plane are not strictly comparable
with what is generally accepted as similar climates in the horizontal plane.
With the rise in elevation in the geomorphologic setting of a changing topography, certain elements of climate that are specific for the mountains appear and they impart specific modifications in the zonal features of the soil
profiles.

Variations in Elements of Climate.—The two principal elements of
climate, temperature and precipitation, in the vertical plane take on characteristics that can not be encountered in the horizontal plane. For example,
at greater altitudes, rainfall is more frequent and, up to a certain altitude,
more abundant. In the Himalayas, precipitation increased up to the 1200
meter altitude; in Java up to 600-1200 meters, and in the Swiss Alps up to
3200 meters, above which the precipitation drops sharply.

In the main, the atmosphere tends to become rarer and colder with
elevation, the temperature falling on the average about 1°F. with each 330
feet in elevation. Albright and Stoker (1) cite measurements taken at
two points, the distance between them being ½ mile and 134 feet difference
in elevation. At the slough, there were only 32 successive frost-free nights,
whereas on the hilltop there were 106 such nights. The hilltop has better

air drainage and is much warmer. As a result of the differences in temperature, the ecological difference is as if the hilltop was 380 miles farther south.

The intensity of insolation and of radiation, both increase aloft in the clearer, drier, and thinner air of the mountain climate. Jenny (7) cites observations made by various investigators on the temperature variations in the mountains. Some days the fluctuations in temperature might amount to 70°C. in Tibet, temperatures were recorded as low as -8°C. in the shade and 16.3°C in the sun.

Because of the cool dry air and sharp fluctuations in temperature between day and night, conditions for organic matter decomposition by microbes are apparently not favorable; hence, organic matter accumulates in mountain soils.

Kovalevskii (10) pointed out that in the mountains, at an altitude of 2600 meters, the chemical activity of the sun's rays are 11 per cent greater than at sea level. He cited an air temperature of 10.1°C at 2877 meters while the soil temperature was 33.8°C. Such wide variations are due to the higher insolation at higher altitudes; the air is clear and no heat rays are lost. By the same token, the loss of heat from the soil at night is accelerated, but the net result is positive. Mirimanyan (Ch. 9, 60, pp. 41-57) presents interesting data on the climatic factors prevailing in mountainous Armenia in relation to soil forming processes and agriculture.

Slpoe Effects.—Slope effects on soil characteristics have been recognized ever since mountain peoples took to tilling the soil. Sprengel (29), more than 100 years ago, spoke of a slope of 15° as almost unsuitable for cultivation and had recommended pastures and meadows in place of cultivated land. Zakharov (Ch. 2, 91) classifies mountain soils arbitrarily according to slope as follows:

5° *slope*: Little erosion takes place, and the soil cover is uniform and continuous.

5° *to* 20° *slope*: Erosion is marked, and even sliding effects, caused by force of gravity without the aid of water, are common. The so-called *deluvial* processes are prominent, and in places the native rock outcrops. The soil cover is therefore neither uniform nor continuous.

Steep slopes from 20° *to* 45°: Sliding of material is the chief force in moving the weathered material. Erosion is deep, the soil cover is highly dissected, and the native rock is exposed very prominently.

Slope with an angle greater than 45°: Practically no soil is to be found, except on rock shelves, crags and ledges, in hollows and cracks in the native rocks.

Slope has a direct effect on the moisture regime of the soil. As the rainwater runs off the steeper slopes, the moisture content on the bottom of the slope increases, affecting the leaching of the soil. An enrichment with the finely dispersed particles takes place at the bottom of the slope.

Slope exposure is another important factor in the vertical distribution of the zonal soil types. Geobotanists have recognized long ago the effects of exposure on the type of vegetation, which would naturally affect the soil-forming processes. In general, the southern exposures are warmer and drier, with marked fluctuations in temperature and moisture; the northern exposures are the converse; and the western and eastern exposure occupy an intermediate position. Zakharov (Ch. 2, 91, p. 249) points out that on the southern exposures of the Hood mountain of the main mountain chain in the Caucasus there are chernozem-like soils, whereas on the northern exposures there are podzolized soils. In the Armenian mountains, with a drier climate, the chernozem-like soil appears on the slope with a northern exposure, whereas on the southern exposure there are gray soils, often enriched with carbonates.

A succession of soil types is very much in evidence on the slopes of Pikes Peak in the Rocky Mountains. Over a distance of seven miles, one may go from the grassland of the Great Plains to alpine meadow and bog. On the slopes with a northern exposure the conifers prevail, whereas on the southern exposures deciduous or mixed forests prevail. The processes of podzolization are more clearly expressed in the forest soils of the northern exposures.

Kostychev (Ch. 2, 41) described changes in soil type due to exposure even in the chernozem belt on the plains. He noted a quantitative difference in the organic matter content of the soils of a northern and southern exposure. The soils on the northern exposures were more leached, showing signs of degradation, whereas the soils of the southern exposure showed solonetzic properties. Dimo and Keller (Ch. 2, 11) observed on the southern exposures of the steeper slopes, in the Penza government, an eroded condition, a thin soil cover, and exposed skeleton soils, whereas on the northern slopes in the neighborhood, the soil was deep, fully developed, and remained intact.

Zakharov considers plateaus, altitude, and geologic formations in relation to the formation of mountain soils. The soil features as influenced by topography are characterized by Zakharov (Ch. 2, 91, p. 248) as follows:

1. The soils of low mountains, hills, and plateaus resemble in a large measure well-developed soils.

2. The soils of the medium height mountains are characterized by (a) the skeletal nature in the upper portions of the slope and the fine texture at the bottom; (b) an increase in soil depth in the same direction; (c) the frequent absence of a genetic relation between the soils on the lower portion of the slope and the underlying parent rock; (d) the frequent occurrence of veins of deluvial material in the soil profile, and the occurrence of buried soils in the deeper layers.

3. The soils of the high mountains are characterized by (a) highly developed skeletal features; (b) shallowness; (c) weakly expressed horizon differentiation; (d) strongly eroded soil cover.

4. The soils in the valleys and glens are characterized by; (a) a marked change in mechanical composition and (b) by a poor differentiation into horizons or layers.

Discussing the soils of the mountain regions in the temperate climate, Zakharov recognizes the following types: mountain steppe, mountain forest, mountain meadow, and mountain tundra soils.

Mountain Steppe Soils

In the mountain steppe soils, the analogous horizontal zonal types, the brown soils, the chestnut brown, and chernozem, are encountered. In each one of these, the stony character of the soil material, or the so-called "foreign intrusion element," is very much in evidence.

Brown Soils.—The following morphological description of a mountain brown steppe soil is given by Zakharov on a soil cut in Armenia, near the railroad station Alagez:

A_1: Humus-rich horizon, 15 cm. deep, brownish-gray in color, whitish at the bottom, structureless, friable, with angular pebbles or stones; it effervesces throughout.
A_2: A transitional horizon, 15 cm. deep, whitish, structureless, very friable, silty with angular stones; it effervesces throughout.
B: The illuvial horizon, about 25 cm. deep, milky white, structureless, more compact, less stony, rich in carbonates; it effervesces violently.
C: Parent material, stony marl, mantle rock from weathered andesite.

It is to be noted that the mountain brown steppe soils are not similar in their characteristics to the horizontal brown-steppe soils. They are distinguished by their stony nature and shallowness.

Chestnut Brown Soils.—These soils have been studied very little, but Zakharov notes that they are distinguished by their stony character and by deep horizons not so distinctly differentiated. The horizon of eluviation has a brownish chestnut coloration and a crumbly to granular structure. Among the Turkestan mountain chestnut soils, one encounters moist areas (the water table at times comes to the surface) which give rise to a darker type of soil known locally as "saz."

Mountain Chernozem.—Because of the inherent topographic features, the chernozem in mountainous country has peculiarities of its own. Its depth is not constant, but depends on the degree of slope and microrelief. On the plateaus, it attains the depth of chernozem in the plains, but on the slopes it is shallower and the profile is, so to speak, *dwarfed*.* The organic matter content is very high in the A horizon—12 to 20 per cent and even more. The zone of lime accumulation, with a high lime content, is found at comparatively shallow depths, 30 to 50 cm. below the surface. Because of their peculiar position in the landscape, the chernozem soils on the slopes receive the drainage waters from the soil zones of the higher altitudes. This prob-

---

*The term *dwarf profile* is introduced as another link in the chain of evidence showing the similarity between the soil as a natural body and other natural bodies. Thus we may speak of *dwarf soil* types within the various soil zonal types just as we speak of dwarf types in biological species.

ably is responsible for the high lime content of the former. These sources of underground moisture also modify the conditions for microbiological activities. A more intensive decomposition takes place in the lower part of the A horizon in this type of chernozem than in the ordinary chernozem of the plains. For this reason, the organic matter content of the chernozem on the slopes decreases rather sharply with depth. In the organic matter of the deep A_0 layer, features of peat-like formations (a highly developed A_0 is not found in ordinary chernozem) are noted, which in turn give a brownish tinge to the color of this chernozem. On the other hand, the nearness of the lime zone to the surface imparts to the lower part of the A horizon a grayish tinge. In the zone of lime accumulation, spots of iron are infrequently found. They are, in all probabilities, due to the precipitation of the iron from the horizontally moving ground waters which come from higher levels. In general, there is no apparent vertical movement of the R_2O_3 constituents in this chernozem, a characteristic of a genuine chernozem type of soil formation.

In table 142, analyses of a typical mountain slope chernozem, adopted

Table 142

Composition of a mountain slope chernozem from Turkestan

(After Glinka)

Constituents	Depth			
	0-5 cm.	25-30 cm.	45-50 cm.	70-80 cm.
	per cent	*per cent*	*per cent*	*per cent*
SiO_2	44.52	53.51	62.19	53.72
Fe_2O_3	3.89	4.27	5.90	4.71
Al_2O_3	11.92	14.47	16.18	16.33
CaO	3.76	3.75	3.83	9.75
MgO	0.58	1.22	1.11	1.12
K_2O	1.46	2.02	1.85	1.33
Na_2O	2.74	3.68	2.69	1.68
P_2O_5	0.47	0.27.	0.13	0.19
Organic matter	24.27	9.05	1.04	—
N	1.06	0.42	0.08	0.05
Loss on ignition	30.79	16.87	5.67	10.54 ·

from Glinka (6), bear out the point made about these soils. Additional data on this point may be found in the monograph by Mirimanyan (Ch. 9, 60) on the mountain soils of Armenia.

Referring to the mountain chernozem, Zakharov (Ch. 2, 91, p. 355) states:

The distinguishing morphological features of mountain chernoozem are variations in depth of profile and prominence of the genetic horizons. This depends on the location of the profile with respect to the various elements of the mountain topography. On the level spots or on the minor depressions, with the fine-textured weathered mantle rock as the parent material, all the horizons included the carbonate-rich illuvial, are well expressed. More or less weathered rock débris is scattered throughout the soil cut, especially in the horizon of illuviation. On the more elevated areas, horizons A_1 and A_2 are discerned, as if they were covering the parent rock material. Horizon B is to be found in the cracks of the parent rock. On the outcrops, horizon A_1 only develops, as if it were "glued" on to the parent rock.

The black coloration of mountain chernozem has a slightly brownish hue which is due to the abundance of semidecomposed roots in horizon A. In some cases, a grayish tinge is apparent due to the presence of carbonates. The structure is well expressed in typical cases, but the abundance of decaying materials, in some cases, and of carbonates in others, hinders at times the formation of thorough granulation.

The chernozem of mountain slopes is distinguished by a high organic matter content in A_1 and by an extensive carbonate-rich B, located at times not deeper than 30 to 50 cm. from the surface. The B horizon has a high lime content and occasional admixtures of the oxides of iron. This condition is brought about by the ground waters descending from the higher elevations.

Chemically, mountain chernozems are distinguished by comparatively high percentages of organic matter, 12 to 19, and of nitrogen, 0.6 to 0.89, even though the percentage of nitrogen in the organic matter is relatively not high, about 5. They are noted for a higher content of chemically combined water, 6 to 7 per cent, and of "zeolitic substances," than the chernozem of the plains. The composition of the zeolitic substances, however, is alike in both types of chernozem, except that the mountain chernozem contains less potassium.

More water-soluble substance are found in the A horizon of mountain chernozem, 0.113 to 0.191 per cent. then in the chernozem of the plains, but the mineral fraction is the same, 0.053 to 0.037 per cent. This indicates that in horizon A the humic acids prevail with depth, the ratio of mineral to organic substances narrows.

Mechanical analyses reveal a pronounced skeletal nature of the deeper horizons. The fine-textured materials are about equally distributed throughout the profile, except for the degraded types.

In general, chernozem formation in mountainous countries leads to a high accumulation of organic matter. This is due to the short period within which mineralization of organic residues can occur and to the leached condition of the upper horizons.

Mountain chernozems vary greatly in morphology and in chemical and mechanical composition. In Transcaucasia, we may distinguish the following subtypes:

1. Mountain carbonate chernozem (chocolate-colored) which effervesces from the surface.
2. Typical mountain chernozem which effervesces at B.
3. Deep mountain chernozem, depth of A up to 75 cm.
4. Leached deep chernozem, with a brownish hue.
5. Degraded chernozem, with a grayish line in A_1, free from carbonates.

In a later paper (39), Zakharov presents analytical data on mountain chernozem of Armenia and discusses the mountain soils of Russia, particularly of the Caucasian mountains. An extensive English summary is given. A wealth of data on the chernozem of Armenia is presented by Mirimanyan (Ch. 9. 60).

Thorp (31) describes the mountain chernozem on the slopes of the Big Horn Mountain in Wyoming: "The A horizon is from 12 to 15 inches thick, laminated in the upper part and structureless in the lower part, and is neutral to slightly acid in reaction. The heavy layer is thicker than in the chestnut brown soils. It is somewhat granular in structure and the granules are coated with brown colloidal material from the A horizon. The horizon of lime accumulation is thinner than in the chestnut brown soils." The layerlike structure of the surface of the A horizon has been noted earlier by Neustruev (19).

Mountain Forest Soils

Zakharov divides the mountain forest soils into a number of subtypes:

(a) Dark-colored forest nutty soil; (b) light-colored forest soils; (c) pod-zolized forest soils; (d) sod forest soils.

Among the dark-colored mountain forest soils, one might distinguish: the *dark-gray* (very similar to those of the plains), containing from 4 to 8 per cent humus in A_1, and 2 to 3 per cent in the nutty A_2 horizon; *brownish-gray,* with a dark brown A, which has a well developed granular to cloddy structure; *brown-gray,* with a well developed A_2, which has a nutty-granular structure and a brown color and which forms on marly parent material (the A, ocntains from 7 to 10 per cent humus; A_2, 1.5 to 2 per cent) ; and *dark humus-carbonate* soil, 6.5 to 7 per cent humus in A. These dark-colored soils form under a deciduous forest cover, elm and oak, and are found in the mountains of the Caucasus, Crimea, and Turkestan.

Among the light-colored mountain forest soils, one might distinguish: the *gray forest* soils with 3 to 4 per cent humus in A_1, *light gray forest* soils with 2 to 3 per cent humus, and *grayish-yellow.* These soils also form under a deciduous forest cover. beech and elm, the climatic conditions being more humid and cooler than that of the dark-colored soils.

The *podzol soils* vary in the degree of podzolization and in mechanical composition. The following subtypes are recognized: podzolic, weakly podzolic, and secondary podzolic with deep dark-colored horizons. In the Caucasus, the mountain podzol soils contain 12 to 8.5 per cent humus in the upper layer, 3.4 to 1.7 per cent in A_1, and 1 to 1.3 per cent in A_2. Thus, these podolized soils are richer in organic matter than the corresponding soils in the plains. Morphologically, the horizons are distinguished by being less differentiated than those in the podzols of the plains and by a lack of concretions. Chemical analyses show, however, that the upper layers become impoverished of sesquioxides and clay with the subsequent enrichment of the illuvial horizons with these substances. On the steep slopes, the podzolization is weakly expressed, with the A_2 horizon superimposed directly on the parent material.

A description of mountain podzolized forest soils is given by Thorp (31), as follows:

A_0: About 0.5″ deep; raw humus of rotted pine needles, roots, wood, etc.
A_1: About 1.0″ deep; dark brown structureless loam.
A_2: About 4.5″ deep; ash gray structureless loam.
B_1: About 6″; pale yellowish, heavy gravelly loam, streaked with dark colored material from above.
B_2: About 14″; reddish yellow and yellow mottled gravelly loam, less heavy than B_1.
C: Yellow, mottled, with reddish-yellow rotten granite fragments.

The entire profile is strongly acid in reaction. In several places, it was observed that the forest was gradually encroaching on the adjacent prairie.

Sod forest soils are, as described by Zakharov (Ch. 2, 91).

encountered at the upper limits of the forest zone. In the Caucasus, grayish sod-soils are found on the northern slopes and brownish-gray on the southern slopes. They are distinguished by the shallow sod layer, gradual lightening of color, and pronounced skeletal nature, about 35 per cent stones and angular pebbles. The A, horizon may contain 8 per cent organic matter: A_2, 2 per cent: and B, from 1 to 0.5 per cent. There is no sharp morphological differentiation of horizons, but chemical analyses reveal the translocation of R_2O_3 in the profile from the surface to the lower horizons. In the sod soils in the mountain regions, the effect of the parent material is sharply expressed.

Bogatyrev (3) cites a condition in the Ural mountains where the forest soils are not podzolized because the seepage waters from the upper slopes

supply Ca and Mg. The gray color noted near the B horizon is due to reduction reactions caused by waterlogged conditions. A similar observation
has been made by Antipov-Karataev and Antipova-Karataeva (2). They
present extensive data on the physical and chemical composition of mountain forest and mountain meadow soils. A study on the microbiological
characteristics of these mountain soils is presented by Simakova (26).

Mountain Meadow Soils

This type of soil formation is unique inasmuch as it has no counterpart
in the horizontal zonal distribution of soils. Its location is above the timber
line, with climatic conditions not found anywhere in the lowlands. The
number of cloudy days decreases at that altitude, with the consequent high
solar insolation, which is also conditioned by the purity of the air and its
low density. According to Neustruev, the conditions enumerated are re-

PLATE 38

*Alpine humus soil profile in the Alps of Switzerland; the A_1 horizon is 60 cm. deep;
the A_2, B, and C horizons merge one into the other; the pH is 4 to 5;
average temperature -1°C.; average rainfall—about 1000 mm;
the prevailing vegetation is carex curvula.*

(After Jenny)

sponsible for the prevailing belt of grass and even for the xerophytic vegetation in mountain regions.

These soils are also known as "alpine humus soils." A discussion of them is to be found in the paper by Jenny (7), who in his studies of the alpine humus soil observed that the distinctive feature of these soils is that the A_1 horizon dominates all other horizons.

On the morphological features of the mountain meadow soils, the following are, according to Zakharov, the most significant:

A more or less dark brown colored A_0 layer and A horizon and a brownish straw-colored B horizon. The profile is not deep, varying from 25 to 60 cm, depending on the topography. Its upper layer is characteristically "rooty" or peaty, and the deeper layers are skeletal in nature. Because of the incomplete disintegration of the lithosphere, remains of the vegetation and rock fragments are abundant in the mountain meadow soils.

Of the chemical features, the organic matter content is outstanding. Judging from the data in table 143, the majority of mountain soils have a considerable quantity

Table 143

Percentage of organic matter in various subtypes of mountain meadow soils

(After Zakharov)

Soil	Horizon and depth			
	A_0 0-5 cm.	A_1 5-25 cm.	A_2 25-40 cm.	B >40 cm
Light gray subalpine meadow sod	9 to 7	6	4 to 3	1 to 2
Brownish gray	14	5	3	—
Dark brown subalpine meadow sod	20 to 18	18 to 14	10 to 4	6 to 1
Chernozem-like alpine meadow	23 to 17	16 to 10	6 to 5	—
Humus alpine meadow	25 to 20	24 to 16	12 to 6	—
Brownish gray alpine meadow sod	30 to 20	22 to 10	15 to 6	—
Peaty alpine meadow	44 to 21	23 to 18	8 to 4	6

of organic matter which increases with altitude. Thus, the mountain forest soils, as pointed out above, are generally poorer in organic matter than the mountain meadow soils. The soils of the subalpine high mountain meadows are high in organic matter, the brownish-gray sod soils of the alpine meadows are still higher in organic matter, and finally the peaty soils are the richest, with 40 per cent organic matter. Some of the mountain meadow soils approach in their organic matter content the quantity of the meadow peat soils in the plains.

As to the composition of the organic matter, data on hand seem to indicate a high content of crenic and apocrenic acids. The nitrogen content of mountain soils is fairly high. In the sod soils, it reaches 1.0 per cent, which is higher than in the chernozem. In the peaty soils it goes up to 1.5 and 2 per cent. With depth, the percentage of nitrogen rapidly decreases to about 0.1 per cent in B. With altitude, the percentage of nitrogen, like that of organic matter, increases, but the percentage of nitrogen in the organic matter differs somewhat. In the lower zone of the mountain regions, the relative quantity of nitrogen in the organic matter is 4 to 6 per cent; a litle htigher it increases to 6 to 7 per cent; at the highest point, in the peaty meadow soils, it drops to 2 to 3 per cent; the chernozem-like and the sod meadow soils seem to have organic matter richest in nitrogen.

The percentage of zeolitic substances (soluble in 10 per cent HCl) is high in mountain meadow soils, 27 to 35 per cent in the upper horizons and 34 to 44 per cent in the lower horizons.

A closer examination of the distribution of the various elements in the horizons of the mountain meadow soils reveals a slight accumulation of sesquioxides in the B horizon. Lime accumulates in the surface horizon, apparently in the form of humate, and again in the lower horizons. Potassium accumulates in A. Mountain meadow soils are richer than mountain forest soils in P_2O_5 and *zeolitic* potassium. There is also a relatively high sulfur content in the A horizon.

In table 144, Zakharov gives the total analysis of a mountain meadow humus stony soil. The data corroborate the conclusions, made on the basis of the composition of zeolitic substances, that in the process of formation of the mountain meadow soils there is an accumulation of lime, potassium, phosphoric acid, and, to some extent, manganese in the upper horizon. The other elements distribute themselves more or less uniformly through the profile. In some cases one may find an increase of R_2O_3 in the B horizon.

In table 145, Zakharov presents data on a water extract of mountain meadow soils. He says:

The water extract of the sod is golden yellow; of the chernozem-like soil it is brownish-yellow, with a more or less definite acid reaction that decreases in intensity with depth. Most of the residue is organic matter, the mineral portion amounting to 12-25 per cent of the total dry residue in A_1, 30-40 per cent in A_2, and 42-54 per cent in B. Silica and R_2O_3 constituents are also found in the mineral portion.

Of the physical properties of mountain meadow soils, we are to note especially the high hygroscopic moisture content, 7 to 8 per cent in A, and the high moisture holding capacity which decreases with depth.

Mountain Tundra Soils

Zakharov (Ch. 2, 91) points out that:

the mountain tundra soils have not been studied to any extent, but the data available indicate that these soils are quite variable, depending on the moisture content of the corresponding altitudes and the character of the vegetation. Thus on the main Caucasian mountain chain they are of a peaty nature, weakly podzolic, very shallow, with 20 to 30 per cent organic matter. Under a rhododendron cover, peat soils with a 60 to 70 per cent organic matter are found. In the Altai mountains, we encounter lichen tundra soil, slightly podzolized, stony, 15 to 25 cm. deep; and bush and moss tundra soil which resembles the soils of the tundra in the plains, about 40 cm. deep, stony, and without a layer of perpetual freezing.

Table 144

Total analysis of a mountain meadow humus stony soil from the eastern slope of Tskhra-Tskaro mountain

(After Zakharov)

Horizon	Depth in:	Organic matter	Loss on ignition	SiO_2	Al_2O_3	Fe_2O_3	CaO	MgO	K_2O	Na_2O
	cm.	per cent	per cent	per cent	per cent	per cent	per cent	per cent	per cent	per cent
A_1	0-10	25.17	32.29	36.26	15.74	7.61	2.76	2.87	2.23	2.00
A_2	10-25	13.99	22.96	41.56	17.39	8.88	3.03	2.06	2.96	2.39
B_1	30-45	4.37	12.62	45.69	21.57	10.61	4.03	1.16	2.20	2.25
B_2	45-55	1.69	8.60	48.11	21.85	10.26	4.63	2.45	3.32	2.75
C	55-70	0.95	7.33	50.90	20.49	8.08	3.35	1.85	4.73	2.74

At the highest points in the mountains, one encounters the *primitive mountain soils*. They represent, as pointed out by Zakharov, "the first stages in the process of soil formation, the beginnings of the conquests of the lithosphere by the phytosphere. They are also found on the steep rocky slopes where the primitive forms of vegetation get a foothold." A number of interesting profiles of mountain soils and their composition have been described by Vilenskii (33), Zakharov and Troitzkii (40), and Gedevanishvilli (5).

General Statement.—The mountain soils, in their geographic distribution along the lines of vertical zonation, are not the same in the various mountain regions. Neustruev (Ch. 2, 50, p. 221) points out that "in the

Table 145

Dry residue from a water extract on several subtypes of mountain meadow soils

(After Zakharov)

Soil	A_0	A_1	A_2	B
	per cent	*per cent*	*per cent*	*per cent*
Chernozem-like	0.295	0.143	0.080	0.071
Humus-stony	0.321	0.231	0.049	0.046
Peat	0.150	0.045	0.004	0.054

mountains of Turkestan and in some sections of the Caucasian mountains, there is a belt of chernozem-like mountain meadow soils; in the Ural mountains, the marshy mountain meadow soils prevail; in the Siberian mountains, the mountain marsh tundra soils are found; and in the tropics, the chernozem-like mountain meadow soil is missing, and above the timber line there are the genuine mountain meadow or mountain desert soils." In some mountain regions, the forest zone is missing, and from the chernozem zone we enter dirctly into the mountain meadow soils. All of these pecularities are a result of the specific climatic conditions of the mountain regions, and for that reason the principle of vertical zonation of soils is an effective aid in the study of mountain soils.

Lithogenic Soils

As indicated earlier, lithogenic soils, because of the specificity of the parent material, attain characteristics of their own and thereby mask or subdue the climatogenic characteristics. Glinka (Ch. 2, 27, p. 208) describes them as "soils in which the chemical properties of the parent material take, so to speak, the upper hand over the climatic influences." In Glinka's nomenclature, these soils are endodynamomorphic.

Rendzina.—This is one of the more prominent lithogenic soils. According to Tanfiliev (Ch. 14, 147), this name was first used by Sibirtsev.

The peasantry in Poland uses the name to designate soils forming on calcareous limestone or gypsum. The exact etymology of the word *rendzina* is not known. It should be pronounced, according to Miklaszewski (18), *rhindzina*. He claims that the word originated from the Polish verb *rzedzic* (to tremble), owing to the sound heard when it is being cultivated. The Russian pedologists describe rendzinas as *humus-carbonate soils*. A review of the literature on rendzina up to 1934 may be found in the paper by Sprihanzl (28).

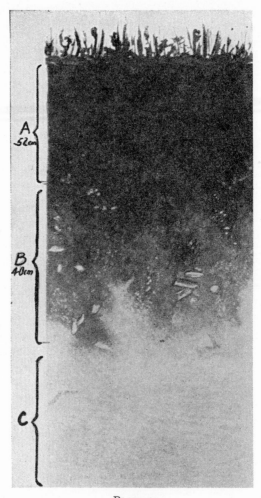

PLATE 39

Rendzina on limestone
(After Kassatkin and Krasyuk)

Rendzina forms on limestones, marls, and gypsum. Any one crossing the English channel can not fail to note the black layer of soil superimposed on the chalk-cliffs of Dover and Normandy. The sharp line between the black of the soil and the white of the chalk deposits makes these soils outstanding. An example of rendzina on gypsum of the *Gaza* or *Gadza* (a local name for rendzina) in the Caucasus, described by Gedeva-nishvilli (5). It is generally believed that rendzina does not form on the hard crystalline limestones.

Kubiena (11) studied rendzina by his microscopic method of examining soils in their natural position. He has differentiated two groups of rendzina. One is characterized by the presence of mull and an abundance of earthworms. The other has neither of these characteristics, being shallow, skeletal in nature and droughty. It is claimed that the desiccation of this soil is responsible for the absence of earthworms.

Johnston and Hill (8) name the Houston and Austin soil series in Texas as representatives of the rendzina type. Actually, these soils are skeletal prairie soils and are for that reason shallow. Johnston and Hill describe them as gray brown to black in color in the A horizon, 25 cm. thick, with a poor "mull-like humus." The B horizon is 15-20 cm. deep, intensely colored, ochre-red to ochre-yellow, very compact and hard when dry. The horizon transitional to the parent material is looser than the B, with some lime concretions. The C horizon is either marl or dolomitic limestone.

The workers of the United States Soil Survey (Ch. 8, 41, p. 1106) have this to say on rendzina. "These soils develop from chalk, soft limestone, or marl and may be regarded as immature. They have derived large amounts of black organic matter from a grass vegetation. The most extensive soils of this group are in the black lands of northern and central Texas and the black prairie of Alabama and Mississippi." This description does not convey the true genetic characteristics of rendzina. The association of rendzina with grass vegetation is contrary to the general understanding of rendzina as a soil type associated with forest vegetation.

Stebut (Ch. 11, 34, p. 387) attributes the formation of rendzina to the abundance of Ca ions which cause the formation of stable zeolites and an accumulation of organic matter. del Villar (35) describes some areas in Spain where rendzina soils are found. Sigmond (Ch. 14, 130) presents analytical data on rendzina in Hungary.

Typical rendzinas are dark in color, resembling chernozems. They differ from them in depth, being shallow, 15 to 30 cm., and having no true B horizon. The A horizon is rich in organic matter, 4 to 10 per cent and more, with fragments of limestone in the lower portion. It is resting directly on the limestone parent material. In some rendzinas, a transition layer, brown in color, resembling a B horizon, may be noted. This is an indication of the degradation of rendzina into a podzolic soil. Of the early contributions on the transformation of humus-carbonate soils (rendzina), the one by Lebedev (12) is as comprehensive as any reported.

Tyurin (Ch. 10, 64, p. 213) points out that the rendzinas occurring among the podzols lose their free lime and subsequently the exchangeable bases. "The replacement of calcium, accompanied by an increase in dispersion and decomposition of organic matter, may begin before the complete removal of free lime. There is the chance for the separation of silica on the surface of the structural units, while whithin these, limestone is still present." An intensified leaching of rendzina, or a change in forest cover, from species of a high to a species of a low ash content, may further degrade it and bring about the formation of a brown forest soils. Kubiena (11) points out that limestone brown soils (*terra fusca*) are a kind of transition between terra rossa and rendzina. The minerals prevailing are metahalloysite, whereas those of terra rossa are primarily kaolinite. It is questionable whether this type of mineralogical makeup is to be found in the alkaline or neutral terra rossa.

Glinka (Ch. 2, 27, p. 435) has this to say on the genesis of rendzina:

No rendzina is formed in Irkutsk and Enissei regions where soils over wide areas are developed from limestone. Well developed podzols are formed rather than rendzina.

In the first stages of their development, the humus carbonate soils are usually marked by skeleton like characteristics. On the soil surface and in the surface horizon, limestone and marl fragments are found, becoming more abundant with depth until the transition to the loose and fissured parent rock is reached. In more advanced stages of soil development, the percentage of such fragments becomes smaller, the materials of the surface horizon are uniformly of fine texture, and only the deeper horizons are spotted by the presence of rock fragments.

The noted characteristics may depend upon other factors. If we imagine two regions in which the external soil-forming conditions are the same, but in one of which the rock is a hard limestone and the other is loose marl, two kinds of skeleton-like soils will develop. On the former the soil will be coarse, rich in fragments of parent rock, and thin. On the latter it will be finer in texture and deeper, because of the more rapid weathering of the loose marl.

In Russia, the humus-carbonate soils do not occur in large unbroken areas, but only as isolated spots and islands. This is natural for European Russia where the whole surface is covered with unconsolidated deposits, and it is only here and there that native limestone or marls are to be found. The unconsolidated deposits are rarely marly. And yet, rendzina is widely distributed. In the government of Leningrad, it formed on Silurian limestone; in Pskov, on Devonian and occasionally on the brackish limestone tuff; in Kaluga, on Cretaceous marl; in Poland, on Triassic, Jurassic, Cretaceous, and Post-Tertiary limestone, marls, and marly clays.

Rendzina in the chernozem zone is associated with existing or former forested regions. Under steppe conditions, limestones and marls are ultimately converted into soils which cannot be differentiated from normal chernozem.

Rendzina, containing 14 per cent organic matter has been reported by Tanfiliev (Ch. 14, 147) in the forests at Gagry, along the eastern shore of the Black Sea, where the climate is subtropical with a rainfall of 1300 mm.

The presence of rendzina has been reported in the podzol zone of Germany, Sweden, and other European states.

Starzynski (30), describing rendzina in the highland area of Lublin, Poland, separates a division which has developed not on calcareous parent rock *in situ,* but on rendzina-like soil material. It has a deep layer of organic matter, attaining in places a depth of 1 m. The profile is not fully developed and does not have as much Ca as the true rendzina.

A description of rendzina on calcareous clays in Latvia is given by Wityn (36). Marbut (15) cites the presence of small areas of rendzina in Alabama and Mississippi. The Houston series of soils in northeastern Texas on lime marls and the Fairmount series in Kentucky have been identified as rendzina.

Dranitsyn describes a rendzina profile among the red soils of the temperate warm region in Africa as follows: (Quoted from Glinka (Ch. 2, 27, p. 436)).

A_1: Gray to dark gray surface layer, in places almost black, containing more or less fragmental marly material; occasionally it is free from limestone or marl fragments; its thickness varies, ranging from 15 to 30 cm.

A_2: Whitish gray, faintly colored with organic matter, at times brownish, containing a considerable quantity of fragments of the parent rock, limestone or marl.

C: Mass of parent rock fragments.

Very little is known about rendzina forming on gypsum. Glinka mentions Tkachenko's observations on such soils in the Arkhangelsk region and Kwaschnin-Samarin's observations in the hills of Saxony. A description of the latter follows:

A_0: Sod, with inclusions of coarse materials, dark gray, 5-cm. thick.

A_1: Lighter than A_0, gray when dry and dark brown when wet, with no definite structure; it contains coarse and fine materials, 36 cm. thick.

A_2: Grayish yellow, rich in fine materials, 20 cm. thick.

C: Stratified gypsum.

Chemical Analyses.—Until recent years, investigations on the chemistry of rendzina have been meager and fragmentary, with very few references to profile analyses. Of the early reports, the analyses presented by Lüdecke (14) on three surface samples (HCl extract) of rendzina are familiar. More valuable are the analyses of rendzina by Councler (4), reproduced in table 146. Glinka's presentation of data on the gypsum rendzina described by Dranitsyn are given in table 147.

The analytical data indicate podzolization tendencies in these soils. There is a definite shift of the R_2O_3, and most of the Ca has been lost.

Because of the large circulation of Ca in these soils, the exchange complex is, as a rule, saturated with this element. As the leaching process proceeds, the Ca is lost, and the soil attains the characteristics of a podzolic or genuine podzol soil. It is the Ca which resists the podzolization process; it

Table 146

Analyses of a rendzina soil, Thüringen

(After Councler)

Constituents	1*	2*	3*	4*
	per cent	*per cent*	*per cent*	*per cent*
H_2O	7.59	4.26	8.70	0.21
CO_2	0.14	0.56	1.11	41.74
SiO_2	63.57	67.74	54.13	2.06
Al_2O_3	9.83	12.13	17.60	0.90
Fe_2O_3	3.82	2.90	6.53	0.51
GaO	1.14	1.16	1.16	52.98
MgO	0.94	0.99	0.83	0.76
K_2O	2.32	2.64	2.65	0.39
Na_2O	0.66	1.09	0.93	0.30
P_2O_5	0.21	0.22	0.20	0.03

*1. Organic matter, uniformly colored, 2-4 cm.   2. Gray or dark brown loamy horizon, 23-30 cm.   3. Yellowish clay, 5-16 cm.   4. Parent rock.

TABLE 147

Analyses of a rendzina on gypsum; in 10 per cent HCl solution
(After Glinka)

Constituents	A_1	A_2	C
	per cent	*per cent*	*per cent*
Organic matter*	8.08	2.27	——
SiO_2	0.18	0.16	0.37
$Fe_2O_3 + Al_2O_3$	1.78	2.86	0.97
Mn_3O_4	0.07	0.01	——
CaO	14.35	25.99	36.41
MgO	0.89	1.61	0.91
$K_2O + Na_2O$	0.41	0.86	0.79
CO_3	0.36	0.87	40.71
P_2O_5	0.05	0.06	——
CO_2	10.59	26.55	3.69

*Organic matter content is on basis of total soil.

is the Ca that is primarily responsible for the accumulation of organic matter; it is the Ca that gives rise to fairly insoluble and stable humates; and it is the Ca that keeps the soil at a rather high pH. Glinka cites an example of a rendzina soil in the Leningrad government which has a pH value of 7.2-7.5.

See (25) studied a number of humus-carbonate (rendzina) soils, showing the stages in the evolution of podzols from rendzina. Zvorykin (41) pointed out that rendzina in its process of degradation goes to the forest gray subtype and finally into true podzols. The latter stage is the exception in the rendzina soils of the Moravian Karst.

Tikheeva (32), in her studies on the genesis and evolution of the forest soils in the Leningrad region, described and presents analytical data on a series of rendzina and rendzina-like profiles formed on Silurian dolomitic limestone. Tikheeva considers rendzina as a prepodzolic state, a concept introduced by Polynov. These soils are, so to speak, in a *hidden podzolic state.*

To illustrate the striking changes that have occurred in the course of rendzina formation, Tikheeva calculated the *petrographic coefficient of acidity, a,* introduced by Levinson-Lessing (13) in his research in petrography. For quartz diorite in Finland, a is 2.9; for granites, 2.72; for the earth's crust (based on Clark's data), 2.41; for the A horizon in genuine rendzinia, 4; and for the A horizon of a strongly podzolized soil, 10. With depth in the profile, the value for a decreases. By the numerical value of $a,$ it is possible to judge the state of podzolization of the soils of the rendzina series, or of podzols in different types of parent material. The 15 tables of data, presented in the original paper by Tikheeva, on the chemical and mechanical analyses of rendzina and its different subtypes and divisions offer a comprehensive understanding of the processes involved. An excellent summary in English is given. In it, the ideas of Polynov on the evaluation of rendzina are presented.

The contribution by Zaitsev (37) supplements the data of Tikheeva. He points out that the rendzina on the Silurian plateau (on different types of dolomitic limestone) in the Leningrad region is found in spots, not very widespread. In table 148, data compiled from Zaitsev's paper (it contains a bibliography of the early work on rendzina), are given.

The two profiles do not differ much in their chemical makeup. The only distinct difference between these two profiles is the Ca and Mg content. It is of interest to note that the degraded rendzina, with its low base content, has a high pH in neutral salt extract. This shows that the soil complex is saturated with bases. There is some difference in the organic matter con-

Table 148

Analyses of a rendzina and degraded rendzina in the Leningrad (U.S.S.R.) region

(After Zaitzev)

Horizon	At depth in cm.	Per cent of dry soil (at 105°C.)									pH neutral salt extract	Exchangeable bases: m.e. per 100 gms.	
		SiO_2	SO_3	P_2O_5	Al_2O_3	Fe_2O_3	MnO	CaO	MgO	Organic matter		Ca	Mg
												I. Rendzina	
A	0-10	68.4	0.088	0.159	9.99	3.83	0.16	2.34	1.83	3.44	6.9	11.5	6.34
B	20-30	38.1	0.182	0.221	9.56	3.86	0.12	14.49	9.27	0.91	7.0	9.0	6.28
B	30-40	33.4	0.011	0.205	7.39	3.19	0.05	17.83	9.74	0.23	7.0	6.0	5.44
C	80-90	25.5	0.005	0.197	5.39	2.58	0.03	24.27	8.99	0.11	7.1	—	
												II. Degraded Rendzina	
A₁	0-10	73.7	0.083	0.255	10.45	5.20	0.16	1.19	0.78	3.01	6.6	9.95	4.92
A₂/B₁	30-40	74.6	0.046	0.367	11.41	5.84	0.07	1.49	0.86	0.22	6.8	7.17	3.22
B₂	55-65	75.9	0.017	0.379	13.08	6.00	0.12	1.20	0.83	0.17	6.9	5.75	2.63

*The N content of the A horizon in I is: 0.22 and in II 0.18 per cent.

tent. The degraded rendzina shows a sprinkling of SiO_2 on the structural units. Still they effervesce when treated with HCl.

In general, the two profiles exhibit, chemically, chernozem characteristics, to wit, granular structure, no movement of R_2O_3, high P content in the A horizon, high pH, and relatively high organic matter content.

An examination of Zaitsev's analytical data of several subdivisions of podzolized soils (given in the original paper) on the limestone parent material hardly justifies the name. The composition of these soils varies but little. Table 148 on the composition of the rendzina and degraded rendzina brings out this point again; except for the low Ca and Mg content, these podzolized soils have no podzolic attributes and characteristics. The pH is not below 6.5 and no H is in the exchange complex.

Other Lithogenic Soils.—An example of the enduring influence of parent material on the soil profile constitution is the Penn series of soils of the Piedmont region. One of the characteristic features of this soil is the chocolate-red color which predominates throughout the profile and down in the C horizon. Even the more mature soils which indicate some evidence of podzolization show very little difference in color. Analyses on the composition of one textural class of this series presented in table 149. The data show that very little of the constituents have been translocated in the profile. Soils neighboring the Penn soils, but on different parent material, do manifest definite podzolization effects.

The reason for the lack of profile development in the Penn soils lies in the makeup on the parent material—Triassic shale. Apparently, the shale represents a consolidated material of eroded soil and weathered rock of a period when the climate was conducive to lateritic weathering and soil formation. This means a larke quantity of end-products of weathering, the R_2O_3 constituents, with very little of other primary minerals. When the shale was exposed, and the agents of weathering and the factors of soil formation began their work, there were very few primary minerals that could be translocated and distributed in the profile. In short, there have not been enough reaction products to affect a differentiation into distinct horizons.

There are many other soils that may be placed in the category of lithogenic soils as the Penn has been placed. The Lansdale and Berks series are good examples.

The Sandhills of Nebraska may be considered as lithogenic. They are located in the zonal belts of the dark brown and chernozem soils, occupying an area of 21,500 square miles. The predominant color of the soils is grayish brown to grayish-yellow, with no layer or horizon of effervescence in the profile.

Table 149

Chemical composition of a Penn silt loam

Horizon	Depth of horizon	Reaction		SiO_2	Fe_2O_3	Al_2O_3	P_2O_5	CaO	MgO	Mn_3O_4	Base-exchange capacity	Unsaturation (H)	
		H_2O extract	Neutral salt extract										
	cm.	pH	pH	per cent	per cent	per cent	per cent	per cent	per cent	per cent	m. e.	m. e.	per cent
A_0	3–4	5.2	4.3	52.55	6.08	17.06	0.131	0.744	1.729	0.445	26.4	18.64	70.6
A_1	12	4.9	4.5	57.85	8.15	18.09	0.071	0.304	1.743	0.487	14.1	7.56	53.6
A_2	26	4.8	4.5	56.7	8.53	19.53	0.056	0.342	1.993	0.238	10.7	7.56	70.6
B	38	4.9	4.3	54.97	9.54	20.36	0.0467	0.206	·2.166	0.425	11.4	7.56	66.3
C	—	5.1	4.3	55.10	9.21	20.20	0.055	0.206	2.053	0.437	11.2	7.64	68.2

*The splashing of mineral material from below the forest litter incorporates large large quantities of this material into the A_0; this layer is therefore not a true A_0.

The sandhill region, as described by Marbut (Ch. 8, 20), presents a landscape of rounded hills and irregular ridges, often capped by drifting sand and pitted by blowouts. This sand originated from the Tertiary sandstone formations of western Nebraska and was carried to its present position by wind and stream action. A part, however, has been derived from a sand sheet underlying much of the loessial mantle in Custer county and adjoining areas. The sands from the two sources have been so mixed, reassorted, and shifted about, that it is not possible to make a definite statement in regard to their origin in a given locality.

From the meager analyses available on the soils of the Sandhill region, it seems that the paucity of calcium in the parent material is responsible for the endodynamomorphic characteristics of these soils.

References

1. Albright, W. D. and Stoker, J. G. 1944 Topography and minimum temperatures. *Sci. Agr.* (Canada) 25: 146-155.
2. Antipov-Karataev, I. N., and Antipova-Karataeva, T. F. 1936 The mountain forest and mountain meadow soils of the Teberda region, N. Caucasia. *Trans. Dokuchaev Soil Inst.* 13: 367-382.
3. Bogatyrev, K. P. 1946 Several peculiarities in the development of mountain soils. *Pedology* (U.S.S.R.) No. 8: 492-500.
4. Councler, C. 1883 Untersuchungen über Waldstreu. I. *Ztsch. f. Forst u. Jagdwesen* 15: 121-136.
5. Gedevanishvilli, D. P. 1930 Natural conditions on the route from Tiflis to Bakuryany. Guide-book for the excursion of the Second International Congress of Soil Science. *Inter. Soc. Soil Sci. Organiz. Committee,* Moscow, II, pp. 159-194 (English).
6. Glinka, K. D. 1910 A note on the soils of mountain slopes. *Pochovedenie* (Pedology) 21: 297-308.
7. Jenny, H. 1930 Hochgebirgsboden. Blanck's *Handbuch der Bodenlehre* 3: 96-118; see also: Die Alpinen Boden. *Denkschr. der Schweiz. Naturforsch. Gesel.* 63 (2): 295-340 (1926).
8. Johnston, J. R., and Hill, H. O. 1944 A study of the shrinking and swelling properties of rendzina soils. *Proc. Soil Sci. Soc. Amer.* 9: 24-29.
9. Klingebiel, A. A., Walker, R. H., and Stewart, G. 1938 Soil profile development in Utah as related to climate and native vegetation. Paper presented before Western Soc. Soil Sci. at San Diego, Cal. (Quoted from Martin and Fletcher).
10. Kovalevskii, G. V. 1932 The problem of utilizing the mountain regions of the U.S.S.R. *Vsesoyuznaya Akad. Sel'sko-Khoz. Nauk im. Lenina,* Ser. A., No. 3: 29-36.

11. Kubiena, W. 1944 Beiträge zur Bodenentwicklungslehre: der Kalksteinbraunlehm (terra fusca) als Glied der Entwicklungsserie der Mitteleuropäischen Rendsina. *Bodenk. u. Pflanzenernähr.* 35: 22-45; see also: Entwiklung und Systematik der Rendsinen 29 (1943): 108-119.

12. Lebedev, A. F. 1906 Humus carbonate soils and their transition to podzols. *Zhur. Opyt. Agron.* (Russian) 7:571-592.

13. Levinson-Lessing, F. Yu. 1922 On the chemical composition of the petrographic provinces of Russia. (Quoted from Tikheeva).

14. Lüdecke, C. 1932 Untersuchungen über Gesteine und Boden auf Muschelkalkformation in der Gegend von Göttingen, *Ztsch. für Naturwissensch.* 65, No. 4-5: 219-348.

15. Marbut, C. F. 1928 The excursion. *Proc. and Papers First Inter. Cong. Soil Sci.* 5: 40-88.

16. Martin, W. L. and Fletcher, J. E. 1943 Vertical zonation of great soil groups on Mt. Graham, Arizona, as correlated with climate, vegetation and profile characteristics. *Ariz. Sta. Tech. Bul.* 99, pp. 87-153.

17. Mikhailovskaya, O. N. 1936 The problem of the genesis of high mountain soils. *Trans. Dokuchaev Soil Inst.* 13: 315-366.

18. Miklaszewski, S. 1924 Contribution à la connaissance des sols nommés 'rendzinas'. Compt. Rend. I. Vième Conférence Agropédologique, Prague (1922), pp. 312-337.

19. Neustruev, S. 1911 A soil-geological survey of Chikment at the Syr-Dar region. *Zhur. Opyt. Agron.*, p. 213 (After Kossovich).

20. Nikiforoff, C. C. 1937 The inversion of the great soil zones in Western Washington. *Geogr. Rev.* 27: 200-213.

21. Powers, W. L. 1940 Vertical zonation in the Umatilla area, Oregon. Paper presented before the Western Soc. Soil Sci. at the Univ. of Washington (Quoted from Martin and Fletcher).

22. Prasolov, L. I. 1909 On the study of vertical soil zones in Tyan-Shan. *Pochvovedenie* (Pedology) 11: 90-92.

23. Prasolov, L. I. 1922 The soil regions of European Russia. Soobshcheniya otdela pochvovedeniya, Sel'sko-Khoz. Komiteta, Bul. 31.

24. Sabanin, I. G. 1943 Some agrohydrologic peculiarities of the soils of the Bogar zone in Central Asia. *Pedology* (U.S.S.R.) No. 7: 34-47.

25. See, K. von. 1921 Observations on residual soils on limestone: The question of rendzina soils. *Inter. Mitteil. Bodenk.* II: 85-104.

26. Simakova, L. T. 1936 Microbiological characteristics of the soils in the Teberda region, in the high mountains of the Caucasus. *Trans. Dokuchaev Soil Inst.* 13: 382-398.

27. Spilsbury, R. H. and Tisdale, E. W. 1944 Soil-plant relationships and vertical zonation in the southern interior of British Columbia. *Sci. Agr.* (Canada) 24: 395-436.

28. Spirhanzl, J. 1934 On rendzina soils. Zemled. Archiv (Prague) 9-10. Abstract in *Proc. Inter. Soc. Soil Sci.* 10, No. 1, p. 61.

29. Sprengel, K. 1837 Die Bodenkunde oder Lehre von Boden nebst einer vollständigen Einleitung zur chemischer Analyse der Ackererde. Leipzig.

30. Starzynskii, Z. 1923 Studies on the formation of rendzina soils (Polish) *Pamietnik Panstwow Inst Naukov. Gospod. Wiejskw Pulaw.* 4, pt. A: 244-301.

31. Thorp, J. 1931 The effects of vegetation and climate upon soil profiles in northern and northeastern Wyoming. *Soil Sci.* 32: 283-301.

32. Tikheeva, L. V. 1936 On the genesis and evolution of forest soils in the Leningrad region. *Trans. Dokuchaev Soil Inst.* (U.S.S.R.) 13: 267-314 (English summary 308-311).

33. Vilenskii, D. G. 1930 Soils in the region of the Caucasian mineral waters. Guide-book of the Second International Congress of Soil Science. Inter. Soc. Soil Sci. Organizing Committee, Moscow, II: 120-145 (English).

34. Villar, E. H. del. 1937 Soils of the Lusitano-Iberian Peninsula (Engglish and Spanish). Thomas Murby & Co., London.

35. Vysotskii, G. N. 1939 Hydroamelioration of our plains with the aid of forests. *Pedology* (U.S.S.R.) No. 1: 76-89.

36. Wityn, I. 1924 Die Hauptphasen des Podsolbildung Prozesses, II. Die Fruchtbarkeit des Bodens in ihrer Beziehung zur Bodenazidität. Riga, Lativa.

37. Zaitsev, A. A. 1935 The soils of the Silurian plateau and fertilizers. *Khimizatsiya Sotsialis. Zemledeliya* No. 5: 3-12.

38. Zakharov, S. A. 1924 The principal results and fundamental problems of soil investigations in Georgia. *Trudy Gosudar. Polytech. Inst.,* Tiflis, 1: 1-56.

39. Zakharov, S. A. 1937 The soils of the mountain regions in the U.S.S.R. *Pedology* (U.S.S.R.) No. 6: 810-848 (Extensive English summary).

40. Zakharov, S. A. and Troitskii, N. A. 1930 Soils on the route from Vladikavkaz to Tiflis. Guide-book for the excursion of the Second International Congress of Soil Science. Inter. Soc. Soil Sci. Organizing Committee, Moscow II, pp. 146-158 (English).

41. Zvorykin, J. 1929 A contribution to the degradation of rendzina in the Moravian Karst. *Mitl. der Tschechoslov. Akad. der Landw.* 5, p. 598 (Abstract in *Proc. Inter. Soil Sci. Soc.* 5 (1930):59-60).

INDEX OF AUTHORS

INDEX OF SUBJECTS

Microorganisms—*continued*

autotrophic, 76, 95

contribution of, to organic matter resources, 211

energy in crust of weathering and, 76

factor of soil formation, 144-147

in A horizon, 172, 173

infusion of, from chernozem, podzol, and solodi, effect on mineral solubility, 96

in Saraha desert, 219

mineral decomposition by, 95

mineral synthesis by, 96

numbers, in soils, 61

structure and, 51, 55

Microrelief—*see* Macrotopography

Minerals—

accessory, 98

amphiboles, 101, 102

beidellite, 108

calcite, 104

calculating losses in, by weather, 87, 98, 105

classification basis of, 98

clay, 106, 108, 109; *see* also Clay

composition of solonetz profile, 561

composition of, in river waters, 93

decomposibility of, order, 98

decomposition in podzolization, 351

decomposition, protection against, 129, 487

effect of, on soil formation, 129

essential, 98

feldspar, 99, 101

feldspathoids, 100

formation of, by microbes, 96

gibbsite in podzols, 366

gypsum, 104

halloysite, 109, 467

humic acid effect on, 96

humus effect on, 96

hydrated, 82

illite, 108

kaolinite, 108; *see* also Kaolinite

limonite in podzols, 366

losses of, by weathering, 87

metamorphic rocks, in 106

metastabillites, 111

micas, 102, 103, 111

montmorillonite, 108; *see* also Montmorillonite

movement of, constituents in profile, 141

Minerals—*continued*

mutabillites, 111

others than silicates, 104

oxidation of, 81

percentage composition of, in igneous rocks, 98

pyroxenes, 101, 102

quartz, 104

resilication of, 466

resistance of, 98

sericite mica and laterization, 466

sesquioxide coatings on, 487

silicate, 99

soil types, in, 113

solubility, in carbonated water, 84, 85

specific gravity of, 98

types of, and weathering, 98, 111

Mineralization—

definition and discussion, 169-171

phytosphere and, 141

Moisture—

capillary movement of, 55

factor in podzol process, 338

movement of, relation to soil structure, 55

mulching conserving, 55

percolation, 135, 140

relationships in chernozem, 302

soil formation and, 18

topography and soil, 130

translocation of constituents in profile by, 135

Montmorillonite—

cation sorption by, 109, 296

discussion, 108

in profile, 112

Moor—*see* Bog, Marsh, Peat

lowmoor and highmoor, 596

soils, 597, 607

Morphology—

erosion and, 43

experimental study, 68

methods of studying, 39-69

science and, 41

Mounds and chernozem, 131

Mountain soils—

discussion, 20, 182, 526, 609-629

exposure and soil type, 131

slope measurement and horizons, 130